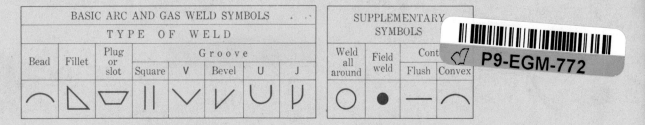

BASIC ARC AND GAS WELD SYMBOLS								SUPPLEMENTARY SYMBOLS			
TYPE OF WELD											
Bead	Fillet	Plug or slot	Groove					Weld all around	Field weld	Cont	
			Square	V	Bevel	U	J			Flush	Convex

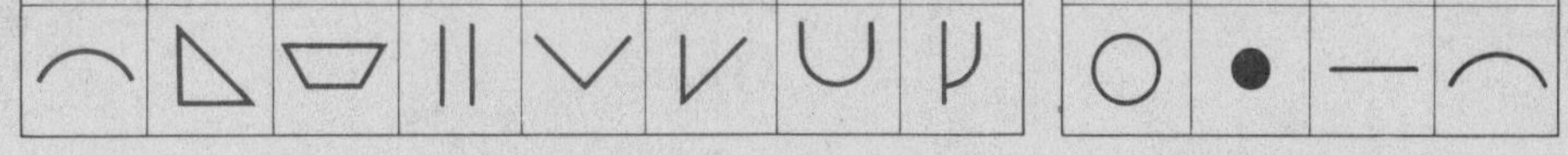

Arc- and gas-welding symbols.

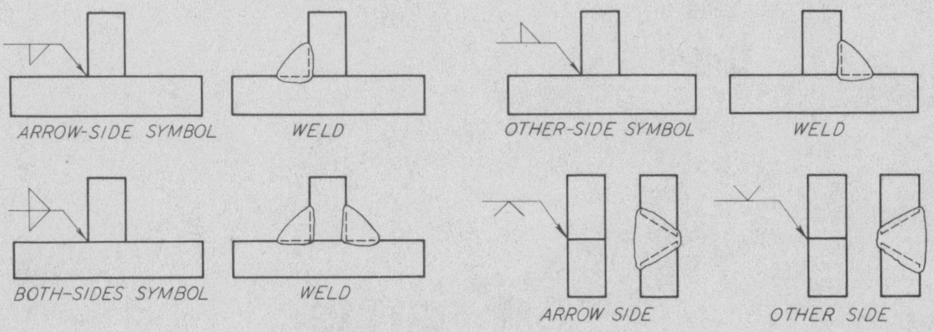
ARROW-SIDE SYMBOL
WELD
OTHER-SIDE SYMBOL
WELD
BOTH-SIDES SYMBOL
WELD
ARROW SIDE
OTHER SIDE

Arrow side and other side.

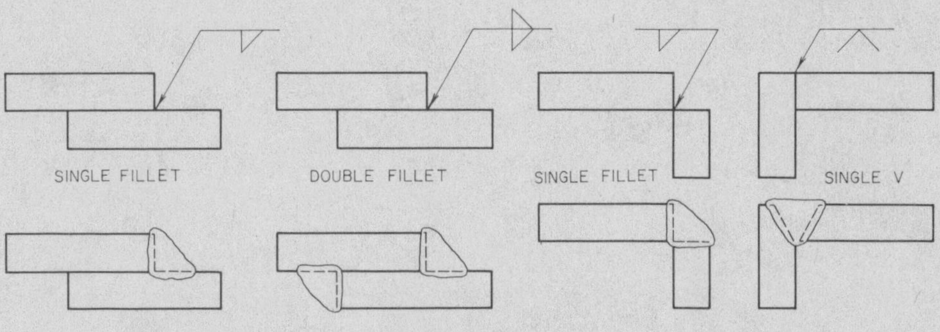
SINGLE FILLET
DOUBLE FILLET
SINGLE FILLET
SINGLE V

Lap joints. Corner joints.

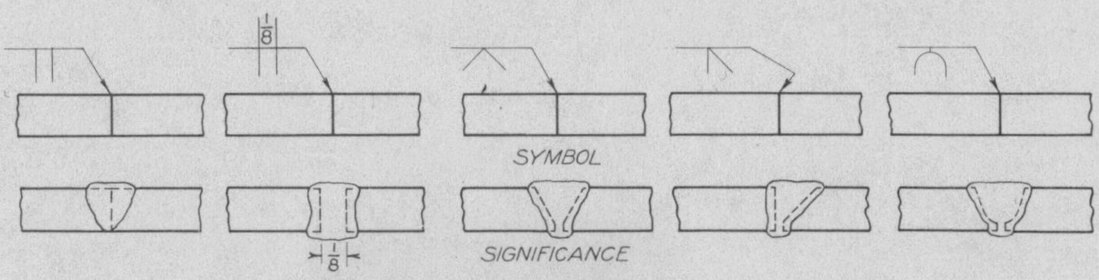
SYMBOL
SIGNIFICANCE

Butt joints.

MECHANICAL DRAWING

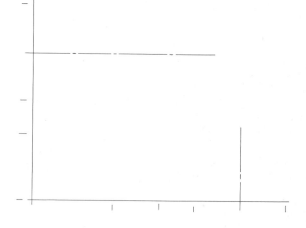

seventh edition revised and enlarged by Carl L. Svensen

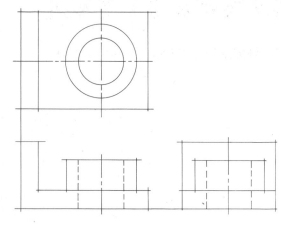
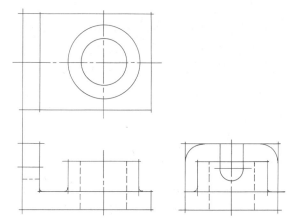

WEBSTER DIVISION, McGRAW-HILL BOOK COMPANY

ST. LOUIS   NEW YORK   SAN FRANCISCO   DALLAS   TORONTO

MECHANICAL
DRAWING

THOMAS E. FRENCH / CARL L. SVENSEN

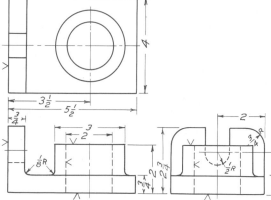

Library of Congress Catalog Card Number: 57-6389
22296

LONDON   SYDNEY

1 2 3 4 5 6 7 8 9 10   RM   76 75 74 73 72 71 70 69 68 67 66

Contents

Preface

This, the Seventh Edition of *Mechanical Drawing,* is completely rewritten. The basic plan and purpose have been adapted to meet the changing needs of this important and growing subject. The continuing interest, advice, and assistance of the long line of progressive instructors who have used *Mechanical Drawing* over the years are responsible for many of the important improvements.

The authors wrote the first edition of *Mechanical Drawing* to help students learn to visualize in three dimensions, to develop and strengthen their technical imagination, to think precisely, to read and write the language of the industries, and to gain experience in making working drawings according to modern commercial practice. These continue to be the objectives of the Seventh Edition.

A larger page size is used to provide for better illustrating and more efficient study. The use of a three-column format permits the placement of illustrations near the descriptive text. Illustrations are numbered to identify them with the article in which they are described. Color is used throughout the book to provide emphasis and clarify basic principles. Careful research has been done to adapt the text and problems to changing courses of study, revised standards, and the latest practices in the engineering drafting rooms of progressive industries. New chapters have been added and others have been revised

to meet these changing requirements. Chapter 24, "Graphic Charts and Diagrams," is included because of the extensive use of graphic charts, models, and mock-ups. Chapter 25, "Functional Drafting," is needed to explain the meaning of a term which is related to *simplified drafting* and has important applications. The greater use of pencil drawings in industry suggests less emphasis on inking practice; hence, inking is covered in a brief, separate chapter. The treatment of architectural drafting has been enlarged and provides necessary material for separate instruction.

Chapter 26 includes a variety of problems which apply to courses of different content, difficulty, or length. There are a great number of new problems and many revised problems. Most tried and true problems in previous editions which have proven value have been retained. The problems have been arranged in groups and numbered to correspond with the chapters to which they apply. In each group the problems have been numbered consecutively and the problem statements placed under or close to the problem illustration to make assignment and identification definite. Suggestions for the selection of problems are given at the ends of the chapters in graded lists for convenient use in helping to organize courses to meet different requirements.

The content and arrangement of text and problems are such that the book is

suitable for use in drafting courses such as:

1. Basic courses of one, two, or three years
2. Pre-engineering course
3. Industrial arts courses
4. A general survey course
5. Machine drawing
6. Architectural drafting
7. Technical institute courses
8. A course for training draftsmen

As was true of previous editions, this Seventh Edition reflects the benefit of actual use. Additions and improvements have been suggested by today's progressive instructors. Conformity with industrial and engineering practice has been provided by information, material, and criticism from many companies.

Credit and appreciation is here expressed to the author's friends, the instructors, for their professional assistance which makes it possible to meet the greater needs of today's courses in engineering graphics and mechanical drawing. Special credit is due the many companies who have cooperated so freely in so many ways.

Sincere thanks are here expressed to all who have done so much for this and previous editions. In particular, special thanks for major contributions are due to Mr. Herbert Brasher, Mr. Peter Buban, Mr. Douglas Ross, and to Mrs. Catherine Givens for untiring care in preparing the manuscript and in checking proof. Instructor's comments and suggestions are always welcome and appreciated.

CARL L. SVENSEN

1
Language of drawing

1•1 Maps to missiles. From the earliest times the language of drawing has been one of the most important tools of mankind. It was the first written language and is the most exact language for many purposes. From ancient maps to modern missiles (Figs. 1-1a and 1-1b), drawings have made it possible to develop and record man's knowledge and progress. Without the early drawings man's progress would have been much slower.

1•2 The language of industry and science. By putting mechanical drawings to many uses, industry supplies us with the goods we need; in doing this, industry has steadily raised our standard of living. People who grow up and work in twentieth-century America find their life better and their jobs easier because of mechanical drawing. Drawings help ensure that the products we buy are manufactured to the standard set by the designer.

Fig. 1-1a. Captain John Smith's map of Virginia, 1655. Early map makers were artists as well as draftsmen. *(United States Coast and Geodetic Survey).* Fig. 1-1b. The Nike Zeus missile. *(Douglas Aircraft Company, Inc.)*

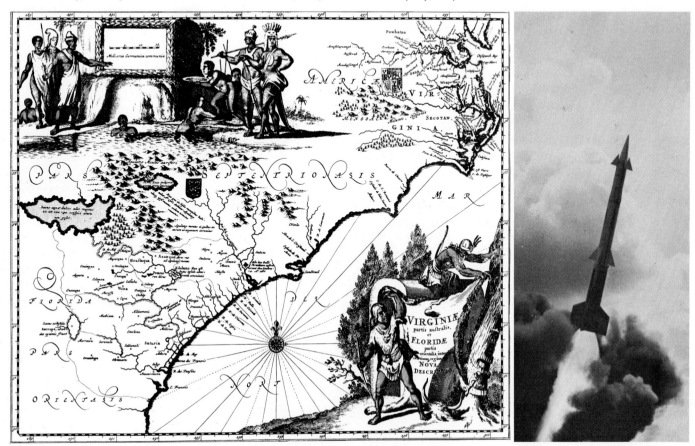

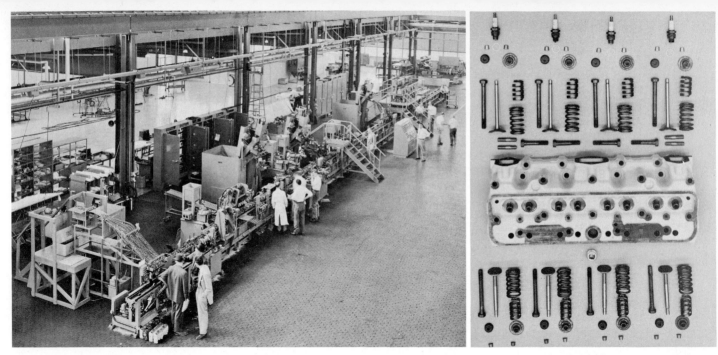

Fig. 1-2a. The machine above puts together 400 automobile V-8 engine cylinder heads per hour. Hundreds of drawings were needed to build the machine. Right, more than 70 parts make up the cylinder head. Many drawings are needed to make the parts and to show how they go together. *(Oldsmobile Division, General Motors Corporation)*

The machines (Fig. 1-2a) which make the parts for our automobiles are made from drawings which start out as sketches on an engineer's pad of sketch paper. Drawings tell the workmen in the factories how to make the cars, jet airplanes, television sets, motorboats, telephones, and refrigerators. All these and many other products originate on the drafting board. Machines provide us with food and clothing—machines that inventors or engineers first describe in mechanical drawings. Civil engineers design our highways, bridges, tunnels, and airports. Electronic engineers design our radio and television sets. Architects draw plans for homes, churches, and schools.

Mechanical drawing plays a part in the life of everyone. Drawings have made possible explorations and travel on the earth and under the seas, in the air and in the space beyond (Figs. 1-2b and 1-2c).

Fig. 1-2b. Santa Fe Railway's "Chief" winding through Johnson's Canyon near Williams, Ariz. This train has thousands of parts, and a drawing has to be made for every part. It would be almost impossible to build the train without these drawings. *(Santa Fe Railway Photo)*

Fig. 1-2c. The oceangoing passenger ship "France" is a city afloat. The design and equipment required the services of draftsmen in every field of engineering.

rough maps of the world they knew. Perhaps the Romans made the best mechanical drawings of ancient times when they drew pictures and plans for their buildings, aqueducts (Fig. 1-3c), and forts.

For centuries men struggled with the problem of drawing solid objects on flat surfaces. It was difficult to show accurately the dimensions of length, width, and height on drawings of two dimensions. Leonardo da Vinci, an Italian genius of the fifteenth century (1452–1519), made a study of drawing and painting. His sketches were easy to understand (Figs. 1-3d and 1-3e), and for several years he taught others his method. After his death other Europeans continued da Vinci's studies, but his teachings were not published until 1651. Among his followers were scholars and mathematicians who explored different ways to show exact shapes and measurements on their drawings.

1•3 First, a pictorial language. Even in ancient times men drew pictures to show others what they had in mind. Only drawings give the directions that are easy for builders to follow.

Some of the earliest builders made crude sketches on clay tablets that still exist. It is probable that they also made detailed plans of their buildings on parchment or papyrus, but we have not found any fragments of such drawings. The people of Mesopotamia used drafting materials as early as 2200 B.C. A statue of one of their kings, Gudea (Fig. 1-3a), shows him with a drawing of a building on his lap.

Ancient Egyptian stonemasons made plans for the pyramids and other buildings on papyrus, slabs of limestone (Fig. 1-3b), and sometimes wood. Lines were drawn on the ground to locate the first layer of big stone blocks for a building or other structure. Sailors of ancient Greece and Rome made

Fig. 1-3a. At A, headless statue of Gudea, engineer, ruler (2000 B.C.). Inscription on statue tells about the design and building of the temple of Ningirsu. At B, a plan view drawn on the stone tablet on Gudea's lap. *(From Ernest de Sarzec, Decouvertes en Chaldee, 1891)*

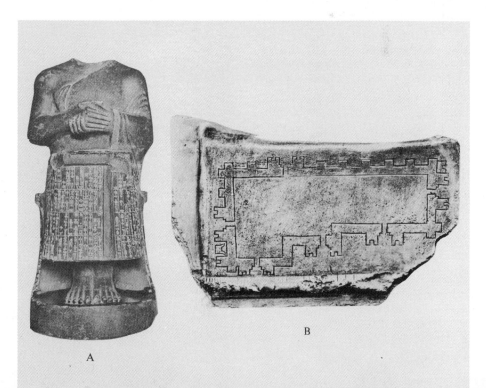

A

B

Fig. 1-3b. The plan on limestone of the tomb of an Egyptian king. *(From Clark and Engelbach, Ancient Egyptian Masonry)*

1•4 Graphic science. Arthur Dobbs, Member of Parliament and distinguished army engineer and pioneer of Castle Dobbs, County Antrim, Ireland, who became the governor of North Carolina in 1754, was an expert on the fine draftsmanship of plans. He left script instructions from which the following is quoted: "The scenographic plan [Fig. 1-4a] was known to the Roman engineer, Vitruvius, and is the fortress or building in the perspective drawn geometrically and receded in correct proportion as on the scroll and line shadowed to produce sun shadow effect."[1]

Fig. 1-3c. Engineers of ancient Rome knew the importance of making drawings. The Pont du Gard, near Nimes, France, is a good example of the aqueducts they built. *(From T. Schreiver, Atlas of Classical Antiquities, 1895)*

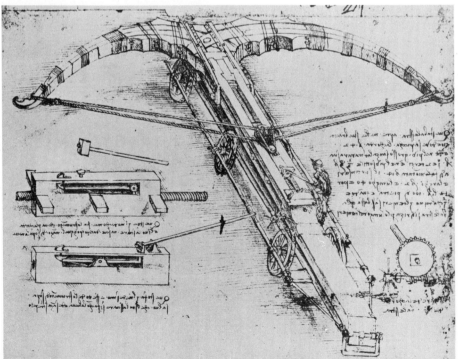

Fig. 1-3d. Leonardo da Vinci's sketch of a giant crossbow. Notice the two suggestions showing the tripping action of the crossbow. Da Vinci often wrote his comments from right to left as a mirror image of ordinary writing. In this way he kept many of his ideas as private as possible. *(Lieb Museum)*

Americans can take pride in the wide use they make of the graphic language and in the advances they contribute to the art. George Washington and his officers used drawing instruments (Fig. 1-4b). In Figs. 1-4c and 1-4d we can see the plans that Thomas Jefferson made for Monticello, his beautiful home in Virginia.

Gaspard Monge (1746–1818), a Frenchman of Napoleon's time, discovered the principles from which the system we use today has been developed. For some time his methods were considered a military secret. At the United States Military Academy, where every cadet learns to describe his ideas of roads, bridges, machines, buildings, military operations, and so on, in draw-

ings, another French scholar, Claude Crozet, taught Monge's projection methods of drawing for the first time in this country. American teachers and engineers added to Crozet's work and further developed the graphic language. West Point graduates, among whom were the first trained engineers of our country, have often contributed to our technical progress. They have drawn plans for railroads, bridges, public buildings, lighthouses (Fig. 1-4e), canals, and atomic energy plants.

We usually find it difficult, and in most cases impossible, to describe in words the appearance of the things we want to make or build. Since words fail to give a complete or accurate description, we use sketches, drawings,

Fig. 1-4a. A scenographic plan shows a plan and building in perspective.

Fig. 1-4b. George Washington's drawing instruments. At the top are parallel rulers, useful in drawing parallel lines and transferring angles; in the middle, dividers and pens; at the bottom, a protractor for laying out angles. (*Mount Vernon Ladies Association, Mount Vernon, Va.*)

Fig. 1-3e. Leonardo da Vinci's sketch of a sprocket chain. Notice the many different views. (*Lieb Museum*)

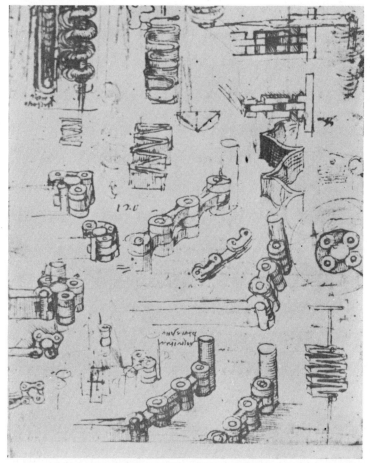

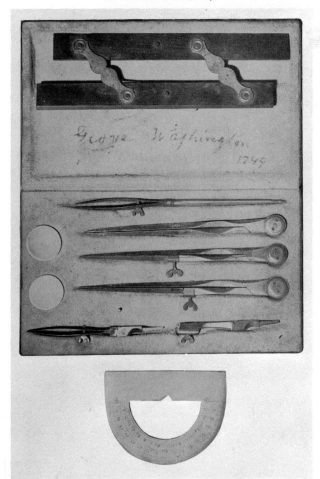

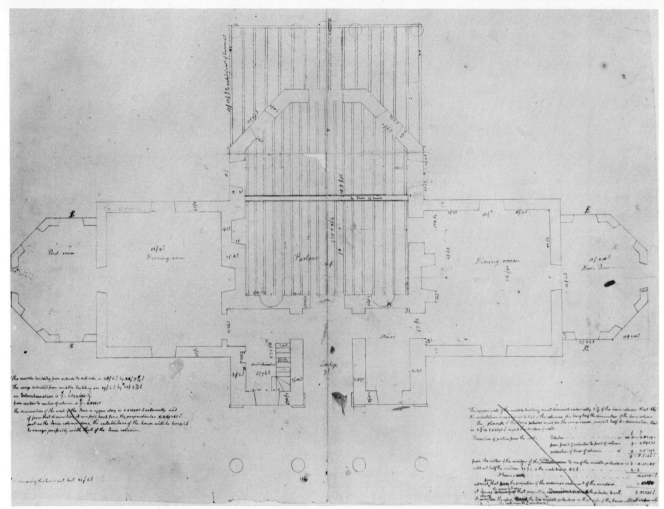

Fig. 1-4c. Thomas Jefferson's plan for the first story of his home, Monticello. *(Massachusetts Historical Society)*

and diagrams. Today there is hardly a newspaper, magazine, catalogue, or book without them.

1·5 A precise language. Photographs (Fig. 1-5a) are often used today to show what something looks like. We also use perspective drawings (Fig. 1-5b) to show a bridge, building, or other structure as it appears to our eyes. However, such drawings and photographs do not show the exact shape and size of all the details of an object. A photograph or perspective drawing does not show the inside parts or the exact ways in which the parts fit together. We need another kind of

Fig. 1-4e. Minot's Ledge Lighthouse in Boston Bay was designed by West Point graduates. *(U.S. Military Academy)*

Fig. 1-4*d*. An early drawing for Monticello by Thomas Jefferson. *(Massachusetts Historical Society)*

Fig. 1-5*a*. Silorsky helicopters. The S-61R is hovering; on the ground is its military counter-part, the U.S. Air Force CH-3C, which is used for long-range rotary-wing support aircraft to carry cargo and personnel. *(Sikorsky Division of United Aircraft Corporation)*

drawing to show this information. Fortunately, another form of description has been developed by which exact shapes can be defined accurately. This method, known as *mechanical drawing,* consists of a series of views arranged according to a definite system (orthographic projection, discussed in Chap. 5) with figures added to tell sizes.

Mechanical drawings provide the builder or manufacturer with the exact description that he needs to build what the designer has in mind. Such view drawings are more widely used than any other type of drawing. To make such a drawing (Fig. 1-5*c*), we draw the views as seen from the front, top, and side.

We draw its shape and the outline of its parts. We use different types of lines according to definite rules. We make the lines exact lengths (or proportional lengths), and we add measurements to show their true lengths. In this way we project each view onto the drawing paper.

We study mechanical drawing and the rules of orthographic projection so that we can not only make accurate mechanical drawings of our own but also understand the mechanical drawings made by others. In Chaps. 2 through 10 of this book are most of the rules for the precise language of mechanical drawing. By applying these rules and making good view drawings by orthographic projection, we can show other people exactly what we want to make or build. Accurate drawings prevent mistakes.

1•6 A universal language. Because views made by orthographic projection give an exact description of what is to be made, they mean the same thing to everyone. Drawings that are made correctly can be used not only in this country but also, with few changes, in countries where people speak a different language. In this country many different workmen read and use the same drawings.

Different kinds of industry have developed special symbols that are useful in their daily work and save time in making and reading drawings. Other methods of saving time in the study and explanation of complex drawings include models and mock-ups (full-size models). Scale models in connection with plan drawings are especially useful to determine the best arrangement of machinery and equipment, as for a plant layout (Fig. 1-6a). A mock-up is useful as a means of checking a design as it appears in three dimensions for comparison with the two-dimensional views of the drawing.

Special drafting machines (Fig. 1-6b) are used for many engineering and scientific purposes where a high degree of accuracy in measurements and a high degree of excellence in drawing are required. Chaps. 11 through 24 of this book tell how to make the drawings for machinists, aircraft workers, sheet-metal workers, electricians, electronic technicians, carpenters, and other workmen. Since mechanical drawing is the language of industry, draftsmen who can make good view drawings are necessary.

Learning drawing, then, is much more than simply learning how to draw. It is learning to read and write a new language, just as real a language as English or French. A knowledge of this graphic language is a necessary part of the education of professional engineers and scientists. Its mastery requires study and practice with close attention to details. Its importance to anyone who expects to go into any branch of technical designing, manufacturing, or building justifies all the time spent in studying it.

1•7 Problem suggestions. Group 1, page 398. A few names are listed in this group for possible reading assignments. The instructor may add others according to his interest and with regard to local industries. Men who have the ability to think in space and to record such thinking are responsible for the development of science and technology. Mechanical drawing is the graphic language used in science and engineering.

Fig. 1-5b. A perspective drawing of the San Francisco–Oakland Bay Bridge. Notice how it gives the effect of distance. *(Designed by California Department of Public Works. Constructed by American Bridge Division of United States Steel)*

2
Learning to draw

Fig. 2-1. Partial view of the engineering department of Ling-Temco-Vought, Inc.

TO LEFT-HANDED
STUDENTS
Directions are given for right-handed students. In most cases left-handed students can reverse directions. However, this is not always the case, and some variations may be necessary to permit good work to be done without difficulty.

2•1 The drafting room. The necessary plans and directions for accomplishing engineering work of all kinds are prepared in the drafting room (Fig. 2-1). Here the designs are worked out and checked. Chapter 1 explained why drawing is really a language and why drawings are used in industrial, engineering, and scientific work. Sometimes designers or scientists make freehand sketches for preliminary study or to present ideas, but for purposes where accuracy is necessary, drawings are made with instruments. In learning to read and write this language we must learn what tools and instruments to use and how to use them skillfully, accurately, and quickly.

Most of the usual instruments and equipment are named in the following list.

Drawing board (Art. 2·3)
T-square (Art. 2·4)
Drawing sheets (Art. 2·6)
Drafting tape, thumbtacks, etc. (Art. 2·7)
Drawing pencils (Art. 2·8)
Pencil sharpener (Art. 2·9)
Eraser (Art. 2·11)
Erasing shield (Art. 2·11)

Triangles, 45° and 30°–60° (Arts. 2·15 and 2·16)
Architect's scales (Art. 2·25)
Irregular curve (Art. 2·36)
Case instruments (Art. 2·30)
Lettering instruments (Art. 3·3)
Black drawing ink (Art. 8·2)
Penholder and pens (Art. 3·5)
Penwiper
Brush or dust cloth
Protractor (Art. 2·14)
Decimal-inch scale (Art. 2·24)
Engineer's scale (Art. 2·23)
Cleaning powder

The instructor can list and specify the required items, sizes, and other necessary information.

The directions in this chapter apply to the basic equipment used for making drawings. However, other equipment designed to save time and increase efficiency is coming into regular use in drafting offices. Such equipment includes parallel-ruling straightedges, the several types of drafting machines, and desk-type drafting tables using regular office chairs (Arts. 2·21 and 2·22). These devices increase the efficiency of the draftsman.

Fig. 2-3. Drawing boards are made in many types.

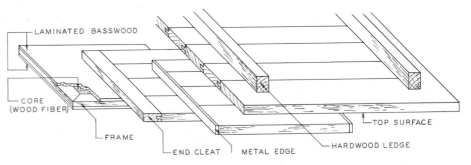

LAMINATED BASSWOOD
CORE (WOOD FIBER)
FRAME
END CLEAT
METAL EDGE
TOP SURFACE
HARDWOOD LEDGE

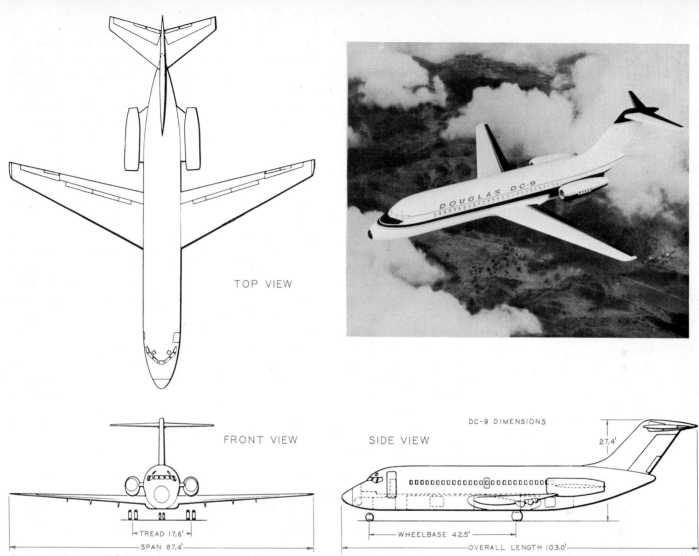

TOP VIEW

FRONT VIEW

SIDE VIEW

DC-9 DIMENSIONS

27.4'

TREAD 17.6'

SPAN 87.4'

WHEELBASE 42.5'

OVERALL LENGTH 103.0'

Fig. 1-5c. Douglas DC-9 twin-jet transport plane. The three-view orthographic projection drawing shows the outline and overall dimensions of the plane. Notice the difference between these views and the photograph. (Douglas Aircraft Company, Inc.)

Fig. 1-6a. Drawings are put to many uses. This model of a factory is built over a plan. (Factory Management and Maintenance)

Fig. 1-6b. Drafting machines of various kinds are often used in industry. The operator of this machine has made a map by tracing many key features from an aerial photograph. (Wild Heerbrugg Instruments, Inc.)

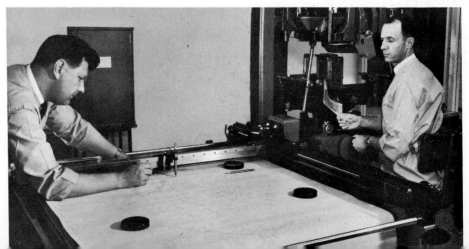

Special drafting machines made for very accurate drawing work are used for laying out, plotting, and tape operation (Fig. 1-6b).

2·2 Drawing tables and desks vary greatly in size and design. They may have a fixed top to hold a separate, movable drawing board, a fixed top made for use as a drawing board, an adjustable top to hold a separate drawing board at a desired slope, or an adjustable top made for use as a drawing board.

They may be "stand-up" tables for use with high stools. They may be "sit-down" regular desk-high drawing tables. Or they may be various combinations of desks and tables for sit-down and stand-up use. The combination of a drafting table and desk used with a regular office chair provides a comfortable and efficient arrangement and is replacing the high drawing table in drafting rooms and engineering offices.

2·3 Drawing boards (Fig. 2-3). The sheet upon which a drawing is made is attached to a drawing board. Usual sizes for student or personal use are 9" × 12", 16" × 21", and 18" × 24". Larger sizes for engineering and architectural designs may have any necessary dimensions. Boards are generally made of soft pine or basswood and constructed so that they will stay flat and have the guiding edge (or edges) straight. Hardwood or metal (steel or aluminum) strips are used at the ends on some boards to provide true guiding edges.

2·4 T-squares (Fig. 2-4) are made of various materials, but most have plastic-edged wood blades or clear plastic blades and heads of wood or plastic. Stainless steel or hard aluminum blades with alloy heads are used where great accuracy is required. The blade (straightedge) must be straight and attached securely to the top surface of

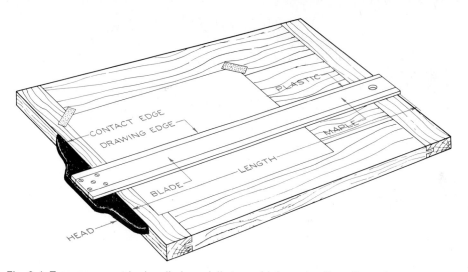

Fig. 2-4. T-squares must be handled carefully to avoid damaging the ruling edge.

the head. This permits the contact surface of the head to be held against the guiding edge of the drawing board and so keep the blade in a working position.

Some T-squares are made with an adjustable head which allows the blade to be lined up with the drawing or set to any angle if the head has a protractor (Art. 2·14). The size of a T-square is the length of the blade measured from the contact surface of the head.

2·5 American Standard trimmed sizes of drawing sheets. Two series of sizes are listed. One is based upon the standard-size letter paper, 8½" × 11", and the other upon a sheet 9" × 12". Multiples of these sizes are used for larger sheets, as follows:

Size	First series	Second series
A	8½" × 11"	9" × 12"
B	11" × 17"	12" × 18"
C	17" × 22"	18" × 24"
D	22" × 34"	24" × 36"
E	34" × 44"	36" × 48"

2·6 Drawing sheets. Drawings are made on many different materials. Papers include white and tinted papers

(cream and pale green). They are made in many thicknesses and qualities. For some purposes they are mounted on muslin or aluminum sheets. Most drawings are made directly in pencil on tracing paper, vellum, tracing cloth, glass cloth, or film. When such materials are used, copies can be made by blueprinting or other reproduction methods (Arts. 8·13 to 8·15).

Vellum is tracing paper which has been treated to increase its transparency. Tracing cloth is a finely woven cotton cloth treated to provide a good working surface and good transparency. Polyester films are coming into use as a material on which to make drawings. They have great transparency, high strength, and exceptional durability. A matte surface is provided for drawing purposes and is suitable for both pencil and ink work.

2·7 Mounting drawing sheets on the board. The sheet may be held in place on the board by various methods (Fig. 2-7a). Drafting tape may be placed across the corners of the sheet and at other places, if needed. Stik-tacks (thin disks with adhesive on both sides) may be placed on the board and under the sheet. They may be removed and re-

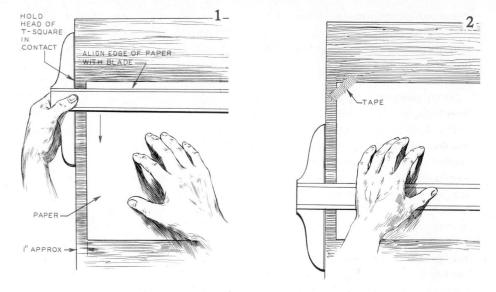

Fig. 2-7a. Some ways of fastening the drawing sheet to the drawing board.

Fig. 2-7b. Adjusting and fastening the drawing sheet on the drawing board.

used. Similar material may be obtained in squares or as tape. A small amount of rubber cement may be placed on the board under the corners of the sheet. These methods leave the surface of the sheet entirely clear for the free movement of the T-square and triangles. They do not damage the corners or the edges of the sheet. They also can be used on composition or other hard-surface boards and are preferred by most draftsmen. Thumbtacks, if used, should be pushed straight down until the heads are in complete contact with the sheet. Small wire staples may be used but may damage the sheet. Thumbtacks and staples can only be used on soft pine or similar soft boards.

To fasten the paper, or other drawing sheet (Fig. 2-7b), place it on the drawing board with the left edge an inch or so away from the left edge of the board. Left-handed students will work from the right-hand edge. The lower edge of the sheet should be placed about four inches up from the bottom of the board, or as much more as will provide a comfortable working position. Then line up the sheet with the

T-square blade as shown at Space 1. Hold the sheet in position. Move the T-square down as at Space 2, keeping the head of the T-square against the edge of the board. Then fasten each corner of the sheet with drafting tape (or by other means). Drawing sheets 8½" × 11" and up to 12" × 18" may be held in place by fastening the two upper corners.

2•8 Drawing pencils. There are presently four types of drawing-pencil leads. The first type is the conventional graphite lead used in pencils for over 200 years and made chiefly of graphite, clay, and resins. Drafting pencils of this type are normally made in 17 degrees of hardness (grades), as follows:

6B (softest and blackest)
5B (extremely soft)
4B (extra soft)
3B (very soft)
2B (soft, plus)
B (soft)
HB (medium soft)
F (intermediate, between soft and hard)

H (medium hard)
2H (hard)
3H (hard, plus)
4H (very hard)
5H (extra hard)
6H (extra hard, plus)
7H (extremely hard)
8H (extremely hard, plus)
9H (hardest)

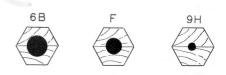

These pencils are made primarily for use on paper or vellum and for secondary use on cloth.

The right grade of pencil to use will depend upon the surface of the material on which the drawing is made, the kind of line required for blackness, or opacity, and the width of the line. For laying out views on fairly hard-surfaced drawing paper, the usual grades are 4H and 6H. For finished views on tracing paper or cloth for reproduction, the H or 2H pencil is favored. Grades sometimes used for sketching, lettering, arrowheads, symbols, border lines, and so forth, include HB, F, H, and 2H, according to the result desired on the surface of the material on which the drawing is made.

Since film has come into use for drawings, new types of pencil lead have been developed. Three types are described, based upon information furnished by the Joseph Dixon Crucible Company. The first type, developed for use on film, is called a *plastic pencil*. This type has a black crayon extruded lead formed by a "plasticizing" process; it is not fired. It has good microfilm reproduction characteristics. The second type has a "combination" part-plastic and part-graphite fired lead. This type holds a point well, gives a good opaque line, does not smear easily, erases well, and has good microfilming qualities. Also, it can be used on paper or cloth as well as on film. The third type has an unfired combination lead of part plastic and part graphite. This type differs from the second type in that it is not fired but is extruded under pressure. It does not hold a point well, gives a

fairly opaque line, erases well, does not smear easily, and has good microfilming qualities. It is made primarily for use on film. The three types of lead are made in a limited number of grades (five or six). The grades do not correspond to the grades used for the conventional leads. Different systems of letters and numbers are used by the pencil makers to tell the type of lead and the relative hardness of their products.

2•9 Sharpening the pencil. Sharpen the pencil by cutting away the wood at a long slope, as at A in Fig. 2-9a. Always cut from the plain end so as to keep the grade mark. Be careful not to cut the lead. Leave it exposed for about ³⁄₈ to ½ in. Then shape the lead to a long conical point by rubbing it back and forth on a sandpaper pad (or on a fine file), as at B, while revolving slowly to form the point, as at C or D. Some draftsmen prefer the flat, or chisel, point shown at E, especially for drawings with a large number of straight lines. Keep the sandpaper pad at hand

so that the point can be kept sharp by frequent rubbing.

Mechnical sharpeners (Fig. 2-9b) are made with special draftsman's cutters to remove the wood as shown. Special pointers are made for shaping the lead, as in Fig. 2-9c. Such devices may be operated either by hand or electrically.

Refill pencils are widely used by draftsmen. They hold plain leads by means of a clutch which permits the exposed lead to be adjusted to any length. The lead is shaped as described for wood-encased leads; however, some refill pencils have a built-in sharpener that shapes the lead.

Pencil lines must be clean and dark enough to bring out the views using the standard lines of Fig. 2-10. You can avoid using too much pressure and grooving the drawing surface if you use the proper grade of lead. Develop the habit of rotating the pencil between the thumb and forefinger as the line is being drawn. This will help you to keep a uniform line and will keep the point from wearing down unevenly. *Never sharpen a pencil over the drawing*

Fig. 2-9a. Sharpening the pencil properly is important.

Fig. 2-9b. A draftsman's pencil sharpener cuts the wood but not the lead.

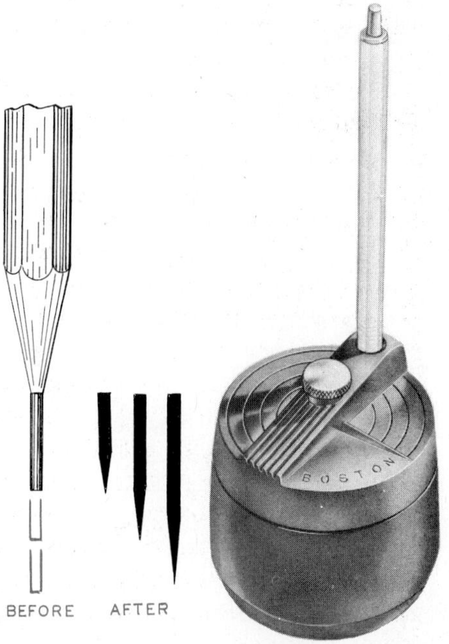

Fig. 2-9c. This lead pointer allows a choice of points. *(Hunt Manufacturing Company)*

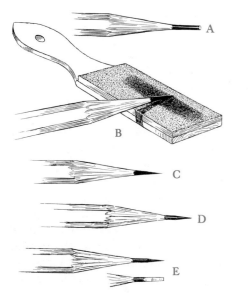

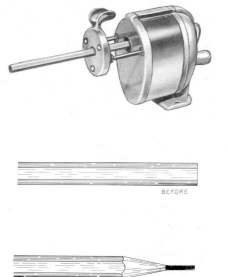

board. *Wipe the lead with a cloth to remove the dust and the extra-fine or sharp needle point.* Care in such matters will do much to keep the drawing clean and bright. This is especially important when the original pencil drawing must be used to make copies (see Arts. 8·13 to 8·16).

2·10 Alphabet of lines. The different lines, or line symbols, used on drawings represent a kind of graphical alphabet. The line symbols recommended by the

Fig. 2-10. The alphabet of lines for pencil drawings and how they are used. (See Fig. 8-3 for ink lines.)

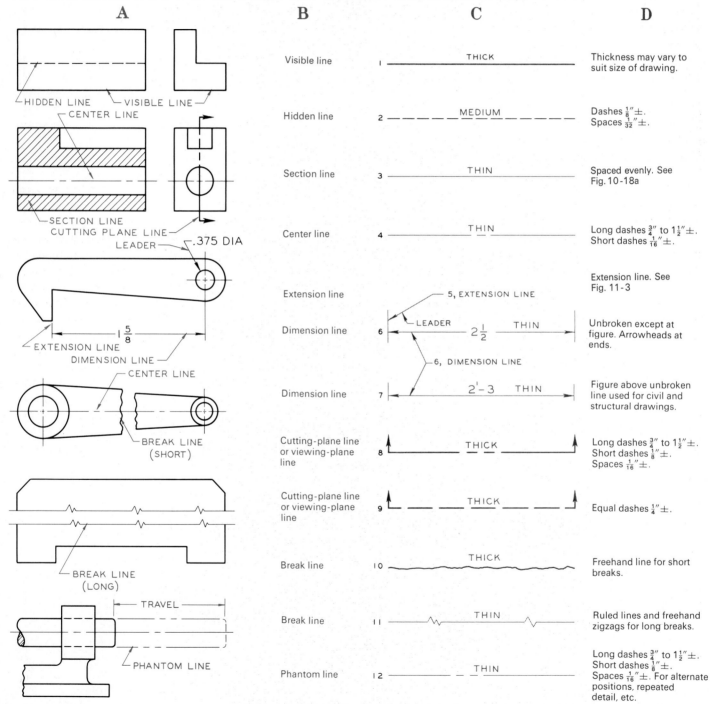

	B	C	D
A	Visible line	1 — THICK —	Thickness may vary to suit size of drawing.
	Hidden line	2 — — — MEDIUM — —	Dashes $\frac{1}{8}''\pm$. Spaces $\frac{1}{32}''\pm$.
	Section line	3 — THIN —	Spaced evenly. See Fig. 10-18a
	Center line	4 — THIN —	Long dashes $\frac{3}{4}''$ to $1\frac{1}{2}''\pm$. Short dashes $\frac{1}{16}''\pm$.
	Extension line	5, EXTENSION LINE	Extension line. See Fig. 11-3
	Dimension line	6 LEADER $2\frac{1}{2}$ THIN	Unbroken except at figure. Arrowheads at ends.
	Dimension line	7 $2'-3$ THIN	Figure above unbroken line used for civil and structural drawings.
	Cutting-plane line or viewing-plane line	8 — THICK —	Long dashes $\frac{3}{4}''$ to $1\frac{1}{2}''\pm$. Short dashes $\frac{1}{8}''\pm$. Spaces $\frac{1}{16}''\pm$.
	Cutting-plane line or viewing-plane line	9 — — THICK — —	Equal dashes $\frac{1}{4}''\pm$.
	Break line	10 THICK	Freehand line for short breaks.
	Break line	11 —∧— THIN —∧—	Ruled lines and freehand zigzags for long breaks.
	Phantom line	12 — THIN —	Long dashes $\frac{3}{4}''$ to $1\frac{1}{2}''\pm$. Short dashes $\frac{1}{8}''\pm$. Spaces $\frac{1}{16}''\pm$. For alternate positions, repeated detail, etc.

American Standards Association are shown in Fig. 2-10 for pencil drawings (see Art. 8·3 for ink lines). Three widths of lines—thick, medium, and thin—are generally used. Sometimes a medium-thick line may be used in place of the thick and medium lines, but the result is not so good. Drawings are much easier to read when there is good contrast between the different kinds of lines. Pencil lines should be uniformly sharp and black.

2•11 Erasers and erasing shields. Soft erasers, such as the vinyl type, the Pink Pearl, or the art gum, are used for cleaning soiled places or light pencil marks from drawings. Rub-kleen, Ruby, or Emerald erasers are good for most purposes to remove pencil or ink. Ink erasers contain grit and have to be used with extreme care, if used at all, to avoid injuring the surface. Electric erasing machines (Fig. 2-11) are in common use in drafting rooms.

Metal or plastic erasing shields have openings of various sizes and shapes.

Fig. 2-11. An electric erasing machine saves time. *(Eugene Dietzgen Company)*

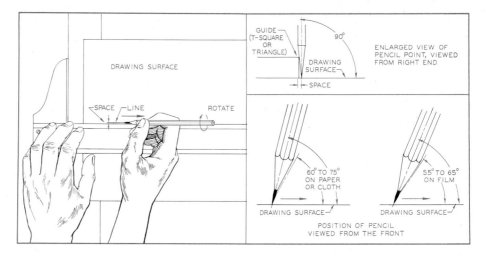

Fig. 2-12. Drawing a horizontal line.

They are convenient for protecting lines which are not to be erased. Lines on paper or cloth are erased along the direction of the work. Lines on film are erased *at right angles to* the direction of the work. A vinyl-type or other eraser without grit should be used. Erasing on film is done very carefully by hand.

2•12 To draw horizontal lines (Fig. 2-12). The upper edge of the T-square blade is used as a guide for drawing horizontal lines. Place the head of the T-square in contact with the left edge of the board with the left hand. Keep it in contact and move the T-square to the desired position. Hold the pencil about an inch from the point and inclined in the direction in which the line is being drawn. On film it is necessary to keep the pencil at a constant angle (55° to 65°) for the whole length of the line and to use less pressure than on paper or other material. The point of the lead should be kept a slight distance away from the corner between the guiding edge and the drawing surface, as shown, so that the draftsman can see where the line is being drawn and also to avoid a poor or smudged line. *Care must be taken to keep the line parallel to the guiding edge.*

2•13 To draw vertical lines (Fig. 2-13). A triangle in combination with a T-square is used for drawing vertical lines. Place the head of the T-square in contact with the left edge of the board. Keep it in contact and move the T-square to a position below the start of the vertical line. Place a triangle against the T-square blade and move it to the desired position. Keep the vertical edge of the triangle toward the left and draw upward. Incline the pencil at an angle in the direction in which the line is being drawn. Be sure to keep this angle constant when drawing on film. Keep the point of the lead far enough out from the guiding edge that you can see where the line is being drawn. Keep the line parallel to the guiding edge.

2•14 Angles (Figs. 2-14a and 2-14b). An angle is formed when two straight lines meet at a point. The point is called the *vertex,* and the lines are called the *sides* of the angle. The unit of measurement for angles is called a *degree* and is marked by the symbol °. If the circumference of a circle is divided into 360 parts, each part measures an angle of 1°. Then one-fourth of a circle would measure $^{360}/_4 = 90°$, as at A in Fig. 2-14a. This is called a *right angle*. An *acute*

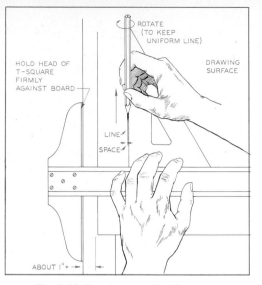

Fig. 2-13. Drawing a vertical line.

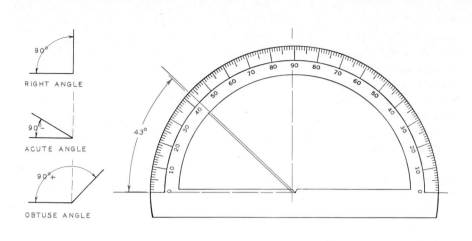

Fig. 2-14b. A protractor is used to lay out, or measure, angles.

angle (B) is less than 90°. An *obtuse angle* (C) is greater than 90°. For closer measurements, degrees are divided into 60 equal parts called *minutes* (') and minutes, into 60 equal parts called *seconds* ("). Notice that the size of an angle does not depend upon the length of the sides; therefore, the number of degrees in an angle will be the same regardless of the diameter of the circle.

An instrument used in measuring or laying out angles is called a *protractor.* A semicircular form is shown in Fig. 2-14b, where an angle of 43° is measured. Drafting machines and adjustable-head T-squares have an adjustable protractor for laying out angles. Angles of 45°, 30°, and 60° can be drawn direct-

ly, and angles varying by 15° can be drawn with the triangles, as described in Arts. 2·15 and 2·16.

2·15 To draw lines inclined at 45°, 30°, and 60°. The 45° triangle (Fig. 2-15a) has two angles of 45 ° and one of 90°. Slanted, or inclined, lines at 45° with horizontal or vertical lines are drawn with the triangle held against the T-square blade, or horizontal straightedge, as shown at A, B, and C in Fig. 2-15a. The 45° triangle may be used to lay off eight equal angles of 45° about a center and for many constructions. The 30°–60° triangle (Fig. 2-15b) has angles of 30°, 60°, and 90°. Inclined lines at 30° and 60° with hori-

zontal or vertical lines are drawn with the triangle held against the T-square blade or horizontal straightedge, as shown at A and B in Figs. 2-15b and 2-15c. The 30°–60° triangle may be used to lay off equal angles, 6 at 60° or 12 at 30°, about a center and for many constructions.

2·16 To draw lines at angles varying by 15°. The 45° and 30°–60° triangles, alone or together and in combination with the T-square, may be used to draw angles increasing by 15°, as 15°, 30°, 45°, 60°, 75°, and so forth, with the horizontal or vertical line. Some arrangements of the triangles for drawing angles of 15° and 75° are suggested at

Fig. 2-14a. Angles are measured in degrees, minutes, and seconds.

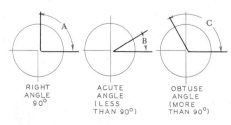

Fig. 2-15a. The 45° triangle has angles of 45° and 90°.

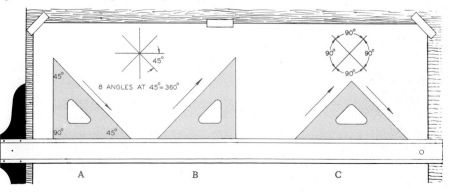

A, B, C, and D in Fig. 2-16a. Methods of obtaining the different angles are shown in Fig. 2-16b. In Space 15 the lines have been drawn for all the positions, and all the angles are 15°. By using the arrangements of Spaces 2 and 13 or Spaces 6 and 9, two angles of 30° and two angles of 15° may be obtained. Try different combinations of triangles until you are familiar with the various arrangements. Any angle may be laid off with the protractor (Art. 2·14).

2•17 To draw parallel lines. Parallel horizontal lines can be drawn with the T-square. Parallel vertical lines can be drawn by using a triangle in combination with the T-square. Parallel lines at regular angles may be drawn with the triangles, as suggested in Fig. 2-16b. Parallel lines in any position may be drawn by using a triangle in combination with the T-square or another triangle, as shown in the steps of Fig. 2-18, or they may be drawn directly with a drafting machine (Art. 2·21).

2•18 To draw a line parallel to a given line (Fig. 2-18). Place a triangle against the T-square blade (Space 1) and move them together until one edge of the triangle matches the given line (Space 2). Hold the T-square firmly and slide the triangle along the blade until the desired position is reached. Then draw the parallel line (Space 3). In Fig. 2-18 the hypotenuse of the triangle is used to draw the parallel line, but other edges or the 30°–60° triangle may be used. In Space 4 a triangle is used in place of the T-square. Parallel lines may be drawn directly with a drafting machine.

2•19 To draw perpendicular lines. Lines at right angles (90°) with each other are perpendicular. A vertical line is perpendicular to a horizontal line. Perpendicular lines may be drawn using triangles and T-square or drawn directly with a drafting machine.

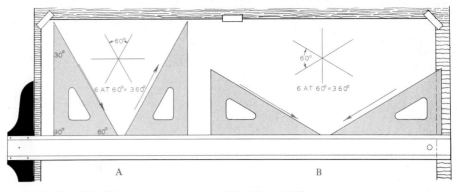

Fig. 2-15b. The 30°–60° triangle has angles of 30°, 60°, and 90°.

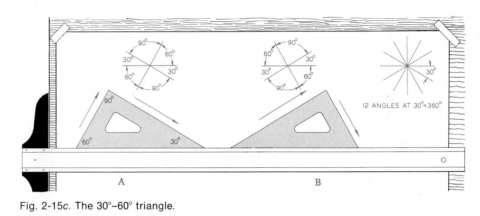

Fig. 2-15c. The 30°–60° triangle.

Fig. 2-16a. Drawing lines at 15° and 75° using the two triangles.

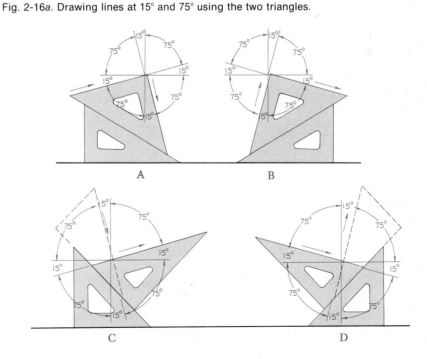

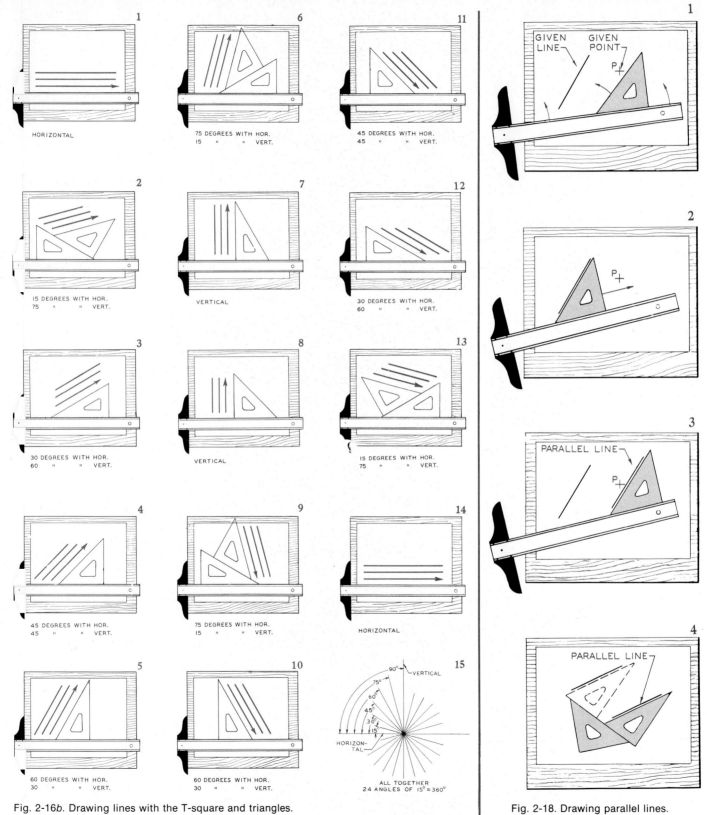

Fig. 2-16b. Drawing lines with the T-square and triangles.

Fig. 2-18. Drawing parallel lines.

2•20 To draw a perpendicular to any line. Two methods can be used.

First method (Fig. 2-20a). Place a triangle and the T-square together so that one edge of the triangle matches the given line, as in Space 1. Hold the T-square firmly. Slide the triangle along the blade to the desired position, as in Space 2, and draw the perpendicular. The 45° triangle may be used instead of the 30°–60° triangle, as in Space 3. A triangle may be used instead of the T-square, as in Space 4.

Second method (Fig. 2-20b). Place a triangle and the T-square together so that the hypotenuse of the triangle matches the given line, as in Space 1. Turn the triangle about its right-angled corner, as in Space 2, and slide it until it is in the desired position (Space 3); draw the perpendicular. The 45° triangle may be used instead of the 30°–60° triangle. A triangle may be used instead of the T-square, as in Space 4.

2•21 Drafting machines. There are two types of drafting machines in general use. One type, shown in Fig. 2-21a, uses an anchor and two arms to hold an adjustable protractor head with two scales, ordinarily at right angles. The arms allow the scales to be moved any place on the drawing parallel to the starting position. Another type, Fig. 2-21b, uses a horizontal guide rail at the top of the board and a moving arm rail at right angles to the top rail. An adjustable protractor head and two scales, ordinarily at right angles, move up and down on the arm. The scales may be moved any place on the drawing parallel to the starting position. This type is convenient on large boards or boards in a vertical position or at a steep angle.

It is estimated that over 60 percent of the industrial drafting departments now use drafting machines. Many school drafting departments teach drawing with drafting machines. Draft-

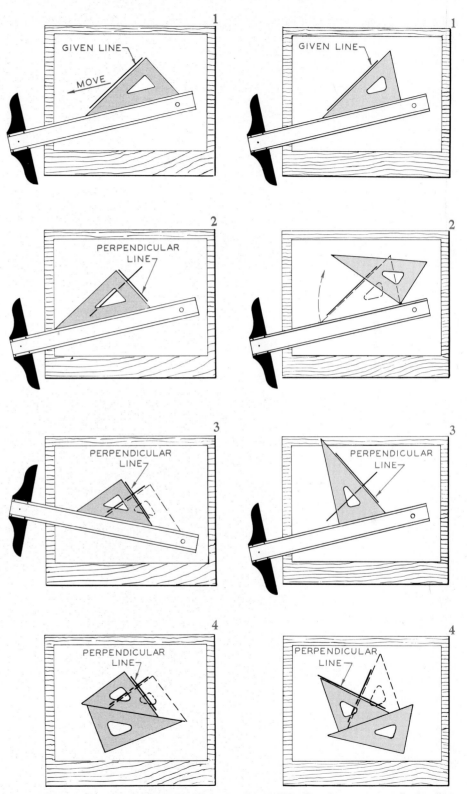

Fig. 2-20a. Drawing a perpendicular line, first method.

Fig. 2-20b. Drawing a perpendicular line, second method.

Fig. 2-21a. This drafting machine is one type used to save time. *(Universal Drafting Machine Corporation)*

ing machines combine the functions of the T-square, triangles, scales, and protractor. Lines can be drawn the exact lengths in the required places and at any angles by moving the scale ruling edge to the desired positions. This results in greater speed with less effort in making drawings. A complete understanding of the possibilities, efficient use, and care of the drafting machine will reveal its value.

A portable drafting machine (Fig. 2-21c) has many advantages where drawings are not over 14" × 20". The "drawing board" is a sheet of plexiglass which allows light to diffuse from under the sloping board to prevent shadows. This is especially convenient for tracing or seeing through tracings for checking.

2•22 Parallel-ruling straightedges (Fig. 2-22) are used by many draftsmen. They are especially convenient when working on large boards in a vertical or nearly vertical position. A guide cord, clamped to the ends of the straightedge, runs through a series of pulleys on the back of the board so that the straightedge may be moved up and down in parallel positions.

2•23 Scales are made in different shapes (Fig. 2-23) and of different materials, such as boxwood, white plastic on boxwood, plastic, and metal. They are made with different divisions to meet the requirements for making different kinds of drawings. Commonly used scales include the architect's scale (Fig. 2-25), the mechanical engineer's scale (Fig. 2-24a), and the civil engineer's scale (Fig. 2-26). These may be of any of the shapes shown in Fig. 2-23.

Scales are used for laying off distances and for making measurements, whether full size or in proportion to

Fig. 2-21b. This track-type drafting machine is especially adapted for wide drawings, in addition to use for regular sizes of drawings. *(Keuffel & Esser Company)*

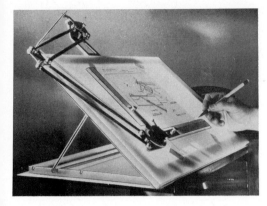

Fig. 2-21c. This portable compact drafting unit, the Techno-Graph, combines a balanced drafting machine with a plexiglass drafting board. *(Alexander Drafting Equipment Company)*

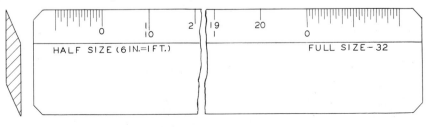

Fig. 2-22. A parallel-ruling straightedge is another convenient device used to save time. *(Eugene Dietzgen Company)*

full size. See Arts. 2·28 and 2·29. Scales may be obtained *open divided* (Figs. 2-24a and 2-25), with only the end units subdivided; or they may be *chain divided* (Figs. 2-24b and 2-26), with subdivisions the entire length of the scale.

2·24 The mechanical engineer's scale. The conventional mechanical engineer's scale (Fig. 2-24a) has inches and fractions of an inch divided to represent inches. The usual divisions are:

Full size, 1 in. divided to read in 32nds.

Half size, ½ in. divided to read in 16ths.

Quarter size, ¼ in. divided to read in 8ths.

Eighth size, ⅛ in. divided to read in 4ths.

These scales are used for drawing parts of machines or where larger reductions are not required. The scale to which the views are drawn should be given on the drawing, either in the title or, if several parts are drawn to different scales, near the views, as:

$$\text{Full size} \quad \text{or} \quad 1'' = 1''$$
$$\text{Half size} \quad \text{or} \quad \frac{1}{2}'' = 1''$$

The decimal-inch system[1] uses a scale divided for measurements in decimals of an inch (Fig. 2-24b). For full size, 1 in. is divided into 50 parts (each part of $\frac{1}{50} = 0.02''$) so that measurements can be readily made to hun-

─────────

[1]See latest American Standard *Scales for Use with Decimal-Inch Dimensioning.*

dredths of an inch by sight. Some usual divisions are:

Full size, 1 in. divided into 50ths.
Half size, ½ in. divided into 10ths.
Three-eighths size, ⅜ in. divided into 10ths.
One-quarter size, divided into 10ths.

The decimal-inch system has been used in the automotive industry for many years, and it is increasing in favor and use in other engineering fields. The use of decimal dimensioning is explained in Chap. 11.

2·25 The architect's scale (Fig. 2-25) is divided into proportional feet and inches. The triangular form shown is used a great deal in schools and in some drafting offices because it con-

Fig. 2-23. Some shapes of scales.

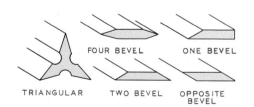

TRIANGULAR   TWO BEVEL   OPPOSITE BEVEL
    FOUR BEVEL   ONE BEVEL

Fig. 2-24a. Mechanical engineer's scale, open divided.

HALF SIZE (6 IN.=1 FT.)   0   10   2   19   20   0   FULL SIZE-32

tains a variety of scales on a single stick. Many draftsmen prefer flat scales, especially when frequent changes of scale are not required. The symbol ′ is used for feet and ″ for inches. Thus three feet four and one-half inches is written 3′–4½″. When all dimensions are in inches, standard practice is to omit the symbol.

The usual proportional scales are:

Full size, 12″ = 1′–0″
¼ size, 3″ = 1′–0″
⅛ size, 1½″ = 1′–0″
1/12 size, 1″ = 1′–0″
1/16 size, ¾″ = 1′–0″
1/24 size, ½″ = 1′–0″
1/32 size, ⅜″ = 1′–0″
1/48 size, ¼″ = 1′–0″
1/64 size, 3/16″ = 1′–0″
1/96 size, ⅛″ = 1′–0″
1/128 size, 3/32″ = 1′–0″

These scales are used in drawing buildings and in making many mechanical, electrical, and other engineering drawings. They are much used as a general-purpose scale. The scale to which the views are made should be given on the drawing, either in the title or, if several parts are drawn to different scales, near the view, as:

6″ = 1′–0″
3″ = 1′–0″
1½″ = 1′–0″

2·26 The civil engineer's scale (Fig. 2-26) has inches divided into decimals. The usual divisions are:

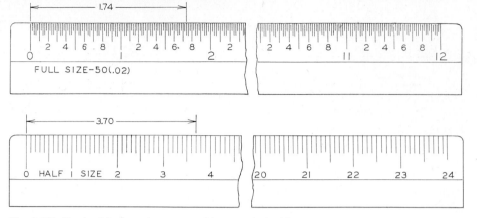

FULL SIZE–50(.02)

HALF SIZE

Fig. 2-24b. Decimal-inch scales are used in many industries.

10 parts to the inch

20 parts to the inch

30 parts to the inch

40 parts to the inch

50 parts to the inch

60 parts to the inch

70 parts to the inch

With this scale 1 in. may be used to represent feet, rods, miles, and so forth, or to represent quantities, time, or other units. The divisions may represent single units or multiples of 10, 100, and so on. Thus the 20 parts to an inch scale may represent 20, 200, or 2000 units. This scale is used for civil engineering work, such as maps (Chap. 23), roads, and other public projects. It is also used where decimal divisions are required, such as plotting data, drawing graphic charts (Chap. 24), and so forth.

The scale used should be given on the drawing or other presentation as:

1″ = 100 feet
1″ = 500 miles
1″ = 200 pounds

For some purposes a graphic scale is placed on a map, drawing, or chart.

EXAMPLE:

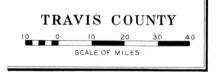

TRAVIS COUNTY

SCALE OF MILES

2·27 Metric scales (Fig. 2-27) are divided into centimeters (cm), with centimeters divided into millimeters (mm) (10 divisions) or into half millimeters (20 divisions). Some scales are made with metric divisions on one edge and inch divisions on an opposite edge.

Fig. 2-25. Architect's scale, open divided. The triangular form has many proportional scales.

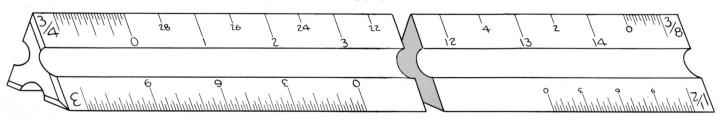

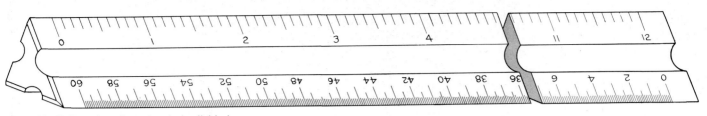

Fig. 2-26. Civil engineer's scale, chain divided.

The length of a 30-cm scale approximates the length of a 12-in. scale. $1'' = 2.54$ cm, and $12 \times 2.54 = 30.48$ cm. See the Appendix for a table of metric units and equivalents.

The metric system is used in France, Germany, Italy, the countries of South America, and many other countries, while the English system is used throughout the English-speaking world. The metric system is favored and used in laboratories and for certain industries in this country, such as for spark plugs and ball bearings. Industry as a whole favors the decimal-inch system (Art. 2·24).

2·28 Full-size drawings. When the object is not too large for the paper, it may be drawn full size, using the inches and fractions scale. *To make a measurement,* put the scale on the paper in the direction to be measured. Make a short, light dash opposite the zero on the scale (Fig. 2-28a) and another dash opposite the division at the desired distance. Do not make a dot or punch a

hole in the surface. Note the short marks on Fig. 2-28b, where a full-size distance of $1\frac{7}{16}''$ is laid off.

2·29 Drawing to scale. If the object is large or has little detail, it may be drawn in a *reduced proportion.* The first reduction is to the scale of $6'' = 1'-0''$, commonly called *half size.* A full-size scale can be used to draw a half size by considering each half inch to represent 1 in. and each 12-in. scale to represent a 24-in. scale. This is illustrated in Fig. 2-29a, where $3\frac{5}{8}''$ is laid off by three half inches and five-eighths of the next half inch. Always think full size. If one is available, a scale divided and marked for half size (Fig. 2-24a) is more convenient to use.

If smaller views are required, the next reduction that may be used is the scale of $3'' = 1'-0''$, often called *quarter size.* Find this scale on the architect's scale and examine it. The actual length of three inches represents one foot divided into 12 parts, each representing one inch and further divided into

eighths. Learn to think of the 12 parts as representing real inches.

EXAMPLE: To lay off the distance of $1'-0\frac{1}{2}''$ (Fig. 2-29b). Notice the position of the zero mark, placed so that inches are measured in one direction from it and feet in the other direction, as shown in the figure.

A regular mechanical engineer's scale may be used with a scale of $\frac{1}{4}'' = 1''$. For other reductions the scales mentioned in connection with Figs. 2-24a and 2-25 are used. For small parts enlarged scales may be used, such as $24'' = 1'-0''$ for double-size views. Very small parts may be drawn four or eight times size or for some purposes 10, 20, or more times full size. The views of large parts and projects must be drawn to a small scale.

2·30 Case instruments. The two patterns of instruments in general use are shown in Fig. 2-30a, the flat pattern at A and the square pattern at B. Some

Fig. 2-27. Metric scales. Most foreign countries use the metric system.

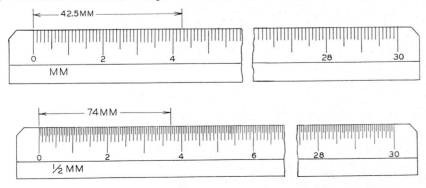

Fig. 2-28a. To make a measurement.

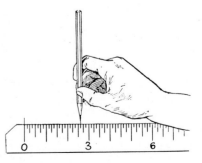

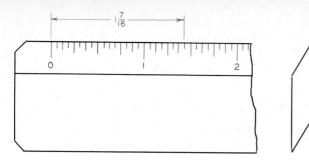

Fig. 2-28b. Making a measurement (1$\frac{7}{16}$″) with the full-size scale.

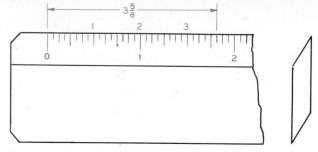

Fig. 2-29a. Measuring to half size.

draftsmen prefer one pattern to the other. The usual set (Fig. 2-30b) includes compasses with pen part, pencil part, and lengthening bar, dividers, bow pen, bow pencil, bow dividers, and one or two ruling pens.

Large bow sets (Fig. 2-30c) are favored by some users of drafting instruments. They are known as *master,* or *giant,* bows and are made in several patterns. Large bows (6 in. or more) are capable of drawing circles up to 13 in. in diameter or, with lengthening bars, up to 40 in. in diameter. Large bow sets provide the convenience of using one instrument in place of the regular compasses, dividers, and small bow instruments. Large bow instruments provide a means of securely holding the radius at any required distance. The set illustrated permits quick setting with provision for accurate adjustment for small distances.

2•31 The dividers. Dividing lines and transferring distances are done with dividers. The bow dividers (Art. 2·33) are used for small distances. The dividers are held in the right hand and adjusted as illustrated in Space 1, Fig. 2-31.

To divide a line into three equal parts, adjust the points of the dividers until they appear to be about one-third the length of the line, and place one point on one end of the line and the other point on the line (Space 2). Turn the dividers about the point that rests on the line, as in Space 3, then in the alter-

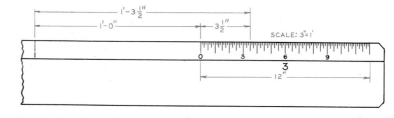

Fig. 2-29b. Reading the scale.

nate direction, as in Space 4. If the last point falls short of the end of the line, increase the distance between the points of the dividers by an amount estimated to be about one-third the distance *mn* and start at the beginning of the line again. Several trials may be necessary. If the last point overruns the end of the line, decrease the distance between the points by one-third the extra distance. For four, five, or more spaces, proceed as described except that the correction will be one-

fourth, one-fifth, and so forth, of the overrun or underrun. An arc or the circumference of a circle is divided in the same way by using the distance between the points of the dividers as a chord. The small knurled screw on one of the legs is used to regulate a hairspring to make small adjustments in the distance between the points.

A line may be divided into any number of equal parts or into proportional parts geometrically, as explained in Chap. 4.

Fig. 2-30a. The two patterns of drawing instruments.

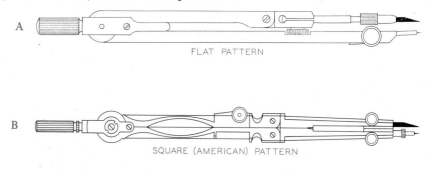

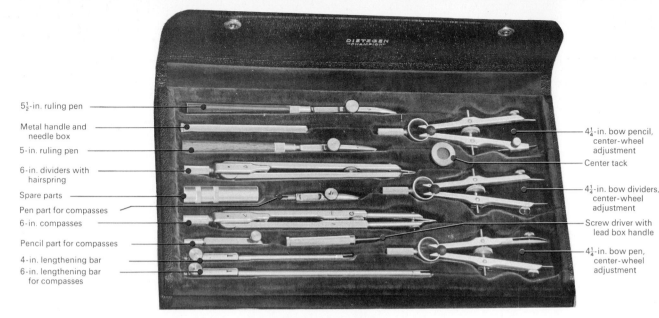

5½-in. ruling pen

Metal handle and
needle box

5-in. ruling pen

6-in. dividers with
hairspring

Spare parts

Pen part for compasses

6-in. compasses

Pencil part for compasses

4-in. lengthening bar

6-in. lengthening bar
for compasses

4¼-in. bow pencil,
center-wheel
adjustment

Center tack

4¼-in. bow dividers,
center-wheel
adjustment

Screw driver with
lead box handle

4¼-in. bow pen,
center-wheel
adjustment

Fig. 2-30b. A three-bow set of case instruments. *(Eugene Dietzgen Company)*

2·32 The compasses. Views on drawings are composed of straight lines and curved lines. Most of the curved lines are circles or parts of circles (arcs) and are drawn with the compasses (Fig. 2-32a). The legs of the compasses may be left straight for radii under 2 in. For larger radii the legs should be adjusted perpendicular to the paper (Fig. 2-32b). A lengthening bar (Fig. 2-32c) may be inserted when a very large radius is needed (over 8 in. usually).

The compasses should be prepared for use by sharpening the lead as in Fig. 2-32d at A and allowing it to extend about ⅜ in. A long bevel on the outside of the lead will keep a sharp edge when the radius is increased (Fig. 2-32d at B). Then adjust the shouldered end of the needle point until it extends a very little beyond the lead point, as illustrated at A. The pressure used on the lead in the compasses cannot be as much as on the pencil. Therefore, it is desirable to use lead which is one or

two degrees softer in the compasses in order to produce the same weight.

When ready to use the compasses, locate the center of the required arc or circle by two intersecting (crossing) lines and lay off the radius by a short, light dash (Fig. 2-32a in Space 1). The compasses are used entirely with the right hand (Fig. 2-32a). They are opened by pinching them between the thumb and second finger (Space 1) and are set to the proper radius by placing the needle point at the center and adjusting

Fig. 2-30c. A large bow set of case instruments. *(Gramercy Guild Group, Inc.)*

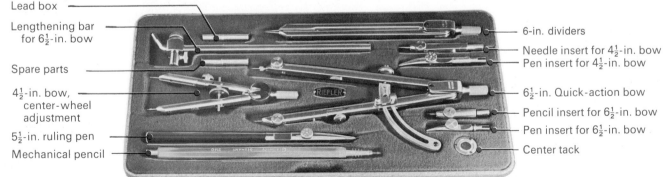

Lead box

Lengthening bar
for 6½-in. bow

Spare parts

4½-in. bow,
center-wheel
adjustment

5½-in. ruling pen

Mechanical pencil

6-in. dividers

Needle insert for 4½-in. bow

Pen insert for 4½-in. bow

6½-in. Quick-action bow

Pencil insert for 6½-in. bow

Pen insert for 6½-in. bow

Center tack

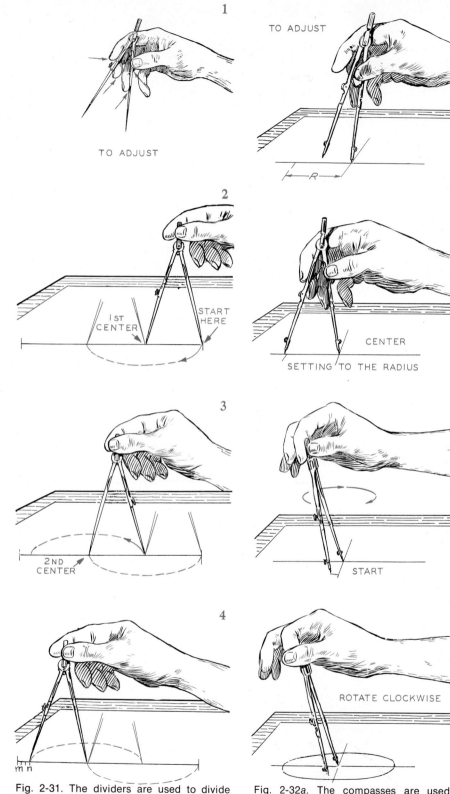

the pencil leg with the first and second fingers (Space 2). When the radius is set, raise the fingers to the handle (Space 3) and revolve the compasses by twirling the handle between the thumb and finger. Start the arc near the lower side and revolve clockwise (Space 4), inclining the compasses slightly in the direction of the line. *Do not force the needle point way into the paper.* Use only enough pressure to hold the point in place. Long radii are obtained by using a lengthening bar in the compasses to extend the pencil leg. For extra-long radii, beam compasses are used (Art. 2·35).

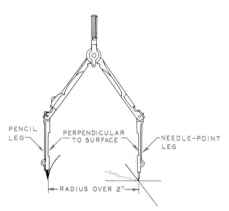

Fig. 2-32*b*. Adjusting the compasses for large circles.

Fig. 2-31. The dividers are used to divide distances and to transfer distances.

Fig. 2-32*a*. The compasses are used to draw circles and arcs.

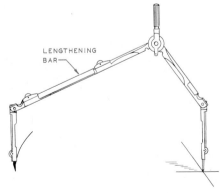

Fig. 2-32*c*. The lengthening bar is used in the compasses for large radii.

2·33 A set of bow instruments (Fig. 2-33a) consists of the bow pencil (A), the bow dividers (B), and the bow pen (C). Any of them may have the center-wheel adjustment, as at A and C, or the side-wheel adjustment, as at B. They may be of the hook-spring type, as at A, or the fork-spring type, as at B and C. The usual size is about 4 in. high.

The bow dividers are used for taking off (transferring) small distances, for marking off a series of small distances, and for dividing a line into small spaces. The bow pencil is used for drawing small circles. The choice of center- or side-wheel adjustment is a matter of personal preference. The lead for the bow pencil is sharpened and adjusted as at A in Fig. 2-33b. The inside bevel holds an edge for small circles and arcs, as indicated at B. For larger radii the outside bevel at C is better. Some draftsmen prefer a conical center point or an off-center point, as at D, E, and F. The bow instruments are convenient and accurate for small distances or radii (less than 1¼ in.), as they hold small distances better than the large instruments. Large adjustments can be made quickly with the side-wheel bows by pressing the fork and spinning the adjusting nut (Fig. 2-33c). Small adjustments are made by the adjusting nut on both the side-wheel and the center-wheel bows. The bow pencil (Fig. 2-33c) is used with one hand. Set the radius as in Space 1. Start the circle near the lower part of the vertical center line (Space 2). Revolve clockwise, as in Space 3.

2·34 The drop-spring bow (Fig. 2-34) is convenient for drawing very small circles, especially where the same size has to be repeated many times, as for rivets and similar conditions. The marking point (pencil or pen) is attached to a tube which slides on a pin. In use the pin remains stationary while the pencil point revolves about it. The radius is

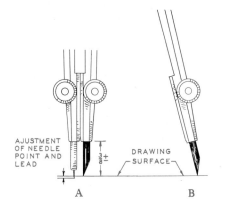

Fig. 2-32d. Adjusting the point and shaping the lead of the compasses.

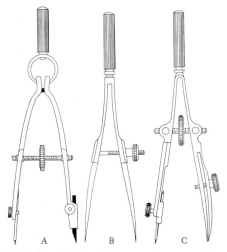

Fig. 2-33a. The bow instruments are used for drawing small circles and arcs.

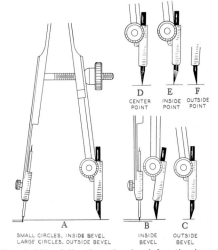

Fig. 2-33b. Adjusting the lead for the bow pencil.

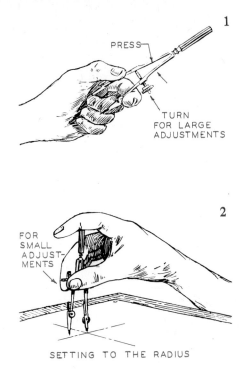

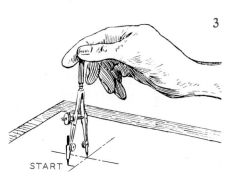

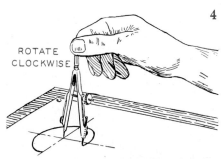

Fig. 2-33c. Adjusting the radius for the bow pencil.

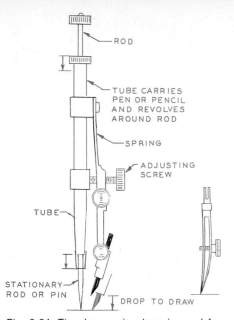

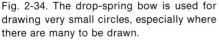

Fig. 2-34. The drop-spring bow is used for drawing very small circles, especially where there are many to be drawn.

set by the adjusting-spring screw. The marking point is held up while the pin is placed on the center, then dropped and revolved. Circles drawn will all be the same size, as set.

2·35 Beam compasses (Fig. 2-35) are used for drawing arcs or circles with large radii. They consist of a bar (beam) upon which movable holders for a pencil part and a needle part may be positioned along the bar and fixed at any desired distance apart. The pencil part is interchangeable with a pen part. The pencil point may be replaced with a needle point in order to use the beam

Fig. 2-35. Beam compasses are used for large radii.

compasses as dividers or to set off long distances. The usual bar is about 13 in. long, but a coupling may be used to add extra length to permit drawing circles of almost any desired size.

2·36 Irregular or French curves (Fig. 2-36a) are used for drawing many non-circular curves (involutes, spirals, ellipses, and so forth), for curves on graphic charts (Chap. 24), and for plotting motions, forces, and some engineering and scientific graphs. French curves are made of sheet plastic and in a very large variety of forms, a few of which are illustrated. Sets are made for ellipses, parabolas, hyperbolas, and many special purposes.

To use a curve (Fig. 2-36b), locate points through which the curve is to pass. This is done by construction, from tests, by computation, or otherwise. Then establish the path of the curve by drawing a light line, freehand, through the points or adjust as necessary for a smooth curve for experimental or other data. Next, fit the irregular curve by trial (Fig. 2-36b) against a part of the curved line and draw a portion of the line. Move the irregular curve to match the next portion, and so forth. Each new position should fit enough of the part just drawn to make sure of continuing a smooth line. It is very important to notice whether the radius of the curved line is increasing or decreasing and to place the irregular curve in the same

way. Do not attempt to draw too much of the curve with one position. If the curved line is symmetrical about an axis, the position of the axis may be marked on the irregular curve with a pencil for one side and then reversed to match and draw the other side. Various flexible or adjustable curves are made which are useful for certain special kinds of work. Other special curves are available, but for ellipses and many other purposes, templates are preferred.

2·37 Templates (Fig. 2-37) are an important part of the equipment for engineers and professional draftsmen, as they save a great deal of time in drawing shapes of details, such as bolt heads, nuts, electrical symbols, architectural symbols, plumbing symbols, outlines of tools and equipment, and many other outlines which are used often or repeated. Regular and special templates are made for drawing all kinds of symbols and many details for electronics, electrical and mechanical engineering, civil engineering, architecture, geometry, mathematics, and so forth. There are two general forms of templates.

One form in wide use is made of sheet plastic with openings of various sizes and shapes which can be drawn by inserting a pencil (or pen) in the opening and tracing the outlines. Another form consists of strips of plastic material with grooves to form outlines of

Fig. 2-36a. Some irregular curves. They are made in a great variety of forms.

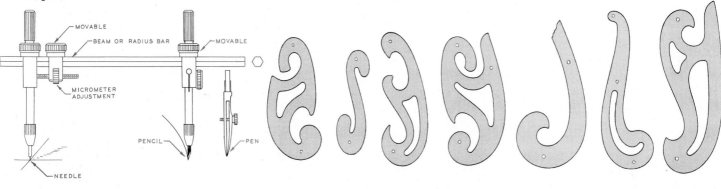

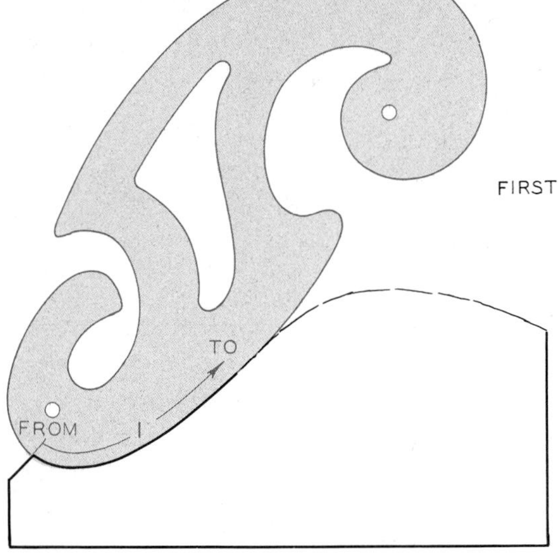

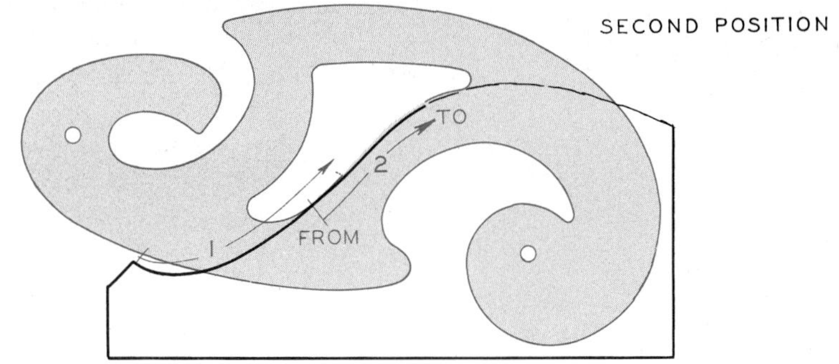

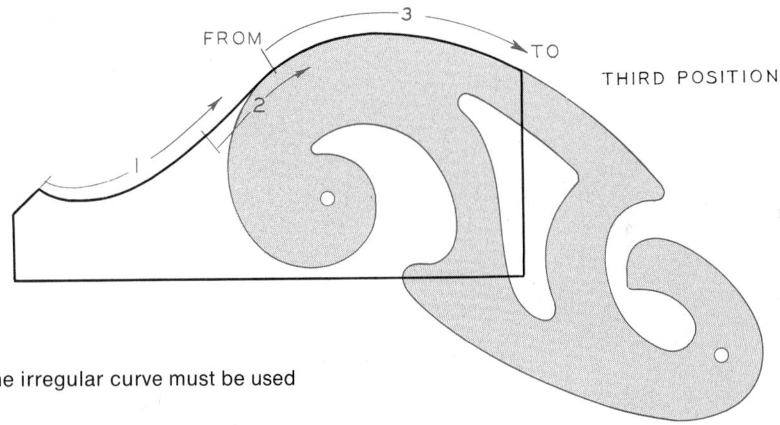

FIRST POSITION

SECOND POSITION

TO

FROM

2

1

TO

FROM

1

THIRD POSITION

FROM

3

TO

2

1

Fig. 2-36b. The irregular curve must be used properly.

symbols and characters. The anchoring tail pin of a scriber is moved in the groove and transfers the outline of the drawing by guiding a pen or pencil in the same manner as for lettering (Art. 3·19).

2·38 Problem suggestions. Group 2, page 399. Three lists are presented. List 1*a* includes basic problems that, in general, are more elementary than those in Lists 2 and 3. A selection from all lists may be used according to the time available and the purpose of the course. Some instructors may prefer the type of problems in Lists 1*b*, 2*b*, and 3*b*. Additional assignments may be made as desired. For a more complete course with older or advanced students, make selections to suit their ability. Two lists of starting problems are provided.

List 1a: Designed for 11″ × 17″ sheets and provides a progressive series. Problems 2·1, 2·4, 2·6, 2·10, 2·13.

List 1b: An alternative set of problems for 8½″ × 11″ sheets, or 11″ × 17″ sheets can be divided into two parts. Problems 2·17, 2·19, 2·22, 2·23, 2·27, 2·13.

List 2a: For 11″ × 17″ sheets. Problems 2·1, 2·5, 2·8, 2·11, 2·12, 2·14.

List 2b: For 8½″ × 11″ sheets. Problems 2·18, 2·20, 2·21, 2·25, 2·28, 2·31.

List 3a: For 11″ × 17″ sheets. Problems 2·1, 2·7, 2·9, 2·12, 2·14, 2·16.

List 3b: For 8½″ × 11″ sheets. Problems 2·24, 2·26, 2·29, 2·33, 2·39.

Fig. 2-37. Some templates. They are made for all possible uses and save a lot of time. (*Rapidesign Inc.*)

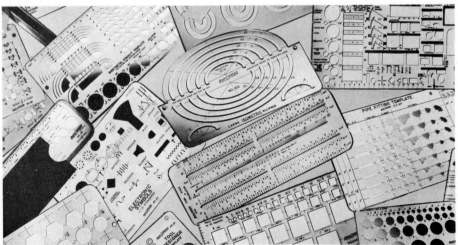

3

Lettering

3·1 Lettering. Machines and structures; engineering projects, such as roads, airports, and bridges; natural features, such as rivers, lakes, and mountains; the operation of laboratory equipment and the presentation of the resulting data—all require the use of drawings, the graphic language of engineering and science. However, it is necessary to use the written language to make the description complete; to tell the kinds of materials and sizes, distances, and amounts; to identify units; and to give other information. The written language used is always in the form of *lettering* (not handwriting).

Simple freehand lettering (Fig. 3-1), perfectly legible and quickly made, is an important part of the operation of business, industry, and engineering.

3·2 Various styles of lettering. There are many kinds of letters, a few of which are suggested in Fig. 3-2.

Fig. 3-1. American Standard letters. (Extracted from *American Drawing and Drafting Room Practice,* Y14.2–1957, with the permission of the American Society of Mechanical Engineers)

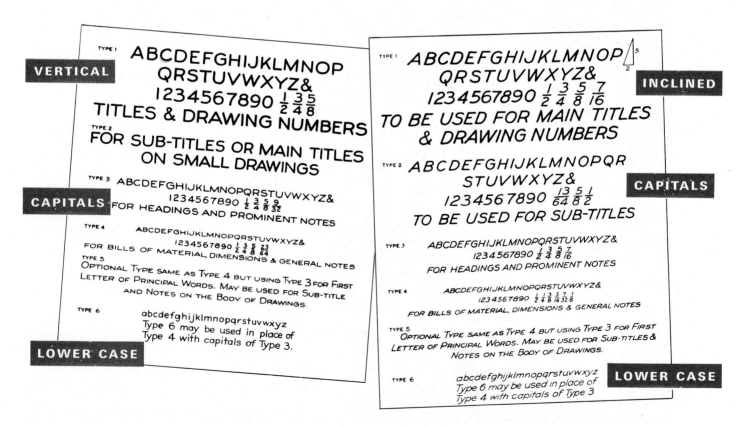

Each style is appropriate for a particular use and for hand lettering or for printing. The standard letters used on working drawings are the style known as *single-stroke commercial gothic* (Fig. 3-1). This style is appropriate because it is easy to read and easy to hand-letter. Lettering consists of capital letters and lower-case (small) letters. There are two kinds of capital and lower-case letters, vertical and inclined (Fig. 3-1). Some companies use vertical letters exclusively; some use inclined letters exclusively; others use vertical letters for titles and inclined letters for dimensions and notes, or other combinations. When accepting a position with a company, one must use the standard of that company. In learning both styles, it is better to take up vertical lettering first. The single-stroke letters presented in this chapter are in agreement with the forms presented in the *American Drafting Standards Manual,* Section 2, Y14.2–1957. The Standard recommends widths of strokes and heights of letters for certain purposes. For example, in regular dimensions and notes, dimensions and capitals are made $\frac{1}{8}$ in. high.

The ability to letter well and rapidly can be gained only by constant and careful practice. The forms and proportions of each of the letters must be thoroughly mastered by study and practice. Frequent and short practice periods will lead to a mastery of the required skill. The letters must then be combined into uniformly written, easily read words.

3•3 Guidelines. In order to make letters the same height and in line so as to be easily legible, it is necessary to rule guidelines for the top and the bottom of each line of letters. Draw lightly with a sharp pencil. The clear distance between lines of letters varies from $\frac{1}{2}$ to $1\frac{1}{2}$ times the height of the capitals. Figure 3-3a illustrates one method of spacing guidelines when several lines of letters are to be made. Mark the height of the letters and the space between lines of letters as at A. Set the bow dividers to a distance equal to the height of the letters plus the distance between lines of letters, as shown. Now, as at B, step off the required number of lines; then, draw the horizontal guidelines as at C. The vertical direction lines on Fig. 3-3a are drawn to assist in keeping the letters vertical and are spaced by eye as needed. For direction lines for inclined letters, see Figs.

Fig. 3-2. Some styles of lettering.

VERTICAL

lower case

INCLINED

COMPRESSED

EXTENDED

BOLD FACE

SLANT *Italics*

𝕺𝖑𝖉 𝕰𝖓𝖌𝖑𝖎𝖘𝖍

MODERN

OLD ROMAN

Fig. 3-3a. Spacing guidelines for capital letters.

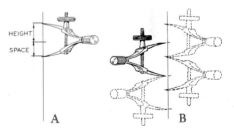

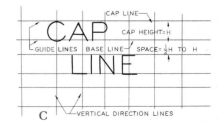

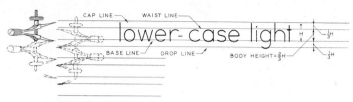

Fig. 3-3*b*. Spacing guidelines for lower-case letters.

Fig. 3-3*c*. Spacing guidelines for caps and small caps.

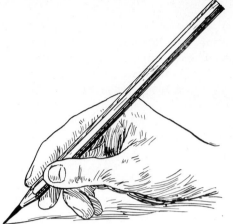

Fig. 3-4. Position of the pencil for lettering.

3-3*e* and 3-11*a*. The same method of spacing lines may be used for lower-case letters (Fig. 3-3*b*) or for capitals and small capitals, as suggested in Fig. 3-3*c*.

The Braddock-Rowe triangle (Fig. 3-3*d*) and the Ames lettering instrument (Fig. 3-3*e*) are timesaving and useful devices for ruling guidelines. Lines are ruled by inserting a sharp pencil point in the holes of either of these devices and moving it back and forth, guided by the T-square edge. The different spacing of groups of holes provides for different sizes of letters, either capital or lower-case. The numbers give the heights of capital letters in thirty-seconds of an inch.

Thus, No. 4 is $4/32$, or $1/8$, in. between the top and the bottom of the group of three holes.

3•4 Lettering practice should precede the lettering of words and sentences. Particular attention should be given to numbers and fractions because these form a very important part of every working drawing. The order of strokes and the proportions of the letters should be learned by practicing until the letters can be made without effort. Since pencil tracings are used for most drawings, everyone should be able to do good pencil lettering. Use an HB, F, or H pencil that gives a firm, opaque line on the tracing material

being used. ☞ *Opaque means not reflecting or passing light.* Such tracings allow good copies to be made (see Chap. 8). On film, use a pencil made for such use. To prepare the pencil, cut away the wood and sharpen the lead to a long conical point (Fig. 3-4). Learn to use an even pressure and to turn the pencil in the fingers after every few strokes to get uniform lines. Hold the pencil just firmly enough to control the strokes.

3•5 Pen lettering. In some professions, and for certain purposes, lettering done with pen and ink is necessary. The instructions given in Arts. 3·6 to 3·14 apply to both pencil and pen letter-

Fig. 3-3*d*. Braddock-Rowe triangle.

Fig. 3-3*e*. Ames lettering instrument.

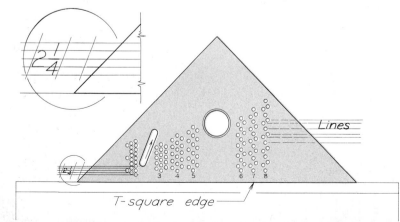

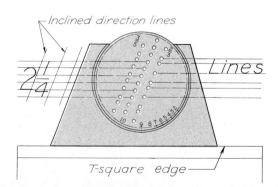

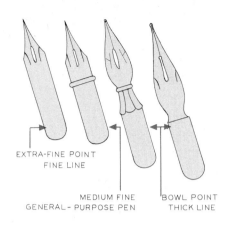

EXTRA-FINE POINT
FINE LINE

MEDIUM FINE
GENERAL-PURPOSE PEN

BOWL POINT
THICK LINE

Fig. 3-5a. Some pen points.

Fig. 3-5b. Position of the pen for lettering.

ing with the following additions for pen lettering. ☞ *The term single stroke means the width of the stem of the letter is the width of the stroke of the pen.* A pen for single-stroke lettering must, therefore, make the required width of line in any direction without pressure enough to spread the two halves of the pen point (the nibs) (Fig. 3-5a). For large letters ¼ in. high, Esterbrook's 802 and Hunt's 512, which are bowl-pointed pens, are among the most desirable. For ordinary dimensions and notes, both Esterbrook's 819 and Gillott's 404 are satisfactory. (Do not use a ruling pen for lettering.) The pen should be held in the position shown in Fig. 3-5b. The strokes are drawn with a steady, even motion of the fingers and a slight uniform pressure, not enough to spread the nibs. Some special lettering pens are described in Art. 3·17. The tube-point fountain pen (Fig. 3-17a) is convenient for making freehand letters with strokes of uniform width.

3·6 Single-stroke vertical capitals. The shapes of the letters can be learned best by a study of the vertical capitals. These are arranged in groups in Figs. 3-6a to 3-6i so that they may be studied in detail. Each letter is shown in a square 6 units high. These squares

are divided into unit squares so that the shapes, proportions, and strokes may be easily learned. Certain characteristics of the letters will be noted as they are described. These have to do with stability,[1] the proportion of space used, the order of drawing the strokes, and other details.

In learning to letter, the first step is to study the shapes and proportions of the individual letters and the order in which the strokes are made. The order and directions for drawing the strokes to form the letters as shown are suitable for most people. Some variations are possible and, of course, necessary for left-handed students, who should experiment until an order is found which is suitable to their personal needs and will enable them to do good lettering. Vertical strokes are made from the top down. Horizontal strokes are made from left to right.

Figure 3-6a: I, L, T. These letters are made up of vertical and horizontal

---

[1] *Rule of stability means to keep letters from appearing top heavy,* such as making the top stroke of the E and Z shorter than the bottom stroke, placing the horizontal stroke of the H slightly above the center, making the upper part of the B and S smaller than the lower part, and making the K and X narrower at the top than at the bottom.

strokes. The I is a single vertical stroke; keep it vertical. The L is 5 units wide and is made of a vertical stroke, 1, and a horizontal stroke, 2. Keep the angle between strokes 1 and 2 a right angle. The T is 6 units wide with the vertical stroke down from the center of the top stroke. Learn to spot the center without hesitation.

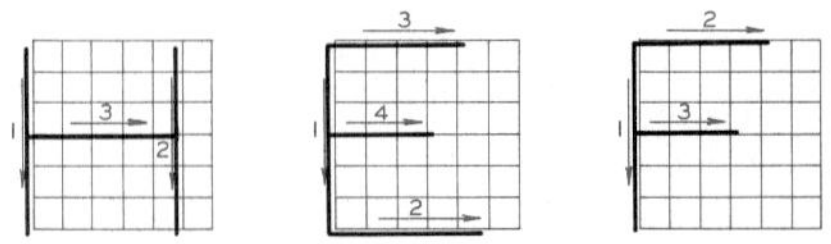

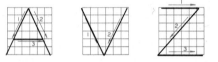

Figure 3-6b: H, E, F. The H and the E are 5 units wide. Stroke 3 of the H is spaced just above the center. Stroke 3 of the E is one-half unit shorter than the bottom stroke. Stroke 4 is two-thirds as long as the top stroke. The F is the same as the E without the bottom stroke.

Figure 3-6c: A, V, Z. These letters have inclined and horizontal strokes. They are 6 units wide. The bar (or bridge) of the A is placed at one-third of the height (2 units up). Be sure the point of the A is at the center of the width. Be sure the point of the V is at the center of the width. The top stroke of the Z is 5 units long and is centered over the bottom stroke. The inclined stroke is drawn last.

Figure 3-6d: K, N, M. These letters have vertical and inclined strokes. The K is 5½ units wide at the bottom and 5 units wide at the top, measured from the left. Stroke 2 starts at the top and ends at one-third the height (2 units up). Stroke 3, if continued up, would end at the top of stroke 1. The N is 5 units wide. The vertical strokes are drawn first to fix the width. Some find it easier to draw the inclined stroke after stroke 1. The M is 7 units wide. The vertical strokes are drawn first to fix the width, but the strokes may be drawn in order from left to right.

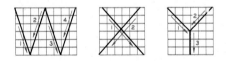

*Figure 3-6*e: *W, X, Y.* These letters have inclined strokes. The W is 8 units wide. It is made of two Vs, each 4 units wide. Be sure to make stroke 3 parallel to stroke 1 and stroke 4 parallel to stroke 2. The X is 6 units wide at the bottom. It is 5 units wide at the top, centered over the bottom. The strokes cross above the center. The Y is 6 units wide and strokes 1 and 2 meet at the center.

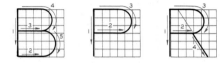

*Figure 3-6*f: *D, U, J.* These letters have vertical and curved strokes. The D is 5 units wide. Strokes 2 and 3 are horizontal and make smooth joints with the curve of stroke 3. The U is 5 units wide. Be sure that strokes 1 and 2 are parallel. Stroke 3 makes smooth joints with strokes 1 and 2. The J is 4½ units wide and is similar to a one-sided U.

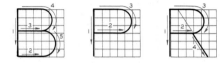

*Figure 3-6*g: *B, P, R.* These letters have straight lines and curves. They are 5 units wide. For the B, strokes 2 and 3 and the start of stroke 4 are horizontal. Stroke 3 is just above the center. The width of the upper part of the B is 4½ units wide. For the P and R, stroke 2 is

at the middle of the height (3 units up). Stroke 4 of the R, if extended upward, would meet stroke 1 above stroke 3 and pass through stroke 2 at (or to the left of) the tangent point.

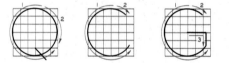

*Figure 3-6*h: *Q, C, G.* These letters are formed on a circle. Note that stroke 1 extends to the right well beyond the top and bottom tangent points. The kern of the Q may be either straight or curved. The C and G are 5½ units wide. Note that the top curves stop at 5 units from the left. Stroke 3 of the G is made up of two parts, a horizontal bar which starts at the center and a vertical part which turns down to meet stroke 1.

*Figure 3-6*i: *O, S, S.* The O is formed of a circle. The S is 5 units wide. The upper part is 4 units wide and is cen-

tered over the lower part. The upper and lower parts meet above the center. Some like to draw the S in a circle, as suggested.

*Figure 3-6*j shows all the letters arranged in alphabetical order for reference.

3·7 Numerals require special attention. Notice how they differ from those used in ordinary figuring, especially the 2, 4, 6, and 9. All the numerals are 5 units wide except the 1.

*Figure 3-7*a: *1, 4, 7, 2.* The 1 is a single vertical stroke. Stroke 1 of the 4 is 4 units from the left. Stroke 3 is 2 units up (one-third the height) and is sometimes made 5½ units long. Stroke 2 of the 7 starts as a straight line toward a point 2 units up on a vertical center line. It curves and ends in a vertical line 1 unit long under the center of stroke 1. The top part of the 2 is 4 units wide and is centered over stroke 2. Keep stroke

Fig. 3-6j. Single-stroke vertical capitals and numerals.

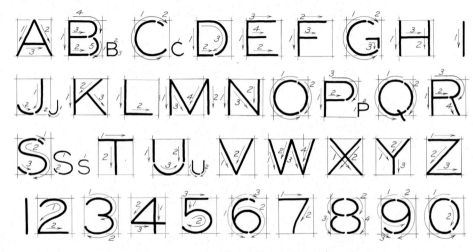

2 horizontal. The curve of stroke 1 reverses at the center.

Figure 3-7b: 5, 3, 8. Stroke 1 of the 5 is ½ unit from the left. Stroke 2 is 4 units high and 5 units wide. Stroke 3 is 4 units long and is centered over stroke 2. The top part of the 3 is about 4 units wide and is centered over the lower part. Note that strokes 1 and 2 meet about one-third of a unit above the center. The 8 is made with two ellipses (or it may be made of a 3 and a "turned around" 3). The upper part of the 8 is about 4 units wide, centered over the lower part and joined to it about one-third unit above the center.

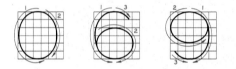

Figure 3-7c: 0, 6, 9. The 0 (or cipher) is an ellipse. Stroke 1 starts at the right

of the top tangent point and ends at the right of the bottom tangent point. The lobes of the 6 and 9 are ellipses 4 units high (two-thirds the height of the numeral) and slightly less than 5 units wide, as shown. For the 6 the lobe is tangent to the limiting line at the right. Stroke 1 is tangent to the lobe. (Some draw the lobe first and 5 units wide, which increases the width of the numeral slightly.) Stroke 3 stops ½ unit from the right. The 9 is made in a similar manner to the 6. The lobe is at the top and is tangent to the limiting line at the left. Stroke 3 starts ½ unit from the left.

Figure 3-7d: alternative numerals. The forms shown for the 3, 4, and 5 are used in the aircraft and some other industries, as well as for government contracts. The purpose is to open up the spaces so as to make the numerals clear, especially on inked tracings.

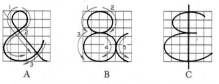

3•8 Ampersands (Fig. 3-8). This is a character used to represent the word "and." Three different forms are shown. The one at A is preferred. The type at B is formed on the figure 8. A simple type is shown at C.

3•9 Fractions (Fig. 3-9) are always made with a horizontal division line. Fractions may have a total height of twice the height of whole numbers. The fraction numbers may be about three-fourths the height of the whole numbers. A clear space must always be left above and below the division line. Some prefer to make the fractions two-thirds or five-sixths the height of the whole number and so reduce the total height. Notice that the numerator is always centered over the denominator. Reference to Figs. 3-3d and 3-3e will show how to rule guidelines with the lettering instruments.

Fig. 3-9. Vertical fractions.

$$1\frac{1}{2} \quad 2\frac{7}{8} \quad 3\frac{5}{16} \quad 4\frac{3}{4} \quad 5\frac{9}{16}$$

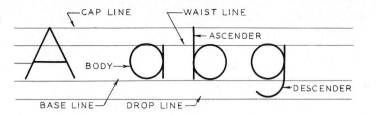

Fig. 3-10*a*. Terms used with lower-case letters.

Figure 3-10*b*. Lower-case monogram.

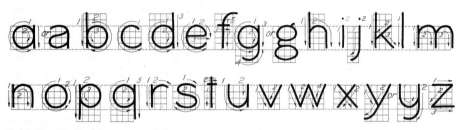

Fig. 3-10*c*. Vertical lower-case letters.

Fig. 3-11*a*. Inclined direction lines.

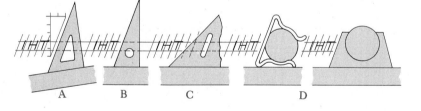

Fig. 3-11*b*. Effect of inclination.

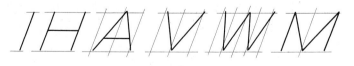

Fig. 3-11*c*. Effect of inclination.

3•10 Single-stroke vertical lower-case letters (Figs. 3-10*a*, 3-10*b*, and 3-10*c*) are based on the combination of circles and straight lines. Terms used with lower-case letters are illustrated in Fig. 3-10*a*. The bodies are made two-thirds the height of the capitals with which they are used. The ascenders extend up to the cap line and the descenders drop a like distance below the base line. The monogram in Fig. 3-10*b* contains 18 of the 26 letters. Vertical lower-case letters for study and reference are given in Fig. 3-10*c*.

3•11 Single-stroke inclined capitals. When inclined direction lines are used, inclined letters are formed (Figs. 3-11*a*, 3-11*b*, and 3-11*c*). Inclined direction lines may be drawn by one of the methods shown in Fig. 3-11*a*. At A a slope of 2 to 5 is set by marking 2 units on a horizontal line and 5 units on a vertical line and then using the T-square and triangle. This is the American Standard slope.

A lettering triangle (with an angle of about 67½°) is shown at B; the use of the slot in the Braddock-Rowe triangle is shown at C, and the use of the Ames instrument is shown at D.

The effect of inclined direction lines is shown in Fig. 3-11*b*. Note that the crossbar of the H is horizontal. Note also the slope of the lines of the A, V, and W as fixed by the direction lines through the "points."

The form taken by rounded letters is illustrated in Fig. 3-11*c* at A, B, and C. When the sides of the square are inclined, an enclosed circle becomes an ellipse with the curves sharp in the upper right-hand and lower left-hand corners and flattened in the other two corners. The effect of inclination on a few other letters is shown at C.

An alphabet of inclined capitals is given in Fig. 3-11*d* with the order and direction of the strokes for study and reference. Observe carefully the effect

An alphabet of inclined capitals

Fig. 3-11*d*. An alphabet of inclined capitals.

Fig. 3-12*a*. Inclined numerals.

Fig. 3-12*b*. Inclined fractions.

Group I: ijkltvwxyz. This group contains the straight-line letters. Keep the slope uniform by following direction lines penciled lightly on the sheet. The dot for the i and the j is placed halfway between the waist line and the cap line. The top of the t is in line with the dots. Be particularly careful about the slant of the angle letters v, w, x, and y and the sloping center line.

of the inclined direction lines on the shapes of the letters. There are two things in particular to watch: (1) Keep a uniform slope, and (2) make the correct shape on the curves and rounded letters.

3·12 Inclined numerals are shown in Fig. 3-12*a*. All, except the 1, are 5 units wide. Note how the shapes are changed by the inclination. Special care must be taken to make the correct shapes for the curves.

Inclined fractions center on an inclined direction line (Fig. 3-12*b*).

3·13 Single-stroke inclined lower-case letters are shown in Figs. 3-13*a* and 3-13*b*. This style of lettering, sometimes called the *Reinhardt letter,* is in general use for notes on drawings because it is very legible and effective and can be made very rapidly. The bodies are two-thirds the height of the capitals, with the ascenders extending to the cap line and the descenders dropping the same distance below the base line.

For purposes of study, the letters may be divided into four groups (Fig. 3-13*a*).

Fig. 3-13*a*. Inclined lower-case letters for study.

CAP LINE

WAIST LINE

BASE LINE

DROP LINE

GROUP I

GROUP II

GROUP III

GROUP IV

Fig. 3-13b. An alphabet of inclined lower-case letters.

Group II: a b d f g p q. This group contains letters made up of a straight line and an ellipse or part of an ellipse. Note the direction of the long axis of the "flat" ellipse (less than 45° with the base line).

Group III: h m n r u y. This group contains the "hook" letters made up of a straight line and parts of a "flat" ellipse.

Group IV: c e o s. The c, e, and o are based on an ellipse which makes a greater angle with the base line than the one in Groups II and III. The s has the same form as the capital S.

An alphabet of inclined lower-case letters is given in Fig. 3-13b for study and reference.

3•14 ☞ **Composition in lettering** *means the arrangement and spacing of words and lines with letters of appropriate style and size.* After the shapes of the separate letters have been mastered, all practice work should be with words and sentences. The keynote of success is uniformity. Uniform height is obtained by having each letter meet the top and bottom guidelines; uniform weight, by making all strokes of the same thickness; uniform direction, by drawing and following direction lines, either vertical or inclined; uniform shade, by careful spacing (Figs. 3-14a, 3-14b, and 3-14c).

Letters in words are not placed at equal distances from each other but are spaced so that the areas of the spaces included between the letters are, or appear to be, about equal. In this way the spacing appears to be approximately uniform. Thus, two adjacent letters with straight sides would be spaced much farther apart than two curved letters. Note the variation in spacing in the word "lettering" in Fig. 3-14a. In general, keep letters fairly close together.

In spacing words, the clear distance between them should not be more than the height of the letters, or they may be spaced by allowing room for the letter O between them. Many variations in letters are possible, such as extending or compressing them (Fig. 3-14b).

In such cases all the letters of an alphabet must be extended or compressed in proportion.

Words in lower-case letters (Fig. 3-14c) are read by the "shape" of the word for familiar words. The letters, especially the round-body letters, should be kept fairly close together and carefully spaced.

3•15 The Old Roman alphabet. Our modern letters have developed from the Old Roman alphabet (Fig. 3-15a). The traditional lettering used on architectural drawings is based on this alphabet. The letters may be solid or in outline. Such letters are used for inscriptions, in titles or important drawings, and on display drawings. The Arabic numerals shown in Fig. 3-15a are designed to match the style of the Old Roman letters. The Romans used a selection of capital letters arranged to designate numbers (Fig. 3-15b).

Fig. 3-14a. Composition. Spacing of words. Capital letters.

LETTERING COMPOSITION
INVOLVES THE SPACING OF LETTERS
WORDS AND LINES AND THE CHOICE
OF APPROPRIATE STYLES AND SIZES.

Fig. 3-14b. Compressed and extended letters.

NORMAL   COMPRESSED
EXTENDED

Fig. 3-14c. Composition. Spacing of words. Lower-case letters.

drilling compound

Fig. 3-15a. An Old Roman alphabet.

They had no symbol for the zero, which did not come into use until the sixth century or later. The numerals we now use (called *Arabic numerals*), including the zero, came to the Arabs from India, but it was the twelfth or thirteenth century before they came into wide use in Europe. Roman numerals are still used for inscriptions on buildings for dates, sometimes on diplomas, on certain formal papers or certificates, and for numbering chapters in books.

For architectural working drawings the lettering is usually done in single-stroke letters, as shown in Figs. 3-15c and 3-15d. In Fig. 3-15c the Old Roman form is retained. In the interest of speed the terminals may be left off, as in Fig. 3-15d. The letters may be inclined to provide italic letters. Some architectural draftsmen use the single-stroke letters shown in Arts. 3·6 to 3·12 for office lettering on working drawings.

Fig. 3-15b. Roman numerals.

I = 1	LX = 60
II = 2	LXX = 70
III = 3	XC = 90
IV = 4	C = 100
V = 5	CL = 150
VI = 6	CC = 200
VII = 7	CD = 400
VIII = 8	D = 500
IX = 9	DC = 600
X = 10	CM = 900
XIX = 19	M = 1000
XX = 20	MC = 1100
XXX = 30	MD = 1500
XL = 40	MCM = 1900
L = 50	MM = 2000

A line over a symbol means multiplied by 1000, as:

$$\overline{L} = 50,000$$
$$\overline{C} = 100,000$$
$$\overline{CD} = 400,000$$

Fig. 3-15c. Single-stroke Roman letters.

ABCDEFGHIJKLMN
OPQRSTUVWXYZ&
1234567890
abcdefghijklmnopqrstuvwxyz

Fig. 3-15d. Single-stroke letters.

ABCDEFGhijklmnopqrs
ABCDEFabcdefghijklmno
1234567890

ABCDEFGHI
JKLMNOPQR
STUVWXYZ
abcdefghijklm
nopqrstuvwxyz
1234567890

Fig. 3-16a. A modern Roman alphabet.

3•16 Modern Roman alphabets vary somewhat in proportions and details. They may be extended or compressed. One alphabet is illustrated in Fig. 3-16a. Note the great contrast between the heavy strokes and the thin hairline strokes. This is one of the ways in which it differs greatly from Old Roman. The heavy stroke may be more or less than one-seventh the height. Modern Roman letters are used by civil engineers on fine maps for names of civil divisions (states, counties, cities, and so forth). The Modern Roman lower-case letters are used for names of towns.

Inclined Roman letters (Fig. 3-16b) must be well done if they are used and require great skill and care.

3•17 Special pens. The lettering used for most scientific and engineering work has been described in Arts. 3·1 to 3·12.

Fountain pens (Fig. 3-17a) for lettering or for ruling lines are made in many sizes. They include Wrico, Leroy, Koh-I-Noor Rapidograph, Pelikan Graphos, Osmiroid, Speedball, Auto-Feed, Techagraph, and Tacrograph. Wide-stroke and large letters can be made in single strokes with special pens, such as the Speedball pen (Fig. 3-17b), or other wide-stroke pens, such as the Drawlet, Payzant, Leroy, and Wrico pens. Brush pens for strokes from $1/16$ to $1/4$ in. wide and felt-tip pens for wide strokes are especially convenient (Fig. 3-17a). Wide-stroke pens can be selected to draw almost any width of stroke, as for charts, diagrams, or posters for audio-visual instruction.

3•18 Commercial gothic letters. An alphabet of commercial gothic letters is shown in Fig. 3-18a. They may be drawn freehand or, if rather large, with

Fig. 3-16b. Inclined Roman.

ABCDEFGHI
JKLMNOPQR
STUVWXYZ
abcdefghijklm
nopqrstuvwxyz
1234567890

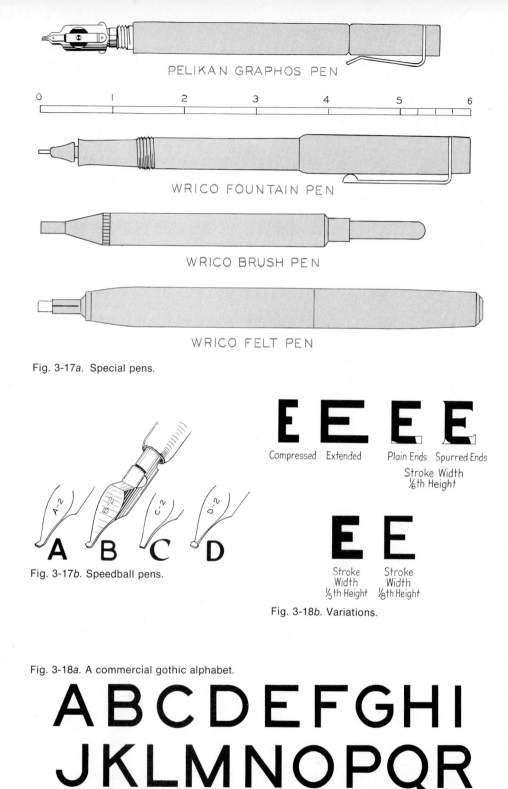

PELIKAN GRAPHOS PEN

0   1   2   3   4   5   6

WRICO FOUNTAIN PEN

WRICO BRUSH PEN

WRICO FELT PEN

Fig. 3-17a. Special pens.

A   B   C   D

A-2 B-2 C-2 D-2

Fig. 3-17b. Speedball pens.

Fig. 3-18a. A commercial gothic alphabet.

ABCDEFGHI JKLMNOPQR STUVWXYZ&

E E E E

Compressed Extended   Plain Ends Spurred Ends
                        Stroke Width
                        ⅛th Height

E E

Stroke   Stroke
Width   Width
⅕th Height   ⅛th Height

Fig. 3-18b. Variations.

instruments and filled in with a brush. For some purposes the letters may be left in outline, as shown for V, W, and X in Fig. 3-18a. Commercial gothic letters may be compressed or extended and may have either plain or spur ends (Fig. 3-18b). Width of stroke may be from one-eighth to one-fifth the height of the letters.

When commercial gothic letters are drawn with the round-point pens mentioned in Art. 3·17, the ends of the letters may be left rounded as formed by the pen or they may be squared or spurred with a fine-point pen.

3·19 Lettering devices and guides. Draftsmen use such instruments to produce uniform lettering in standard sizes ranging from 0.09 to 0.5 in. high for regular drawings and on up to 4 in. high for other purposes. Different sizes of pen points are used to obtain different widths of strokes. Guides and templates are also made for many of the symbols used on drawings, such as welding symbols, map symbols, geological symbols, and electronic symbols. There are templates for fractions, mathematical symbols, and other characters. Well-known guides include Wrico, Wricoprint, Wrico Scriber, and Leroy Scriber.

Wrico guides (Fig. 3-19a) consist of strips of plastic with openings shaped like parts of the letters and numerals. Letters are formed by moving a special pen in contact with the sides of the openings.

Wrico scriber guides (Fig. 3-19b) consist of strips of plastic in which letters are engraved. The scriber pen or pencil forms the letters as the tracer point is moved in the grooves.

Leroy scriber templates (Fig. 3-19c) consist of laminated strips with engraved grooves to form letters. A tracer pin moved in the grooves guides the scriber pen or pencil in forming the letters. Guides for different sizes and

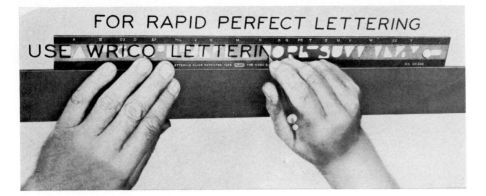

ABCDEFGH *W&1234* JKLM9 *K90* **LM**
TUV*KLM* QR abc NOP IJ

Fig. 3-19*a*. Wrico lettering guide. (The Wood Regan Instrument Company, Inc.)

Fig. 3-19*b*. Wrico Universal scriber lettering guide. (The Wood Regan Instrument Company, Inc.)

Fig. 3-19*c*. Leroy scriber lettering guide. (Kueffel & Esser Co.)

kinds of letters can be obtained for any of the lettering devices. Different sizes of points are made for the special pens so that fine lines can be used for small letters and wider lines for larger letters. When scribers are used, they may be adjusted to get vertical or slant lettering of several sizes from a single guide. One of the principal advantages of lettering guides is in maintaining uniform lettering, especially where there are a number of draftsmen. Another important use is for lettering titles, note headings, and numbers on drawings and reports.

The Vari-Typer, a typewriter designed for use with interchangeable type faces, can be used to type on tracing cloth or paper up to 12 ft in width. A special ribbon is used to give clear letters on tracing cloth.

The Grintzner drawing-board typewriter is a miniature unit weighing 2 lb and measuring $5\frac{3}{4}'' \times 6\frac{3}{4}'' \times 3\frac{1}{8}''$. It has gothic type as standard, and special characters, which includes arrowheads. The typewriter operates on the drawing board on a special guide which takes the place of the horizontal guide of a drafting machine.

3·20 Problem suggestions. Group 3, page 416. Lettering is best taught in short, unhurried periods. Problems 3·1 to 3·8 are for vertical lettering. Problems 3·9 to 3·16 are for inclined lettering. As an alternative, lettering exercise books are suggested. They are convenient and save time as guidelines are already ruled. If time permits, Prob. 3·17 should be assigned and kept as a cover sheet for the course drawings.

The use of lettering guides is regular practice in most offices for some purposes. It is, therefore, desirable for students to become acquainted with such devices and how they are used. There should be exercises using tube pens for freehand lettering. Problems for architectural lettering are on page 420.

4

Drafting constructions

4•1 Geometry has always been of great practical importance to mankind. It had its beginning in ancient times when certain geometric constructions were used to lay out right angles, to survey land or measure land, and so forth. In order to locate their temples, the Egyptians constructed right angles to locate north-south and east-west lines. North-south lines were obtained from star observations. East-west lines were then obtained by constructing right angles. For this purpose men called *rope stretchers* (Fig. 4-1 at A) used rope with marks or knots having 12 equal spaces divided into 3-, 4-, and 5-space parts. The 3-space part was stretched along the north-south line and fastened with pegs set in the ground at *B* and *C* (Fig. 4-1 at B). Men pulled the 4-space part of the rope and the 5-space part tight and walked to-

Fig. 4-1. The Egyptian rope stretchers.

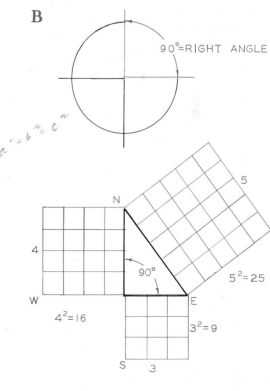

B

$90° = $ RIGHT ANGLE

$a^2 + b^2 = c^2$

5

N

4

$5^2 = 25$

W   E

$4^2 = 16$

$3^2 = 9$

90°

S   3

$4^2 + 3^2 = 5^2$ $16 + 9 = 25$

ward each other around the pegs. When the 4-space knot and the 5-space knot met at *A*, the angle *ABC* was a right angle (90°) and line *BA* was an east-west line. This is just one of the many interesting ancient uses of geometry. It is an application of the Pythagorean theorem. (See Art. 4·13, Figs. 4-13*c* and 4-13*d*.) Geometry is an essential part of the education and practice for surveyors, draftsmen, architects, engineers, and scientists. Some geometric constructions have important uses in making drawings, in solving engineering problems by diagrams, in representing conditions by graphs, and so forth.

The lines forming the views on many mechanical drawings can be located with the instruments and equipment described in Chap. 2. However, it is often necessary, or convenient, to use or to know geometric constructions in order to understand the "how" and "why" in making or reading many kinds of drawings. The student should become familiar with the more commonly used constructions explained in this chapter.

4·2 To bisect a straight line, an arc, or an angle. (☞ *To bisect means to divide into two equal parts.*) Given straight line *AB* (Fig. 4-2*a*) or arc *AB* (Fig. 4-2*b*), with *A* and *B* as centers and any radius *R* greater than one-half of *AB,* draw arcs to intersect at *C* and *D.*

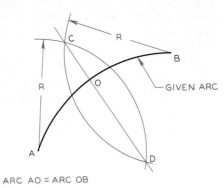

ARC AO = ARC OB

Fig. 4-2*b*. To bisect an arc.

(☞ *To intersect means to cut across.*) Draw line *CD* to cut the given line or arc at *O* and divide it into two equal parts, *AO* and *OB.* A line may be divided into two equal parts by measurement with a scale, by trial with the dividers, or by one of the methods suggested in Fig. 4-2*c.*

To bisect an angle, *AOB* (Fig. 4-2*d*). With *O* as a center and any convenient radius *R,* draw an arc to intersect the sides of the angle at *C* and *D.* With *C* and *D* as centers and any radius R_2 greater than one-half arc *CD,* draw arcs to intersect at *E.* Draw line *OE* to divide the angle *AOB* into two equal angles, *AOE* and *EOB.*

4·3 To erect a perpendicular to a given line *AB* at a point *O* on the line.

First method (Fig. 4-3 at A). With *O* as a center and any convenient radius

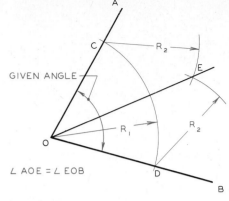

∠ AOE = ∠ EOB

Fig. 4-2*d*. To bisect an angle.

R_1, cut the given line *AB* at *C* and *D.* With *C* and *D* as centers and any radius R_2 greater than *OC,* draw arcs intersecting at *E;* draw *OE,* the required perpendicular.

Second method. When point *O* is at or near the end of the given line *AB* (Fig. 4-3 at B). From any center *C* above *AB* draw an arc of a circle with any convenient radius *R* to pass through *O* and cut line *AB* at *D.* Draw *DC* and extend it to cut the arc at *E;* draw *OE,* the required perpendicular.

4·4 To draw a perpendicular to a given line *AB* from a point *O* outside the line.

First method (Fig. 4-4*a* at A and B). With *O* as a center draw an arc with radius R_1 long enough to cut line *AB* in two points, *C* and *D.* With *C* and *D* as centers and radius R_2 greater than one-

Fig. 4-2*a*. To bisect a straight line.

Fig. 4-2*c*. To bisect a horizontal, vertical, or inclined line.

Fig. 4-3. To erect a perpendicular at a point on a line.

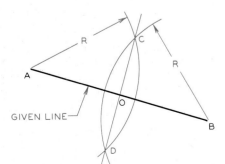

GIVEN LINE

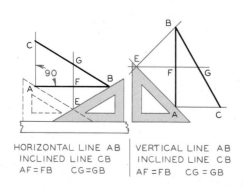

HORIZONTAL LINE AB	VERTICAL LINE AB
INCLINED LINE CB	INCLINED LINE CB
AF = FB CG = GB	AF = FB CG = GB

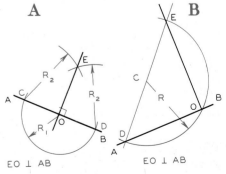

A

B

EO ⊥ AB

EO ⊥ AB

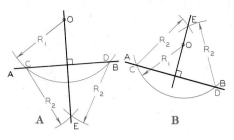

Fig. 4-4a. To draw a perpendicular to a line from a point outside the line, first method.

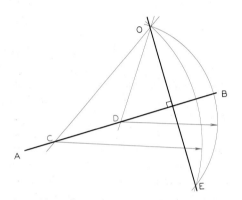

Fig. 4-4b. To draw a perpendicular to a line from a point outside the line, second method.

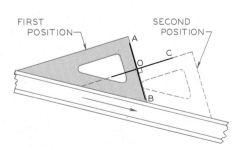

Fig. 4-4c. Perpendicular by triangle and T-square.

Fig. 4-4d. Perpendicular by triangle and T-square.

half *CD*, draw arcs to intersect at *E*. A line through *O* and *E* is the required perpendicular.

Second method (Fig. 4-4b). Draw lines from *O* to any two points, *C* and *D*, on line *AB*. With *C* and *D* as centers and radii *CO* and *DO*, draw arcs to intersect at *E*. Draw *OE*, the required perpendicular.

A perpendicular may be drawn to a given line *AB* through a point outside the line or a point on the line using a triangle and the T-square or another triangle (Figs. 4-4c and 4-4d). Place the triangle and the T-square in the first position. Hold the T-square and slide the triangle to the second position and draw the perpendicular *CO*.

4·5 To draw a line parallel to a given line. The required line may be on either side of the given line.

First method (Fig. 4-5a). Given line *AB* at *A* to draw a line through *P* parallel to line *AB*. With *P* as center and a convenient radius R_1, draw an arc cutting line *AB* at *C*. With center *C* and same radius R_1, draw arc *PE*. With center *C* and radius R_2 equal to chord *PE*, draw an arc to locate point *F*. Draw *PF*, the parallel line.

Second method (Fig. 4-5a). Given line *AB* at *B* to draw a parallel line at a given distance from *AB*. Draw a perpendicular to the given line at any point *O* (Art. 4·3). Lay off the required distance from *O* to *P*. Draw the required parallel *CD* through *P* perpendicular to *OP*.

Third method (Fig. 4-5a). Given line *AB* at *C*, draw two arcs with centers on line *AB* and with a radius *R* equal to the required distance between the parallel lines. Draw parallel line *CD* tangent to the arcs.

Fig. 4-5a. To draw a line parallel to a straight line.

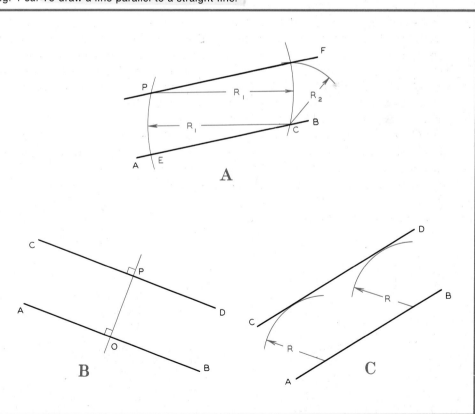

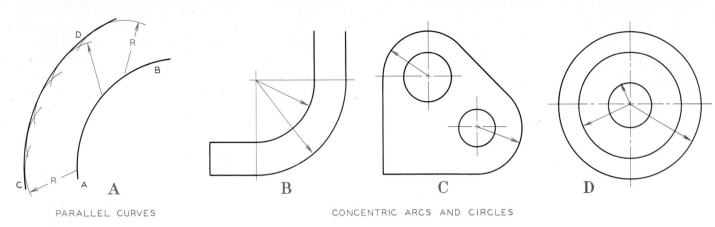

PARALLEL CURVES   CONCENTRIC ARCS AND CIRCLES

Fig. 4-5b. To draw a line parallel to a curved line.

Fig. 4-6a. To divide a straight line into a number of equal parts.

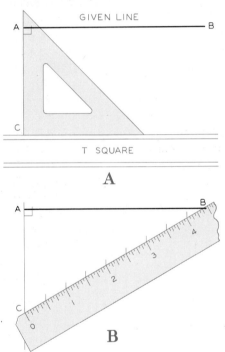

GIVEN LINE

T SQUARE

A

B

C

For a curved line (Fig. 4-5b at A), given curved line *AB*, draw a series of arcs with radius *R* equal to the required distance between the lines and centers on line *AB*. Draw a line touching the arcs; use an irregular curve. Arcs and circles (Fig. 4-5b at B, C, and D) having the same center are concentric, as shown, for two arcs, for a circle and an arc, and for circles. The distance between two concentric arcs or circles is constant and is equal to the difference between the radii.

Fig. 4-6b. To divide a straight line into a number of equal parts.

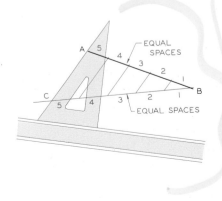

4•6 To divide a straight line into any number of equal parts, use either of the following methods.

First scale method (Fig. 4-6a). Line *AB* is to be divided into nine equal parts. Draw a perpendicular to *AB* through one end of *AB,* as line *AC* at A. Place a scale in such a position that any nine equal divisions are included between a point on line *AB* and point *C,* as shown at B (in this case, nine half-inches), and mark the divisions. Draw lines parallel to *AC*, as at C, through the marks to divide the given line into nine equal parts.

Second scale method (Fig. 4-6b). Line *AB* is to be divided into five equal parts. From *B* draw a line at any convenient angle. On this line step off five equal spaces of any convenient length. From the last point, *C*, draw *CA*. Draw lines through each point on *CB* parallel to *CA*. Line *AB* will be divided in five equal parts.

4•7 To reduce or enlarge linear dimensions (Fig. 4-7a). A special scale may be made for this purpose based on the laws of proportional triangles. Draw parallel lines at a convenient distance apart. Lay off *AB* to the given scale or length. Lay off *CD* to the de-

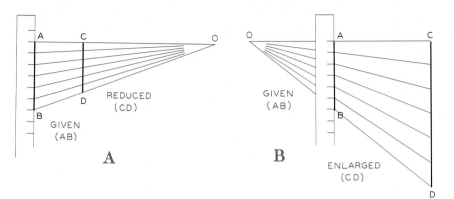

Fig. 4-7a. To reduce or enlarge dimensions.

Fig. 4-7b. To enlarge or reduce a drawing.

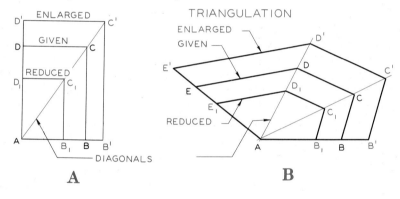

Fig. 4-7c. Use of proportional squares or rectangles.

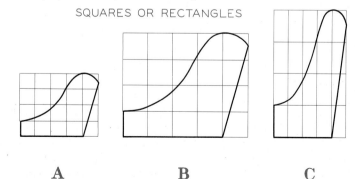

sired length, either shorter (Fig. 4-7a at A) or longer (Fig. 4-7a at B). Draw lines AC and BD and continue them to intersect at O. Lines from O through each division of line AB will divide line CD into proportional spaces to form a new scale.

A line or drawing may be enlarged or reduced by drawing diagonals of a geometrical figure, as in Fig. 4-7b, to form similar triangles (called *method of triangulation*). In Fig. 4-7b at A the rectangle ABCD is shown reduced at $AB_1C_1D_1$ and enlarged at $AB^1C^1D^1$. In Fig. 4-7b at B the polygon ABCDE is shown reduced and enlarged. Proportional squares or rectangles may be used to draw an enlarged or reduced copy of a drawing or sketch (Fig. 4-7c at A and B) or to change the proportions, as at C.

4·8 To copy a given angle AOB (Fig. 4-8). Draw one side O^1B^1 in the new position. With O and O^1 as centers and any convenient radius R_1, draw arcs to cut BO and AO at C and D, and O^1B^1 at C^1. With C^1 as a center and radius R_2 equal to chord CD, draw an arc to locate point D^1 at the intersection of the arc. Draw O^1D^1 to complete the required angle.

Fig. 4-8. To copy an angle.

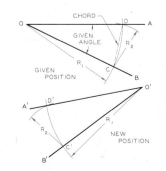

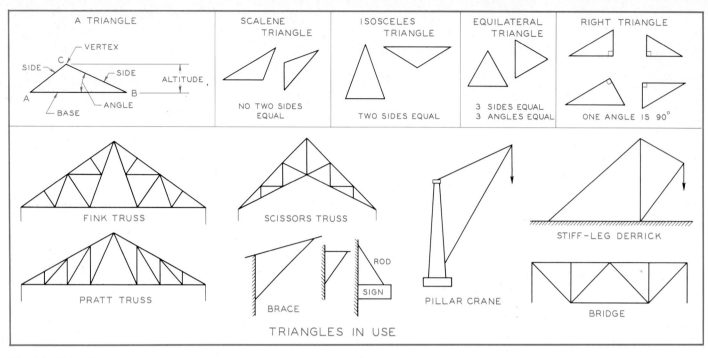

Fig. 4-9a. Triangles.

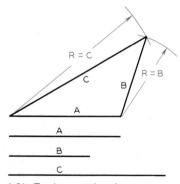

Fig. 4-9b. To draw a triangle.

Fig. 4-10a. To copy a view by triangles.

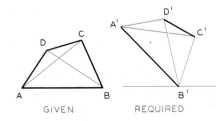

GIVEN   REQUIRED

4·9 Triangles (Fig. 4-9a). A triangle is a part of a plane surface enclosed by three straight lines called *sides*. The sides intersect to form *angles*. The point where two sides meet is called a *vertex*. A side opposite a vertex is called the *base*. Side *AB* is the base corresponding to the vertex *C*. A *scalene* triangle has all sides unequal. An *isosceles* triangle has two sides equal and two angles equal. An *equilateral* triangle has three equal sides and three equal angles of 60°. A *right* triangle has one right angle of 90°. A few ways in which triangles are used are shown in Fig. 4-9a.

To draw a triangle given the sides *A, B,* and *C* (Fig. 4-9b), draw one side, as *A,* in the desired position. With the ends of side *A* as centers and radii equal to sides *B* and *C,* draw intersecting arcs.

4·10 To copy a view in a new position. To copy by triangles (Fig. 4-10a), given view *ABCD,* draw *A¹B¹* in the required position equal to *AB.* Construct

triangle *A¹B¹C¹* equal to *ABC,* and triangle *A¹B¹D¹* equal to *ABD* to locate points in the required position.

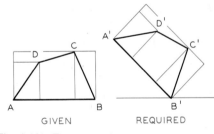

GIVEN   REQUIRED

Fig. 4-10b. To copy a view by "boxing."

Fig. 4-11. To draw an isosceles triangle.

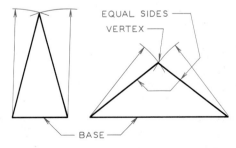

EQUAL SIDES
VERTEX
BASE

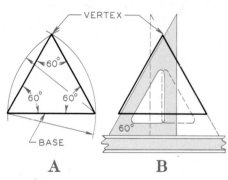

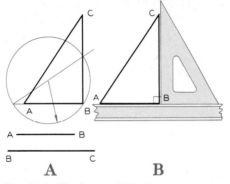

Fig. 4-12. To draw an equilateral triangle.

Fig. 4-13a. To draw a right triangle.

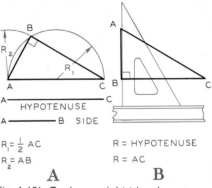

Fig. 4-13b. To draw a right triangle.

To copy by boxing or offsets (Fig. 4-10b), draw a rectangle about the given view. Draw an equal rectangle in the required position. Draw rectangles in the given view and equal rectangles in the required position to locate the points.

4•11 To draw an isosceles triangle (Fig. 4-11). Draw the base in the desired position. With the ends of the base as centers and a side as a radius, draw intersecting arcs to locate the vertex.

4•12 To draw an equilateral triangle (Fig. 4-12). At A draw one side as a base in the desired position. With the ends of the base as centers and the side as a radius, draw intersecting arcs to locate the vertex. At B draw 60° lines through the ends of the base with the 30°–60° triangle.

4•13 To draw a right triangle. Given two sides, AB and BC (Fig. 4-13a at A), draw one side AB in the desired position. Erect a perpendicular to AB at B equal to BC. (Use method of Fig. 4-3.) Draw AC. In Fig. 4-13a at B the triangle and T-square are used as shown. To draw a right triangle, given the hypotenuse AC and one side AB (Fig. 4-13b at A), draw a semicircle on AC as a diameter. With center A and radius

equal to side AB, draw an arc to cut the semicircle at B. Draw AB and BC to complete the right triangle. In Fig. 4-13b at B the triangle and T-square are used as shown. The right triangle by the 3-4-5 method (Fig. 4-13c) is the method used by the rope stretchers, as illustrated in Fig. 4-1. This method was known by the Egyptians and Babylonians some five or six thousand years ago. Pythagoras, who lived in the sixth century B.C., is credited with the proof of the theorem which bears his name, the Theorem of Pythagoras: "The square on the hypotenuse of a right-angled triangle is equal to the sum of the squares on the other two sides."

In Fig. 4-13c, $5 \times 5 = 3 \times 3 + 4 \times 4$, or $25 = 9 + 16$. Any other values having the same ratio 3:4:5 may be used, as 6:8:10 where $36 + 64 = 100$. To construct a right triangle by the 3-4-5 method (Fig. 4-13d), given any two of the three sides, as one side AB and hypotenuse AC, from one end of AB at B, lay off three equal spaces of any convenient length to locate E. From center B draw an arc with a radius equal to four spaces. From center E draw an arc with a radius equal to five spaces to intersect the other arc at F. Draw line BF extended. From center A and radius AC draw an arc to cut BF extended at C. Draw AC to complete the triangle.

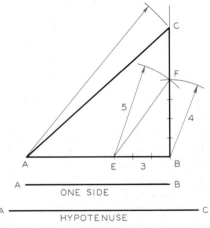

Fig. 4-13c. The 3–4–5 triangle.

Fig. 4-13d. To draw a right triangle by the 3–4–5 method.

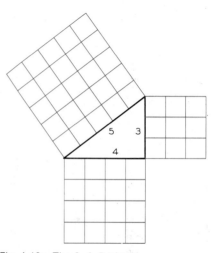

4·14 A square may be drawn about a circle or in a circle (Fig. 4-14 at A) using diameters at 45°, as shown, or a horizontal and a vertical diameter. A square may be drawn with lines in the numbered order, as in Fig. 4-14 at B.

4·15 A pentagon is a part of a plane enclosed by five straight lines called *sides.* A regular pentagon (Fig. 4-15*a* at A) has equal sides and equal angles. The famous government building the Pentagon (Fig. 4-15*a* at B) takes its name from the plan, which is a pentagon. Observe the stem on a fire hydrant (Fig. 4-15*b*), which has five sides (a pentagon).

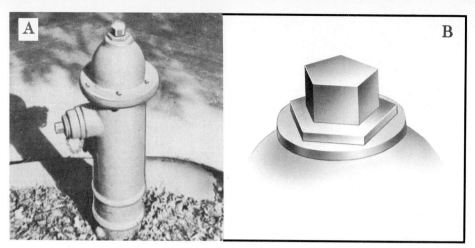

Fig. 4-15*b*. Fire hydrant—a pentagon.

Fig. 4-14. To draw a square.

4·16 To draw a regular pentagon given one side *AB* (Fig. 4-16). Draw perpendicular *AC* equal to one-half *AB*. Draw *BC* and extend it to make *CD* equal to *AC*. With radius *AD* and centers *A* and *B* draw arcs to intersect at *O*. With the same radius and center *O* draw a circle. Step off *AB* as a chord to locate points *E, F,* and *G*. Connect the points to complete the pentagon. This construction and the one in Art. 4·17 require very accurate work.

Fig. 4-16. To draw a regular pentagon given one side.

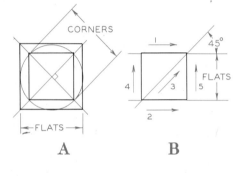

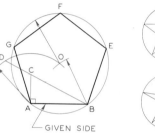

Fig. 4-15*a*. The Pentagon.

PENTAGON

S T A R

A

B

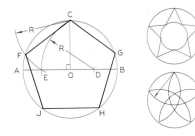

Fig. 4-17. To draw a regular pentagon in a circle.

4•17 To draw a regular pentagon in a given circle (Fig. 4-17). Draw a diameter *AB* and a perpendicular radius *OC*. Bisect *OB* to locate *D*. With *D* as center and radius *DC* draw an arc to locate *E*. With *C* as center and radius *CE* draw an arc to locate *F*. Chord *CF* is one side of a pentagon. Step off chord *CF* on the circle to locate points *G*, *H*, and *J*. Another method is to use the dividers and locate the points by trial.

4•18 A regular hexagon (Fig. 4-18 at A) has six equal sides and six equal angles. Notice that the hexagon is made up of six equilateral triangles of equal size and that one side of a triangle is equal to the radius of the circumscribing circle (one-half corners) and will go six times as a chord in the circumference. The hexagon is used in many designs, such as the tile pattern (Fig. 4-18 at B). Metal rods and tubes, columns, bases, and other parts often have the hexagonal form. Hexagonal bolt-heads and nuts (Fig. 4-18 at C) are used to such a large extent (Chap. 12) that it is necessary to know how to draw a regular hexagon. There are many other places where the hexagon is used.

4•19 To draw a regular hexagon given the distance across flats *AB*.

First method (Fig. 4-19a): circumscribed about a circle. Draw a circle with a diameter equal to distance across flats. With the T-square and 30°–60° triangle draw tangents in the order indicated.

Second method (Fig. 4-19b). Draw parallel lines at a distance apart equal to the flats. With the T-square and 30°–60° triangle draw lines in the order indicated.

Fig. 4-18. The hexagon.

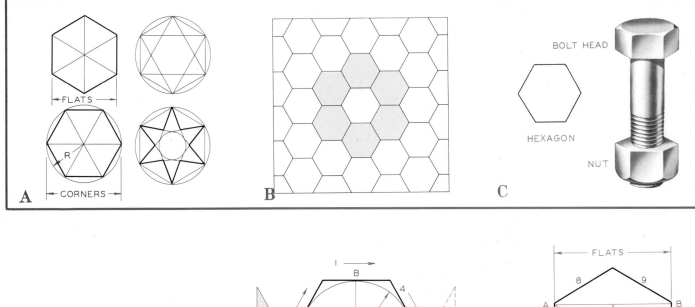

Fig. 4-19. To draw a regular hexagon, given flats.

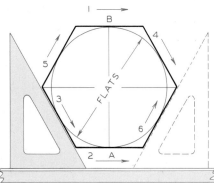

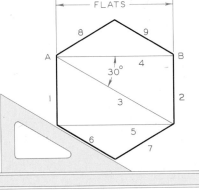

4•20 To draw a regular hexagon given the distance across corners *AB.*

First method (Fig. 4-20a): inscribed in a circle. Draw a circle with *AB* as diameter. With *A* and *B* as centers and the same radius draw arcs to intersect the circle in points 1, 2, 3, and 4. Connect the points to complete the hexagon.

Second method (Fig. 4-20b). Draw line *AB* equal to the distance across corners. With the T-square and 30°–60° triangle draw lines in the order indicated.

4•21 A regular octagon has eight equal sides and eight equal angles (Fig. 4-21a at A). Examine a pipe union (used to connect two pipes) and note its octagonal shape (Fig. 4-21 at B). To draw a regular octagon in a square given distance across flats *AB* (Fig. 4-21b), draw a square *ABCD*. Draw the diagonals *AC* and *DB*. With centers *A, B, C,* and *D* and radius *R = AO* draw

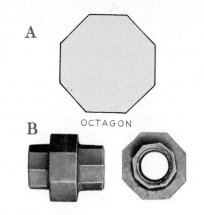

OCTAGON

Fig. 4-21a. The octagon.

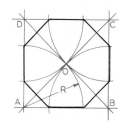

Fig. 4-21b. To draw a regular octagon in a square.

arcs to cut the sides of the square. Connect the points as shown to complete the octagon.

4•22 To draw a regular octagon in or about a circle. About a circle (Fig. 4-22 at A): draw tangents with T-square and 45° triangle. In a circle (Fig. 4-22 at B): draw diameters *AB* and *CD* at right angles. Bisect the right angles to locate *E, F, G,* and *H.* The bisector *EF* and *GH* may be drawn with the 45° triangle.

4•23 To draw a circle through any three points not in a straight line (Fig. 4-23). Given points *A, B,* and *C,* draw lines *AB* and *BC.* Draw perpendicular bisectors of *AB* and *BC* to intersect at *O.* Draw the required circle with center *O* and radius *R = OA = OB = OC.*

4•24 To draw a tangent to a circle at a given point *T* **on the circle.**

First method (Fig. 4-24a). Draw radial line *OT.* Erect a perpendicular to *OT* at *T.* The perpendicular *TA* is tangent at *T.*

Second method (Fig. 4-24b). Place a triangle so that the hypotenuse passes through *T* and *O* as at first position on the T-square. Hold the T-square, turn the triangle about the right-angle corner, slide to second position, and draw the tangent *TA.*

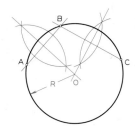

Fig. 4-23. To draw a circle through three points.

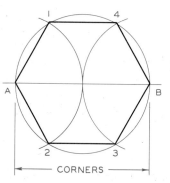

Fig. 4-20a. To draw a regular hexagon, given corners.

Fig. 4-20b. To draw a regular hexagon, given corners.

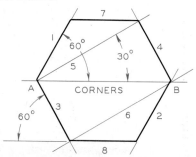

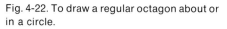

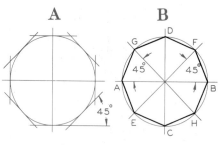

Fig. 4-22. To draw a regular octagon about or in a circle.

Fig. 4-24a. To draw a tangent to a circle at a point on the circle.

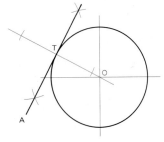

Fig. 4-24b. To draw a tangent to a circle at a point on the circle.

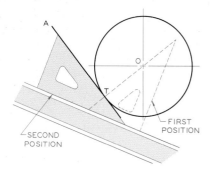

$$R = \frac{1}{2} OP = OA$$

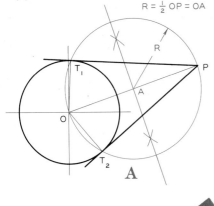

A

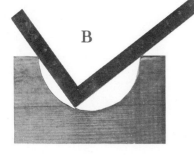

B

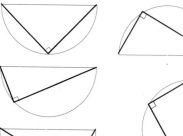

C

4•25 To draw a tangent to a circle from a point P outside of the circle (Fig. 4-25 at A). Draw *OP* and bisect it to locate point *A*. Draw a circle with center *A* and radius $R = \frac{1}{2}OP$ to intersect the given circle at T_1 and T_2. Then draw PT_1 and PT_2, which will be tangent to the circle, as angles OT_1P and OT_2P are right angles. An angle in a semicircle is a right angle (Fig. 4-25 at A and C). Mechanics make use of a steel square to check a semicircular cut by moving it to different positions (Fig. 4-25 at B).

When accuracy is not necessary, draftsmen place a triangle so that an edge passes through point *P* and draw the tangent to the circle by eye.

4•26 To draw an arc tangent to two straight lines. Three conditions are shown in Fig. 4-26a for an acute angle, for an obtuse angle, and for a right angle. Figures 4-26b and 4-26c show tangents to an acute angle and to an obtuse angle. Given radius *R* and lines *AB* and *CD*, draw lines parallel to *AB* and *CD* at a distance *R* from them. The intersection *O* will be the center of the required arc. Draw perpendiculars from *O* to *AB* and *CD* to locate the

Fig. 4-26a. Arcs tangent to two straight lines.

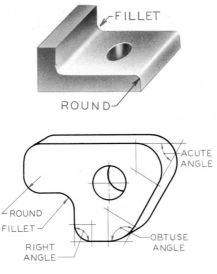

points of tangency *T*. When the angle between the lines is a right angle, we have the usual conditions of rounds and fillets (Fig. 4-26a).

To draw a tangent arc to lines at right angles (Fig. 4-26d at A and B), draw an arc with given radius *R* and center at *B*.

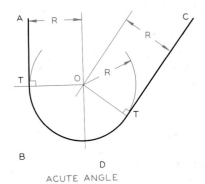

ACUTE ANGLE

Fig. 4-26b. To draw an arc tangent to lines at an acute angle.

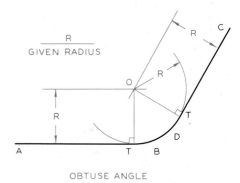

OBTUSE ANGLE

Fig. 4-26c. To draw an arc tangent to lines at an obtuse angle.

Fig. 4-26d. To draw an arc tangent to lines at a right angle.

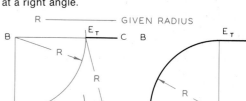

A

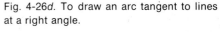

B

RIGHT ANGLE

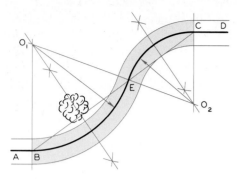

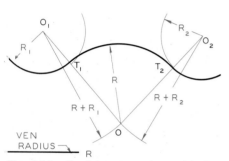

Fig. 4-27. To draw a reverse, or ogee, curve.

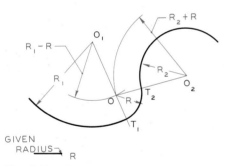

VEN
RADIUS
R

Fig. 4-28a. To draw an arc tangent to two arcs.

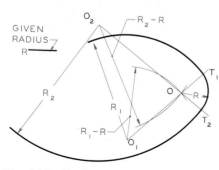

GIVEN
RADIUS
R

Fig. 4-28b. To draw an arc tangent to two arcs.

GIVEN
RADIUS
R

Fig. 4-28c. To draw an arc tangent to two arcs.

This will locate the tangent points D_T and E_T, as at A. With D_T and E_T as centers and same radius R draw arcs to locate the center O of the required arc. With center O and radius R draw the required arc, as at B.

4·27 To draw a reverse or ogee curve (Fig. 4-27). (To connect two straight lines by a smooth curve composed of arcs of circles.) Given lines *AB* and *CD,* draw line *BC*. Select a point, *E*, on line *BC* through which the curve is to pass. Draw perpendicular bisectors of *BE* and *EC*. Draw perpendiculars to *AB* at *B* and to *CD* at *C* to intersect the bisectors of *BE* and *EC* at O_1 and O_2. Draw one arc with center O_1 and radius O_1E and another with center O_2 and radius O_2E to complete the required curve. Note the tangent points at *B, C,* and *E*. The line of centers O_1 and O_2 must pass through *E*, the point of tangency of the two arcs.

4·28 To draw an arc of given radius R tangent to given arcs of radii R_1 and R_2 (R_1 and R_2 may be equal or may differ).

First case (Fig. 4-28a). To locate center O of the required tangent arc. Draw an arc with center O_1 and radius $= R + R_1$. Draw an arc with center O_2 and radius $R + R_2$. The intersection at O is the center of the required arc. Draw lines of centers O_1O and O_2O to locate tangent points T_1 and T_2.

Second case (Fig. 4-28b). Draw arc from center O_1 with radius $R_1 - R$ to intersect arc from center O_2 with radius $= R_2 + R$ to intersect at O.

Third case (Fig. 4-28c). Draw arc from center O_1 with radius $= R_1 - R$ to intersect arc from center O_2 with radius $= R_2 - R$ to intersect at O.

4·29 To draw an arc of given radius R tangent to an arc of radius R and a straight line *AB* (Fig. 4-29). For conditions shown at A and B draw a line

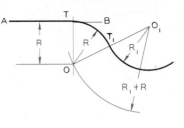

A

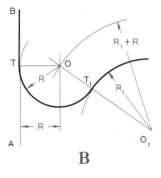

B

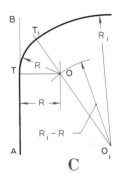

C

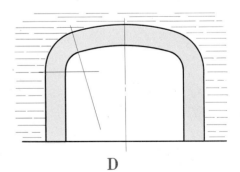

D

Fig. 4-29. To draw an arc tangent to an arc and a straight line.

parallel to AB at a distance R from it. Draw an arc with radius $= R_1 + R$ to intersect the parallel line at O. Intersection O will be the center of the required arc. Draw a perpendicular from O to AB to locate tangent point T on AB. Draw line of centers O to O_1 to locate tangent point T_1 of arcs. For the conditions shown in Fig. 4-29 at C draw a line parallel to AB at a distance R from it. Draw an arc with radius $= R_1 - R$ to intersect the parallel line at O; then O is center of required arc. Draw a perpendicular from O to line AB to locate tangent point T on AB. Draw line of centers O_1O and extend it to locate tangent point of arcs T_1. The construction shown at C is applied to an arc at D.

4·30 To draw an exterior common tangent to two circles of unequal radii (Fig. 4-30). This is the case for an open belt on pulleys. Given circles with radii R_1 and R_2, with center O_1 and radius $R = R_1 - R_2$ draw a circle. From O_2 draw a tangent O_2T to the circle of radius R (by method of Art. 4·25). Draw radius O_1T and extend it to locate T_1. Draw O_2T_2 parallel to O_1T_1. Draw the required tangent T_1T_2 parallel to TO_2.

4·31 To draw an interior common tangent to two circles of unequal radii (Fig. 4-31). This is the case for a crossed belt on pulleys. Given circles with radii

R_1 and R_2, with center O_1 and radius $R = R_1 + R_2$ draw a circle. From O_1 draw a tangent O_1T to the circle of radius R (by method of Art. 4·25). Draw the required tangent T_1T_2 parallel to TO_2.

4·32 To lay off the approximate length of an arc on a straight line (Fig. 4-32). Given arc AB, draw a line tangent to the arc at A. Set the bow dividers to a small space. Start at B and step along the arc to a point nearest A (close to the tangent point). Without lifting the dividers, step off the same number of spaces along the tangent line to locate point C. AC is the length of the arc (approximately).

4·33 To lay off the approximate length of the circumference of a circle (Fig. 4-33). Given a circle of radius R, draw perpendiculars to A and B. Make BD equal to $3R$. Lay off angle AOC equal to $30°$. Draw CD, which is one-half the circumference (approximately; the error is less than 1 in 100,000).

4·34 To approximate a noncircular curve with arcs of circles (Fig. 4-34). Given a curve, by trial locate the center of an arc that will closely approximate a portion of the curve. Connect the end of the arc with the center. The center of an arc tangent to the first arc must

lie on the radius just drawn, extended if necessary. Continue in the same way for each new arc. Remember that the point of tangency must lie on the "lines of center," as T_1 on O_1O_2 and T_2 on O_2O_3.

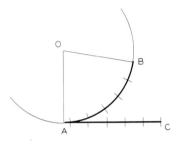

Fig. 4-32. To lay off the approximate length of an arc on a straight line.

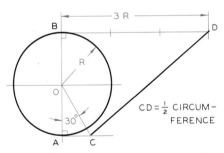

Fig. 4-33. To lay off the circumference of a circle on a straight line.

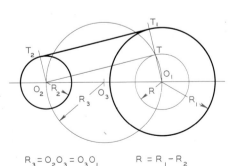

$R_3 = O_2O_3 = O_3O_1$ $R = R_1 - R_2$

Fig. 4-30. To draw an exterior common tangent to two circles.

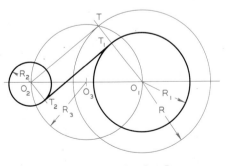

$R_3 = O_2O_3 = O_3O_1$ $R = R_1 + R_2$

Fig. 4-31. To draw an interior common tangent to two circles.

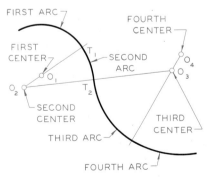

Fig. 4-34. To approximate a noncircular curve with arcs.

4·35 The involute (Fig. 4-35). If a nonstretching cord is kept taut while it is being unwound from around a stationary figure, a point on the cord will trace a curve called an *involute*.

4·36 To draw the involute of a square (Fig. 4-36). With center 1 and radius 1–4, draw an arc to intersect side 2–1 extended to 1^1. With center 2 and radius 2–1, draw an arc to intersect side 3–2 extended at 2^1. Continue in like manner with centers at the corners of the square, and increase each radius by the length of one side of the square.

4·37 To draw the involute of a circle (Fig. 4-37). Divide the circumference of the circle into a number of equal parts. Lay off the length of the arc from point 1 to point 2 on tangent $2–2^1$. On the tangent at 3 lay off the length of arc $1–3^1$ to locate point 3^1. Continue in like manner for other points. Sketch a light line through the points and brighten the curve, using an irregular curve. The involute of a circle is the curve of the involute gear system.

4·38 To draw a spiral of Archimedes (Fig. 4-38). Draw a circle; divide the circle into a number of equal parts; draw radial lines. Divide one radial line, O–6, into the same number of equal

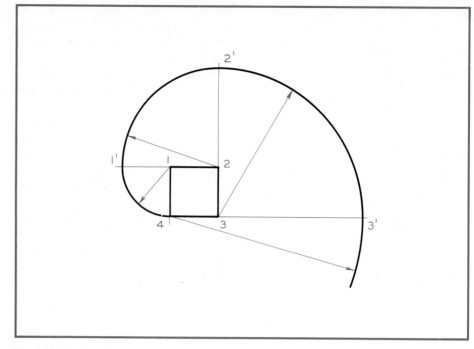

Fig. 4-36. To draw the involute of a square.

Fig. 4-37. To draw the involute of a circle.

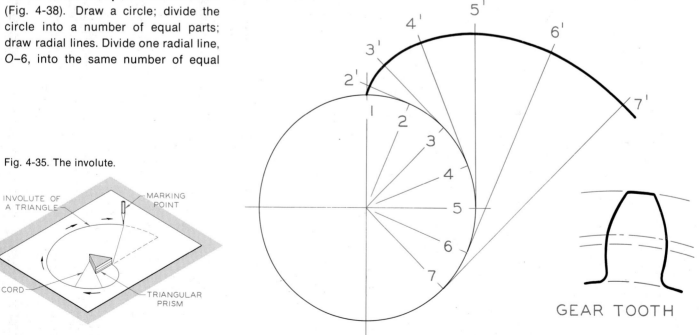

Fig. 4-35. The involute.

GEAR TOOTH

Fig. 4-38. To draw a spiral of Archimedes.

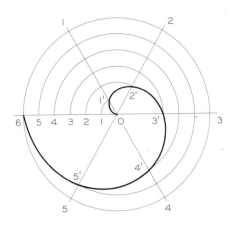

parts. With center *O* and radius *O*–1 draw an arc to locate point 1¹. In like manner draw arcs with radii *O*–2, *O*–3, and so forth, to locate other points as shown. Sketch lightly through the points and brighten the curve, using the irregular curve.

4•39 The ellipse. The lampshade in Fig. 4-39*a* at A has been tipped back. The base of the circular bottom shows as an ellipse when viewed from in front. If a circle is parallel to a plane and if every point on the circle is carried over to that plane by straight lines perpendicular to the plane, another circle will be formed on the plane. The second

circle is known as the *projection* of the first. (☞ *Projection means thrown forward.*) If a circle is perpendicular to a plane, its projection will be a straight line. If it is at an angle, its projection will be an ellipse. A square board with a circular hole drawn in two positions, as in Fig. 4-39*a* at B, illustrates the foregoing statement. Views of a circle at different angles are shown at C. ☞ *An ellipse* (Fig. 4-39*b*) *is defined as a curve generated (formed) by a point moving in a plane so that the sum of its distances from two fixed points, called foci, F₁ and F₂, is a constant (is always the same) and is equal to the major axis, AB, or longest diameter. The two foci*

Fig.₄-39*a*. The ellipse.

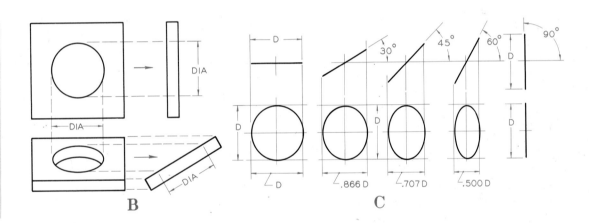

A

B

C

Fig. 4-39*b*. Terms and parts of an ellipse.

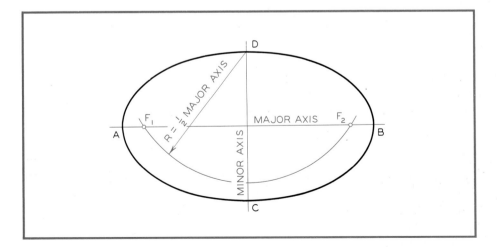

are always on the major axis of the ellipse. A line through the center perpendicular to the major axis is called the *minor axis (CD)* or *short diameter.* To find the foci (Fig. 4-39b) draw an arc with its center at one end of the

minor axis and a radius equal to one-half of the major axis. This arc will cut the major axis at the foci F_1 and F_2.

4·40 To draw an ellipse by the pin and string method (Fig. 4-40). Given major axis *AB* and minor axis *CD* at 1, with center *D* and radius *AO* (one-half the major axis) draw an arc to locate the foci *(F₁* and *F₂)*. Place pins at *F₁, D,* and *F₂*. Tie a cord tightly around the three pins. Remove pin *D;* insert the point of a pencil in the loop. Keep the cord taut and move the point as indicated at 2 and 3.

4·41 To draw an ellipse by the trammel method (Fig. 4-41). Cut a strip of paper or plastic (called a *trammel*). Mark the distance *ao* equal to *AO* (one-half the major axis) and *ad* equal to *DO* (one-half the minor axis). Place the trammel as shown. Move the trammel as indicated by arrows, keeping point *d* on the major axis and point *o* on the minor axis. At each position make a light pencil mark at *a* to locate points on the ellipse.

4·42 To draw an ellipse by the concentric circle method (Fig. 4-42). With *O* as a center draw circles on the major

and minor diameters. Draw a number of radial lines, as *OP* and *OQ*, cutting the large circle at *P, Q,* and the small circle at *P¹, Q¹*. From *P* draw a vertical line to intersect a horizontal line from *P₁* to locate *p*, a point on the ellipse. Draw vertical lines from points on the large circle to intersect horizontal lines from corresponding points on the small circle to locate more points on the ellipse. To draw a tangent to an ellipse at any point *H* (Fig. 4-42), draw a line perpendicular to the major axis from the point *H* to cut the outer circle at *K*. Draw *KL* tangent to the outer circle to cut the major axis extended at *L*. From *L* draw *HL*, the required tangent.

4·43 Approximate ellipses. When a true ellipse is not required, a curve having the general appearance of an ellipse (an approximate ellipse) may be drawn with arcs of circles.

First method (Fig. 4-43a). When the minor axis is at least two-thirds of the major axis, lay off *OF* and *OG*, each equal to *AB* minus *CD*. Lay off *OJ* and *OH*, each equal to three-fourths of *OF*. Draw and extend lines *GJ, GH, FJ,* and *FH*. Draw arcs with centers *G* and *F* and radius *GD*. Draw arcs with centers *J* and *H* and radius *JA* to complete the approximate ellipse. Note the tangent points marked *T*.

Fig. 4-40. To draw an ellipse by the pin-and-string method.

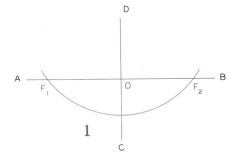

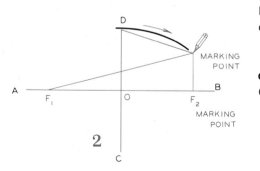

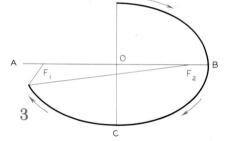

Fig. 4-41. To draw an ellipse by the trammel method.

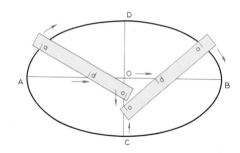

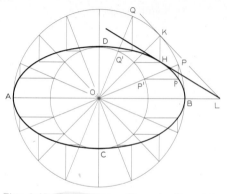

Fig. 4-42. To draw an ellipse by the concentric-circle method.

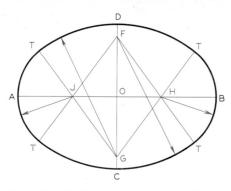

Fig. 4-43a. To draw an approximate ellipse.

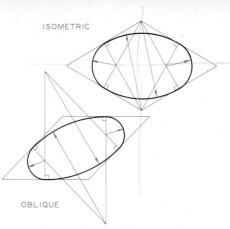

Fig. 4-43b. To draw an approximate ellipse.

Fig. 4-43c. Isometric and oblique ellipses.

Second method (Fig. 4-43b). Draw line *AD;* draw an arc with center *O* and radius *OA* to locate point *E*. Draw an arc with center *D* and radius *DE* to locate point *F*. Draw the perpendicular bisector of *AF* to locate points *J* and *H*. With center *J* and radius *JA* draw arc *TAT*. With center *H* and radius *HD* draw arc *TDT*. Lay off *OK* = *OJ* and *OL* = *OH* to locate centers for arcs *TBT* and *TCT*.

Circular arc approximations for ellipses are used in isometric, oblique, and other pictorial drawings (Chap. 14), where the method is to draw perpendicular lines from the points of tangency to locate centers for arcs (Fig. 4-43c).

There are many methods of using arcs of circles to closely approximate ellipses, but it is about as easy to draw a true ellipse, especially if ellipse templates are available.

4·44 Ellipse templates (Fig. 4-44a) are made of sheet plastic with ellipses cut out to guide a pen or pencil. They are made in a great variety of sizes and proportions, so almost any desired size can be drawn. Templates for ellipses from circles at angles with 5° intervals are usual. Note illustrations of the diameter and the angle in Fig. 4-44b. Professional engineers, draftsmen, and illustrators use such templates as regular equipment.

Fig. 4-44a. Ellipse templates.

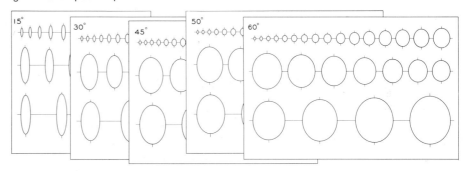

Fig. 4-44b. The ellipse angle.

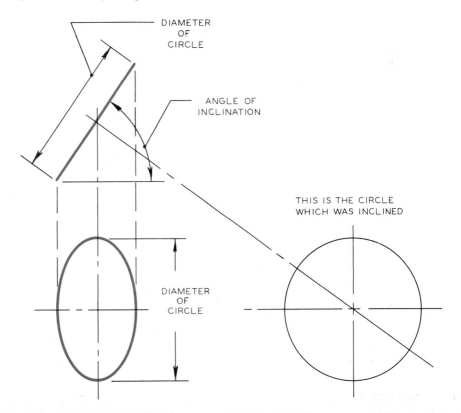

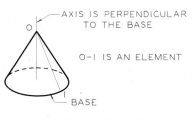

RIGHT CIRCULAR CONE

—AXIS IS PERPENDICULAR
TO THE BASE

O-I IS AN ELEMENT

BASE

Fig. 4-45a. A right circular cone.

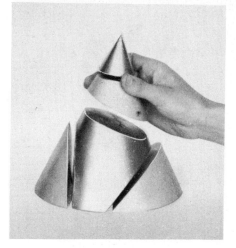

Fig. 4-45b. The conic sections. *(Photo courtesy Professor Spencer Hokenson, North Dakota School of Science)*

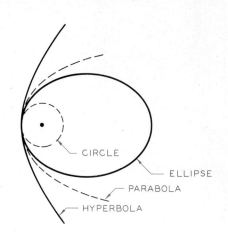

CIRCLE

ELLIPSE

PARABOLA

HYPERBOLA

Fig. 4-45d. Possible orbit forms.

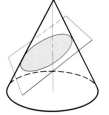 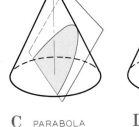

A CIRCLE   **B** ELLIPSE   **C** PARABOLA   **D** HYPERBOLA

Fig. 4-45c. The conic sections.

4·45 Conic sections. A right circular cone (Fig. 4-45a) has a circle for a base and an axis perpendicular to the base at its center. A right circular cone may be cut by planes to obtain curves known as *conic sections* (Figs. 4-45b and 4-45c). If the plane is parallel to the base, the curve is a *circle,* as at A, Fig. 4-45c. The circle is a familiar curve and is drawn with the compasses. If the cutting plane makes a greater angle with the axis than the elements make, the curve is an *ellipse* (Fig. 4-45c at B). The ellipse is defined in Art. 4·39, and methods of drawing ellipses are given in Arts. 4·40, 4·41, and 4·42. If the cutting

plane is parallel to an element of the cone, the curve is a *parabola* (Fig. 4-45c at C). If the cutting plane makes a smaller angle with the axis than the elements make, the curve is a *hyperbola* (Fig. 4-45c at D).

The path, or orbit, of satellites about a central body, such as the earth, may take the form of one of the conic-section curves (Fig. 4-45d). For earth satellites the curve is an ellipse. The circle is a special case of the elliptical orbit. A guided missile may climb to a desired height and then follow the curve of a hyperbola before it dives on its intended target.

4·46 The parabola is one of the conic-section curves. It is one of the paths followed into space (Fig. 4-46a). A parabola (Fig. 4-46b) is defined as a plane curve traced by a point moving so that its distance from a fixed point (focus) and its distance from a straight line (directrix) are equal.

A parabola may be drawn by locating points from the focus (F) and the directrix (AB) (Fig. 4-46b). Draw a line parallel to the directrix as line 1–1 at a distance R_1 (greater than EO). With center F and radius R_1 cut the line 1–1 at points marked P_1. For P_1 note that R_1 is the distance from AB and is the same as the distance R_1 from F. Proceed in the same way to locate sufficient points on the parabola.

A parabola may be drawn by tangents (Fig. 4-46c at A and B where GM and HM are tangent). Divide GM and HM, each into the same number of equal parts, numbered as shown. Draw lines 1–1, 2–2, etc., and draw the parabola as a smooth tangent curve. The vertex, O, will be halfway between M and N. If ON and GH are given, extend ON to make OM = ON. Draw GM and MH, and proceed as before.

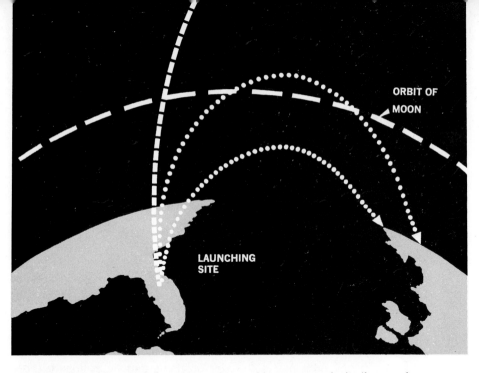

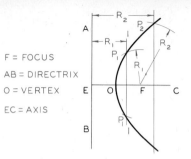

ORBIT OF MOON

LAUNCHING SITE

■■■■ Parabolic path followed by probe reaching escape velocity (from surface of Earth 25,000 miles per hour).

●●●●● Elliptical paths followed by probes not reaching escape velocity.

Fig. 4-46a. Parabolic space path.

F = FOCUS
AB = DIRECTRIX
O = VERTEX
EC = AXIS

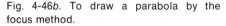

Fig. 4-46b. To draw a parabola by the focus method.

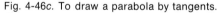

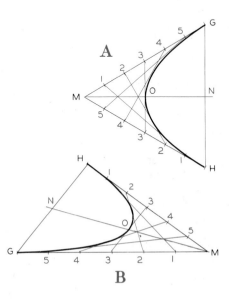

A

B

Fig. 4-46c. To draw a parabola by tangents.

4·47 The hyperbola (Fig. 4-47).
☞ *The hyperbola is defined as a plane curve traced by a point so moving that the difference of the distances from two fixed points (foci) is a constant and equal to the transverse axis.*

A hyperbola may be drawn by locating points from the foci (F_1 and F_2) and the transverse axis AB (Fig. 4-47). With centers F_1 and F_2 and any radius as R_1 greater than F_1B draw short arcs. With centers F_1 and F_2 and radius $R_2 = R_1 + AB$ draw arcs to intersect (cut across) the arcs drawn with radius R_1. This will locate four points marked P_1. Locate other points in the same way. In each case the shorter radius plus AB = the longer radius (R_2) [or the longer radius (R_2) minus AB = the shorter radius].

4·48 Problem suggestions. Group 4, page 422. Three lists are presented. Since List 1 includes basic problems, it would be desirable to use all of them in any course which includes geometrical constructions. Additional assignments from Lists 2 and 3 and Probs. 4·34 to 4·62 may be made according to the age group of the students, the time that is available, and the purpose of the course.

List 1: Problems 4·1, 4·3, 4·5, 4·7, 4·8, 4·13, 4·16, 4·17, 4·18, 4·24, 4·25, 4·28.

List 2: Problems 4·2, 4·9, 4·11, 4·14, 4·19, 4·20, 4·22, 4·26, 4·29, 4·31.

List 3: Problems 4·6, 4·10, 4·12, 4·15, 4·21, 4·23, 4·27, 4·30, 4·32, 4·33.

Fig. 4-47. To draw a hyperbola by the focus method.

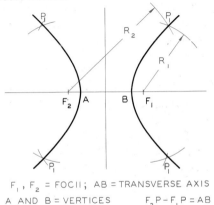

F_1, F_2 = FOCII; AB = TRANSVERSE AXIS
A AND B = VERTICES $F_2P - F_1P = AB$

5
Theory of shape description

5•1 Mental pictures made visible. Communication may be carried out by the oral and written language, by mathematics, and by graphic methods. Graphic methods include mechanical drawing and the many purposes for which it can be used. It is a universal language used and understood in all countries. For the description of shape, operation, arrangements, and all purposes where visual understanding is involved, it is the most exact method of communication.

To use the graphic language the designer, scientist, engineer, or draftsman must be able to do two things: (1) He must be able to visualize, or see clearly in his mind's eye, what an object, machine, device, or project looks like. (2) He must be able to describe it completely by graphic information (a drawing). Such a drawing, properly made, will give a more accurate and clearer description than a photograph or written description; and, of course, a photograph cannot be made of something which does not exist. Lines drawn according to definite principles enable views to be drawn which give exact descriptions. Shape description is based upon orthographic projection (Art. 5·7). The ability to describe real shapes accurately and completely with lines and the ability to read and understand such descriptions require a thorough knowledge of the principles set forth in this chapter.

5•2 Describing objects by views. For the graphic description of an object we should have available the paper, pencils, and instruments described in Chap. 2. On the paper we can make measurements in a single plane only. All objects have dimensions that may be at angles or perpendicular to the paper as well as parallel to it. A picture could be made that would show, just as a photograph would, the general appearance of the object, but it would not show the exact forms and relations of the parts of the object. It would show it as it appears, not as it really is.

Our problem, then, is to represent objects on a sheet of paper in such a manner as to tell the exact shape and proportions. This is done by drawing views of the object as seen from different positions and by arranging these views systematically.

5•3 Views from different directions. Three directions would be suggested for viewing the concrete steps pictured in Fig. 5-3a to obtain three views. This is illustrated in Fig. 5-3b. From in front the width and height would show; this is a front view. From one side the depth and height would show; this is a side view. From above, the depth and width would show; this is a top view.

If the steps are 4 ft wide and each step has a tread of 12 in. and a rise of 6 in., we can draw three views as shown in Fig. 5-3c. In order to keep down the size of the drawing, a scale of 1 in. equals 1 ft might be used. For the steps, the front and side views give the required information and the top view could be omitted. Some things can be shown in two views, but others require three views; it depends upon the shape.

Views of two different shapes are shown in Fig. 5-3d. At A arrows indicate directions for viewing a rectangular prism; views in each of these directions are shown and named. At B a picture of a cylinder is shown, together with

Fig. 5-3a. Concrete steps at front entrance to house.

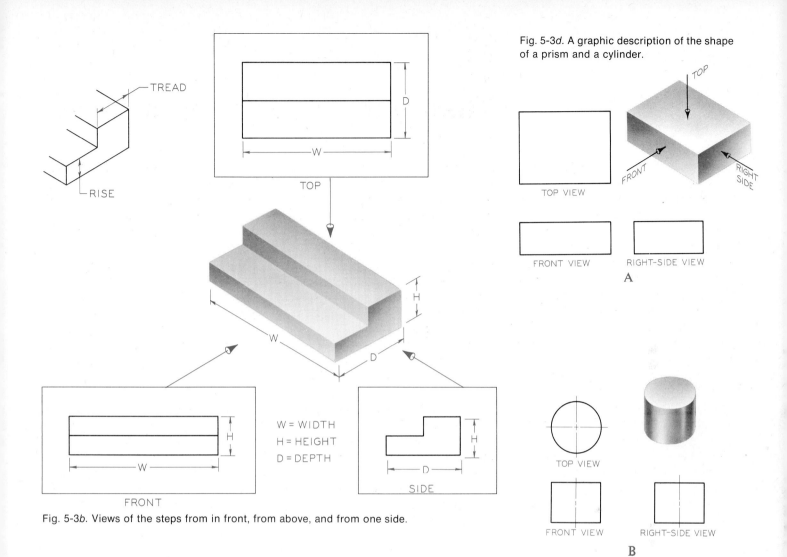

TREAD

RISE

D

W

TOP

H

W

D

W = WIDTH
H = HEIGHT
D = DEPTH

FRONT

H

SIDE

D

H

Fig. 5-3b. Views of the steps from in front, from above, and from one side.

Fig. 5-3d. A graphic description of the shape of a prism and a cylinder.

TOP

FRONT

RIGHT SIDE

TOP VIEW

FRONT VIEW

RIGHT-SIDE VIEW

A

TOP VIEW

FRONT VIEW

RIGHT-SIDE VIEW

B

Fig. 5-3c. A three-view drawing of the steps, showing the proper arrangement of the views.

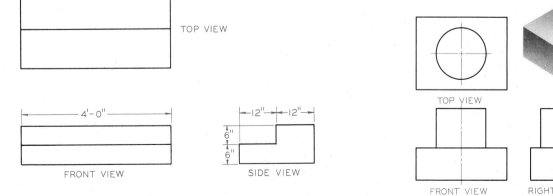

TOP VIEW

4'-0"

FRONT VIEW

12"   12"

6"
6"

SIDE VIEW

TOP VIEW

FRONT VIEW

RIGHT-SIDE VIEW

C

Theory of shape description   63

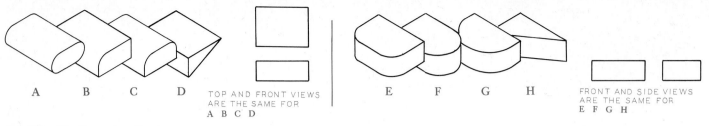

A   B   C   D

TOP AND FRONT VIEWS
ARE THE SAME FOR
A B C D

E   F   G   H

FRONT AND SIDE VIEWS
ARE THE SAME FOR
E F G H

Fig. 5-3e. Why three views?

Fig. 5-4a. Picture of a slide projector. *(Society for Visual Education, Inc., Chicago, Ill.)*

TOP

SIDE

FRONT

Fig. 5-4b. The front view of the projector.

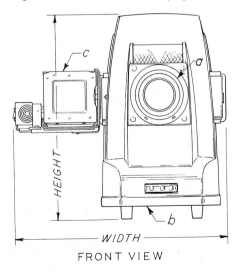

c

a

HEIGHT

b

WIDTH

FRONT VIEW

three views. Notice that the top view shows the true circular shape of the cylinder as seen from above. The front and side views appear as rectangles and are the same size, so the cylinder might be described by two views; the top view shows the shape and the front view shows the diameter and height. The side view is not needed. At C the cylinder has been placed on the prism. Notice how the views at A and B combine to form the views at C. Complete views are composed of views of separate parts. Two views, top and front or top and side, might be used, but we would have to be sure the prism had all square corners. In Fig. 5-3e notice that two views might be the same for many different third views.

5•4 The relation of views. A picture of a slide projector (Fig. 5-4a) shows the projector as it ordinarily appears to us, but it does not show the true shapes of the parts. The front of the lens tube appears as an ellipse, although we know it is really circular. This is because the circular end is not in a plane perpendicular to our line of sight. The projector has, in effect, been tilted at an angle in order to show more sides. If we look at the projector from directly in front, we obtain a view showing the exact shape of the end of the tube and the outline of the other parts as seen from in front. This is called a *front view* (Fig. 5-4b). This view shows the width and height of the projector, but it does not tell us the depth (or distance from front to back), so it is nec-

sary to have another view from a position directly above (called a *top view*) or else a view from one side (called a *side view*). In this way either the top view or a side view will show the depth. Often, as in this case, both a top view and a side view, in addition to the front view, are needed to describe the object (Fig. 5-4c).

The lens tube is shown as a circle, as at *a* in the front view, but in the top view and the side view it is shown as a straight line, as at *a*, Fig. 5-4c. The outline of the base is shown in the top view at *b,* but the bottom of the base is shown as a straight line at *b* in the front and side views. The three views taken together define the shapes of all the visible parts of the projector and their exact relationships to each other. It is evident that the front and side views are exactly the same height. When drawn, they are placed directly across from each other. The top view is placed directly above the front view, and the three views together appear as in Fig. 5-4c.

5•5 Left-side view (Fig. 5-5). Sometimes a left-side view describes an object more clearly than a right-side view, and in such cases it should be used. Figure 5-5 shows the top, front, and left-side views of the projector. Notice at *c* that it shows the slide magazine, which can not be seen in the right-side view. For some objects it may be necessary to show both the right- and the left-side views in order to provide a complete description of the object to be drawn.

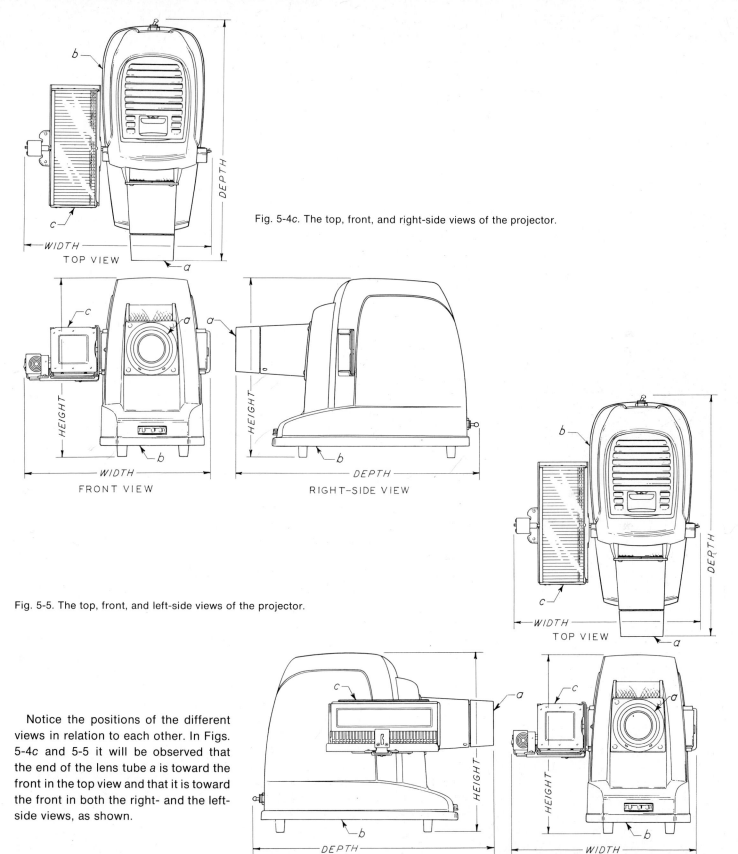

Fig. 5-4c. The top, front, and right-side views of the projector.

TOP VIEW

FRONT VIEW

RIGHT-SIDE VIEW

Fig. 5-5. The top, front, and left-side views of the projector.

TOP VIEW

Notice the positions of the different views in relation to each other. In Figs. 5-4c and 5-5 it will be observed that the end of the lens tube *a* is toward the front in the top view and that it is toward the front in both the right- and the left-side views, as shown.

LEFT-SIDE VIEW

FRONT VIEW

5·6 Width, depth, and height. As a further explanation of the relation of the three views, study the drawing of the steel desk shown in Fig. 5-6. Notice that the typewriter shelf is at the right in the top and front views and that it projects toward the front view. Also, notice that it projects toward the front view in both the right-hand and the left-hand views. The height, *H*, of the desk shows in the front and the side views. The width, *W,* shows in the top and the front views. The depth, *D*, shows in the top and the side views. Notice how the side views differ.

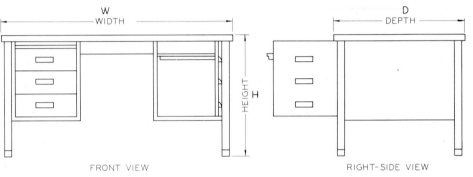

TOP VIEW

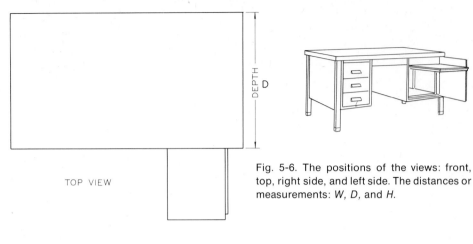

Fig. 5-6. The positions of the views: front, top, right side, and left side. The distances or measurements: *W, D,* and *H.*

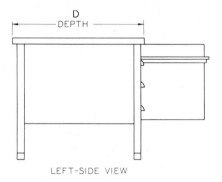

LEFT-SIDE VIEW

FRONT VIEW

RIGHT-SIDE VIEW

5·7 Orthographic projection. The use of different views to describe objects, as shown in the previous articles, is based upon the principles of orthographic projection. This theory must be well understood before complicated or difficult drawings can be made or read.

Ortho- means "straight or at right angles" and *-graphic* means "written or drawn." *Projection* comes from two old Latin words, *"pro,"* meaning "forward," and *"jacere,"* meaning "to throw." Thus, orthographic projection literally means "thrown forward, drawn at right angles." The following definition has been given: ☞ *"Orthographic projection is the method of representing the exact form of an object in two or more views on planes, generally at right angles to each other, by perpendiculars from the object to the planes."*

Observe Fig. 5-7, where three planes make right angles to each other. A point *A* is below the *H* plane and inside the *F* and *P* planes. The line *A–A* is perpendicular to the frontal plane and projects point *A* to the frontal plane at *A.* The line *A–A* is perpendicular to the horizontal plane and projects point *A* to the horizontal plane at *A.* The line *A–A* is perpendicular to the profile and projects point *A* to the profile, or side plane, at *A.*

5·8 Planes of projection. Suppose the bookend shown in Fig. 5-8*a* is to be drawn. The draftsman imagines himself to be looking through a transparent plane set up in front of the bookend (Fig. 5-8*b*). If, from every point of the bookend, perpendiculars are imagined as extended or projected to the plane, the result on the front of the plane would be the projection on that plane called the *frontal projection,* or *front view;* or, in architectural drawing, the *front elevation.* This view will show the true width and height of the bookend.

Fig. 5-7. Orthographic projection. The three views of a point.

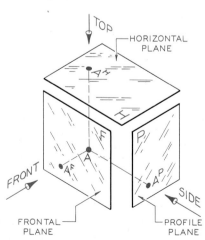

Fig. 5-8a. Picture of a bookend.

Fig. 5-8b. The frontal plane, F.

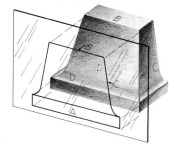

Fig. 5-8c. The horizontal plane, H.

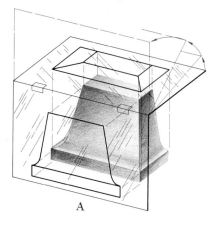

A

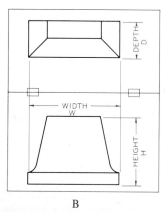

B

In Fig. 5-8c at A a horizontal plane is hinged at right angles to the frontal plane. If the observer looks down through the plane, he will see the top of the bookend. Perpendiculars from the bookend to this plane will give the *horizontal projection,* or *top view;* or, in architectural drawing, the *plan.* This view will show the depth of the bookend from front to back as well as the width already shown on the front·view. These two planes represent the drawing paper. If the horizontal plane is imagined as swung up on the hinges until it lies in the extension of the front plane, as at B in Fig. 5-8c, the two views will be shown in their correct relationship

Fig. 5-9a. The glass box.

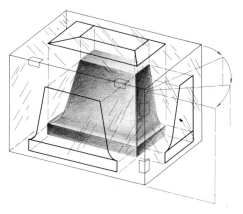

Fig. 5-9b. Opening the glass box.

as they would be drawn on the paper. Together they give the width, *W;* the depth, *D;* and the height, *H.* This explains the reason for the statement made in Art. 5·4 that the top view is always drawn directly over the front view. The side view is obtained in like manner by a plane at right angles to both the frontal and the horizontal planes (Fig. 5-9a).

Three planes have been mentioned, and these are considered the "regular" planes used to obtain the three regular views:

The front view on the frontal plane, indicated by the letter *F*
The top view on the horizontal plane, indicated by the letter *H*
The side view on the profile plane, indicated by the letter *P*

5·9 The glass box. As mentioned in Art. 5·8, the side view, side elevation, or profile projection is imagined as made on a plane perpendicular to both the front and top planes. Thus, the object can be thought of as being inside a glass or other transparent box, as in Fig. 5-9a. The projections on the sides of this box would be the views which we have discussed. In Fig. 5-9b the sides of the box are being opened.

When fully opened up into one plane (Fig. 5-9c), the views take their relative positions as they would be drawn on the paper. These figures show the views as projected onto all six planes, or faces, of the box and are arranged according to accepted practice for the six views.

Notice that some views give the same information contained in other views. They may also be, for practical purposes, mirror images of one another. It is not necessary to show all six views for a working drawing, though an extra view may be desirable in some cases. The top, front, and right-side views, as ordinarily drawn, are shown in Fig.

5-9d. When a left-side view is drawn, it is placed as shown in Fig. 5-9e.

5·10 Studies. As an explanation of how the theory of projection is applied, study the drawings of the objects in the following figures: In Space 1 of Fig. 5-10a each view represents a single surface. In Space 2 the top view shows two surfaces, A and B, at different levels; as shown by the front view, surface A is above surface B. In the side view surfaces C and D are shown, but it is necessary to look at the front view to see which surface is closer to the side plane. In Space 3 surface B is inclined and is shown slightly short-

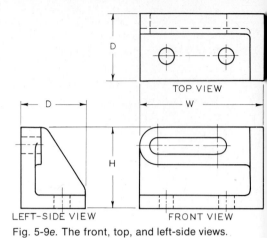

Fig. 5-9e. The front, top, and left-side views.

Fig. 5-10a. Views for study. Plane surfaces.

Fig. 5-9c. The glass box opened.

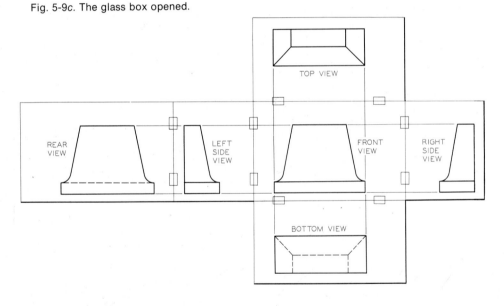

Fig. 5-9d. The front, top, and right-side views.

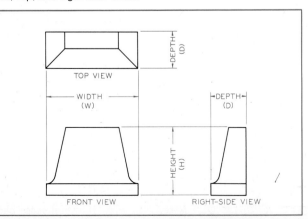

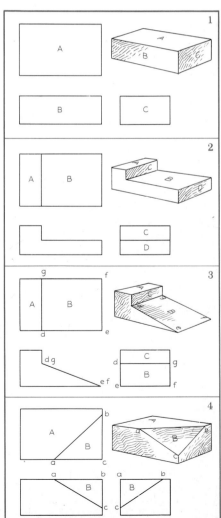

ened in the top view and very much shortened in the side view. To obtain the true size of surface B, the distance de must be taken from the front view, where it shows in its true length (it is parallel to the front plane), and the distance ef must be taken from the top or side view, where it shows in its true length. A surface inclined to all three planes is shown in Space 4 (the corner of the block has been cut away). The true size of surface B can be laid out by taking the distance ab from the top view, ac from the front view, and cb from the side view, where these distances show in their true length. Then construct a triangle (Art. 4·9).

More pictures and drawings are given in Fig. 5-10b for study and comparison. Consider the reason for the views that have been selected and the meaning of each line on the views. Could any of the views be omitted for any of the objects? Notice how the inclined surfaces are represented and that the views do not show the true sizes of such surfaces. In Space 1 of Fig. 5-10b the inclined surfaces make angles with the top and front planes but are perpendicular to the side plane. Study and describe the positions of the inclined surfaces in Spaces 2, 3, and 4.

5·11 Hidden lines. Since it is necessary to describe every part of an object, everything must be represented, whether it can be seen or not. Such features are projected in the same way as for exterior features. The only difference is that parts which cannot be seen in the views are represented by hidden lines composed of short dashes (Fig. 5-11a). Notice that the first dash of a hidden line touches the line at which it starts (Fig. 5-11a at A). If a hidden line is a continuation of a visible line, space is left between the visible line and the first dash of the hidden line, as at B. If the hidden lines show corners, the dashes touch at the corners, as at C.

Dashes for hidden arcs (Fig. 5-11b at A) start and end at the tangent points. When a hidden arc is tangent to a visible line, a space is left, as at B. When a

Fig. 5-10b. Views for study. Inclined-plane surfaces.

Fig. 5-11a. Hidden lines. Starting, continuing, and at corners.

Fig. 5-11b. Hidden arcs. Visible lines have preference over hidden lines.

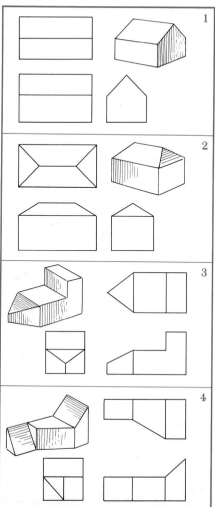

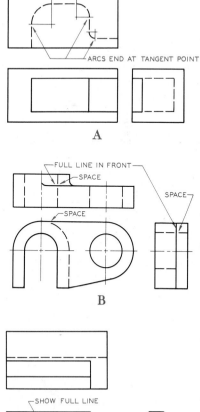

Fig. 5-11c. Technique of representing hidden and visible lines.

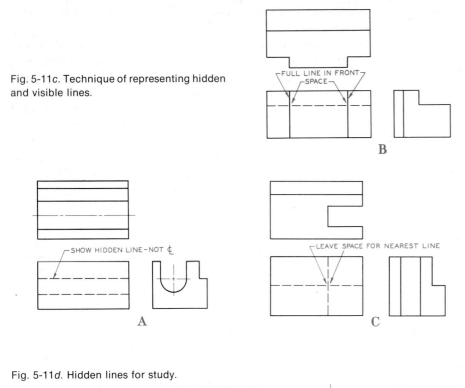

FULL LINE IN FRONT
SPACE

B

SHOW HIDDEN LINE—NOT ℄

A

LEAVE SPACE FOR NEAREST LINE

C

Fig. 5-11d. Hidden lines for study.

RAFTER

DASH STARTS AT TANGENT POINT

JOIST IN BACK OF RAFTER

A   B   C   D

Fig. 5-12a. Center lines, primary and secondary.

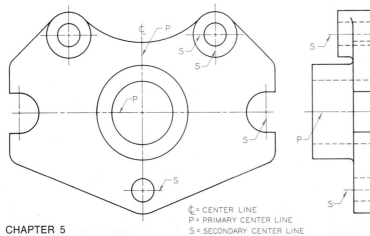

℄ = CENTER LINE
P = PRIMARY CENTER LINE
S = SECONDARY CENTER LINE

hidden line and a visible line project at the same place, show the visible line (Fig. 5-11b at C). When a center line and a hidden line project at the same place (Fig. 5-11c at A), draw the hidden line. When a hidden line crosses a visible line (Fig. 5-11c at B), do not cross the visible line with a dash. When hidden lines cross (Fig. 5-11c at C), the nearest hidden line has the "right of way" and spaces are left as shown. Some hidden lines for study are shown in Fig. 5-11d.

5·12 Center lines are used to locate views and dimensions. (See the alphabet of lines, Fig. 2-10.) Primary center lines, marked *P* in Fig. 5-12a, are axes of symmetry on symmetrical views where one part is a mirror image of another part. Primary center lines are also used as major locating lines to construct the views and as base lines for dimensioning (Chap. 11). Secondary center lines, marked *S* in Fig. 5-12a, are axes for details of a part or construction. Primary center lines are, therefore, the first lines to be drawn, and the views are worked up from them. Note that center lines represent the axes of cylinders in the side view and that the centers of circles or arcs are located first so that measurements can be made from them to locate the lines on the various views. A hidden line is shown in preference to a center line in Fig. 5-12b.

Fig. 5-12b. Center lines and hidden lines.

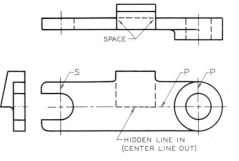

SPACE

HIDDEN LINE IN
(CENTER LINE OUT)

5•13 Curved surfaces. The fact that some curved surfaces, such as cylinders and cones, do not show as curves in all views is illustrated in Fig. 5-13a. A cylinder with its axis (center line) perpendicular to a plane will show as a circle on that plane and as a rectangle on the other two planes. Three views of a cylinder when placed in different positions are shown at B, C, and D. The holes may be considered as negative cylinders. A cone appears as a circle in one view and as a triangle in the others, as shown at E. For a frustum of a cone one view appears as two circles, as at F. In the top view the conical surface is represented by the space between the two circles.

Cylinders, cones, and frustums of cones have single curved surfaces and are represented by circles in one view and straight lines in the other. The handles in Fig. 5-13b at A have double curved surfaces which are represented by curves in both views. The ball handle

has spherical ends, and both views of the ends are circles because a sphere appears as a circle when viewed in any direction. The slotted link in Fig. 5-13b at B and C is an example of tangent plane and curved surfaces. Since the rounded ends are tangent to the sides of the link and the ends of the slot are tangent to the sides, the surfaces are smooth and there is *no* line of separation.

5•14 What views to draw. As already mentioned, the six views in Fig. 5-9c are not needed to describe the bookend. The three views in Fig. 5-9d are sufficient. The six views explain the theory of making drawings, but it is not necessary to draw them in order to tell which views are needed. The general characteristics of an object indicate the views required to describe its shape. Three properly selected views will describe most shapes, but sometimes there are features that will be more

clearly described by using more views or parts of extra views.

Most pieces have a characteristic view by which they can be recognized. This is the first view to consider and generally the first view to draw. Next, consider the normal position of the part when it is in use. This is often desirable but not always necessary. For example, tall parts such as vertical shafts are more readily drawn in a horizontal position; then, views with the fewest hidden lines are easiest to read and take much less time to lay out and draw.

The practical purpose for drawing views is to describe the shape of something. More views than necessary are a waste of time in making the drawing, as well as a waste of time in reading, because all views have to be read (the reader assumes they are necessary and has to be sure). Turned parts, such as the handles shown at A in Fig. 5-13b, and sheet material (Chap. 20), plywood,

Fig. 5-13a. Curved surfaces. Cylinders and cones.

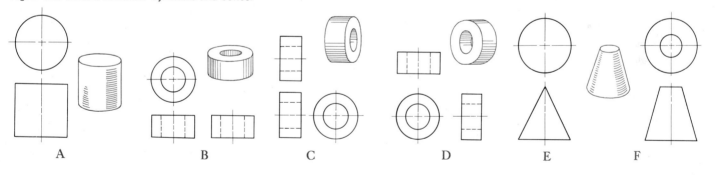

Fig. 5-13b. Curved surfaces.

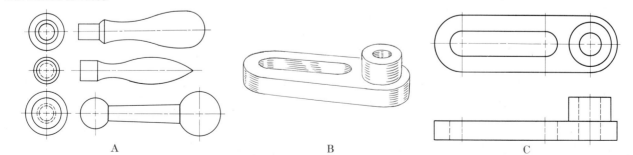

plate material, and parts of uniform thickness, such as the latch and the stamping in Fig. 5-14a at A and B, can often be described in one view. For the handles in Fig. 5-13b at A give the diameter; for the latch or the stamping in Fig. 5-14a at A and B give the thickness. Parts such as the bushing shown at D and the sleeve shown at E could be,

and often are, shown in one view by dimensions for the diameters marked DIA, as indicated.

There are many things which can be described in two views, as indicated in Fig. 5-14b. When two views are used, they must be carefully selected so as to be sure to describe the shape of the object. For the parts at A and B in Fig.

5-14b there would be no question; for the part at A the top view and either front or side view would be sufficient. For the placer cone at C a third view would add nothing to the description. There should be no question about the selection of views for the guide at D or for the wedge cam at E. Figure 5-14c shows some objects which can

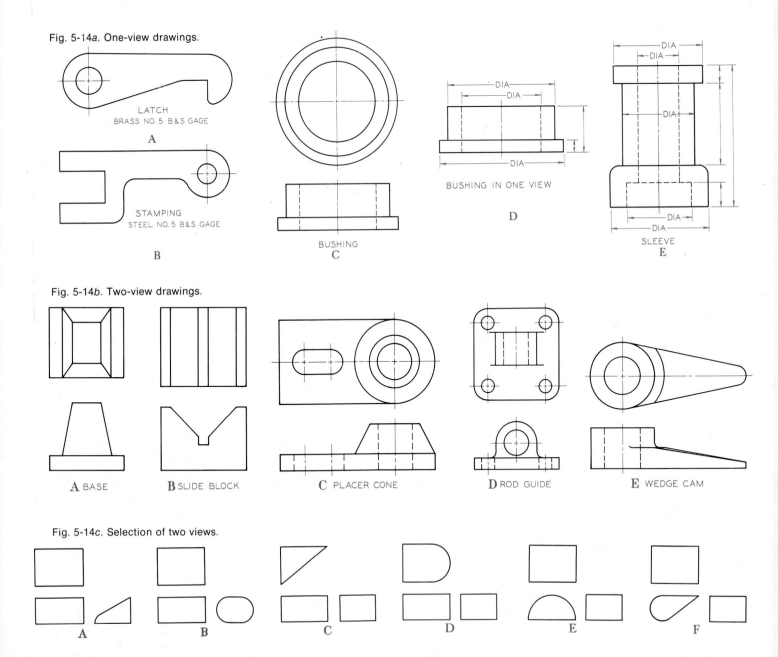

Fig. 5-14a. One-view drawings.

LATCH
BRASS NO. 5 B&S GAGE
A

STAMPING
STEEL NO. 5 B&S·GAGE
B

BUSHING
C

BUSHING IN ONE VIEW
D

SLEEVE
E

Fig. 5-14b. Two-view drawings.

A BASE   B SLIDE BLOCK   C PLACER CONE   D ROD GUIDE   E WEDGE CAM

Fig. 5-14c. Selection of two views.

A   B   C   D   E   F

be described in two views. The top and front views at A and B are the same. Since the side views are necessary, the front and side views would be sufficient. At C and D the top views are necessary, so the top and front views would be sufficient. At E and F the front views are necessary, so the front and top views, or the front and side views, would be

sufficient. Some things, such as the angle in Fig. 5-14d, require three views, as it is necessary to describe shapes in each of the views.

Six views are shown for the sliding base in Fig. 5-14e. A study of the picture and the views will show that the top, front, and right-side views will give the best shape description and

have the fewest hidden lines. The six views are shown here simply to illustrate and explain the selection of views. Only the necessary views would be drawn in practice.

5•15 Second position of the side view. The proportions of an object or the size of the sheet sometimes makes

Fig. 5-14d. Three-view drawings.

Fig. 5-14e. Choice of views.

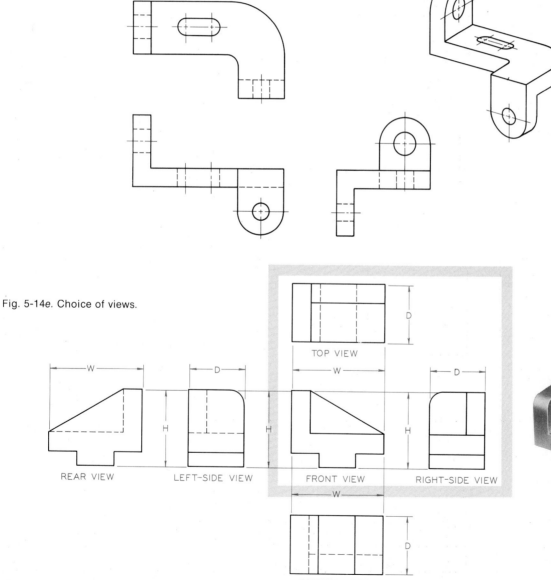

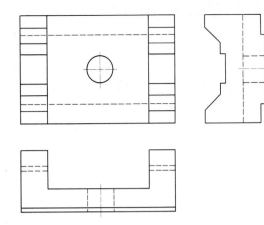

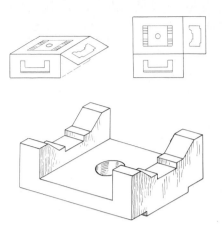

Fig. 5-15. Second position of the side view.

it desirable to show a side view in the second position, or directly across from the top view, as in Fig. 5-15. This position is obtained by revolving the side plane about its intersection with the top plane.

Visualization and careful thought about a "mind's-eye picture" of an object will help decide which views should be drawn to describe its shape.

5·16 Placing views. The location of the views is given for many problems in this book. When drawings are made from the actual part, or for parts yet to be made, it is necessary to be able to place the views so that they will go into the space available on the size of sheet used. This is done by considering the space necessary for each view and comparing the total space required. The size of the drawing sheet selected

should provide for views that will give a clear description of the part. The size suggested in the problems for this chapter is American Standard size A, $8\frac{1}{2}'' \times 11''$ or $9'' \times 12''$. The working space may be as suggested in Fig. 5-16a or as specified by the instructor. The method of working out the positions of the views is the same for any space.

A working space of $10\frac{1}{2}'' \times 7''$ is used to explain how to place the views

of the slide stop in Fig. 5-16b, Space 1. The overall dimensions are: width = $W = 5\frac{1}{4}''$; depth = $D = 1\frac{3}{4}''$; height = $H = 3''$.

1. Space 1. From the left border line lay off the width, $5\frac{1}{4}''$, and the depth, $1\frac{3}{4}''$. Then $5\frac{1}{4}'' + 1\frac{3}{4}'' = 7''$ and $10\frac{1}{2}'' - 7'' = 3\frac{1}{2}'' = R$, the remainder.

2. Space 2. This remainder of $3\frac{1}{2}''$ is to be divided into three parts to provide a space between the front and side

Fig. 5-16a. Sheet layout.

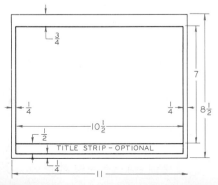

Fig. 5-16b. Placing the views for a three-view drawing.

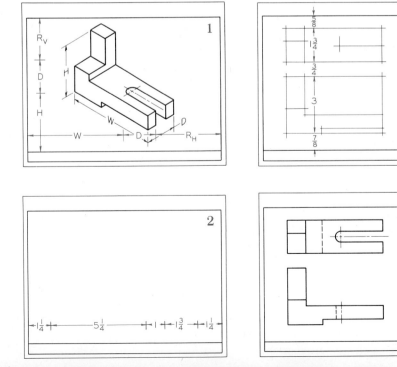

views, a space at the left of the front view, and a space at the right of the side view.

3. Space 2. If a space of about 1″ is used between the front and side views, it will allow left and right spaces of 1¼″. These spaces may be more or less, depending upon the shapes of the views, the space available, and space for dimensions and notes when added.

4. Space 1. Next, from the lower border line lay off the height 3″ and the depth 1¾″ upward. Then $3″ + 1¾″ = 4¾″$ and $7″ − 4¾″ = 2¼″ = R$, the remainder.

5. Space 3. If a space of ¾″ is used between the front and top views, it will allow 1½″ for spaces above and below the views. These could be ¾″ each, but a better balance will result if ⅞″ is used below and ⅝″ above.

6. Space 4. The view as located will appear as shown. More space is generally used below the front view because this gives a better appearance. Spaces between and around views depend upon their shapes, the dimensions required, and the size of the sheet. As experience is gained, the views can be located by a few starting lines and without making computations.

The method of locating views explained for Fig. 5-16b can be used for a two-view drawing. If two views are arranged the long way of the sheet (Fig. 5-16c), lay off W and D as in Space 1 and divide the remainder, R, into suitable spaces, as in Space 2. Then lay off vertical distances H and D as in Space 3. The views as located are drawn in Space 4.

Sometimes two views may be arranged with the long way vertical, as in Fig. 5-16d. Here a vertical center line would be in order. The H and D distances are laid off as in Space 1 and the spaces marked as in Space 2. The starting lines for drawing the views are indicated in Space 3. The views as located are drawn in Space 4.

Fig. 5-16c. Placing the views for a two-view drawing.

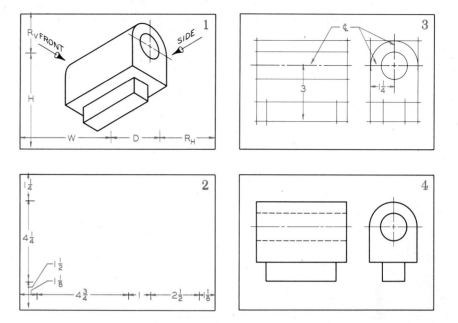

Fig. 5-16d. Placing the views for a two-view drawing.

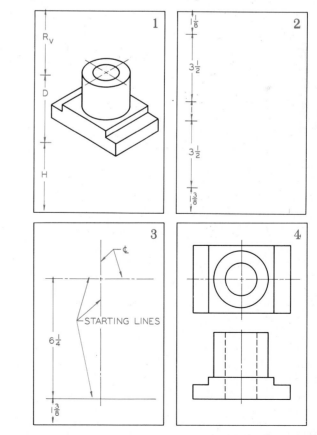

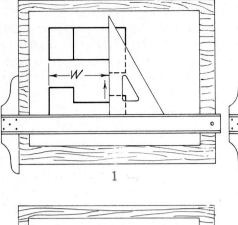

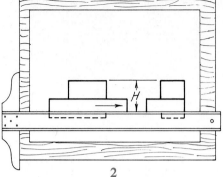

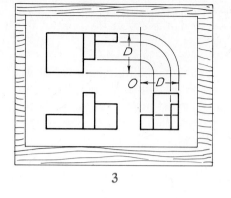

1

2

3

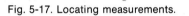

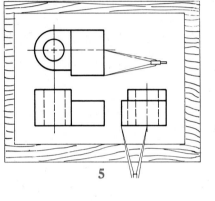

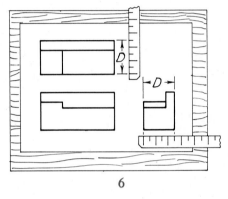

4

5

6

Fig. 5-17. Locating measurements.

5·17 Locating measurements (Fig. 5-17). After lines have been drawn to locate the views, it is necessary to make measurements for details and to draw the views. Measurements made on one view can be transferred to another to save the time of making them again and to ensure accuracy and correctness. Distances in the three directions, width, *W;* height, *H;* and depth, *D,* can be easily transferred, as illustrated in Fig. 5-17.

1. Width, *W,* (horizontal) measurements made on the front view can be located on the top view by drawing up from the front view (Space 1). In like manner, measurements can be projected down from the top view to the front view.

2. Height, *H,* (vertical) measurements on the front view can be located on the side view by drawing a light line across to the side view (Space 2). Measure-

ments can also be located on the front view from the side view in like manner.

3. Depth, *D,* measurements show as vertical distances in the top view and as horizontal distances in the side view. Such measurements can be taken from the top view to the side view by drawing arcs from a center *O* (Space 3), by using a 45° triangle through *O* (Space 4), by using the dividers (Space 5), or by using the scale as shown in Space 6.

5·18 To make a drawing (Fig. 5-18). A systematic method of working should be followed to ensure accuracy and understanding. All views should be carried along together. Do not attempt to finish one view before starting the others. Use a hard pencil (H, 2H, or 4H) and light, thin lines for preliminary lines. Use a soft pencil (F, HB, or B) for final lines. The grade of pencil depends,

to a certain extent, upon the surface of the paper, cloth, or film used. The following order of working is suggested:

1. Consider the characteristic view (Space 1; the front view).

2. Determine the number of views (Space 1; three views needed).

3. Locate the views (Space 2; see Art. 5·16).

4. Block in the views with light, thin lines (Space 3).

5. Lay off the principal measurements (Space 4).

6. Draw the principal lines (Space 5).

7. Lay off the measurements for details (Space 6; centers for arcs, circles, and triangular ribs).

8. Draw the circles and arcs (Space 7).

9. Draw any additional lines needed to complete the views.

10. Brighten the lines where necessary to make them sharp and black and of the proper thickness (Space 8).

Fig. 5-18. Making a drawing.

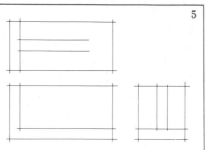

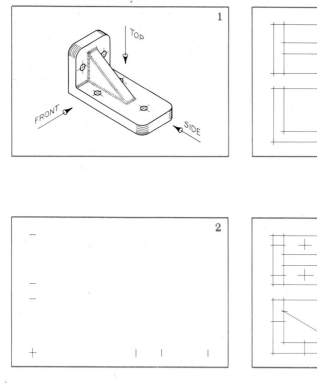

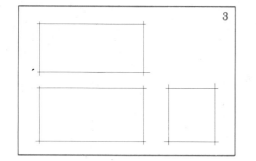

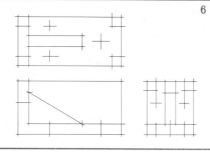

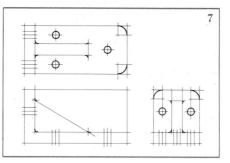

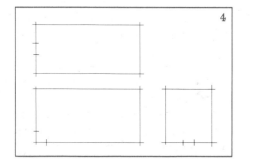

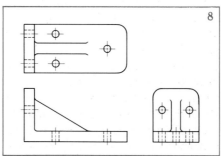

5•19 Problem suggestions. Group 5, page 429. Many instructors have found it possible to secure better results by assigning only a few problems from List 1, proceeding to sketching in Chap. 6, and then returning to Group 5 to work the desired number of problems while studying Chap. 7. Three lists are presented. List 1 includes basic problems which are in general more elementary than Lists 2 and 3. A selection from List 1 should be made according to the time available. Additional or alternative assignments may be made from Lists 2 and 3 according to the age group of the students, the time available, and the purpose of the course. There are sufficient problems listed to provide variation from year to year.

List 3: Problems 5·23, 5·40, 5·44. Additional or alternative problems may be selected from Chap. 26.

List 1: Problems 5·1, 5·2, 5·3, 5·4, 5·5, 5·7, 5·8, 5·9, 5·10, 5·11, 5·12, 5·13, 5·15, 5·16, 5·21, 5·27, 5·29, 5·32, 5·34, 5·35, 5·36, 5·37, 5·42, 5·43, 5·46, 5·47, 5·50, 5·52, 5·53, 5·56, 5·62, 5·65, 5·66, 5·67, 5·72, 5·77, 5·78, 5·80, 5·84, 5·85, 5·88, 5·94.

List 2: Problems 5·14, 5·17, 5·18, 5·19, 5·22, 5·26, 5·28, 5·29, 5·30, 5·31, 5·33, 5·38, 5·39, 5·41, 5·48, 5·51, 5·55, 5·58, 5·61, 5·63, 5·68, 5·69, 5·73, 5·75, 5·76, 5·79, 5·81, 5·86, 5·87, 5·88, 5·90, 5·91, 5·93, 5·95, 5·96.

6
Sketching

6·1 Freehand drawing, or sketching, is one of the most valuable forms of simplified drafting. It is not the easiest, but when the necessary skill and sense of proportion have been attained, it allows clear and accurate space thinking without the handicaps imposed by the use of mechanical drawing equipment. Sketching is the oldest form of writing the graphic language. Sketches have been used from the time of man's picture records on through the ages to present-day engineering design and manufacture.

Sketching is a convenient method of shape description that is helpful in the practice of engineering as well as in the study of view drawing. Views can be made more quickly freehand than with the instruments. Such practice develops accuracy of observation, a good sense of proportion, and sureness in handling the pencil. The ability to make a good sketch is useful for many purposes, such as: (1) making sketches of existing objects; (2) making sketches from "mind pictures"; (3) making sketches for use in place of drawings made with instruments; (4) sketching different parts from assembly or design drawings in order to draw the details; (5) making partial or complete sketches as an aid in reading drawings, explaining drawings, or working up new ideas; (6) planning changes in existing machines or apparatus; (7) working up new mechanisms; and (8) sketching different arrangements for comparison before making drawings.

Skill in freehand sketching is a "must" for draftsmen, designers, and engineers. It is a most important form of graphical communication.

6·2 Sketching equipment. If necessary, any pencil (or pen) and any piece of paper may be used to make a sketch; however, a few simple items will make good sketching easier. These include F, H, and HB pencils properly sharpened to a long conical point, a pencil eraser and a kneaded rubber or plastic eraser, and suitable paper.

Plain or cross-section (graph, or squared) paper may be used, but plain paper is suggested for beginning practice. One should develop the ability to make a good sketch on plain paper without aids of any kind. Usual graph (cross-section) papers are ruled in one-inch squares subdivided into one-quarter-, one-eighth-, or one-tenth-inch squares. Many other rulings are available for both engineering and scientific purposes. A sketch on squared paper is shown in Fig. 6-2a. Such paper is useful in sketching "to scale," or in proportion. Paper may be any convenient size, but standard letter size (8½″ × 11″) is preferred. Separate sheets attached to a stiff cardboard or to a clipboard as well as pads of sketching paper may be used. Working sketches can be made quickly and conveniently with pads of strong tracing paper by placing a sheet of cross-section paper under the top sheet. Isometric ruled paper (Fig. 6-2b) is convenient for making pictorial sketches.

Fig. 6-2a. A sketch on squared paper.

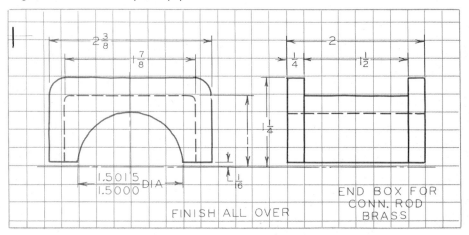

Fig. 6-2b. A sketch on isometric-ruled paper.

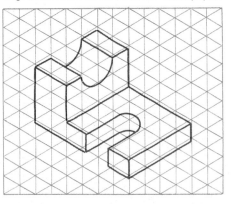

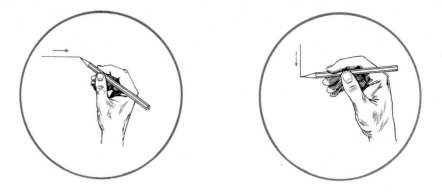

Fig. 6-3a. Sketching a horizontal line.   Fig. 6-3b. Sketching a vertical line.

6·3 Straight lines. First, sharpen the pencil to a long conical point and remove the sharp needle point by wiping it with cloth or paper so that it will not groove the paper. Hold the pencil far enough from the point to allow easy movement of the fingers—about twice the point distance ($1\frac{1}{2}''\pm$)—as in Fig. 6-3a, which shows the position for sketching a horizontal line. The position for sketching a vertical line is shown in Fig. 6-3b.

Lines may be sketched as in Fig. 6-3c, which illustrates: (1) a freely sketched (continuous) line; (2) a line guided by a short dash at the start and end (place the pencil point on the starting dash, keep the eyes on the end dash, and draw toward the ending dash); (3) a line made up of a series of strokes (touching or separated by very small spaces); (4) a line made up of a series of overlapping strokes. In general, freehand lines may be the same as for pencil lines on mechanical drawings, as shown in Fig. 2-10. Kinds of lines used on sketches are shown in Fig. 6-3d. Often only three kinds of lines are used on sketches: thick, dark lines; thin, light lines; and dark, hidden lines. Lines should be sketched very lightly at first so that they may be darkened later for view lines and hidden lines. Preliminary and construction lines should be light enough that they need not be erased.

The student should practice sketching straight lines (Figs. 6-3e, 6-3f, and 6-3g) until he can do creditable work with ease before starting on views. Horizontal lines are drawn from left to right, as in Fig. 6-3e, and vertical

Fig. 6-3c. Some ways of sketching lines.

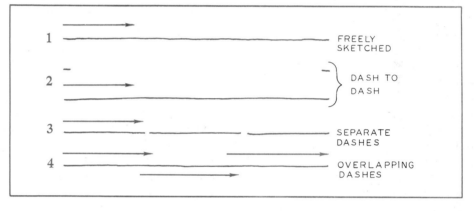

1 — FREELY SKETCHED

2 — DASH TO DASH

3 — SEPARATE DASHES

4 — OVERLAPPING DASHES

Fig. 6-3d. Kinds of lines used on sketches.

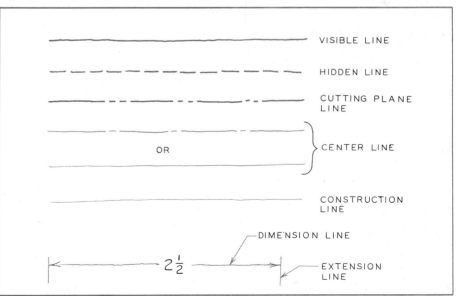

VISIBLE LINE

HIDDEN LINE

CUTTING PLANE LINE

CENTER LINE

OR

CONSTRUCTION LINE

DIMENSION LINE

$2\frac{1}{2}$

EXTENSION LINE

Fig. 6-3e. Sketching horizontal and vertical lines.

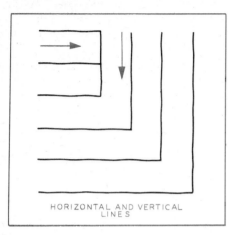

HORIZONTAL AND VERTICAL LINES

Fig. 6-3f. Sketching 45° lines.

45° LINES

Fig. 6-3g. Sketching 30° and 60° lines.

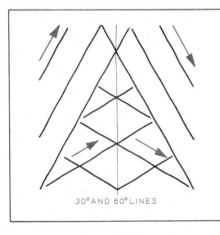

30° AND 60° LINES

lines are drawn from the top down, as in Fig. 6-3e. Inclined lines may be sketched in the directions indicated in Figs. 6-3f and 6-3g. In some cases the sketcher may wish to change his position or to turn the paper so that all lines can be drawn as either horizontal or vertical lines.

6·4 Circles, arcs, and other curves. Two methods can be used.

First method for circles (Fig. 6-4a at A). Draw very light horizontal and vertical center lines and mark off the estimated radii; then, draw a square in which the circle can be sketched.

Second method (Fig. 6-4a at B). Draw very light center lines and extra

Fig. 6-4a. Sketching circles.

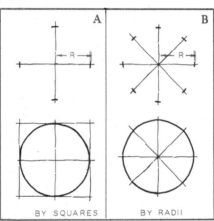

A   B

BY SQUARES   BY RADII

Fig. 6-4b. Sketching arcs and concentric circles.

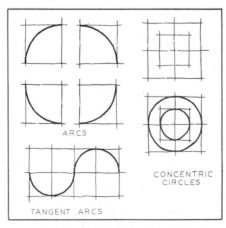

ARCS   CONCENTRIC CIRCLES

TANGENT ARCS

lines through the center and mark off the estimated radii; then, sketch arcs through the marks to form a circle.

Arcs, tangent arcs, and concentric circles are conveniently sketched by blocking in with very light straight lines, as suggested in Fig. 6-4b. In Fig. 6-4c, a strip template as used for large circles is suggested; construction for tangents and part of a circle template are shown. The circle template of thin plastic with holes for drawing many sizes of circles is a help for speed and neatness on sketches or drawings. Ellipses may be sketched as suggested in Fig. 6-4d, or a template may be used. For use of the strip template (trammel), refer to Fig. 4-41.

Fig. 6-4c. Sketching circles with a strip or a sheet template.

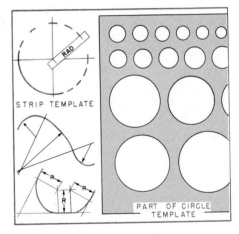

STRIP TEMPLATE

PART OF CIRCLE TEMPLATE

Fig. 6-4d. Sketching ellipses.

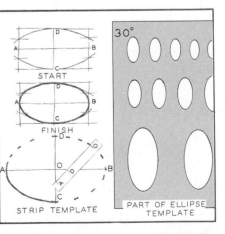

START

FINISH

STRIP TEMPLATE

PART OF ELLIPSE TEMPLATE

6•5 Number and treatment of views. Sketches may consist of one view (Fig. 6-5a; for parts of uniform thickness), two views (Fig. 6-5b), or three views (Fig. 6-5c). Sometimes extra views or part views may be added, or one or more incomplete views may be enough to describe a part completely; half or part views often serve the purpose. .

6•6 A freehand sketch. A V-block is shown in the picture (Fig. 6-6a), and views necessary to describe it have been sketched in Fig. 6-6b. Note that three views are needed. The proportions have been observed. Blocking-in lines have been sketched in for all the views so that they are properly located in the available spaces. Never attempt to sketch one complete view at a time; block them all in and proceed to work up the corresponding details in all the views.

6•7 Making a sketch. Careful practice and systematic methods of work are necessary to develop skill in making sketches.

Fig. 6-5a. A one-view sketch.

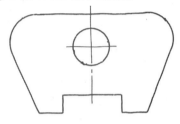

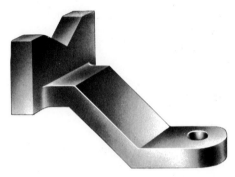

Fig. 6-6a. Picture of a V-block.

Fig. 6-5b. A two-view sketch.

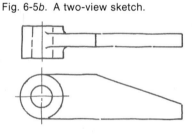

Fig. 6-6b. Sketch of the V-block of Fig. 6-6a.

Fig. 6-5c. A three-view sketch.

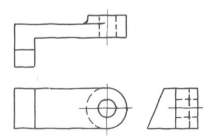

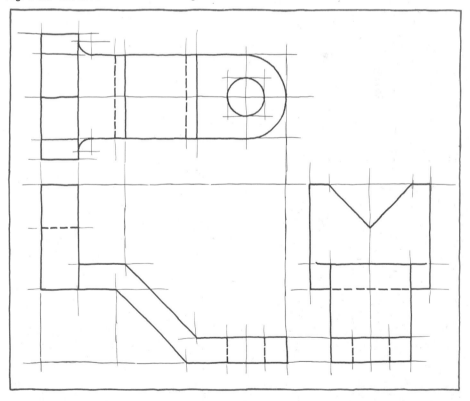

1

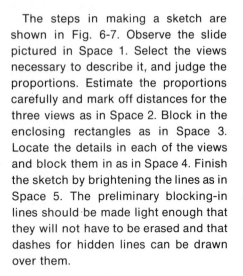

PICTURE OF SLIDE

Fig. 6-7. Steps in making a sketch.

2 — LAY OFF DISTANCES

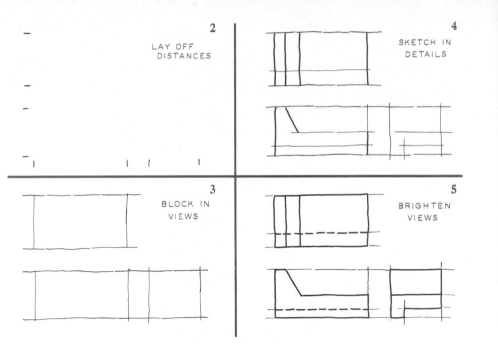

4 — SKETCH IN DETAILS

3 — BLOCK IN VIEWS

5 — BRIGHTEN VIEWS

The steps in making a sketch are shown in Fig. 6-7. Observe the slide pictured in Space 1. Select the views necessary to describe it, and judge the proportions. Estimate the proportions carefully and mark off distances for the three views as in Space 2. Block in the enclosing rectangles as in Space 3. Locate the details in each of the views and block them in as in Space 4. Finish the sketch by brightening the lines as in Space 5. The preliminary blocking-in lines should be made light enough that they will not have to be erased and that dashes for hidden lines can be drawn over them.

6•8 Pictorial sketches provide a convenient way of reading a drawing or of checking to see if a drawing is understood. While there are several types of pictorial sketches and drawings (see Chap. 14), isometric-type sketches are most often used for this purpose.

An isometric sketch is based on three lines, called *axes,* which are used to show the directions in which distances

are laid off for heights *(H),* widths *(W),* and depths *(D),* of an object (Fig. 6-8). The height is laid off on a vertical line *OA.* The width is laid off on *OB* and the depth on *OC,* the lines making 30° with the horizontal, as shown. The 30° lines may be located by estimating one-third of a right angle, as suggested in the figure. Lines parallel to the axes are isometric lines, and distances are laid off on them as shown for the prism in Fig. 6-8. When working freehand, there

is a tendency to make the angle steeper than 30°, which gives awkward or displeasing views. Better views will result if the angle is kept flatter (less) than 30°. Special graph paper with isometric ruling (Fig. 6-2b), if available, will allow good pictorial views to be made quickly and easily.

6•9 To make an isometric sketch of an object, use very light lines most of which need not be erased when the

Fig. 6-8. The three axes for an isometric-type sketch.

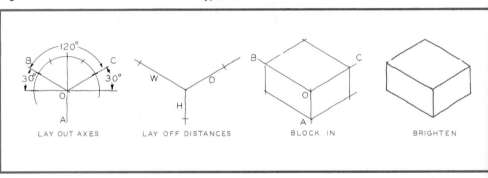

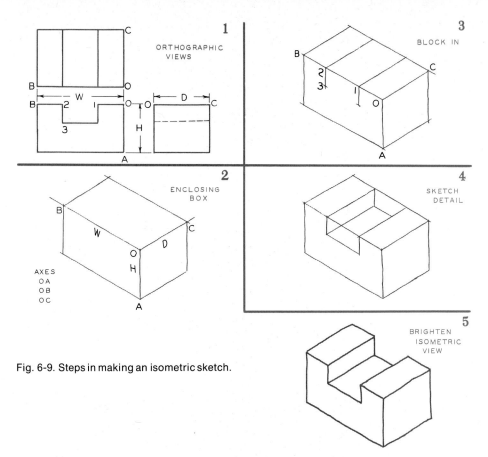

1 ORTHOGRAPHIC VIEWS

2 ENCLOSING BOX

AXES
O A
O B
O C

3 BLOCK IN

4 SKETCH DETAIL

5 BRIGHTEN ISOMETRIC VIEW

Fig. 6-9. Steps in making an isometric sketch.

picture is completed. Follow the steps in Fig. 6-9, where three orthographic views are shown in Space 1. Sketch the three axes as in Space 2. Note that:

$$\text{Height } (H) = OA$$
$$\text{Width } (W) = OB$$
$$\text{Depth } (D) = OC$$

The height (H), the width (W), and the depth (D) have been laid off on the three axes by estimating them from the orthographic views. Block in the enclosing prism, or "box." In Space 3 lay off distances 0–1, 1–2, and 2–3, and sketch lines through points 1, 2, and 3 parallel to the axes. These will indicate the part to be cut out as shown in Space 4. In Space 5 some erasures have been made and lines have been brightened to show the picture of the object.

6·10 Nonisometric lines on isometric sketches. Any object may be enclosed in a box, as suggested in the method of Art. 6·9. Note, however, that the objects in Figs. 6-10a and 6-10b have

Fig. 6-10a. Making an isometric sketch from orthographic views.

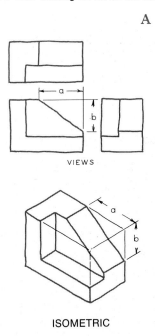

A

VIEWS

ISOMETRIC

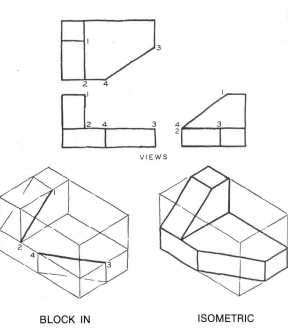

B

VIEWS

BLOCK IN

ISOMETRIC

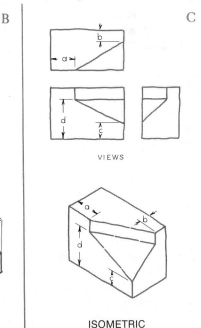

C

VIEWS

ISOMETRIC

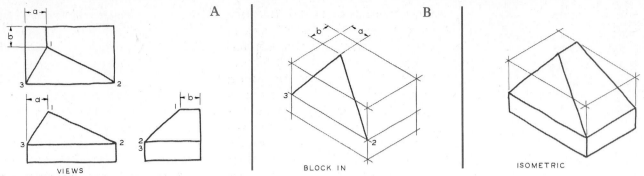

VIEWS   BLOCK IN   ISOMETRIC

Fig. 6-10b. Making an isometric sketch with inclined lines.

some lines which are not parallel to the isometric axes. Lines not parallel to the axes are *nonisometric lines.* In such cases sketch the enclosing box; then, locate points at the ends of the slanting lines by estimating measurements along or parallel to isometric lines and join the points. Lines that are parallel to each other on the object will show parallel on the sketch (Fig. 6-10a). Note how the ends of lines 1–2 and 1–3 are located on the sketch in Fig. 6-10b.

6•11 Circles and arcs on isometric sketches will appear as ellipses or parts of ellipses. To sketch a circle in an isometric view (Fig. 6-11a), first sketch the isometric square as at A. Next, sketch small-end arcs tangent at points *T;* then, sketch the large arcs tangent at points *T* to complete the view. Note that the major diameter (long axis) is longer and the minor diameter is shorter than the diameter of the circle. Circles on the three faces of the isometric cube are sketched at B in Fig. 6-11a.

Some methods of blocking in for cylinders are illustrated at C and D. Some methods of blocking in for conical shapes are shown in Fig. 6-11b. Notice the positions of the axes in Fig. 6-11c for regular axes at A; for reversed axes at B, which shows a view from below; and for long axes horizontal at C, which is convenient for showing long pieces. In all cases the axes must make three equal angles of 120°, as shown.

Fig. 6-11a. Circles on isometric sketches.

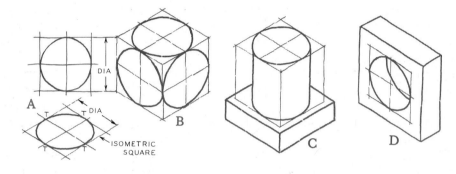

Fig. 6-11b. Isometric sketches of conical shapes.

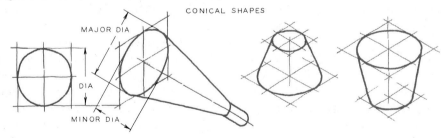

Fig. 6-11c. Different isometric views.

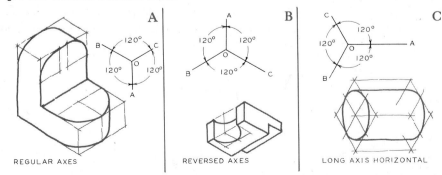

REGULAR AXES   REVERSED AXES   LONG AXIS HORIZONTAL

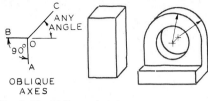

ANY ANGLE

90°

OBLIQUE AXES

Fig. 6-12. Oblique sketches.

6•12 Oblique sketching (Fig. 6-12). Thin pieces, with all or most of the changes in outline parallel to the front face, can be shown easily by an oblique sketch. The method of procedure is the same as for isometric sketching except for the positions of the axes. Note that two axes are at right angles (90°) and that the third axis may be at any angle. An angle of 45° with the horizontal is often used for axis *OC*. The construction of oblique drawings is explained in Chap. 14.

6•13 Measurements for sketches. When sketches are made from machines, parts, and other projects and are to be used to make finished drawings or in place of finished drawings, it is necessary to have dimensions to tell sizes, location of parts, and other information. When sketching from existing items, it is necessary to include other information, such as the material, kinds of surfaces (finished, rough, or other), mating parts (parts which fit together), identification numbers or marks, and any other information that might have any future value. See Chap. 11.

6•14 Dimensioning a sketch. After sketching the views of an object, necessary dimension lines are added in exactly the same way as for views made with instruments (Chap. 11). The piece should be examined and the kind of material noted, together with the kinds of finish and location of all finished surfaces. When everything else is done, it is time to measure the piece and fill in the figures to tell the sizes. For this purpose various measuring tools will be needed: a 2-ft rule, a steel scale, and a pair of calipers will be sufficient for many purposes where great accuracy is not required.

When a pictorial sketch is dimensioned, the dimension and extension lines should be in or parallel to the pictorial planes (Figs. 6-14*a*, 6-14*b*, and 6-14*c*). Vertical-style letters and figures are used on pictorial sketches. There are two methods of placing dimensions and notes:

1. With letters and figures made in pictorial form on the planes, as shown on the key diagram of Fig. 6-14*a* and applied on Fig. 6-14*b*.

2. With all letters and figures in their regular forms and placed to read from the bottom of the sheet (Fig. 6-14*c*). This is in accord with the unidirectional dimensioning (Art. 11·12).

6•15 Problem suggestions. A collection of models and parts of machines from which sketches can be made will provide an interesting and valuable method of learning to sketch. Many of the problems in Chap. 26 can be used for sketching practice. View sketches can be assigned from the pictures in Group 5 and pictorial sketches from view drawings (Chap. 14). Selections can also be made from Probs. 5·65 and 5·74 and from problems in Group 14.

Fig. 6-14*a*. Key diagram for pictorial dimensioning.

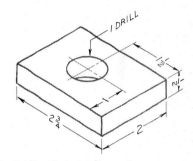

Fig. 6-14*b*. Pictorial dimensions.

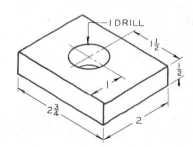

Fig. 6-14*c*. Unidirectional dimensioning on a pictorial sketch.

7

Reading the graphic language

7•1 Communication. For many purposes drawings are the most exact means of communication. Drawings tell the shapes of parts, how they are placed relative to each other, and how they are put together. They show arrangements, relative sizes, and the great store of information involved in engineering, science, and research—whatever can be recorded or conveyed by the drawing of lines.

For graphic communication it is necessary to read and understand the meaning of every line and every symbol. It is equally necessary for anyone who prepares drawings to know the most direct and clearest ways of presenting the required information so that there is only one meaning. The mental pictures of the "reader" must be the same as the mental pictures of the "maker."

For many, or most, purposes, sizes and positions must be given by dimensions. The principles of size specification (dimensioning) are presented in Chap. 11.

7•2 Translation. When learning to read a drawing, one of the good ways to start is by translating the views of a simple object into words. From such a beginning the ability to visualize lines, surfaces, and shapes is developed for constructions which would be very difficult to describe in words. This is the reason mechanical drawing is used for engineering, architecture, and all projects where space and arrangement are involved.

Consider the object shown in Fig. 7-2. At A we have a rectangular prism with a hole; at B, a frustum of a cone with a hole; and at C, the frustum combined with the prism. Note that the picture at C does not show for certain that the hole goes all the way through. The views at D give an exact description. Try to describe this simple object in words, and it will be clear that the combination of lines which make up the views describe it more easily, quickly, and accurately than any word description could do.

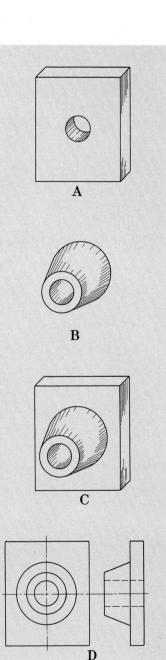

Fig. 7-2. Translation from words into pictures and pictures into orthographic views.

Fig. 7-3. Constructing views from word descriptions.

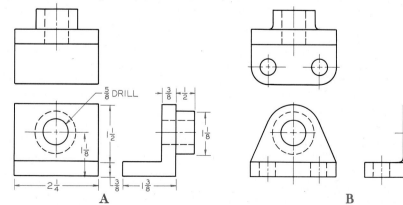

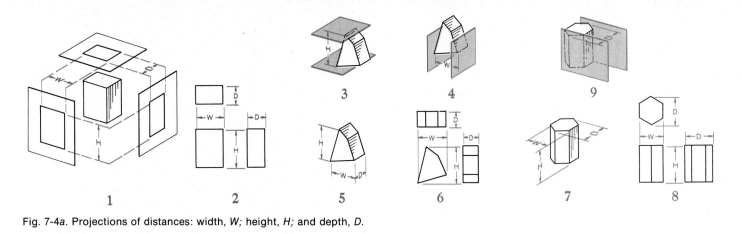

Fig. 7-4a. Projections of distances: width, W; height, H; and depth, D.

7•3 Views from word description. It is desired to make a bracket bearing. It is composed of a rectangular prism 2¼ in. wide, ⅜ in. high, and 1⅜ in. deep. Another prism is placed at the back of, and on, the first prism. It is 2¼ in. wide, 1½ in. high, and ⅜ in. deep. This last prism has a cylinder projecting back from its center; it is 1⅛ in. in diameter and ½ in. long. There is a hole ⅝ in. in diameter through the cylinder and the prism. This very simple object may be translated into views which describe it accurately in much less time, as shown at A in Fig. 7-3. If there were bolt holes, rounded edges and corners, and other details such as shown at B, it would take many more words to describe the bracket bearing.

7•4 Projections of distances: width, height, and depth. We have learned that the height, H, of an object is shown in the front and side views; that the width, W, is shown in the front and top views; and that the depth, D, is shown in the side and top views. This is illustrated in Fig. 7-4a at Spaces 1 and 2 by a prism with its surfaces parallel to the coordinate planes.

The total height distance, H, is the length of a line from the top to the bottom surfaces and perpendicular to them. The total width distance, W, is the length of a line from the left to the right surfaces and perpendicular to them. The total depth distance, D, is the length of a line from the front to the back surfaces and perpendicular to them.

If some of the limiting surfaces of an object are not parallel to the planes of projection (Fig. 7-4a at 3, 4, 5, and 6), parallel planes just touching the object can be assumed. At 3, planes are assumed parallel to the horizontal plane; the height, H, is the perpendicular distance between them, as indicated. At 4, planes are assumed parallel to the profile plane; the width, W, is the perpendicular distance between them, as indicated. The front and rear surfaces are parallel to the frontal plane. The depth, D, is the perpendicular distance between them, as indicated.

The hexagonal prism at 7, 8, and 9 has top and bottom surfaces parallel to the horizontal plane. The height, H, is the perpendicular distance between them. The right and left surfaces are parallel to the profile plane. The width, W, is the perpendicular distance between them. The depth distance, D, is the perpendicular distance between planes touching the front and back of the hexagonal prism and parallel to the frontal plane, as indicated in the figure.

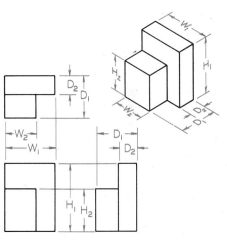

Fig. 7-4b. W, H, and D distances.

The distances indicated in Fig. 7-4a are total width, total height, and total depth. Lesser distances are located in the same way as shown in Fig. 7-4b for W, H, and D.

7•5 Projection of points. In Chap. 5 we learned that the top view is directly above the front view and that the side view is on a line with the front view. Three views of a point would appear as in Fig. 7-5a at A, B, and C. Reading or making a drawing can often be made easier and more certain of correct understanding by using the projections of one point at a time.

A picture of a notched block is shown at A in Fig. 7-5b. To draw three views, lay out the outlines and the notch in the

Fig. 7-5a. Three projections of a point.

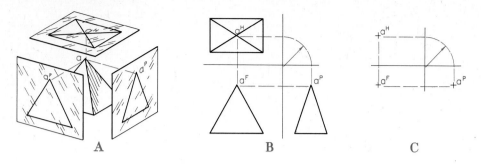

Fig. 7-5b. Projections of points on an object.

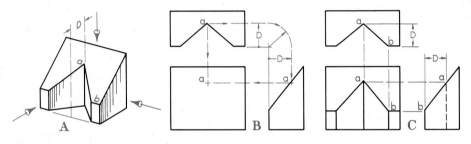

Fig. 7-5c. Given two views, to draw the third view by projecting points.

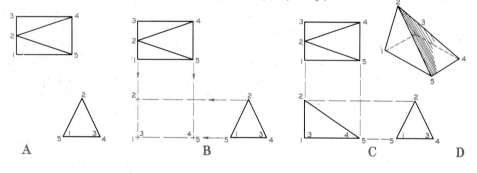

Fig. 7-5d. To locate the projections of any point.

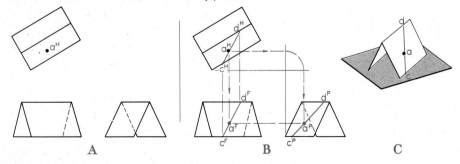

top view as at B. The point a is located in the side view by the distance D, which is taken from the top view. In the front view point a is located by projecting down from the top view and across from the side view. Other points are located by the same method as shown for point b at C.

In Fig. 7-5c at A, two views are given and the third view is to be drawn. Number the points in the top and side views. Project down from the top view and across from the side view to locate the front views of the points, as at B. At C the points have been joined, and we have the three views of the object pictured at D. It is seldom necessary to number and project every point, as a few points will generally serve to make everything clear. Sometimes it is necessary to locate a point in three views from its projection on one view when it is not on a line of the view (Fig. 7-5d). Given point a^H, draw a line, $c^H d^H$, through the top view of the point. Points c^H and d^H end in lines of the top view, as shown. Project points c^H and d^H to the front view and draw line $c^F d^F$. Project point a^H to a^F. Project point a^H from the top view and a^F from the front view to the side view at a^P in the usual way.

7·6 Projection of lines. The position of a straight line is fixed by two points of the line (Fig. 7-6). To project a straight line, project the two points and connect them.

1. A straight line parallel to two planes of projection will show its true length when projected to them. In the picture (Fig. 7-6 at A), the line ab shows its true length in the front and top views. Below the picture, the orthographic views show the top, front, and side views of lines parallel to F and H, F and P, and H and P.

2. A straight line perpendicular to a plane of projection will show as a point when projected to that plane. In the picture (Fig. 7-6 at A), the line ab shows

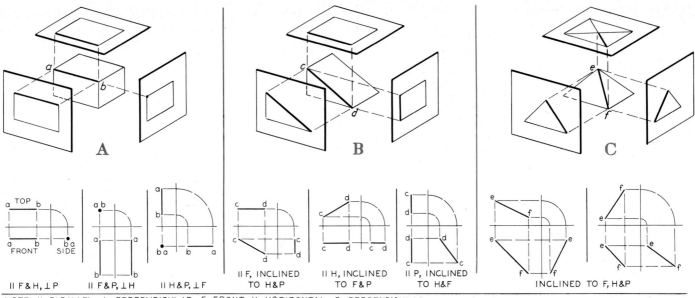

II F&H, ⊥P   II F&P, ⊥H   II H&P, ⊥F   II F, INCLINED TO H&P   II H, INCLINED TO F&P   II P, INCLINED TO H&F   INCLINED TO F, H&P

NOTE: II=PARALLEL, ⊥= PERPENDICULAR, F=FRONT, H= HORIZONTAL, P=PERPENDICULAR

Fig. 7-6. The projections of straight lines.

as a point in the side view. Below the picture, the orthographic views show lines perpendicular to *P*, to *H*, and to *F*.

3. A straight line inclined to two planes of projection and parallel to the other one will show less than its true length on the planes to which it is inclined and will show its true length on the plane to which it is parallel. In the picture (Fig. 7-6 at B), the line *cd* at B shows less than its true length in the top and side views but shows its

true length in the front view. Below the picture (Fig. 7-6 at B), the orthographic views show lines inclined to *H* and *P* and parallel to *F*, inclined to *F* and *P* and parallel to *H*, and inclined to *F* and *H* and parallel to *P*.

4. A straight line inclined to all three planes of projection will show less than its true length in all three views, as shown in the picture (Fig. 7-6 at C). Below the picture, the views show some lines inclined to *H*, *F*, and *P*.

7·7 Projections of curved lines. The position of a curved line is fixed by a number of points on the line. To project a curved line, project as many points as are necessary and draw a smooth curve through them.

1. A curved line in a plane parallel to a plane of projection will show its true shape on that plane. In the picture (Fig. 7-7 at A), the line *ab* is parallel to the frontal plane and shows its true shape in the front view. It shows as a

Fig. 7-7. The projections of curved lines.

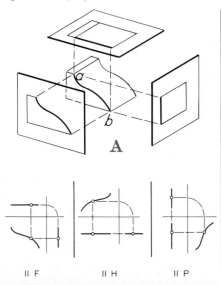

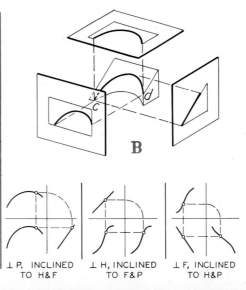

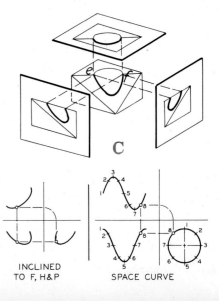

II F   II H   II P   ⊥P, INCLINED TO H&F   ⊥H, INCLINED TO F&P   ⊥F, INCLINED TO H&P   INCLINED TO F, H&P   SPACE CURVE

straight line in the top and side views. Below the picture, the orthographic views show three views of a curved line in a plane parallel to the frontal plane *F*, parallel to *H*, and parallel to *P*.

2. A curved line in a plane inclined to two planes of projection and perpendicular to the other one will not show its true shape on any of the planes. It will show as a straight line on the plane to which its plane is perpendicular. In the picture (Fig. 7-7 at B), the line *cd* does not show its true shape in the front or top view but shows as a straight line in the side view. Below the picture, the orthographic views show curved lines in a plane inclined to *H* and *F* and perpendicular to *P*.

3. A curved line in a plane inclined to all three planes of projection will not show its true shape on any of them. In the picture (Fig. 7-7 at C), the curved line shows as a curved line in all three views. Below the picture, the orthographic views show curved lines in space.

7·8 Projections of plane surfaces are obtained by the projections of the lines which define them (Fig. 7-8).

1. A surface parallel to a plane of projection will show its true shape on that plane. In the picture (Fig. 7-8 at A), the surface is parallel to the frontal plane and shows its true shape in the front. Below the picture, the orthographic views show surfaces parallel to *F, H,* and *P*.

2. A surface perpendicular to a plane of projection will show as a line on that plane. In the picture (Fig. 7-8 at A), the surface is perpendicular to the horizontal and profile planes and shows as a line in the top and side views. Below the picture, the orthographic views show planes perpendicular to *H* and *P, F* and *P,* and *H* and *F*.

3. A surface inclined to a plane of projection will not show its true shape on the plane to which it is inclined. In the picture (Fig. 7-8 at B), the surface is inclined to the frontal and horizontal planes and appears foreshortened in the front and top views. Since the surface is perpendicular to the side plane, it shows as a line in the side view. Below the picture, the orthographic views show planes which are inclined to two planes and perpendicular to the other one.

4. A surface inclined to the three planes of projection will not show its true shape on any of them, as shown in the picture (Fig. 7-8 at C). Below the picture, the orthographic views of some planes inclined to *H, F,* and *P* are shown.

7·9 Projection of curved surfaces. Elementary curved surfaces have been illustrated in Art. 5·13. In Fig. 7-9*a* cylindrical surfaces form a part of each object. Note the location of the center of the radius in each case. At A there is a flat surface joining the two cylindrical surfaces, so a straight vertical line will show in the front view. At B the centers of the two radii are on a line parallel to the frontal plane. Where the curved surfaces meet, there is a limiting line (contour line) for each surface, so a straight vertical line will show in the front view. At C the center of radius 1 is farther back from the frontal plane than the center for radius 2, and there will be no line to project to the front view.

Fillets and rounds occur on a great many parts. A *fillet* is a filled-in corner (Fig. 7-9*b* at A, B, and C). A *round* is a

Fig. 7-8. The projections of plane surfaces.

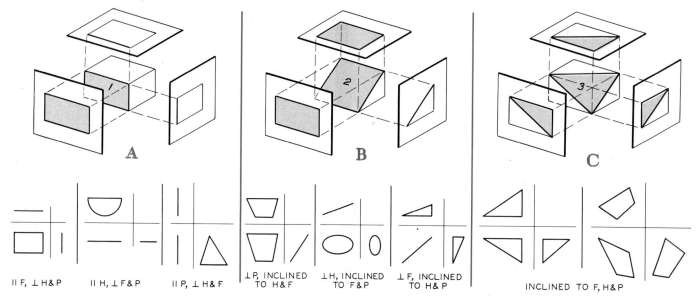

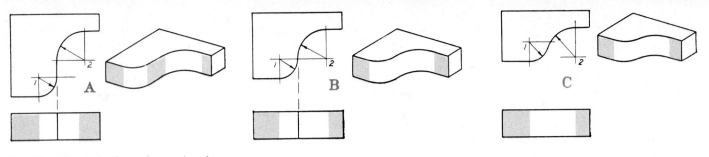

Fig. 7-9a. The projections of curved surfaces.

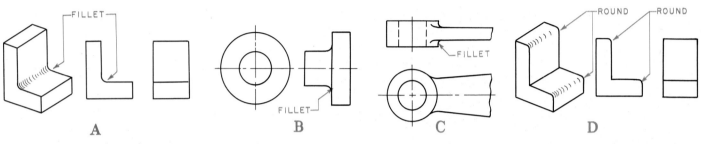

Fig. 7-9b. Fillets and rounds.

rounded-off corner (Fig. 7-9b at D). Fillets and rounds are cylindrical surfaces and are tangent to the surfaces they join, so there will be no lines to project.

7•10 Projections of lines of curved surfaces are found by projecting a series of points. In Fig. 7-10 at A, the top view of the molding is found from the front and side views. Select a number of points, as *a, b,* and *c* on the side view; project them to the front view. The next step is to project from the front and side views to locate the points in the top view. Then draw a smooth curve through the points as shown.

The front view in Fig. 7-10 at B is found by selecting a number of points, as *a, b,* and *c* on the side view, and projecting them to the top view. Next, project them down from the top view and across from the side view to locate the points in the front view.

In Fig. 7-10 at C, the front view is also found by projecting from corresponding points in the side and top views.

7•11 The meaning of lines. A line may represent the edge view of a surface, the intersection of two surfaces, or the outline or contour of a surface. In Fig. 7-11 lines numbered 1 represent edge views of surfaces as well as intersections of surfaces. Lines numbered 2 represent intersections of surfaces where shown. Lines numbered 3 represent elements, or contour lines. All lines are important and necessary to a drawing. No lines should be omitted, and extra lines should not be drawn.

Fig. 7-10. The projections of lines on curved surfaces.

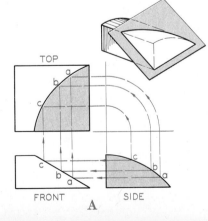

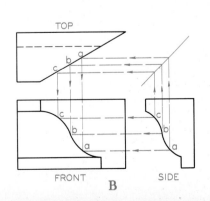

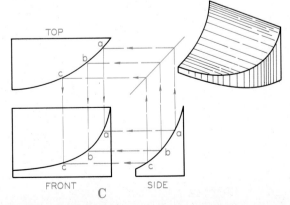

Fig. 7-11. The meaning of lines.

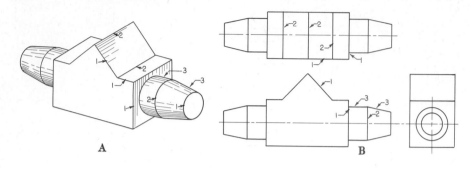

Study each line and see what it means in the views in Fig. 7-11 and on some of the other illustrations.

7•12 Surfaces parallel to the planes of projection. In Fig. 7-12 the surfaces of the object are parallel to the planes of projection. There are three visible surfaces and two hidden surfaces when viewed from in front. Surface *A* is defined by four lines: 1–2, 2–3, 3–4, and 4–1. Locate these points in each of the three views. It will be seen that surface *A* is nearest the observer and shows its true shape in the front view. In like manner locate surfaces *B* and *C*. Surface *B* is farther back than surface *A* and nearer the front than surface *C*, as shown by the lines which represent them in the side and top views. Locate the two hidden surfaces, *D* and *E*, and sketch their outlines. Find the three visible surfaces and the one hidden surface as represented in the top view. In the side view there are two visible surfaces and two invisible surfaces.

7•13 Surfaces inclined to the planes of projection. In Fig. 7-13 observe the inclined surfaces. Surface *A*, which is nearest to the front, is inclined to the frontal and horizontal planes. It is perpendicular to the side, or profile, plane and shows as a line in the side view. Surface *B* is inclined to the horizontal and side planes. It is perpendicular to the frontal plane and shows as a line on that plane. Surface *C* is inclined to all three planes. Each surface may be located by placing numbers at the ends of the lines which define it.

7•14 An example for study. The bearing shown in Fig. 7-14 is made up of cylinders, parts of cylinders, and rectangular prisms. There are flat surfaces and curved surfaces that require visible and invisible (hidden) lines. Notice that surface *A* of the side view

Fig. 7-12. Reading views with surfaces parallel to the planes of projection.

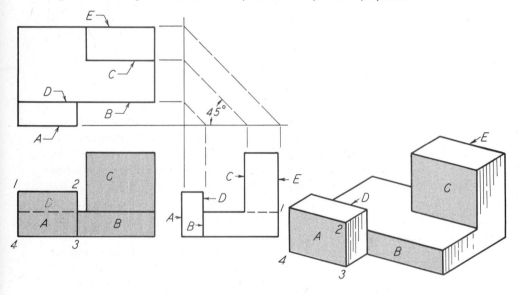

Fig. 7-13. Reading views with surfaces inclined to the planes of projection.

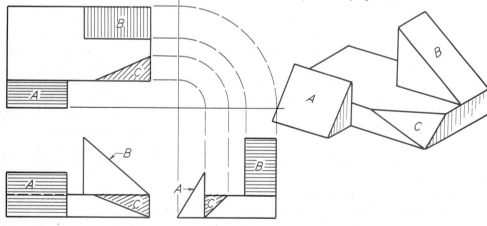

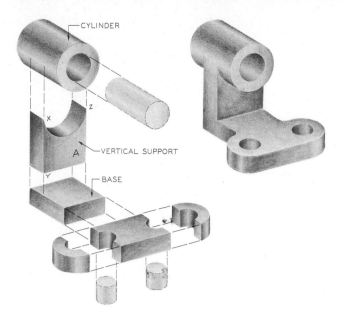

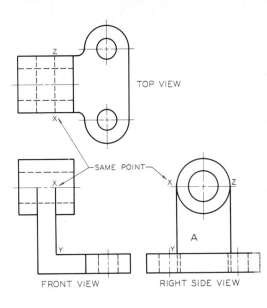

Fig. 7-14. Reading views by taking the object apart. An exploded view.

is shown by a full line, *xy,* in the front view and by a hidden line, *xz,* in the top view. Compare the three views with the picture and notice how the different parts are described in the views. Study the reason for the visible or hidden lines in each case, as well as the necessity for three views in order to give a complete description of the bearing. Considering the three views shown to be the top, front, and right-side views, try to see how the bottom, rear, and left-side views would look. Which lines would be visible and which ones would be hidden? For a casting, the working drawing would show fillets, or rounded-in corners, between the cylinder and the vertical support and between the base and the vertical support. Fillets are omitted in Fig. 7-14 to simplify the views for study purposes and to show how point *a* in the front view is determined by a tangent point in the right-side view.

7·15 Problem suggestions. Models, parts of machines, and selected problems from Group 5 should be used in connection with this chapter. See List 2 at the end of Chap. 5. A few prints from industry to be read, described, and sketched in pictorial views will add much to the understanding and value of this chapter. Review of this chapter can be very helpful before doing the problems in Group 13.

A little theory can be of both interest and value for thinking in space. Such thinking is necessary in engineering and science. It is suggested that at least five problems selected from Probs. 7·1 to 7·19 be assigned.

American Standards

A standard is defined as a model or example which has been set by authority, custom, or general consent.

The American Standards Association, Incorporated, 10 East 40th Street, New York 16, N.Y., has among its members trade associations, technical societies, professional groups, and consumer organizations.

The ASA provides standards that are nationally accepted and used. It avoids duplication and works over conflicting standards that have been proposed. The ASA provides standards for uniform sizes, specifications, and names used in the design, production, and marketing of many goods and services.

American Standards are widely used by industry and commerce, and by city, state, and Federal government agencies. Manufacturers use them to lower production costs, to eliminate misunderstandings, and to operate more efficiently. Consumer groups use them to measure quality. Government agencies use them as a protection to the public in buying items.

Draftsmen and engineers should know the American Standards for the industry in which they work.

8

Inking and reproduction

Fig. 8-3. The alphabet of lines. Purposes for which they are used.

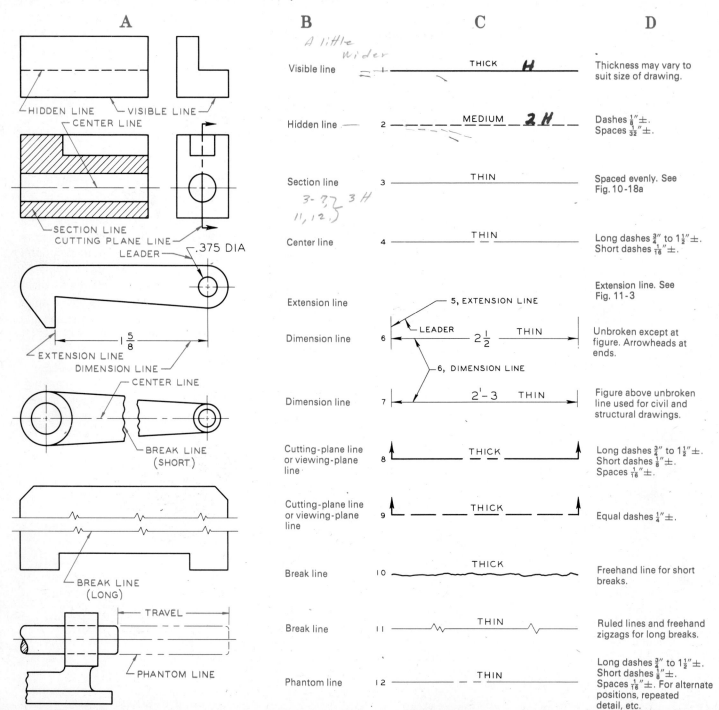

A

HIDDEN LINE — VISIBLE LINE
CENTER LINE
SECTION LINE
CUTTING PLANE LINE
LEADER
.375 DIA
EXTENSION LINE
DIMENSION LINE
$1\frac{5}{8}$
CENTER LINE
BREAK LINE (SHORT)
BREAK LINE (LONG)
TRAVEL
PHANTOM LINE

B		**C**	**D**
	A little wider		
Visible line		THICK H	Thickness may vary to suit size of drawing.
Hidden line	2	MEDIUM 2H	Dashes $\frac{1}{8}"\pm$. Spaces $\frac{1}{32}"\pm$.
Section line	3	THIN	Spaced evenly. See Fig. 10-18a
	3-? 3H 11, 12.		
Center line	4	THIN	Long dashes $\frac{3}{4}"$ to $1\frac{1}{2}"\pm$. Short dashes $\frac{1}{16}"\pm$.
Extension line		5, EXTENSION LINE	Extension line. See Fig. 11-3
Dimension line	6	LEADER $2\frac{1}{2}$ THIN	Unbroken except at figure. Arrowheads at ends.
Dimension line	7	6, DIMENSION LINE $2'-3$ THIN	Figure above unbroken line used for civil and structural drawings.
Cutting-plane line or viewing-plane line	8	THICK	Long dashes $\frac{3}{4}"$ to $1\frac{1}{2}"\pm$. Short dashes $\frac{1}{8}"\pm$. Spaces $\frac{1}{16}"\pm$.
Cutting-plane line or viewing-plane line	9	THICK	Equal dashes $\frac{1}{4}"\pm$.
Break line	10	THICK	Freehand line for short breaks.
Break line	11	THIN	Ruled lines and freehand zigzags for long breaks.
Phantom line	12	THIN	Long dashes $\frac{3}{4}"$ to $1\frac{1}{2}"\pm$. Short dashes $\frac{1}{8}"\pm$. Spaces $\frac{1}{16}"\pm$. For alternate positions, repeated detail, etc.

8·1 Engineering drawings. Present practice is to make most finished drawings in pencil. However, there are certain purposes for which inked drawings or tracings are necessary or required, such as display drawings or where called for in contract specifications. It is, therefore, a desirable qualification to know how to make a good drawing with ink.

Original drawings are seldom used for working purposes. Extra copies are generally required for working, reference, and other purposes. There are many ways of making copies of drawings, and new methods are being developed. A knowledge of some of the ways of reproducing drawings is a necessary part of the preparation for using the graphic language.

8·2 Drawing ink. Waterproof black ink is always used for inking drawings or tracings. Never use writing ink. Waterproof drawing inks have a base of extremely fine ground carbon with shellac and other components necessary to make a satisfactory waterproof solution which will make black, opaque lines. Such ink dries readily and will not smudge when dry. Regular waterproof black is suitable for paper and tracing cloth. A waterproof "plastics"[1] black ink is made for use on plastic film and water-repellent drafting surfaces. Nonwaterproof or general drawing ink can be used on cloth, paper, or plastic but is subject to smudging. It is removable from plastic film by water. Ink may be damaged by freezing, intense heat, exposure to air, and age after being opened.

8·3 The alphabet of lines. Line symbols used in making drawings may be considered as a graphic alphabet. The *American Drafting Standards Manual* recommends three widths of lines:

[1] Higgins Ink Company, Inc.

thick, medium, and thin. The symbols for ink lines are shown in Fig. 8-3. (See Art. 2·10 for pencil lines and details.) Each line is used for a definite purpose and must not be used for anything else. Detail drawings should have fairly wide (thick) outlines with thin center and dimension lines so that the drawing will have contrast and be easy to read. Hidden lines have a medium width. If all the lines are of the same width, the drawing will have a flat appearance and will be hard to read.

Fig. 8-4a. The regular ruling pen has blades which can be adjusted to draw different widths of lines.

NARROW POINT
FOR THIN LINES

OUTSIDE
SPRING
BLADE

INSIDE
STIFF
BLADE

THUMB
SCREW
TO ADJUST
WIDTH OF
LINE

NIBS, OR
POINTS,
OF BLADES

GENERAL- PURPOSE
PEN

DETAIL
PEN

8·4 Inking straight lines. The regular ruling pens used to ink straight lines are shown in Fig. 8-4a. Ruling pens are supplied with ink from a filler (quill, rod, or wire) attached to the stopper of the drawing-ink bottle (Fig. 8-4b). Hold the pen downward and place a small amount of ink between the blades (Fig. 8-4c at A). Drawing ink may also be obtained in a "cartridge" (or plastic tube) from which the pen may be filled (Fig. 8-4c at B); the amount of ink is shown at A in Fig. 8-4d.

Fig. 8-4b. Filling the pen from a bottle of drawing ink.

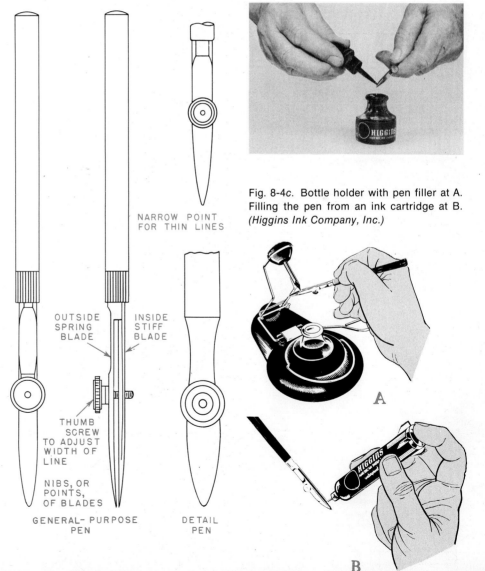

Fig. 8-4c. Bottle holder with pen filler at A. Filling the pen from an ink cartridge at B. *(Higgins Ink Company, Inc.)*

A

B

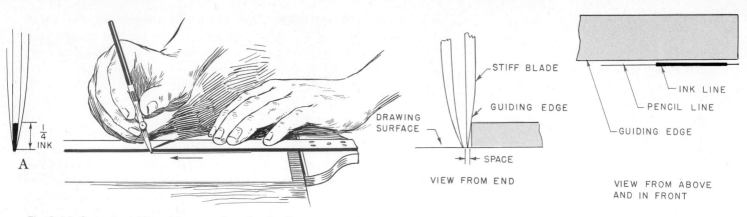

Fig. 8-4*d.* Correct position of the pen when drawing lines.

Fig. 8-4*e.* Some faulty lines and what makes them faulty.

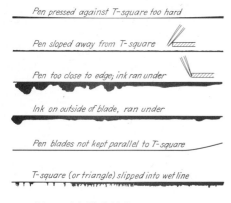

Pen pressed against T-square too hard

Pen sloped away from T-square

Pen too close to edge; ink ran under

Ink on outside of blade, ran under

Pen blades not kept parallel to T-square

T-square (or triangle) slipped into wet line

Not enough ink to finish line

When the pen has been filled, set the nibs to draw the desired width of line by turning the thumb screw. Hold the pen with the inside, or stiff, blade against the T-square blade or other guide in the position shown in Fig. 8-4*d.* Observe the following instructions for using the regular ruling pen:

1. Do not hold the pen over the drawing while filling.

2. Do not put too much ink in the pen; about $\frac{1}{4}$ to $\frac{5}{16}$ in. is generally sufficient.

3. Never dip the pen into the ink bottle or allow ink to get on the outside of the blades.

4. Have a penwiper at hand (a soft, lintless cloth or tissue paper).

5. Keep the pen clean by frequent wiping, outside the blades as well as between them. Always wipe it carefully after using.

6. Keep both nibs of the pen in contact with the drawing surface.

7. Keep the blades of the pen parallel to the direction of the line.

8. Do not press the pen nibs hard against the T-square blade or guide.

9. Do not screw the nibs of the pen too tight.

Faulty lines occur from various causes. The pen may need dressing, or sharpening. The beginner should not attempt to do this himself but should ask the instructor to help him. Fig. 8-4*e* shows some of the common faults and suggests how to avoid them.

The fountain tube-point pen (Fig. 8-4*f*) is made with separate points for drawing different widths of lines. These points ensure constant widths of lines. The fountains hold a good supply of ink, so they do not require frequent filling or cleaning. Most of the "faults"

Fig. 8-4*f.* The tube-point fountain pen and sample widths of lines. *(The Wood-Regan Instrument Company, Inc.)*

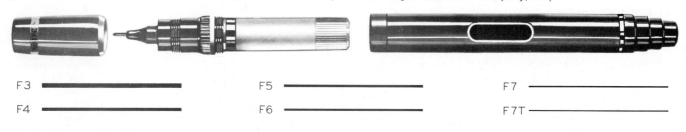

F3

F4

F5

F6

F7

F7T

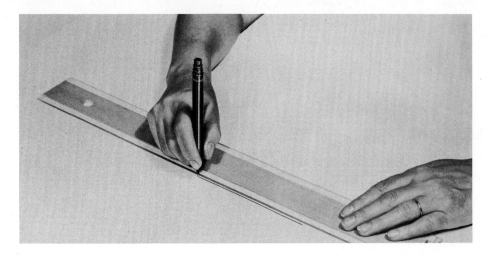

Fig. 8-4g. Correct position of the tube-point pen when drawing a line. *(The Wood-Regan Instrument Company, Inc.)*

indicated in Fig. 8-4e are avoided with the tube pen. They are replacing the regular ruling pens in drafting rooms and offices. The fountain tube pen is held against the guide and in a vertical position to draw a line (Fig. 8-4g).

8·5 Inking circles and arcs. The compasses, giant bow, and bow pen (Arts. 2·32 to 2·35) are used for drawing circles and arcs. To use the compasses, remove the pencil leg and insert the pen leg. Adjust the needle point until it is slightly longer than the pen point (Fig. 8-5a). Adjust the joints of the compasses so that the legs are perpendicular to the drawing surface (Fig. 8-5b). Always draw a circle in one stroke, inclining the compasses slightly in the direction of the line and rolling the handle between the thumb and the finger. Large circles may be drawn by

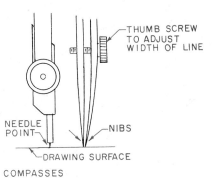

Fig. 8-5a. How to adjust the needle point of the compasses and the pen point.

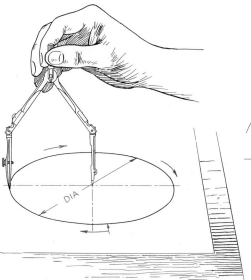

Fig. 8-5b. Inking circles and arcs.

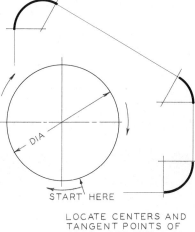

LOCATE CENTERS AND TANGENT POINTS OF ARCS. SEE ART. 4·26

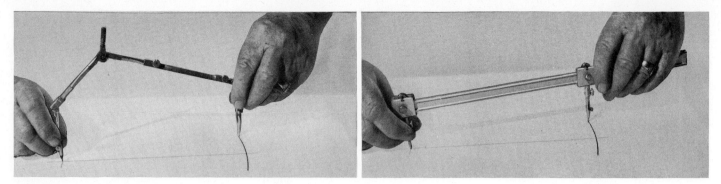

Fig. 8-5c. Using the lengthening bar to draw large circles.

Fig. 8-5d. Using the beam compasses.

Fig. 8-5e. Needle point adjustment for the bow pen.

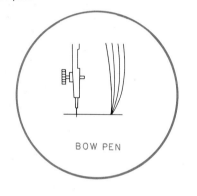

BOW PEN

Fig. 8-5f. Adapter for using tube-point pens in the compasses. *(D. A. Patterson Associates)*

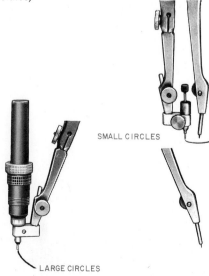

SMALL CIRCLES

LARGE CIRCLES

inserting one or more lengthening bars in the compasses (Fig. 8-5c) or by using the beam compasses (Fig. 8-5d) with the pen part. The bow pen is used for small circles and arcs. The needle point should be adjusted so that it is just very little longer than the pen point (Fig. 8-5e).

Adapters (Fig. 8-5f) are made to allow tube points to be used in the compasses so that arcs and circles will match the straight lines drawn with tube-point pens. Circle templates (Fig. 6-4c) are used with tube-point pens for drawing circles and arcs and have the advantage of exactly matching straight lines drawn with tube-point pens.

Ink lines, regardless of the pen used, must be drawn exactly over the center of the pencil lines (Fig. 8-5g).

Fig. 8-5g. Ink lines must be "centered" over pencil lines.

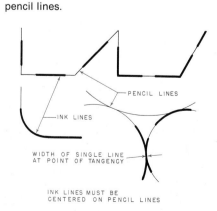

PENCIL LINES

INK LINES

WIDTH OF SINGLE LINE
AT POINT OF TANGENCY

INK LINES MUST BE
CENTERED ON PENCIL LINES

8•6 Inking curved lines. Irregular curves (Art. 2·36) are generally used for guiding the pen when curves other than circle arcs are inked. Match a part of a curve to the pencil line and ink part of the line; then move the curve to a new position. The new position of the irregular curve must always match a part of the line already inked. Observe the following instructions: First, locate the "joining points" by light pencil lines across the curve. Second, always be sure that the radius of the irregular curve matches the direction of the increasing or decreasing radius of the curve being inked. For some purposes adjustable-curve rulers may be desirable (Fig. 23-6c). The tube pen (Fig. 8-4f) is especially convenient for inking curves.

8•7 Tracings are made on tracing cloth, tracing paper, glass cloth, or film. Ordinary tracing cloth is ruined by water or perspiration and should be protected; however, some tracing cloths are not affected by moisture. When using tracing cloth, first tear off the selvage along the edge and fasten the cloth down smoothly over the pencil drawing. The usual cloth has one side smooth and the other side dull finish. Most draftsmen place the dull side up. Dust the surface with pounce or similar powder to remove the gloss so that the ink will take. Then be sure to remove all powder before starting to ink. As tracing cloth is very sensitive to atmospheric changes and will stretch if left overnight, only the views that can be completed the same day should be started. When ready to continue on other views, the cloth should be re-stretched. In restretching, adjust the cloth so that the work already done is in register with (will match) the new work. When using ink on film, read and follow the manufacturer's directions carefully.

8•8 Order of inking. Good inking is the result of two things: careful practice and a definite order of working. Smooth joints and tangents, sharp corners, and neat fillets not only improve the appearance of a drawing but make it easier to read.

The general order of inking or tracing is shown in Fig. 8-8. The arcs are inked first, as in Space 1, and should center over the pencil lines. Horizontal lines should be inked as in Space 2 and the drawing completed as in Space 3. Then the dimension lines, arrowheads, finish marks, and so forth, are added and the dimensions filled in as in Space 4. The order of inking is:

1. Ink main center lines.
2. Ink small circles and arcs.
3. Ink large circles and arcs.
4. Ink hidden circles and arcs.
5. Ink irregular curves.
6. Ink horizontal full lines.
7. Ink vertical full lines.
8. Ink inclined full lines.
9. Ink hidden lines.
10. Ink center lines.
11. Ink extension and dimension lines.
12. Ink arrowheads and figures.
13. Ink section lines.
14. Letter notes and titles.
15. Ink border lines.
16. Check drawing carefully.

8•9 Lettering in ink. The ability to do acceptable freehand lettering with pen and ink is a valuable qualification and sometimes a necessary one. Refer

Fig. 8-8. Order of inking or tracing a drawing.

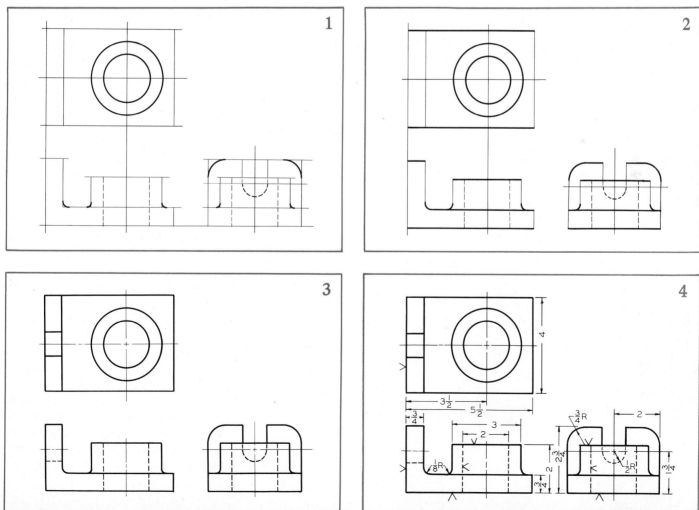

to Chap. 3 for freehand lettering. Tube-point fountain pens with regular drawing ink may be used for freehand lettering in addition to the usual pen points. The pens used with lettering templates may also be used for freehand lettering. Special typewriters, such as the Vari-Typer and the Grintzner Drawing Board typewriter (Art. 3·19), are used in many industrial drafting rooms. For some purposes, printed adhesive letters, words, symbols, and titles are used to save time.

Fig. 8-11. Tube pens are especially good for use with templates and irregular curves.

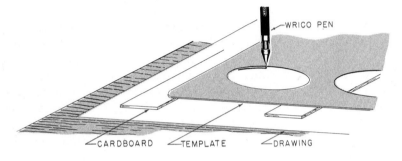

Fig. 8-13. A continuous electric blueprint machine. *(Ditto, Incorporated)*

BLUEPRINT MACHINE

8·10 Erasing ink lines. The ideal is to complete a drawing or tracing without having to do any erasing. Sometimes, however, it is necessary to make an erasure because of a change or a mistake. Ink lines may be removed by rubbing with a pencil eraser, which does not rub off the surface of the paper or cloth as an ink eraser does. Ink may be erased more easily and with less damage to the drawing if a drafting triangle or other hard surface is placed under the part to be erased. *Do not use a knife or scratcher.* An erasing shield is very convenient; these are thin metal shields with slots and openings of various sizes and shapes. Electric erasing machines (Art. 2·11) are convenient and timesaving. On film, lines must be erased at right angles to the direction of the lines, and this must be done very carefully by hand. Nonwaterproof black ink may be removed from plastic film with water.

8·11 Inking with templates. There are many kinds of templates available, including ellipses, circles, arcs, squares, hexagons, and other shapes which can be used to save time. There are also special symbols for use on architectural, electrical, electronic, map, and other drawings. When a template is used for inking, a piece of cardboard or a triangle should be placed under it near the opening to hold it up from the drawing surface unless the template has an undercut to prevent the ink from running under. Tube pens such as are used with lettering guides (Fig. 8-11) will be found most convenient for use with templates.

8·12 Blueprinting. Industrial, engineering, and construction work, in general, is done from blueprints, or from other reproductions called *prints*, made by one of the large variety of available methods. The paper used is chemically treated to give white lines on a blue background. As many copies as desired can be made from a single tracing. Blueprints are made from either pencil or ink tracings. The original drawing is kept in the files of the drawing room.

8·13 To make a blueprint. Blueprint paper is usually bought in rolls ready to expose to the light. Some kinds work fast and some work slow, depending on the degree of rapidity for which they are made. In the past, blueprints were made by sunlight, but electric blueprint machines are now used because they give more uniform results, are faster, and can be used at any time. A continuous blueprinting machine is illustrated in Fig. 8-13; it includes washing and drying facilities.

Tracings are fed into the front of the printer onto blueprint paper. Together they are carried around a contact glass, where they are exposed to the printing rays of electric lamps. After exposure, the blueprint paper passes through a water wash, a potash applicator system, and then through drying drums. The finished prints are delivered at the back of the machine.

Sometimes it is necessary or desirable to make minor changes or corrections on blueprints. This can be done by using an alkaline solution in a writing or drawing pen.

8•14 Other methods of reproducing drawings include vandyke paper, which gives white lines on a dark brown background, and a number of special papers that give dark or black lines on a light background. Vandyke and similar negatives are used to make positive blue- or black-line prints. Diazotype processes give positive prints (dark lines on a light background). Materials may be purchased which produce different colors on cloth or films in addition to paper.

Ozalid prints are made from tracings and provide dark reddish (or other color) lines on a light background. They are developed dry by exposing them to ammonia vapor. An Ozalid copying machine is illustrated in Fig. 8-14. The tracing is placed on the Ozalid paper on the feedboard, *A*, and is carried on printer belts around a light source, *B*. Then it is conveyed across a perforated developer tank, *C*, from which ammonia vapor rises and develops the dry print. The print is then delivered on the front receiving tray, *D*. The machine is operated by an electric motor.

Fig. 8-14. Ozalid or xerography copying machine. *(Ozalid Division of General Aniline and Film Corporation)*

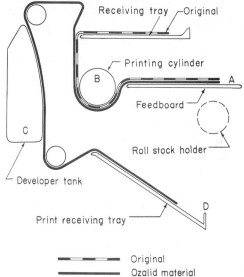

Prints with a light background are easy to read, and they simplify changes and alterations. Photostats are made by a photographic method and may be the same size as the original drawing or a different size. For some purposes copies may be made using the mimeograph or the hectograph. Where a large number of copies are required, they may be reproduced in the same or a different size by offset printing.

8•15 Microfilm copies are made on 35-millimeter film. Duplicates, positives and negatives, clear enlargements, intermediates, and prints can be made from the microfilms. Intermediates are copies of original drawings used in place of originals to save wear and damage. They may be either positives or negatives. Film readers (Fig. 8-15), which show an enlarged view of any film, are convenient as well as time-

Fig. 8-15. Microfilm reader allows reference to any drawing in seconds. *(Recordak Corporation)*

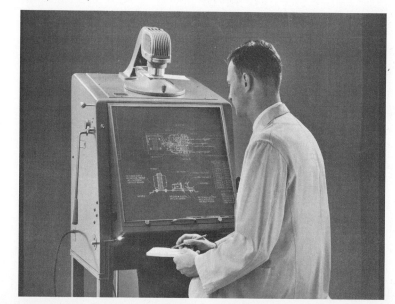

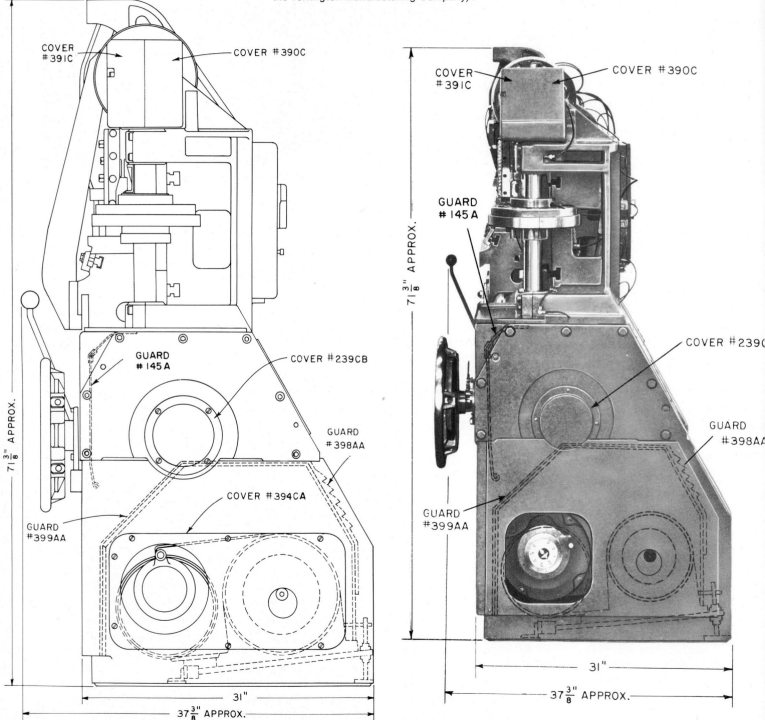

Fig. 8-16a. The line drawing and the photodrawing present the same information. These views demonstrate the value of photodrawings for a representative machine. *(LogEtronics, Inc., and the Torrington Manufacturing Company)*

saving, since any drawing may be referred to without handling a large print or waiting for one to be made.

8•16 Photodrafting. Many uses are being found for photographic methods in connection with mechanical drawing. Photodrafting combines photography and line drawing. It is especially useful and timesaving for assembly and other complicated drawings. To make a photodrawing (Fig. 8-16a at the right), a photograph of an assembled machine is made and enlarged. Notes may be lettered on any necessary line work drawn in to make a detail clear or to show desired interior features by hidden lines. The result is an assembly drawing that is made in a short time and that is more meaningful than a conventional line drawing (Fig. 8-16a at the left), which requires a great amount of time to draw. There are many uses for photodrawing, including the illustrations for instruction manuals, assembly and maintenance instructions, study of changes or modification, and sales literature. Another use of the camera is the process illustrated in Fig. 8-16b, which shows why accurate drawings and a knowledge of technique of drafting are important.

The process illustrated used Kodak Transfax, a light-sensitive solution that can be applied to surfaces with a spray

Fig. 8-16b. The Kodak Transfax process. *(Eastman Kodak Company)*

gun. By using this solution, technicians can print drawings, layouts, wiring diagrams, and instrument dials directly on metals, plastics, or almost any smooth or semiporous material. If necessary to obtain a good bond on the base material, it may be coated with a quick-drying lacquer. The surface is then sprayed with Transfax. When dry, a tracing or high-contrast photographic film negative is placed in contact as at A and exposed to light. Developing and clearing then follow to produce the copy at B. Where complete fabrication instructions are included on the trac-

ing, they are reproduced; the work can be done without further reference to the drawing.

8•17 Problem suggestions. Assign at least two problems to be drawn and traced. A blueprint, xerox, or other reproduction should be made. A visit to a company which makes use of microfilm is a most desirable part of a drafting science course if it can be arranged. Problems may be assigned from Group 5. One or two more tracings may be made later in connection with the problems in Group 13 on working drawings.

Engineering Council for Professional Development (ECPD)

The ECPD is an organization that improves and promotes the status of engineers. It concerns itself with the professional, technical, educational, and legislative phase of engineers' lives. The following national organizations cooperate in the efforts and activities of the ECPD: American Society of Civil Engineers, American Institute of Mining and Metallurgical Engineers, The American Society of Mechanical Engineers, American Institute of Electrical Engineers, The Engineering Institute of Canada, American Society for Engineering Education, Institute of Chemical Engineers, and the National Council of State Boards of Engineering Examiners.

The ECPD recommends procedures and standards to the national organizations. Its work is carried on through committees concerned with student guidance, engineering curricula, professional education and training, engineering ethics, and publicity.

A great deal of valuable information on the subjects mentioned is available at nominal cost in the publications of the ECPD, 345 E. 47th St., New York, N.Y. 10017.

9

Auxiliary views and revolutions

9•1 Explanatory views projected on other planes. In the previous chapters views have been drawn on the three regular planes with the object in a normal (regular) position. The three regular planes are the top, or horizontal plane; the front, or frontal plane; and the side, or profile plane. In this chapter views are drawn of inclined surfaces on planes which are parallel to the inclined surfaces and of objects which have been revolved, or turned about an axis (Fig. 9-1).

9•2 Auxiliary views are "helper views." When an object has slanting surfaces, the usual views do not show the true shapes of such surfaces (Fig. 9-2a at A). However, a view on a plane parallel to the slanting surface will show the true shape of the slanting surface, as at B. This, together with the side view, a bottom view of the base, and a partial front view, will give a better description than the views at A.

☞ *An auxiliary view is a projection on an auxiliary plane parallel to a slant-ing surface.* It is a view looking directly at the slanting surface in a direction perpendicular to it.

Observe the anchor pictured in Fig. 9-2b in Space 1 and that the position of the auxiliary plane in Space 2 is parallel to the inclined face and perpendicular to the frontal plane. In Space

Fig. 9-1. Revolution about a vertical axis. A 15-ton, 80-ft-boom shipyard traveling crane. *(McKiernan-Terry Corporation)*

Fig. 9-2b. An auxiliary view is drawn on a plane parallel to the inclined surface.

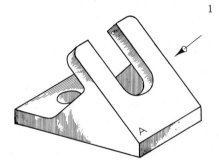

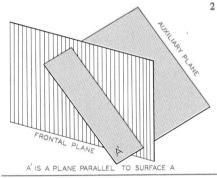

A' IS A PLANE PARALLEL TO SURFACE A

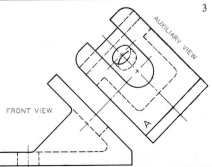

Fig. 9-2a. An auxiliary view gives a better description than regular views.

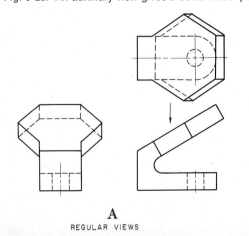

A
REGULAR VIEWS

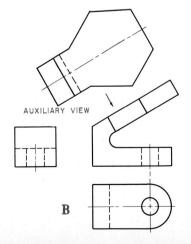

B

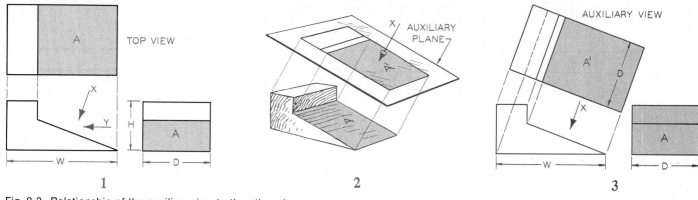

Fig. 9-3. Relationship of the auxiliary view to the other views.

3 the shape of the anchor is completely described by the two views, one of which is an auxiliary view.

Auxiliary views are important for describing the shapes of inclined features, especially when they have an irregular outline. They are also necessary for dimensioning such features.

9•3 The relationship of the auxiliary view to the usual views is illustrated by the simple block in Fig. 9-3. The three regular views are shown in Space 1, the side view being obtained by look-ing in the direction of arrow *Y*. The inclined face, *A*, does not show in its true shape in any view. If we locate a plane parallel to face *A*, as in Space 2, and look in the direction of arrow *X* perpendicular to face *A*, we obtain an auxiliary view on the auxiliary plane that will show the true size and shape of face *A* at *A'*. Such an auxiliary view made on an auxiliary plane and re-volved into the plane of the paper is shown in Space 3. The true size and shape of any inclined surface may be shown in a similar way.

9•4 The auxiliary plane in relation to the usual regular planes is illustrated in Fig. 9-4. At A the object is shown with the frontal, horizontal, and profile planes. At B the planes have been re-volved to show the front, top, and side views. At C the object is shown with the frontal, auxiliary, and profile planes. At D the planes have been revolved to show the front, auxiliary, and side views. Notice that the top and side views are not needed, since the object is completely described by the front and auxiliary views.

Fig. 9-4. The three regular planes and views; the two regular planes and an auxiliary plane.

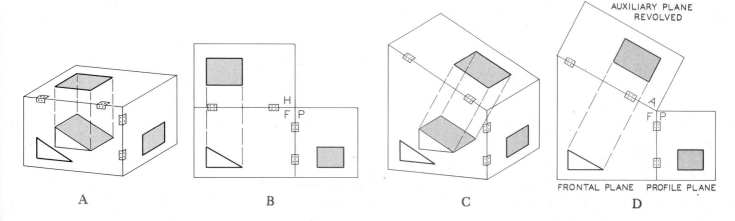

Fig. 9-5a. An auxiliary elevation is drawn on a plane perpendicular to horizontal plane.

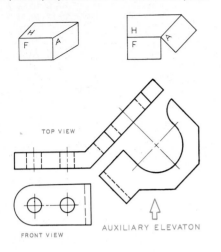

TOP VIEW

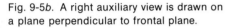

FRONT VIEW

AUXILIARY ELEVATON

Fig. 9-5b. A right auxiliary view is drawn on a plane perpendicular to frontal plane.

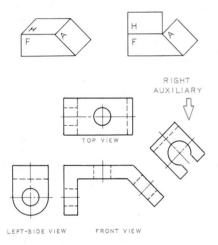

RIGHT AUXILIARY

TOP VIEW

LEFT-SIDE VIEW   FRONT VIEW

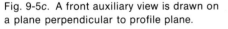

Fig. 9-5c. A front auxiliary view is drawn on a plane perpendicular to profile plane.

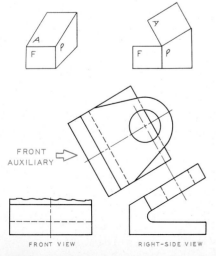

FRONT AUXILIARY

FRONT VIEW   RIGHT-SIDE VIEW

9•5 Kinds of auxiliary views. Auxiliary views may be classified according to the position of the planes upon which they are drawn. There are three primary auxiliary views.

Auxiliary elevations. If the auxiliary plane is perpendicular to the horizontal plane, the view is an auxiliary elevation (Fig. 9-5a). The auxiliary plane shows as a line (edge view) on the horizontal plane.

Right and left auxiliary views. If the auxiliary plane is perpendicular to the frontal plane, the view is a right or left auxiliary (Fig. 9-5b). The auxiliary plane shows as a line (edge view) on the frontal plane.

Front and rear auxiliary views. If the auxiliary plane is perpendicular to the profile (side) plane, the view is a front or rear auxiliary (Fig. 9-5c). The auxiliary plane shows as a line (edge view) on the profile (side plane).

Secondary, successive, or oblique auxiliary views are drawn when the auxiliary plane is inclined to all three regular planes (Fig. 9-5d).

9•6 To draw an auxiliary view, center-plane construction (Fig. 9-6). For a symmetrical object a center line is used to represent the edge of a center plane where it cuts the object (as in Space 1) by the line XY. Number the points on the inclined face. Space 2: Draw the line X'Y' parallel to the edge view of the inclined surface and at a convenient distance from it. Space 3: Draw projecting lines perpendicular to the inclined face from each point in the front view and extending beyond X'Y' as shown. Space 4: On each of the lines just drawn, locate the auxiliary view of the point projected by measuring the distance of the point from the center line XY in the top view and marking off this distance from the center line X'Y' in the auxiliary view. Distances D_1 and D_2 are measured from the center toward the front in the top view and therefore are measured toward the front in the auxiliary view.

Since the figure is symmetrical, the same distances, D_1' and D_2', would be measured on the other side of the line

Fig. 9-5d. A secondary auxiliary view. When a surface is inclined to all three regular planes, two successive auxiliary views are required to obtain a view on a plane parallel to the inclined surface.

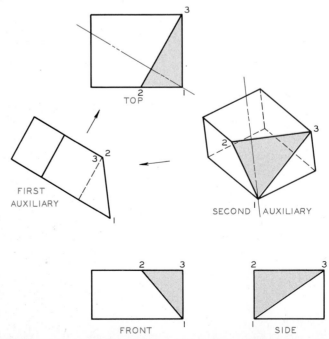

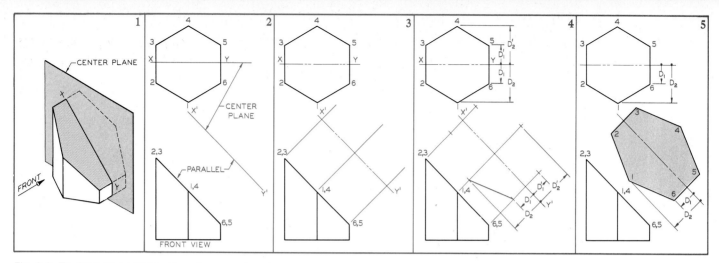

Fig. 9-6. To draw an auxiliary view using a center plane.

toward the back. The auxiliary view of the inclined face is completed by joining the numbered points as in Space 5. In Fig. 9-6 only the inclined face has been drawn, but the entire object would be projected in the same way. This is a *right auxiliary* view.

9•7 To draw an auxiliary view, reference-plane construction (Fig. 9-7). For a nonsymmetrical object, such as Fig. 9-7, a reference plane is used. This plane is placed for convenience in taking measurements. In this case the reference plane is placed at the back of the object. The construction is the same as for Fig. 9-6 except that all distances are laid off toward the front. The entire object has been projected to the auxiliary plane. This is a *left auxiliary* view.

9•8 To draw an auxiliary elevation and a front auxiliary. The auxiliary elevation of a piece of molding is shown in Fig. 9-8a. Given the top and left-side views of the molding, the auxiliary plane will be perpendicular to the horizontal plane. The reference plane, *XY*, will be placed under the molding. Locate points 1 to 6 in the front and top views. Draw projecting lines perpendicular to *X'Y'* from each point in the

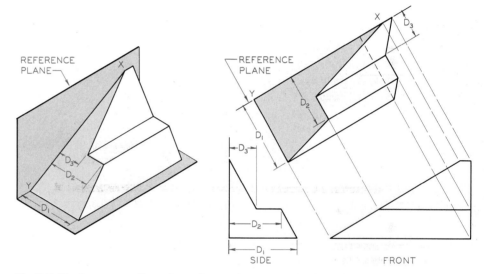

Fig. 9-7. To draw an auxiliary view using a reference plane.

Fig. 9-8a. To draw an auxiliary elevation.

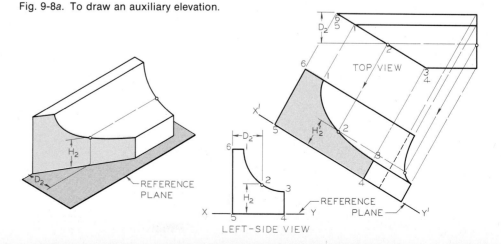

top view. Take distances up from XY in the side view and lay them off up from X'Y' in the auxiliary view, as shown for point 2. Locate as many more points on the curve as necessary to define it properly on the auxiliary view.

The front auxiliary of a wedge is shown in Fig. 9-8b. Given the front and right-side views, the auxiliary plane will be perpendicular to the profile (side) plane. The center plane will be perpendicular to the horizontal plane and will show as indicated by XY and X'Y'. Locate points on the front and side views of the curve. Draw projecting lines perpendicular to X'Y' from points on the side view. Take distances from XY on the front view and lay them off on each side of X'Y' as shown by the distance W for points numbered 1. Locate as many points on the curve as needed to define it properly on the auxiliary view.

9•9 Curves on auxiliary views.
Auxiliary views with curved lines are obtained by locating a number of points on the curves. This is illustrated by the auxiliary view of the inclined surface of a cylinder (Fig. 9-9). In this case the vertical center line (representing a center plane) shows in the side view of the cylinder. It is the line from which measurements are made and transferred to the auxiliary view.

Locate a convenient number of points on the side view. Project these points horizontally to the edge view of the inclined surface (in the front view). Draw the center line X'Y' parallel to the edge view of the inclined surface at a convenient distance from it. From the points on the inclined surface draw perpendiculars to cross the center line of the auxiliary views. Take the distance on each side of XY in the side view, as D_2 for point 2, and set off from X'Y' as for point 2 in the auxiliary view.

9•10 True shape of an oblique plane surface by auxiliary views.
Such views are made on a plane parallel to a surface which is inclined to all three of the normal planes. Surface 1–2–3–4 in Fig. 9-10a is inclined to the three normal planes. At A an auxiliary view has been drawn on a plane perpendicular to the inclined surface. At B an auxiliary view has been drawn from the view at A on a plane parallel to the surface 1–2–3–4. The true shape of the surface is shown at B.

Another example is shown in Fig. 9-10b. A first auxiliary view is drawn at A on a plane perpendicular to the triangular surface 0–1–2. A second auxiliary view is drawn at B on a plane parallel to surface 0–1–2, where the true shape of triangle 0–1–2 is shown.

9•11 Practical auxiliary views.
When working drawings for practical use are being made, the object can often be described by partial views. Notice that the casting in Fig. 9-11a is drawn with a partial auxiliary view, a partial top view, and a complete front view. Another practical use of auxiliary views is the auxiliary section (Fig. 9-11b), where the inclined surface is obtained by a plane which cuts through the object. (See Sectional Views, Chap. 10.)

9•12 Revolution.
Ordinarily drawings are made for objects placed in the regular positions, where they are shown in the usual views. However, views may be made for objects tipped about an edge, resting upon a corner, or revolved about an axis. Sometimes a revolved view is needed to obtain or check the space necessary for operation, find a true length, or draw a pictorial view.

Fig. 9-9. To draw curves on an auxiliary view. The auxiliary view of the cut surface of a cylinder.

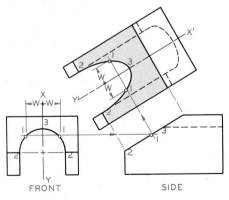

Fig. 9-8b. To draw a front auxiliary.

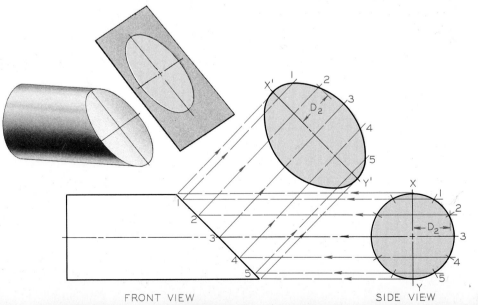

FRONT VIEW   SIDE VIEW

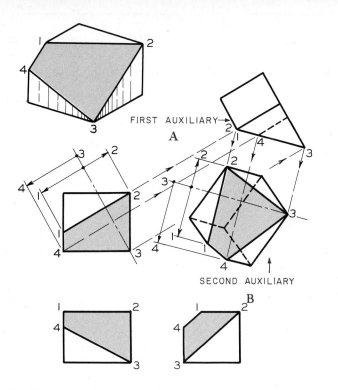

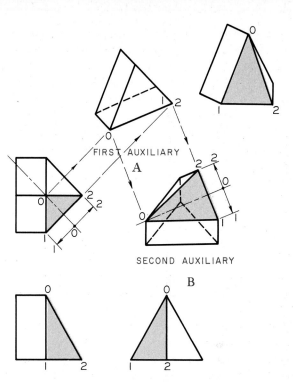

Fig. 9-10a. True shape shown by successive auxiliary views.

Fig. 9-10b. True shape shown by successive auxiliary views.

9·13 The axis of revolution. A convenient method for drawing views of an object in a revolved position is to imagine a shaft, or axis, passed through the object and perpendicular to the horizontal, frontal, or profile plane (Fig. 9-13). The object can be thought of as revolved about an axis and views drawn of the revolved object.

An object may be revolved to the right or to the left about an axis perpendicular to either the horizontal or the vertical plane. An object may be revolved forward or backward about an axis perpendicular to the side plane.

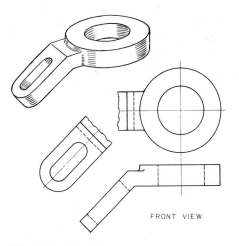

Fig. 9-11a. Partial views; a practical auxiliary view.

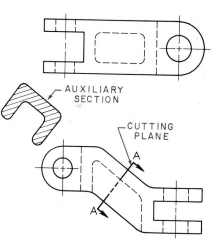

Fig. 9-11b. An auxiliary section is a view on a plane parallel to and showing a cut surface.

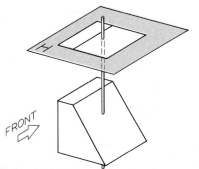

AXIS PERPENDICULAR TO HORIZONTAL

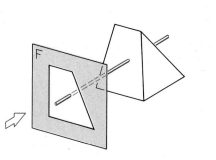

AXIS PERPENDICULAR TO FRONTAL

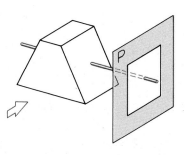

AXIS PERPENDICULAR TO PROFILE

Fig. 9-13. Positions for the axis of revolution.

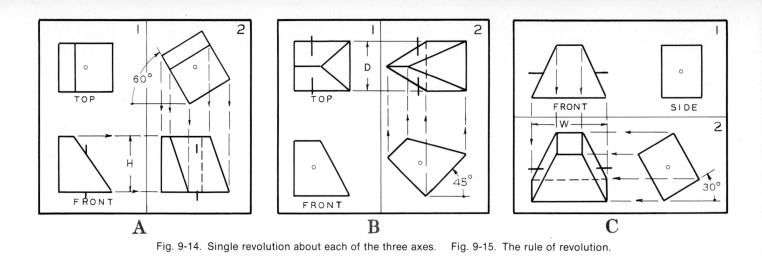

Fig. 9-14. Single revolution about each of the three axes.   Fig. 9-15. The rule of revolution.

9•14 The object revolved (Fig. 9-14). As stated, an axis of revolution may be taken perpendicular to the horizontal, frontal, or side planes. In Fig. 9-14 at A, the usual top and front views are shown in Space 1. The views after the object has been revolved about an axis perpendicular to the horizontal plane are shown in Space 2. Notice that the top view is revolved 60° to the right (clockwise) but otherwise is unchanged. The new front view is obtained by projecting down from the new top view and across from the front view of Space 1 (the height, *H*, has not changed, as it is parallel to the axis).

In Fig. 9-14 at B, the usual front and top views are shown in Space 1. In Space 2 the front view is shown after the object has been revolved to the left (counterclockwise) through 45° about an axis perpendicular to the frontal plane. The new top view is obtained by projecting up from the new front view and across from the top view of Space 1. In Fig. 9-14 at C, the usual front and side views are shown in Space 1. In Space 2 the side view is shown after the object has been revolved forward (counterclockwise) through 30° about an axis perpendicular to the profile plane. The new front view is obtained by projecting across from the

new side view and down from the front view of Space 1. Revolution may be clockwise (to the right), as in Fig. 9-14 at A, or counterclockwise (to the left), as at B. At C, the object has been revolved counterclockwise (to the left) or forward.

9•15 The rule of revolution may be stated in two parts:

———————————

1. The view perpendicular to the axis of revolution is unchanged except in position (Fig. 9-15). This is true because the axis is perpendicular to the plane on which it is projected.

2. Distances parallel to the axis of revolution are unchanged. This is true because they are parallel to the plane or planes on which they are projected. In Fig. 9-15 at A the *H* distances are parallel to the frontal and the side planes. At B the *D* distances are parallel to the side and the horizontal planes. At C the *W* distances are parallel to the frontal and the horizontal planes.

———————————

9•16 Revolution about a vertical axis. Figure 9-16*a* shows the method of drawing the views of an object revolved about a vertical axis. Given the three views, as at A, it is required to draw the views after the piece has been

revolved clockwise through 30° about a vertical axis. First, draw the top view in its new position, as at B. Since the axis is vertical, the height has not been changed; so a horizontal projecting line may be drawn from point 1 of the front view at A and a vertical projecting line from the top view at B. The intersection of the two lines just drawn will locate the position of point 1 in the new front view. Proceed in the same way for each point and join the points to complete the view. The side view is obtained from the front and top views in the usual manner. The object shown in Fig. 9-16*b* is revolved counterclockwise through 45°.

9•17 Revolution about a horizontal axis is illustrated in Fig. 9-17*a*. The method of drawing the views of an object revolved about a horizontal axis is shown in Fig. 9-17*b*. First, draw the views in the usual way; then, revolve to a new position about an imaginary axis taken perpendicular to a plane of projection.

At A in Fig. 9-17*b* we have two views of an object in a natural position. Suppose a hole is drilled through from the front and a shaft is inserted, as shown. The object might be revolved about the shaft, or axis, into a new position, as

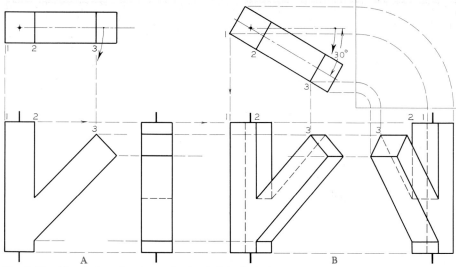

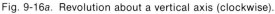

Fig. 9-16a. Revolution about a vertical axis (clockwise).

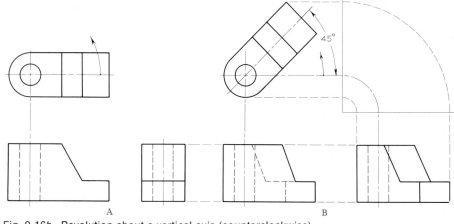

Fig. 9-16b. Revolution about a vertical axis (counterclockwise).

Fig. 9-17a. Revolution about a horizontal axis. A concrete mixer. (The Jaeger Machine Company)

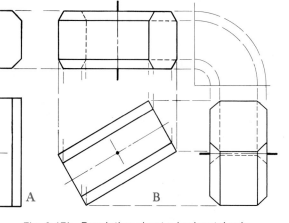

Fig. 9-17b. Revolution about a horizontal axis.

at B. It will be observed that the front view of B is the same as the front view of A except that its position has been changed. The top view of B is obtained by projecting up from the new front view and across from the top view of A. The new side view is obtained in the usual way from the new front and top views.

9•18 Practical revolved views. When working drawings for practical use are being made, objects often can be described best by drawing one of the views, or part of a view, in a revolved position. In Fig. 9-18a the top view shows the angle made by the right-hand part, and the front view shows the true shape in a revolved position. In Fig. 9-18b the angles are shown in the front view, and the true shapes, together with the total length when the parts have been revolved, are shown in the top view.

Fig. 9-18a. Revolution applied: Vertical axis.

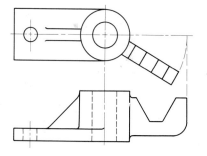

Fig. 9-18b. Revolution applied: Horizontal axis.

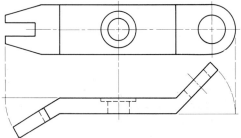

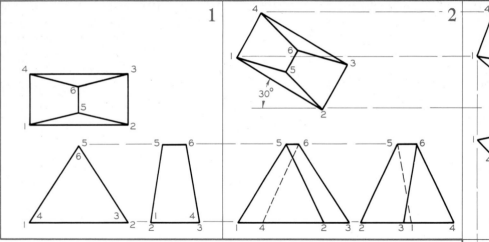

Fig. 9-19. Successive revolution.

9•19 Successive revolutions (Fig. 9-19).
After an object has been revolved about an axis perpendicular to a plane, it may be revolved about an axis perpendicular to another plane. The piece has been revolved about a vertical axis through 30° in Space 2. From the position of Space 2 it has been revolved about an axis perpendicular to the frontal plane through 45°.

The object is shown in Space 1 in the regular position. In Space 2 it has been revolved about a vertical axis through 30° clockwise. In Space 3 it has been revolved from the position of Space 2 about an axis perpendicular to the frontal plane through 45° clockwise. In Space 4 it has been revolved from the position of Space 3 about an axis perpendicular to the profile plane (backward) until line 3–4 is horizontal.

9•20 Auxiliary views and revolved views.
The true size of an inclined surface can be obtained by an auxiliary view (Fig. 9-20 in Space 1) or by revolving the object until the inclined surface is parallel to one of the regular planes (in this case parallel to the frontal plane) (Fig. 9-20, Spaces 2 and 3).

9•21 True shape of an inclined plane by successive revolution.
A surface will show in its true shape when it is parallel to a plane. In Fig. 9-21 the surface 1–2–3–4 of the object pictured in

Space D is inclined to all three of the normal planes. In Space A the object is drawn in its normal position. In Space B the object has been revolved about a vertical axis until the inclined surface is perpendicular to the frontal plane. In Space C the object has been revolved from the position of Space B until the surface 1–2–3–4 is parallel to the profile plane and shows its true shape.

9•22 To find the true length of a line
(Fig. 9-22). Since an auxiliary view of an inclined surface shows its true size and shape, it may be used to find the true length of a line. In Fig. 9-22 at A, the line OA does not show its true length in the top, front, or side view because it is inclined to the planes of

Fig. 9-20. True size shown by an auxiliary view and true size shown by a revolved view.

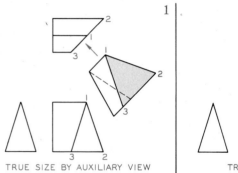

TRUE SIZE BY AUXILIARY VIEW

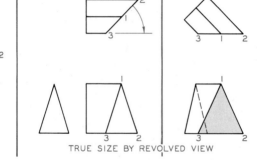

TRUE SIZE BY REVOLVED VIEW

projection. The line *OA* does show its true length (TL) at B, where the auxiliary plane is parallel to the surface *OAB*.

The pyramid in Fig. 9-22 may be revolved about an axis perpendicular to the frontal plane until surface *OAB* is parallel to the profile plane, as at C. The true size of *OAB* will show in the side view, as will the true length of *OA*. Only the surface *OAB* needs to be revolved as shown at D. If the pyramid is revolved as in Fig. 9-22 at E so that the top view of line *OA* is horizontal, the front view of *OA* will then show its true length because the line is then parallel to the frontal plane.

Instead of revolving the whole pyramid, just the line *OA* may be revolved until it is parallel to one of the planes of projection. In Fig. 9-22 at F and G, the line has been revolved until its top view is horizontal at *OA'*. The point *A'* can then be projected to the front view, where *OA'* will be the true length.

Revolution may be such as to make the line parallel to any one of the three planes. Its projection on the plane to which it is parallel will show its true length. In Fig. 9-22 at H, the line has been revolved parallel to the horizontal plane, and the true length is shown at *OA'* in the top view.

9·23 Problem suggestions. Group 9, page 452. Two lists are presented. List 1 includes basic problems which in general are more elementary problems than List 2. Selections should be made according to the purpose of the course. List 2 may be used for additional or alternative assignments.

List 1: Problems 9·1, 9·4, 9·8, 9·17, 9·21, 9·22, 9·24, 9·26, 9·28, 9·30, 9·32, 9·37, 9·39, 9·41, 9·45, 9·46, 9·47.

List 2: Problems 9·5, 9·9, 9·14, 9·19, 9·25, 9·27, 9·29, 9·31, 9·33, 9·34, 9·35, 9·36, 9·38, 9·40, 9·42, 9·43, 9·44, 9·46, 9·47.

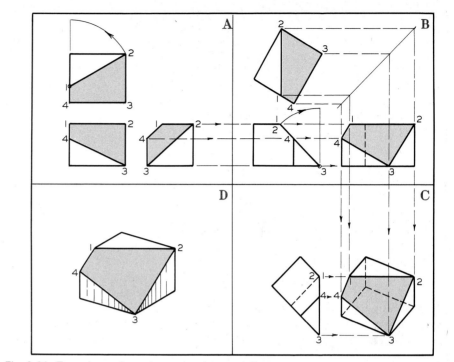

Fig. 9-21. True shape shown by successive revolution.

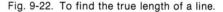

Fig. 9-22. To find the true length of a line.

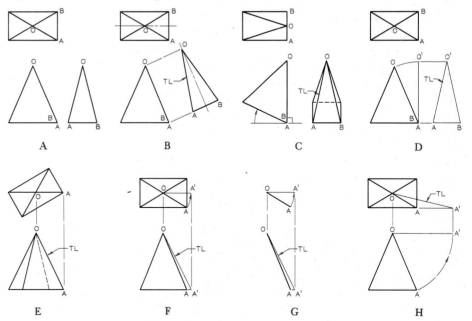

10

Sectional and other conventional views

10•1 Modified views. In the application of the graphic language to everyday uses in industry and science, it is sometimes necessary to use representations which may differ from true projection or be changed in other ways. The reason for this is to make a drawing simpler and easier to read (generally this requires less time than to make the drawing). Such treatments are called *conventional representations* and correspond with the idioms used in our everyday talk. Conventional representations include sectional views of various kinds, revolved or rotated parts of objects to show true shapes, simplified drawings (sometimes called *functional drawings*), diagrams, and symbols of many kinds.

10•2 Sections show hidden details. We have learned that interior or other parts of an object which cannot be seen may be represented or described by *hidden lines* made with short dashes (Art. 5·11). This method is satisfactory if the interior detail is fairly simple. When there are many inside details, or when several parts are shown together, hidden lines make the drawing hard to read. In such cases views, called *sections,* or *sectional views,* are drawn to show the object or construction as if cut apart by using an imaginary cutting plane and removing all that is in front of the cutting plane. The photograph in Fig. 10-2*a* shows the exterior of a check valve. The photograph in Fig. 10-2*b* shows how the valve would look if cut parallel to the frontal plane and the cutaway part removed. A drawing showing the cut valve would be a section, or sectional view. Imagine how an exterior drawing would look if one attempted to show complicated interior details using hidden lines and you will understand why sectional views are necessary.

Fig. 10-2*a*. The exterior of a check valve. *(Charles Wheatley Co.)*

Fig. 10-2*b*. Cutaway showing the interior of a check valve. *(Charles Wheatley Co.)*

10·3 A sectional view is obtained by supposing an imaginary cutting plane to be used and everything in front of the plane removed to show the cut surface and the interior details. This is explained in Fig. 10-3. A picture of a connector plate is shown at 1, and three regular views are shown at 2. At 3 a picture of an imaginary cutting plane that passes through the center, parallel to the frontal plane, is shown. The picture at 4 shows how the piece would look if actually cut apart. Orthographic views of the piece, if actually cut in two, are shown at 5. This does not tell that it is half of the piece or just where it is cut; a cutting plane can be located where necessary to show necessary detail, as will be explained later. Furthermore, such a drawing would *not* be used because the piece has not been cut by a *real* plane. The *correct* drawing, with a sectional view, is shown at 6. Note the following: Show the cut surface by section lining composed of uniformly spaced thin lines, generally at 45° (sometimes called *crosshatching*). Show the edge of the cutting plane by a cutting-plane line with the ends turned at 90° and terminated by arrowheads to show the direction in which the section is viewed (see alphabet of lines, Fig. 8-3). Show the complete top and end views because the cutting plane is imaginary.

10·4 A full section is obtained when the object is cut completely apart, as in Fig. 10-3. The usual full sections are:

Frontal section. Cutting plane parallel to the frontal plane (Fig. 10-4a).
Profile (side, or cross) section. Cutting plane parallel to the profile plane (Fig. 10-4b).
Horizontal (or top) section. Cutting plane parallel to the horizontal plane (Fig. 10-4c).

Such views are generally referred to simply as *sections*.

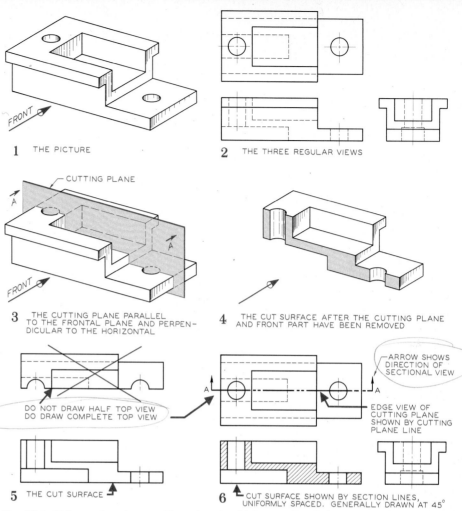

1   THE PICTURE

2   THE THREE REGULAR VIEWS

CUTTING PLANE

3   THE CUTTING PLANE PARALLEL TO THE FRONTAL PLANE AND PERPENDICULAR TO THE HORIZONTAL

4   THE CUT SURFACE AFTER THE CUTTING PLANE AND FRONT PART HAVE BEEN REMOVED

DO NOT DRAW HALF TOP VIEW DO DRAW COMPLETE TOP VIEW

ARROW SHOWS DIRECTION OF SECTIONAL VIEW

EDGE VIEW OF CUTTING PLANE SHOWN BY CUTTING PLANE LINE

5   THE CUT SURFACE

6   CUT SURFACE SHOWN BY SECTION LINES, UNIFORMLY SPACED. GENERALLY DRAWN AT 45°

Fig. 10-3. Using an imaginary cutting plane to obtain a sectional view.

Fig. 10-4a. A frontal section. The cutting plane is parallel to the frontal plane.

Fig. 10-4b. A profile (side or cross) section. The cutting plane is parallel to the profile plane.

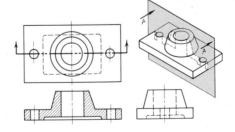

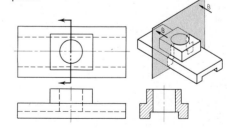

Fig. 10-4c. A horizontal section. The cutting plane is parallel to the horizontal plane.

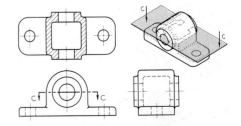

Fig. 10-5a. Section lines are spaced by eye and are farther apart for large areas.

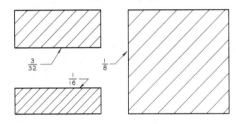

$\frac{3}{32}$ $\frac{1}{8}$

$\frac{1}{16}$

Fig. 10-5b. Blacked-in section for thin areas at A. Outline sectioning for large areas at B. These may be drawn freehand on design drawings.

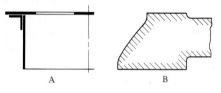

A   B

Fig. 10-5c. Cut surface may be grayed.

Fig. 10-5d. Cut surface may have grayed outline.

Fig. 10-5e. Do not draw section lines parallel or perpendicular to a main line of view.

INCORRECT   POSSIBLE   PREFERRED

Fig. 10-6. The cutting-plane line. Edge view.

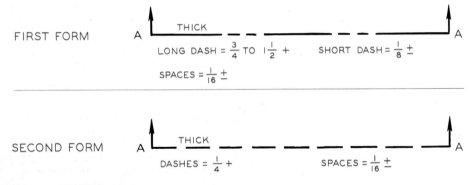

FIRST FORM   A   THICK

LONG DASH = $\frac{3}{4}$ TO $1\frac{1}{2}$ +   SHORT DASH = $\frac{1}{8}$ ±

SPACES = $\frac{1}{16}$ ±

SECOND FORM   A   THICK

DASHES = $\frac{1}{4}$ +   SPACES = $\frac{1}{16}$ ±

10·5 Spacing of section lines. Section lines may be closer together or farther apart, depending upon the area (Fig. 10-5a). American Standards suggests approximate distances between section lines of 1/32 in. to 1/8 in. or more, uniformly spaced, and generally at 45°. Wider spacing is preferred when it can be used to show the sectioned area clearly. A neater drawing will result and time will be saved if section lines are *not* spaced too close together. For most purposes the distance between lines can be about 3/32 in., spaced by eye. For small areas use closer spacing (1/16 in. or less), and for large areas use wider spacing (up to 1/8 in. or more). When the sectioned area is very small, as for thin plates, sheets, and structural shapes, blacked-in sections may be used (as in Fig. 10-5b at A). Note the white space between the parts.

A timesaving method for indicating a large sectioned area is to use outline sectioning, as shown in Fig. 10-5b at B. This method is often used on design drawings with the section lines drawn freehand and widely spaced. Still another method is to gray the sectioned area (Fig. 10-5c), to outline with a pencil (Fig. 10-5d), or to rub pencil dust over the area. A fixative may be applied to prevent smudging.

On any section avoid section lines parallel or perpendicular to an important visible line of the enclosing area (Fig. 10-5e). If necessary, section lines may be drawn with any suitable angles and spacing to identify the parts.

10·6 The cutting-plane line represents the edge view of the cutting plane. Two forms are approved for American Standard (Fig. 10-6). The first form is generally preferred. The second form shows up well on complicated drawings. Short lines at right angles, and with arrowheads to show the direction for looking at the section, are drawn at the ends of the cutting-plane line. Bold capital letters are placed at the corners as shown if needed for reference to the section. Also see Figs. 10-7 and 10-8a.

The cutting-plane line need not be used when it is clear that the section is taken on the main center line of an object or other clearly seen location.

10·7 Offset sections. The cutting plane is usually taken straight through the object, but it may be offset at one or more places in order to show some detail or to miss some part (Fig. 10-7 at A, B, and C). Here the plane is not continuous but is offset to pass through the bolt hole and to miss the rib by passing in front of it. The hole and the

rib are shown more clearly than if the section were continued through the center. If sectioned, the rib would make the part look heavier and the description would not be as clear. Offsets are shown in the edge view of a cutting plane but *not* in the sectioned view. If reference letters are necessary, they are placed at the ends of the cutting-plane line.

10·8 A half section is obtained when two cutting planes at right angles are used to cut out and remove one quarter of the piece, as at A and B in Fig. 10-8a. The half section at C shows one-half the view as a section and the other

half as an exterior view. Such views can be used to advantage with symmetrical pieces to show both the interior and the exterior in one view. A *center line* is used where the exterior and the sectional half views meet because the piece is not actually cut. Also, the complete top view is drawn because no part is actually removed. If dimensions are to be shown, it will be necessary to draw some, or all, hidden lines in the exterior half. If sight direction is required, only one arrow is used, as shown at C. The cutting-plane line could be omitted here, as the location of the section is evident. Sometimes it may be desirable to show two half sections

Fig. 10-7. An offset cutting plane is not continuous.

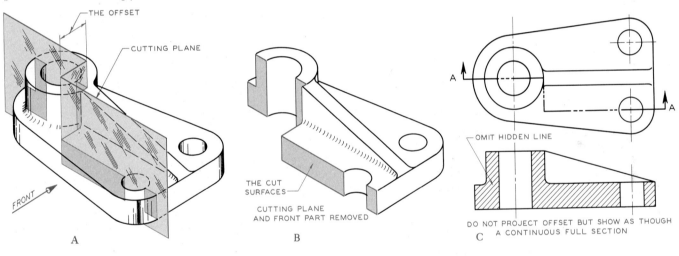

A

B

C

Fig. 10-8a. A half section is obtained by cutting out one-quarter of the piece.

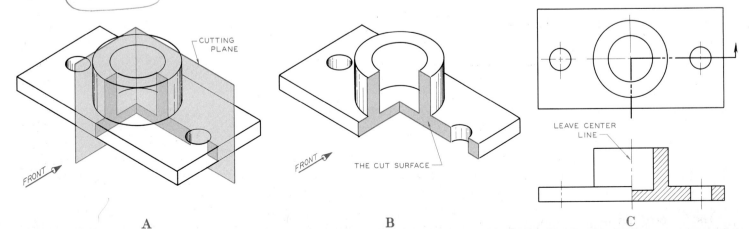

A

B

C

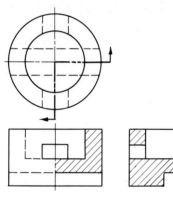

Fig. 10-8*b*. Two half sections, made by cutting out one-quarter of the piece.

(Fig. 10-8*b*). *(Half section* is a general term, as more or less than one-quarter may be removed.)

10•9 Hidden and visible lines on sectional views. Hidden lines should not be drawn on sectional views except when needed for dimensioning or for clearly describing the shape. In Fig. 10-9*a* the hub is clearly described at A with no hidden lines. Compare with the view at B.

On sectional assembly drawings (where several parts are shown assembled, or put together), most of the hidden lines should be omitted to keep the drawing from becoming complicated and hard to read (Fig. 13-5*a*). Sometimes a half section or part section can be used to advantage to avoid hidden lines on an assembly drawing.

Under usual conditions all visible lines on or beyond the plane of the section should be drawn on a sectional view (Fig. 10-9*b* at A). Observe the numbered lines which match the lines on the picture at B. A drawing without these lines, as at C, would have no value and should *never* be used. Without the visible lines beyond the plane

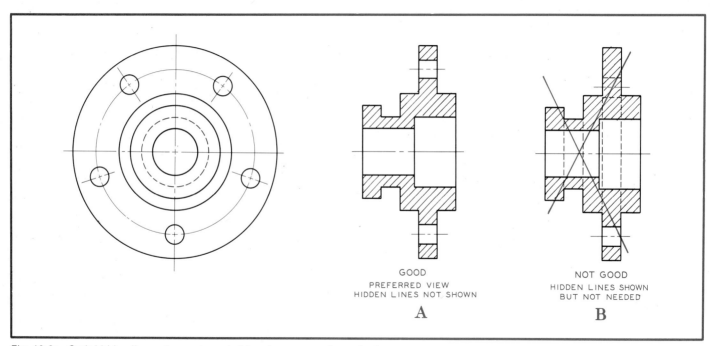

GOOD
PREFERRED VIEW
HIDDEN LINES NOT SHOWN
A

NOT GOOD
HIDDEN LINES SHOWN
BUT NOT NEEDED
B

Fig. 10-9*a*. Omit hidden lines when not needed for clearness or dimensioning.

Fig. 10-9*b*. Show all visible lines beyond the section.

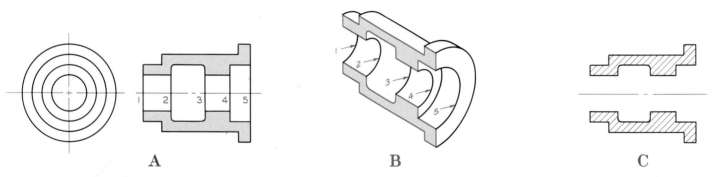

A

B

C

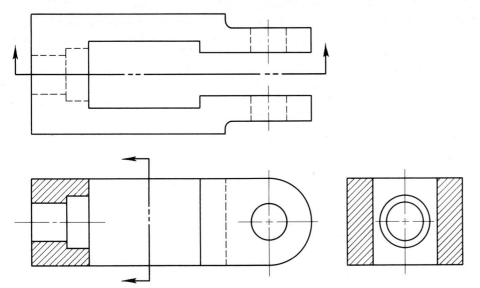

Fig. 10-9c. Visible lines beyond the plane of the section are necessary.

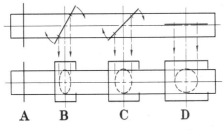

BREAK LINE

BROKEN-OUT SECTION
A

BROKEN-OUT SECTION
B

Fig. 10-10. A broken-out section is useful to show some detail.

Fig. 10-11a. A revolved section is a "cut-across" section turned at right angles and parallel to the view.

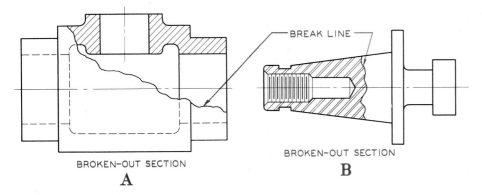

A   B   C   D

Fig. 10-11b. Revolved sections.

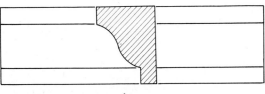

A

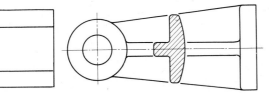

B

of the section in Fig. 10-9c, the view would have no meaning.

10•10 Broken-out sections (Fig. 10-10) may be used when it is desired to show some interior detail without drawing a complete or half section. In such cases a cutting plane is assumed to be passed through the desired detail and "broken out" in front of the plane. Note that the broken-out section is limited by a "break line."

10•11 A revolved section provides a convenient means of showing the shape of a rib, arm, or a long feature by cutting a section perpendicular to the length and then revolving the section through 90° parallel to the plane of the view. This is illustrated in Fig. 10-11a. At A the plane is perpendicular to the length. At B and C the plane is partly revolved about a vertical axis, and at D the cutting plane is revolved parallel to the plane of the view. The revolved section may be "set in" the view, as in Fig. 10-11b at A and B, or set in a "break," as in Fig. 10-11c at A and B. The method shown in Fig.

Fig. 10-11c. Revolved sections in long parts.

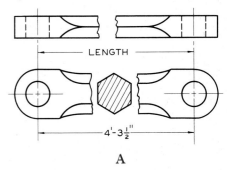

LENGTH

4'-3½"

A

h

PARALLEL
(SAME SLOPE)

B

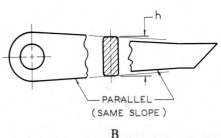

10-11*c* is useful for long, slender parts when the section is uniform. In such cases the length may be shortened (not shown to scale) and given by a dimension. This allows larger revolved views to be drawn.

10•12 A removed section (Fig. 10-12) is a section which has been taken from the regular position and drawn in some other position. However, the edges or center lines of a removed section should be parallel to the corresponding lines as drawn in the regular position. If possible, removed sections should be placed on the same sheet as the regular views. Bold lettering should be used to identify the removed section and the location of the cutting plane on the regular view, as illustrated. If removed sections are not on the same sheet as the regular views (or when there are several sheets), further identification is necessary to tell where the removed section will be found, as: SECTION AA ON SHEET 5, ZONE B2.

A removed section may be a sliced section (the same as a revolved section), or it may contain some additional detail beyond the cutting plane. It may be drawn to an enlarged scale if necessary to show details clearly and to provide more space for dimensions.

Sometimes a removed exterior view (nonsectioned) may be desirable. It may be to the same or an enlarged scale and may be complete or used to show certain features.

10•13 Auxiliary sections. When a cutting plane is passed at an angle, as in Fig. 10-13 at A, the resulting sectional view, parallel to the cutting plane, is an auxiliary section. The method of drawing is the same as for any auxiliary view (Chap. 9).

The usual practice on working drawings is to show only the cut section; however, any part, or all beyond the auxiliary cutting plane, may be shown if needed. In Fig. 10-13 at B, one hidden line is shown on the auxiliary section, and there are three incomplete views.

10•14 Sections through ribs, webs, and similar features. When a cutting plane passes through a rib parallel to the flat side of a rib or web, the section-

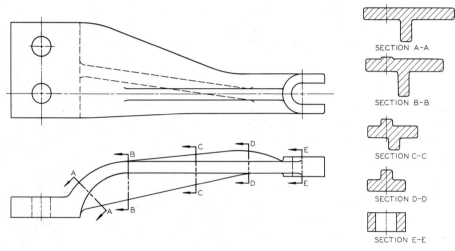

Fig. 10-12. Sections may be removed from regular positions and drawn in a convenient position.

Fig. 10-13. Auxiliary sections. The cutting plane is not parallel to any of the three regular planes.

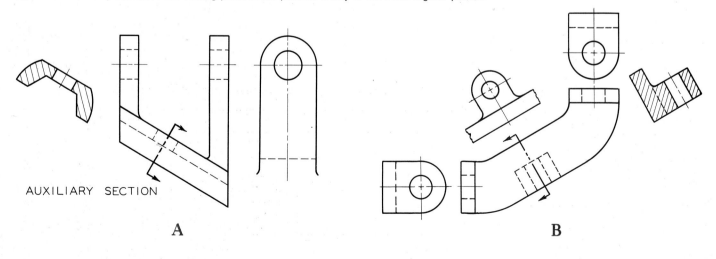

AUXILIARY SECTION

A

B

ing is omitted, as in Fig. 10-14 at B, where the plane is thought of as being just in front of the rib. A true section, as at A, would give the idea of a very heavy, solid piece, which would not be a true description.

If a cutting plane passes perpendicular to the flat side of a rib, web, or other "thin" feature, sectioning is shown.

There are three conditions for showing ribs, webs, and similar features on sectional views: (1) parallel to the flat side; (2) perpendicular to the flat side and crosswise; (3) perpendicular to the flat side and lengthwise.

10•15 Alternate, or wide, sectioning (Fig. 10-15) may be used when a rib (or similar flat feature) does not show clearly in a sectional view. The sectional view at A shows the eccentric as it would be drawn without a rib. It also shows the usual conventional way it would be drawn by not sectioning a rib. This view could mean no rib or a rib. The top and bottom of the rib is even with the surfaces it joins; however, at B alternate section lines are used with hidden lines to show the extent of a rib.

Alternate sectioning is a method of indicating a rib by leaving out every other section line on the rib, as shown. Alternate section lines are useful to indicate a rib in one-view drawings of parts or in assembly drawings.

10•16 The phantom, or hidden, section (Fig. 10-16) is used when it is desired to show on one view the interior and the exterior of a part that is not completely symmetrical. Note that the circular boss is on only one side of the piece. A half section could not be used in this case. A partial phantom section

Fig. 10-14. Ribs are not sectioned when the cutting plane is parallel to the flat side.

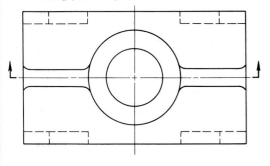

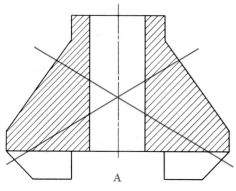

SECTION THROUGH RIB

A

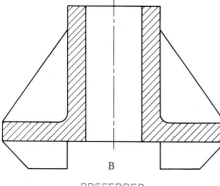

B

PREFERRED
CONVENTIONAL SECTION

Fig. 10-15. Alternate sectioning identifies a rib.

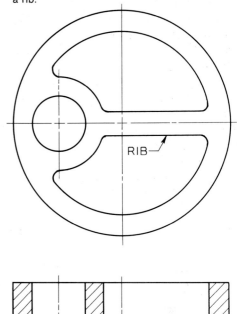

RIB

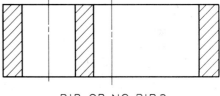

RIB OR NO RIB?

A

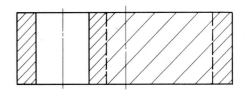

RIB SHOWN BY ALTERNATE SECTION

B

Fig. 10-16. Phantom section shows the inside on the outside (X-ray idea).

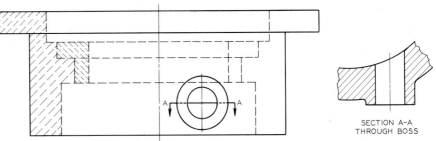

SECTION A-A
THROUGH BOSS

is sometimes useful for showing a detail in section on an exterior view instead of a broken-out section (Art. 10·10).

10·17 Sections through assembled pieces. When two or more pieces are shown together in a sectional view, section lines are drawn in different directions for each piece (Figs. 10-17a and 10-17b). However, each separate piece has the section lines in the same direction wherever any part of it appears as a cut surface.

A picture of a flanged check valve is shown at A in Fig. 10-17c, and sectional assembly views of the valve are shown at B. Note that the pieces which come into contact are sectioned in different directions and that the same pieces are sectioned in the same way in both views. Section lining is sometimes used to indicate different materials, as for part 2, the bronze cover. See Art. 10·18 for sectioning symbols. When there are a number of separate parts, section lines may be drawn at 30°, 60°, 15°, 75°, or other angles in addition to 45° if necessary to identify the separate parts (Fig. 10-17c).

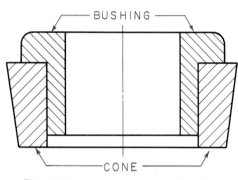

Fig. 10-17a. Two pieces. Section lines in two directions.

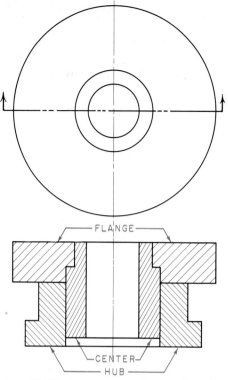

Fig. 10-17b. Three pieces. Section lines in three directions.

Fig. 10-17c. A flanged check valve. Picture and sectional-view drawing. *(Charles Wheatley Co.)*

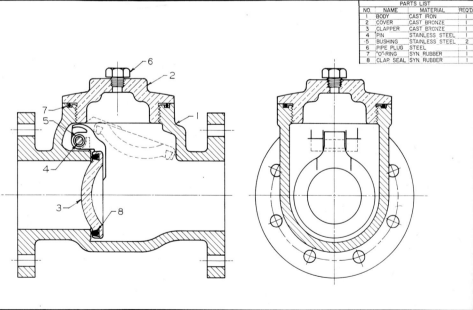

PARTS LIST			
NO.	NAME	MATERIAL	REQ'D
1	BODY	CAST IRON	1
2	COVER	CAST BRONZE	1
3	CLAPPER	CAST BRONZE	1
4	PIN	STAINLESS STEEL	1
5	BUSHING	STAINLESS STEEL	2
6	PIPE PLUG	STEEL	1
7	"O"-RING	SYN. RUBBER	1
8	CLAP. SEAL	SYN. RUBBER	1

AUTHORIZED BY	DATE	DRAWN BY	DATE	CHARLES WHEATLEY COMPANY	FOR		
DEVELOPED FROM DWG.	CODE NO.	TRACED BY	DATE	414 SO. DETROIT · TULSA, OKLA.			
SUPERCEDES DWG.	DATE	CHECKED BY	DATE		TOLERANCES UNLESS OTHERWISE NOTED FRACTIONAL ± 1/64", DECIMAL ± 0.005"	SCALE	REV
SUPERCEDED BY DWG.	DATE	APPROVED BY	DATE		ISSUE NO.	ISSUE DATE OF PRINT	
						DWG. NO.	
				ALL DIMS. IN INCHES IF NOT SPECIFIED			

FILE B—

10·18 American Standard symbols for representing materials (Figs. 10-18a and 10-18b). The general-purpose symbol (cast iron) is used for most purposes, especially on drawings of separate pieces. Sectioning symbols are sometimes used on assembly drawings to indicate different materials, as cast iron, steel, bronze, and others. However, exact specifications by notes or otherwise are necessary to completely describe the material. For some purposes, certain distinctive materials may be indicated on exterior views by using the symbols that are shown in Fig. 10-18b.

10·19 Sections through shafts, bolts, and rivets. When a cutting plane passes lengthwise (through the axis) of shafts, bolts, pins, rivets, or similar elements, sectioning is not used (Fig. 10-19a). Such elements are left in full because there is no interior detail and because sectioning would, or might,

Fig. 10-18a. American Standard symbols for section lining.

 Cast iron and malleable iron. Also for general use for all materials

 Steel

 Bronze, brass, copper, and compositions

 White metal, zinc, lead, babbitt, and alloys

 Magnesium, aluminum, and aluminum alloys

 Rubber, plastic electrical insulation

Cork, felt, fabric, leather, fiber

 Sound insulation

Thermal insulation

 Firebrick and refractory material

Electric windings, electromagnets, resistance, etc.

 Concrete

 Brick and stone masonry

 Marble, slate, glass, porcelain, etc.

Earth

Rock

Sand

Water and other liquids

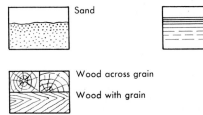 Wood across grain

Wood with grain

Fig. 10-18b. American Standard symbols for outside views.

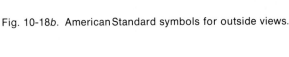

Brick

Uncoursed and coursed rubble

Ashlar

Transparent materials, glass, etc.

Marble

Fig. 10-19a. Do not section when there is no interior detail.

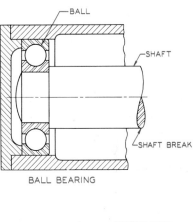 BALL BEARING — BALL, SHAFT, SHAFT BREAK

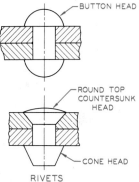 RIVETS — BUTTON HEAD, ROUND TOP COUNTERSUNK HEAD, CONE HEAD

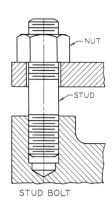 STUD BOLT — NUT, STUD

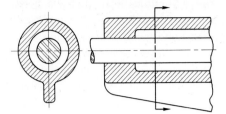

Fig. 10-19b. A cross section.

give a wrong idea of the part. The exterior view is easier to read and requires less time to draw. However, when such parts are cut across the axis, they should be sectioned (Fig. 10-19b). The sectional assembly (Fig. 10-19c) shows and names a number of features which are not sectioned.

10·20 Rule of contour and rotated features. The rule can be stated as follows:

In general, preserve the characteristic contour of an object.

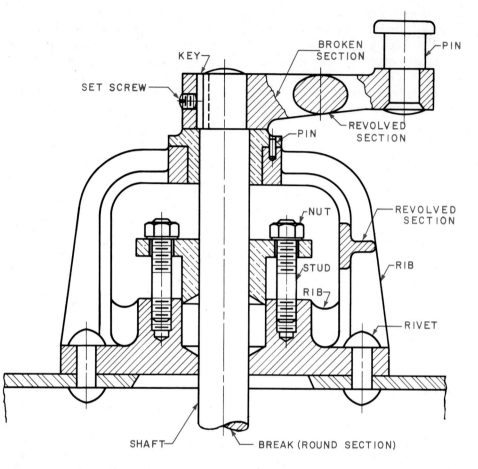

Fig. 10-20a. Rotate to show true shapes. The rule of contour.

Fig. 10-19c. A study in what not to section.

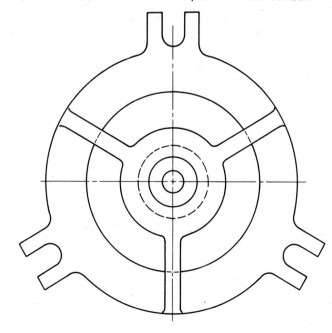

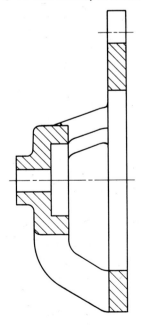

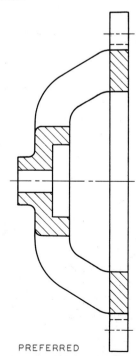

TRUE PROJECTION   PREFERRED

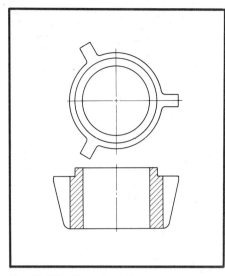

Fig. 10-20*b*. Do not section lugs.

Sections or elevations of symmetrical pieces would sometimes be hard to read (as well as hard to draw) if drawn in true projection. In such cases it is usual to consider features of the object to be rotated until a characteristic or familiar contour shows. In Fig. 10-20*a* ribs and lugs have been rotated parallel to the frontal plane. The ribs show true shape. Only the parts which extend all the way around the vertical axis are sectioned. In Fig. 10-20*b* the lugs are rotated but not sectioned.

The rule of contour applies to exterior views (Fig. 10-20*c*) as well as sections. Note that the true projection does not describe the piece as well and requires more drawing time than the preferred view where the ribs are rotated.

When a section passes through spokes, the spokes are not sectioned (Fig. 10-20*d* at A). Compare this with the drawing for a solid web (Fig. 10-20*d* at B) and notice the sectioning which indicates the web is solid rather than spoked.

Fig. 10-20*d*. A section through spokes.

Fig. 10-20*c*. The rule of contour applies to exterior views.

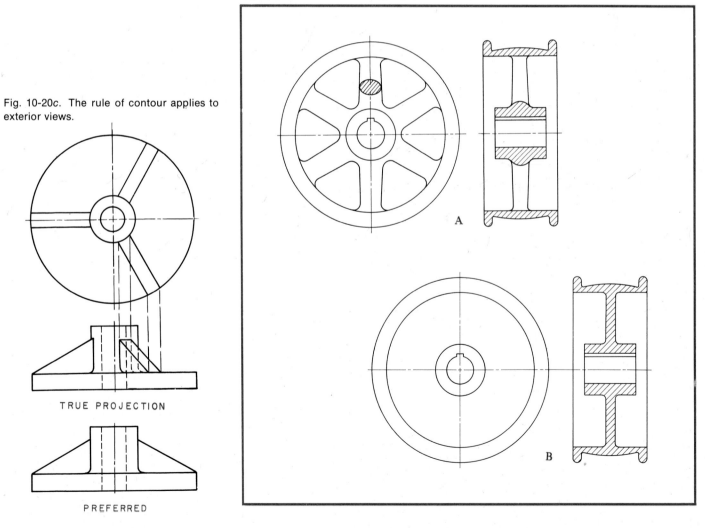

TRUE PROJECTION

PREFERRED

A

B

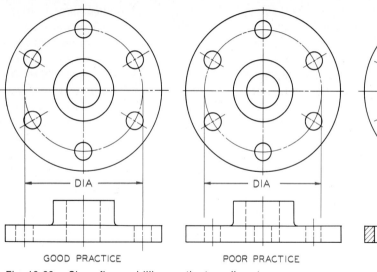

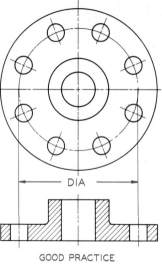

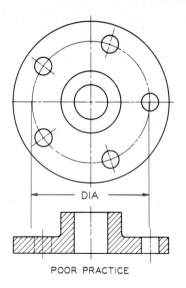

GOOD PRACTICE   POOR PRACTICE   GOOD PRACTICE   POOR PRACTICE

Fig. 10-20e. Show flange drilling on the true diameter.

Fig. 10-20f. Rotation of part of a view to show true shape.

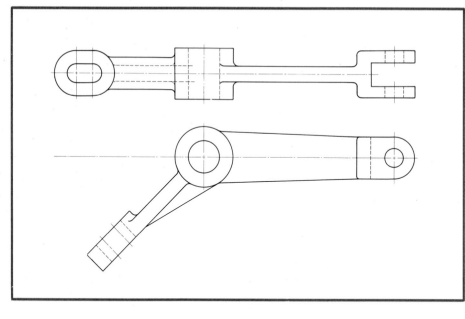

Fig. 10-20g. Stretched-out view to show true length.

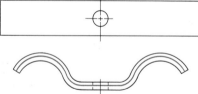

When a section or elevation of a part with holes on a circle of drilling is drawn (Fig. 10-20e), the axes of the holes are rotated until parallel with the frontal plane. This is done so that the section or elevation will show the true diameter of the circle of drilling. The holes show the true distance from the center, regardless of where they would project.

The principle of rotated features has many uses when it is desirable to show true conditions or true distances even though the views do not project. This may be illustrated by the bent lever (Fig. 10-20f), where a part is rotated or stretched out in one of the views. Another form of stretch-out is indicated in Fig. 10-20g, where the true length of the strap-iron holder is shown above the front view.

10·21 Representations of intersections of cylinders and of cylinders and prisms (or pipes and square tubes). Figures 10-21a, 10-21b, and 10-21c show some intersections on sectional views. The line of intersection may be simplified in most cases (Fig. 10-21a). If true projections of intersecting cylinders (or other shapes) are needed, they may be drawn as explained in Chap. 20. Intersections of cylinders often may be approximated by circular arcs (Fig. 10-21b). For two cylinders with equal diameters (Fig. 10-21c at the right-hand side), the intersection is two straight lines. For a square prism having a side equal to the diameter of the cylinder (Fig. 10-21c at the left-hand side), there will be no vertical line of intersection because the surface of the square prism is tangent to the cylinder.

Intersections on exterior views are shown on Figs. 10-21d and 10-21e. For cylinders an approximation is shown at A in Fig. 10-21d and the preferred method at B. Representations for a prism and a cylinder are shown at C and D. For cylinders with little or no difference in diameter (Fig. 10-21e), the intersections may be shown as at A and B. When the joints are filleted, there will be no sharp line of intersection, and the representations may be shown as at C and D.

10·22 Conventional breaks and symbols are representations used in place of true projections to save time and for greater clearness. For showing long, uniformly shaped parts and for "breaking out" parts, the representations of Fig. 10-22a are used. These

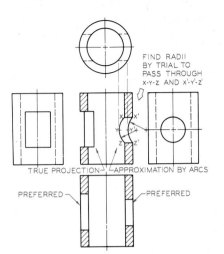

Fig. 10-21b. Approximated and preferred sections.

Fig. 10-21d. Exterior intersections.

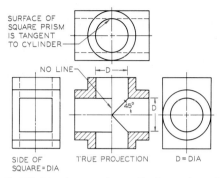

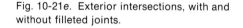

Fig. 10-21c. Intersections of hollow tubes of the same size.

Fig. 10-21e. Exterior intersections, with and without filleted joints.

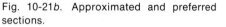

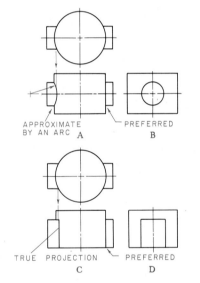

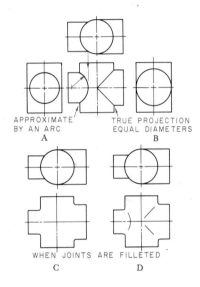

Fig. 10-22a. Conventional breaks and symbols.

Fig. 10-21a. Holes in a sectional view of a cylinder.

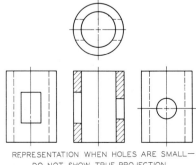

REPRESENTATION WHEN HOLES ARE SMALL— DO NOT SHOW TRUE PROJECTION OF INTERSECTION

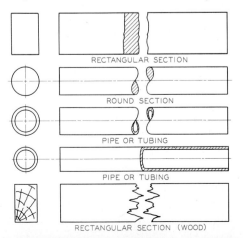

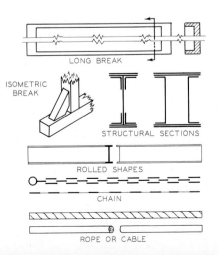

Fig. 10-22b. End breaks for cylinders and pipes.

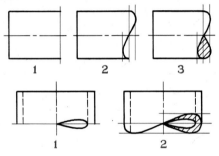

Fig. 10-22c. The phantom, or ditto, line in use.

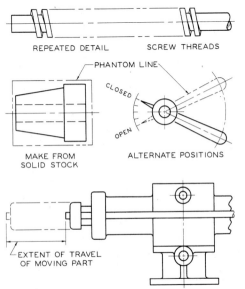

REPEATED DETAIL · SCREW THREADS

PHANTOM LINE · CLOSED · OPEN · ALTERNATE POSITIONS

MAKE FROM SOLID STOCK

EXTENT OF TRAVEL OF MOVING PART

Fig. 10-22d. Some general symbols.

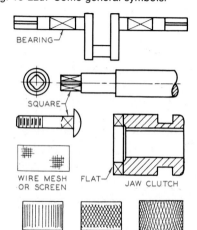

BEARING

SQUARE

WIRE MESH OR SCREEN · FLAT · JAW CLUTCH

STRAIGHT · DIAMOND · KNURLING

permit the use of a larger scale. The length is given by a dimension. The break line for cylinders and pipes is drawn carefully freehand. Note that the curve extends equally on each side of a line at right angles to the center line (Fig. 10-22b).

The phantom or ditto line (Fig. 10-22c) is a useful convention to indicate repeated detail, the rough size of a part (casting, forging, etc.), alternate positions, or the extent of travel of a moving part of a machine to be sure that working space is provided.

Some general symbols commonly used are suggested in Fig. 10-22d. Many standard symbols are used on drawings for architectural, mechanical, electrical, topographic, and other fields of engineering and science. Such symbols are published by the American Standards Association. Templates are available for drawing all standard symbols and save time when symbols must be repeated. Many companies have special symbols for their own machines or products as a part of simplified draft-

ing practice. However, these vary greatly in form and meaning in different industries. They must be understood and used with caution to avoid confusion.

Printed symbols, notes, titles, and other elements which are often repeated on drawings are available in a great variety of forms and sizes. These are ready to apply where needed and save a great amount of time.

10·23 Conventional practice and partial views. Sometimes a half view of a symmetrical part can be used to advantage to draw the views at a desired larger scale in a limited space. The near half (Fig. 10-23a at A) should be drawn with a complete exterior view. The far half (Fig. 10-23a at B and C) should be drawn with a section or a half section. For some purposes on sketches or simplified drawings (Fig. 10-23b), one-half of a section or one-half of an exterior can be used. Notes would be added to indicate diameters and other information.

Fig. 10-23a. How half views are arranged.

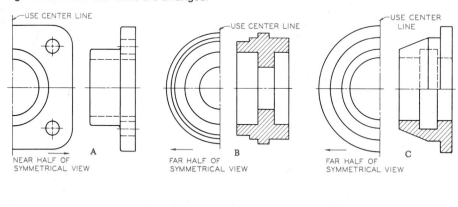

USE CENTER LINE · NEAR HALF OF SYMMETRICAL VIEW · A

USE CENTER LINE · FAR HALF OF SYMMETRICAL VIEW · B

USE CENTER LINE · FAR HALF OF SYMMETRICAL VIEW · C

Fig. 10-23b. These half views describe the shape.

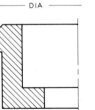 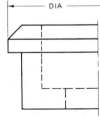

DIA · DIA

When one of the views might be somewhat difficult to read, two incomplete views may be used, as suggested in Fig. 10-23c. The two incomplete end views describe the piece more clearly and are easier to read than one complete end view.

There are conditions where true projection would not show intersections because of fillets and rounds (Fig. 10-23d at A and B). However, conventional lines drawn as if there were no fillets or rounds would present a better description. When to use or not to use conventional lines is determined by the requirement of a clear description. Good judgment is necessary in using conventional representation, and this comes with experience.

10·24 Problem suggestions. Group 10, page 462. Two lists are presented. List 1 includes basic problems and in general more elementary problems than List 2. Selections should be made according to the purpose of the course. List 2 may be used for additional or alternative assignments, or selections may be used in more advanced groups.

List 1: Problems 10·34, 10·35, 10·38, 10·40, 10·42, 10·46, 10·47, 10·49, 10·51.

List 2: Problems 10·36, 10·37, 10·39, 10·41, 10·43, 10·44, 10·45, 10·52, 10·53, 10·54.

Fig. 10-23c. Two incomplete views.

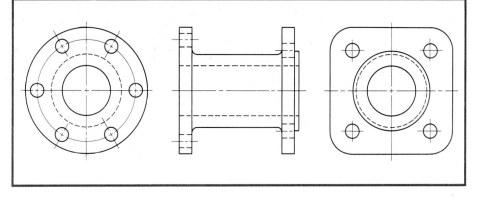

Fig. 10-23d. Conventional intersections.

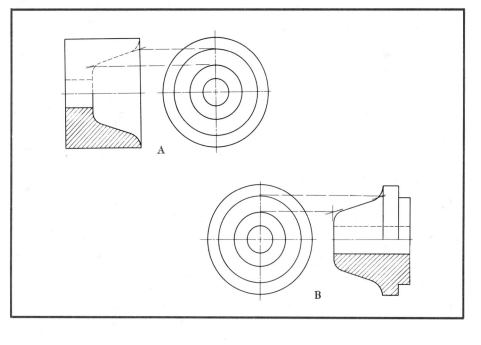

Engineering Registration

All states, and the District of Columbia have laws that require the registration of professional engineers. Engineers are required to obtain a license to practice, as are doctors and lawyers. To obtain such a certificate of registration, it is necessary to present evidence of qualification. The Model law, upon which the laws of most states are based, requires:

1. Graduation from an approved engineering curriculum of four years or more and a record of four years or more of experience of a character satisfactory to the State Registration Board which also shows that the applicant is competent to practice engineering. A written or a written-and-oral examination may also be required. OR **2.** A record of eight or more years of experience in engineering work of a character satisfactory to the Board which shows that the applicant is competent to practice engineering. The applicant must also successfully pass a written or a written-and-oral examination designed to show knowledge and skill approximating that obtained from an approved engineering course.

11
Size description

11·1 Size. We have learned that the two things to be told about an object are its shape and its size. In the previous chapters we studied the methods of showing the shape. Information about the size is called *dimensioning*. It includes numerical values of measurement in inches, or feet and inches, as well as notes and symbols to specify the kind of finish, material, and other information needed to make the particular part. When such information is added to shape description, we have all the elements of a complete *working drawing.*

Size description is an essential part of a working drawing. For some purposes it is enough to specify nominal and ordinary sizes in common fractions of an inch. Sometimes a note is added stating that dimensions are to be plus or minus a specified amount, as $1/64$ in. or $1/32$ in.; for large castings it might be that $1/16$ in. or more would be sufficiently close. Such a note may be placed on the drawing with the views, or it may be placed in the title block, usually in a space provided for this purpose. When accurate dimensions are required, they are given in decimals to hundredths, thousandths, or ten-thousandths of an inch.

Extreme accuracy is necessary in many fields of present-day engineering, especially in aerospace projects. Precision gage blocks (Fig. 11-1) are one device for checking accuracy. Various optical methods are used for checking the measurements of finished parts.

11·2 Dimensioning. The views on drawings describe the shape. Although the views are drawn actual size, or to a proportional scale, it would not be practical to try to obtain the measurements by applying a scale. It would take too much time, and it would not be possible to make measurements of the accuracy necessary for interchangeable manufacture where large numbers of pieces must fit in place with mating parts (parts which fit together) and where there are other requirements.

This size information is provided by adding a system of lines, symbols, and numerical values, called *dimensioning.* To ensure accuracy and efficiency in use, size information is arranged on the drawing in a definite manner.

11·3 Lines and symbols (Fig. 11-3) are used on drawings to show where the dimensions apply. These lines and symbols are recognized by the men who use the drawings. Professional and

Fig. 11-1. Size accuracy. Hoke gage blocks are square. A stack of them pressed together stands solidly on a surface plate. Tie rods placed through the center holes bind the stack rigidly. Here a complicated magnesium casting is being scribed easily and exactly. Precision gage blocks are the basic master standards of measurement which establish the inch as a definite value. Accuracy here is measured in millionths of an inch. The measuring faces of the blocks are guaranteed flat and parallel in all sizes within four millionths of an inch per inch of length. Blocks are used in stacks to make up any desired dimension. *(Pratt & Whitney Company, Penn-Texas Corporation)*

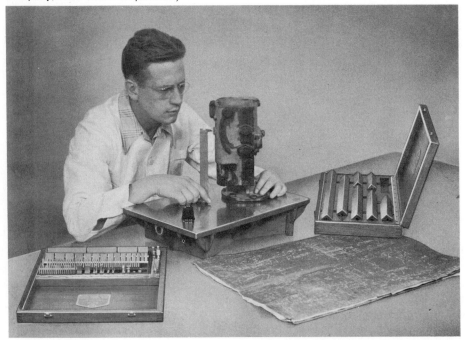

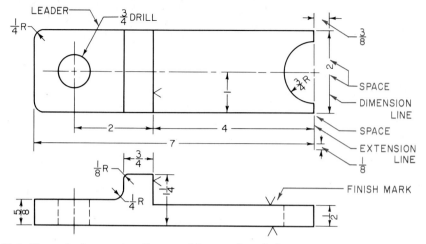

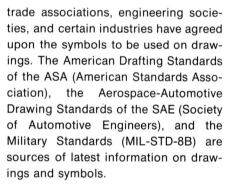

Fig. 11-3. Dimensioning requires the use of lines and symbols.

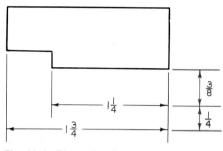

Fig. 11-4. Dimension lines must be spaced to provide clearness.

Fig. 11-5. Arrowheads.

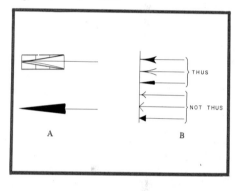

Fig. 11-6. Extension, or witness, lines. A center line may be used as an extension line.

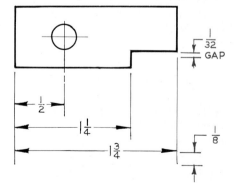

trade associations, engineering societies, and certain industries have agreed upon the symbols to be used on drawings. The American Drafting Standards of the ASA (American Standards Association), the Aerospace-Automotive Drawing Standards of the SAE (Society of Automotive Engineers), and the Military Standards (MIL-STD-8B) are sources of latest information on drawings and symbols.

To make a correct drawing, the draftsman must be familiar with these symbols, and he must know the principles of dimensioning. He must also be acquainted with the shop processes that will be used in building or making the product he is drawing. Symbols are sometimes used to indicate such processes.

11·4 Dimension lines (Fig. 11-4). A dimension line is a thin line used to show the direction of a measurement (where it begins and where it ends) or to show the size of an angle. The dimension line should have a "break" for the dimension numerals. To avoid crowding the numerals, dimension

lines should be ⅜ in. or more from the lines of the drawing and ¼ in. or more from each other.

11·5 Arrowheads (Fig. 11-5) are used at the ends of dimension lines to show where the dimension begins and ends (Fig. 11-4). They are also used at the end of a leader (Fig. 11-9) to show where a note or dimension applies to a drawing. Shapes of arrowheads are shown enlarged at A and reduced to actual size at B. They may be "open" or made solid, as shown. Arrowheads should be carefully drawn and of uniform size on a given drawing; however, a small space may require some variation.

11·6 Extension lines (Fig. 11-6) are thin lines used to extend lines of the views and to indicate points or surfaces for which dimensions are given. Since extension lines are not part of the views, they should not touch the outline. Extension lines start with a visible space, about 1/32 to 1/16 in. gap, and extend about ⅛ in. beyond the last dimension line.

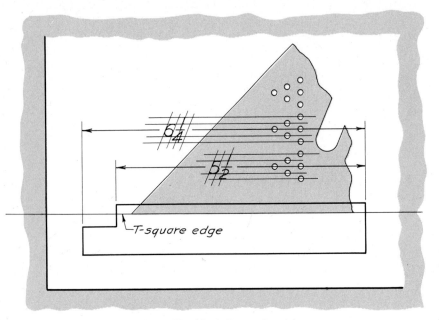

Fig. 11-7. Guidelines for fractions. *(Braddock-Rowe triangle)*

Inside figure: 6/4, 5/2, —T-square edge

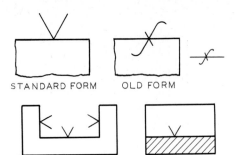

STANDARD FORM   OLD FORM

Fig. 11-8. The finish mark tells which surfaces are to be machined.

11•7 Numerals and notes must be made carefully so that they will be easy to read (Chap. 3). Do not make them so large, however, that they overbalance the drawing. In general, make numerals about 1/8 in. high and fractions about 1/4 in. high, with fraction numerals about 3/32 in. high. Always make the fraction bar (division line) in line with the dimension, never at an angle. Decimals can be about 1/8 in., or .12 in., high.

Light guidelines for figures and fractions may be drawn quickly and easily with the Braddock-Rowe triangle, as illustrated in Fig. 11-7. The group of holes in the left-hand part of the triangle have been spaced for this purpose.

When drawings are made to be reduced photographically for use at a smaller size or when used for microfilming, the numerals must be made larger and with heavier strokes so that they will be clear when reduced. *Capitals,* either *vertical* or *inclined,* are preferred for all lettering on most drawings (Figs. 3-6*j*, 3-11*d*, 3-12*a*, 3-12*b*).

11•8 The finish mark (Fig. 11-8), or surface texture symbol, is used to indicate that a surface is to be machined (finished). The old symbol form, f, is still in use to some extent but is being replaced. The symbol V is now in general use. The point of the V is placed in contact with the edge view of the surface to be finished. Modifications of this symbol are used to provide for an indication that allowance for machining is required, that a certain surface condition is required, and for other conditions described in ASA B46.1, *Surface Texture.*

11•9 Leaders (Fig. 11-9) are thin lines drawn from a note or dimension to the place where it applies. Leaders are drawn at an angle with the horizontal; 60° is preferred, but 45°, 30°, or other angles may be used. A leader starts with a dash, or short horizontal line (about 1/8 in. is preferred but longer if needed), and generally ends with an arrowhead (a dot or other symbol may be used for special identification).

A number of leaders near together are best drawn parallel; a leader to be drawn to a circle or arc should be drawn in a radial direction. Don't cross leaders; don't draw long leaders; don't draw leaders horizontally, vertically, at a small angle, or parallel to dimension, extension, or section lines.

11•10 Scale of a drawing. Scales used in making drawings are described in Arts. 2·23 to 2·27. The scale used should be given in or near the title. If a drawing has views of more than one part and different scales are used, the scale should be given close to the views. Usual scales are:

SCALE: FULL SIZE (or FULL) or 1 = 1
    or 1.00 = 1.00
SCALE: HALF SIZE or 1/2 = 1
    or .50 = 1.00

and so forth, for quarter or eighth size. If enlarged views are used, the scale is shown as:

TWICE SIZE or TWO TIMES FULL
    SIZE or 2 = 1 or 2.00 = 1.00, etc.

11•11 Units and parts of units. Dimensions on drawings are given in units of measurement, such as feet and inches, feet and decimals of a foot, inches and fractions of an inch, inches and decimals of an inch, and (on metric drawings) millimeters (MM).

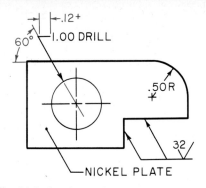

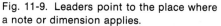

Fig. 11-9. Leaders point to the place where a note or dimension applies.

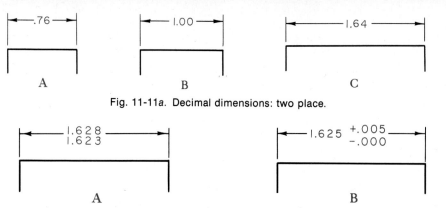

Fig. 11-11a. Decimal dimensions: two place.

Fig. 11-11b. Decimal dimensions: three place.

Common fractions, such as ½, ¼, ⅛, etc., used with whole numbers have been and are used as generally suitable where particular accuracy is not required—say, not closer than ±1/64 in. When all dimensions are in inches, the inch symbol (″) is omitted. Standard practice, when feet and inches are used, is to show the symbol for feet but *not* for inches, as: 7′–5, 7′–0, etc.

Decimals are used where accuracy is required. For parts which must fit accurately, the dimensions are given in decimals, and the workman is required to work within specified limits. Such dimensions are used between finished surfaces, center distances, and places which must be held in a definite relationship to each other. Decimals to two places are used where limits of ±.01 are sufficiently close (Fig. 11-11a at A, B, and C). For two-place decimals fiftieths are preferred, such as .02, .04, .24, etc., rather than .03, .05, etc. Such decimals can be divided by two and result in two-place decimals when used to get the radius from a diameter or for other purposes. The scale of fiftieths (Fig. 2-24b) is used for drawings with decimal dimensioning. The decimal point should be clearly definite, placed on the bottom guideline in a space about the width of a zero. Decimals to three or more places are used where limits of less than ±.01 are required, as in Fig. 11-11b at A and B.

Decimal dimensioning is used in many industries. It is indicated as the preferred method in drafting standards and is coming into general use for all drawings.

Millimeters (MM) are used for giving dimensions on drawings where the metric system of measurements is adopted.

11·12 Placing dimensions for reading. There are two methods in use: the *aligned system* and the *unidirectional system*.

1. The aligned system of dimensioning (Fig. 11-12a) has the dimensions placed in line with the dimension lines. Horizontal dimensions always read from the bottom of the sheet. Vertical dimensions read from the right-hand side of the sheet. Inclined dimensions read in line with the inclined dimension line but should be kept outside the area indicated by the shading in Fig. 11-12b if possible.

2. The unidirectional system of dimensioning (Fig. 11-12c) has all the dimensions placed to read from the bottom of the sheet, no matter where they occur. Automotive and aircraft companies have brought this system into general use. It is accepted practice and is being rapidly adopted by other industries, replacing the old aligned system which was in universal use for many years.

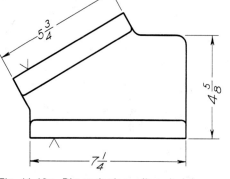

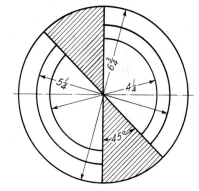

Fig. 11-12a. Dimensioning: aligned system.

Fig. 11-12b. Avoid placing dimensions in the shaded area.

Fig. 11-12c. Dimensioning: unidirectional system.

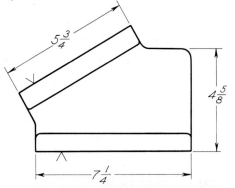

Special typing and dimensioning typewriters (Art. 3·19) for use with drawings make it possible to save a great deal of time by using the unidirectional system. Both systems are in use in industry. Both systems are used in this book, as the student should become familiar with them. The one to use will be determined by company practice. On both systems, notes and dimensions with leaders should read from the bottom of the drawing.

The American Standard, the SAE, the Aerospace Standard, and the Military Standard indicate that the unidirectional system is favored and is coming into general use.

11·13 Theory of dimensioning.
There are two basic kinds of dimensions: (1) *size dimensions* and (2) *location dimensions*. The theory of dimensioning considers any object as made up of a number of geometrical shapes, such as prisms, cylinders, pyramids, cones, and so forth, or parts of such shapes. This is illustrated in Fig. 7-14, where the bearing is separated into simple parts. A hole or hollow part can be considered as having the same outlines as one of these shapes. Such open spaces in an object may be considered

as negative (not solid) shapes. It then becomes a matter of dimensioning a number of simple shapes. When the size of each simple piece is defined and the relative positions are given, the description is complete. Size dimensions are used to define the simple pieces and location dimensions to give relative positions. When a number of pieces are assembled, each piece is first considered separately and then in relation to the other pieces. In this way the size description of a complete machine, a piece of furniture, or a building is simply a matter of following an orderly procedure, as for a single part.

This analysis is applied in the aircraft and some other industries where the weights of parts are calculated by figuring volumes of parts as solid. From these solids the volumes of holes and hollow or open spaces (negative or minus shapes) are subtracted. The result is then multiplied by the weight per cubic inch of the material to obtain the total weight.

11·14 Size dimensions.
The first shape is the prism. For a rectangular prism (Fig. 11-14a), the width *(W)*, the height *(H)*, and the depth *(D)* will be required. Such an elementary shape may appear in a great many ways, a few of which are shown in Figs. 11-14b and 11-14c. Flat pieces of irregular shape

are dimensioned in a similar way (Figs. 11-14d and 11-14e). The rule may be stated thus:

For any flat piece, give the thickness in the edge view and all other dimensions in the outline view.

The outline view is the one which shows the shape of the flat surface or surfaces. The front views in Figs. 11-14d and 11-14e are the outline views.

Fig. 11-14c. The first rule applied.

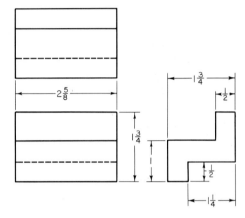

Fig. 11-14d. An irregular flat shape.

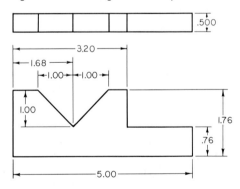

Fig. 11-14e. An irregular flat shape.

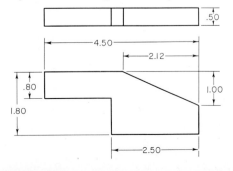

Fig. 11-14a. The first shape.

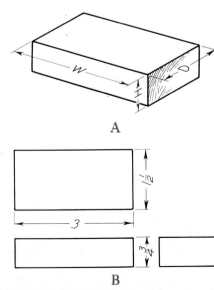

Fig. 11-14b. The first rule applied.

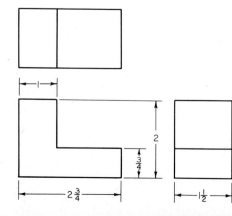

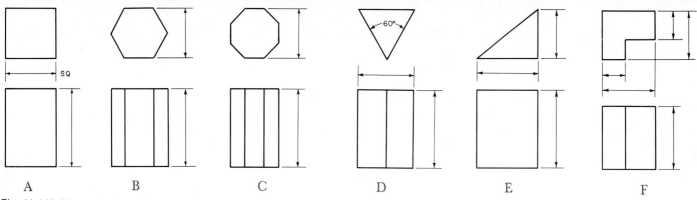

A   B   C   D   E   F

Fig. 11-14f. Dimensioning prisms.

Prisms are illustrated in Fig. 11-14f. A square prism requires two dimensions, a hexagonal or an octagonal prism may use two dimensions, a triangular prism may use three dimensions, and so on for other regular or irregular prisms.

The second shape is the cylinder, which requires two dimensions: the diameter and the length (Fig. 11-14g). Three cylinders are dimensioned in Fig. 11-14h, one of which is the hole. A washer or other hollow cylinder may be thought of as two cylinders of the same length (Fig. 11-14i). The rule is as follows:

For cylindrical pieces, give the diameter and length on the same view.

Fig. 11-14h. The second rule applied.

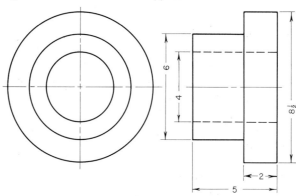

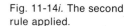
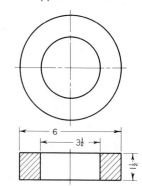

Fig. 11-14i. The second rule applied.

When the circular view of a cylinder is not shown, the abbreviation DIA is placed with the diameter dimension (Fig. 11-14j). When parts of cylinders occur (Fig. 11-14k at A, B, and C), they are dimensioned in the view where the curves show by giving the radius dimension followed by the abbreviation R.

Notes are generally used to specify the sizes of holes. Such a note is usually placed on the outline view, especially when the method of forming the hole is specified (Fig. 11-14k at A).

Fig. 11-14j. Use of DIA on a single view.

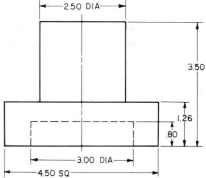

Fig. 11-14g. Dimensioning a cylinder: the second shape.

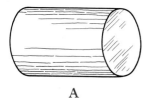

A

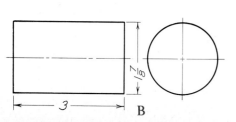

B

Fig. 11-14k. Fillets, rounds, and radii.

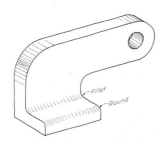

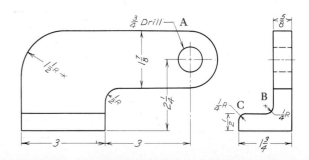

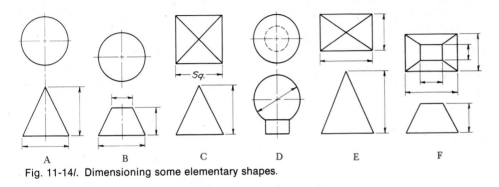

Fig. 11-14*l*. Dimensioning some elementary shapes.

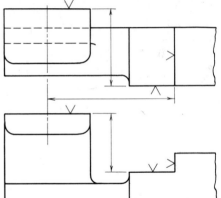

Fig. 11-15*a*. Locating dimensions for prisms.

Fig. 11-15*b*. Locating dimensions for prisms and cylinders.

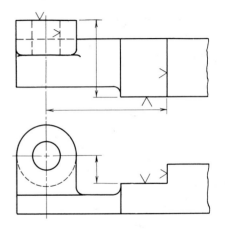

These notes show the operations necessary to form or complete the hole, such as drilling, punching, reaming, lapping, tapping, countersinking, spot facing, and so forth (Fig. 11-24*d*). Either a dimension or a note may be used when a hole is to be formed by boring. When a hole in a casting is to be formed by a core, the word "core" is used in a note or with the dimension.

When parts of cylinders occur, such as fillets (Fig. 11-14*k* at B), rounds (Fig. 11-14*k* at C), and rounded corners, they are dimensioned in the views where the curves show (Fig. 11-14*k*).

Other shapes include the cone, the pyramid, and the sphere. The cone, the frustum, the square pyramid, and the sphere may be dimensioned in one view (Fig. 11-14*l*). To dimension rectangular or other pyramids and parts of pyramids, two views are required.

11·15 Location dimensions are used to specify the relative positions of the elementary shapes. Finished surfaces and center lines, or axes, are important for fixing the positions of parts by location dimensions. In general, location dimensions are necessary in three mutually perpendicular directions (up and down, crossways, and forward and backward).

Prisms are located by surfaces, surfaces and axes, or axes (center lines). Cylinders are located by axes and bases. Three location dimensions are required. Location dimensions also lo-

cate holes, surfaces, and other features. The relative importance of the various surfaces and axes must be studied together so that the parts will go together as accurately as necessary. A knowledge of engineering practice in manufacture, assembly, and use is necessary if the draftsman is to do a good job of including the correct dimensions and notes on his drawing. Finished surfaces and center lines, or axes, are used to define positions with location dimensions. Two general rules will serve as a basis for showing location dimensions:

Prism forms are located by the axes and the surfaces (Fig. 11-15*a*). Three dimensions are required.

Cylinder forms are located by the axis and the base (Fig. 11-15*b*). Three dimensions are required.

Combinations of prisms and cylinders are shown in Figs. 11-15*c* and 11-15*d*. The dimensions at *L* (Fig. 11-15*d*) are location dimensions.

11·16 Datum dimension. Datums are points, lines, and surfaces which are assumed to be exact. Such datums are used for purposes of computation or reference, and location dimensions are given from them. When positions are located from datums, the different features of a part are all located from the datum.

Fig. 11-15*c*. First and second shapes.

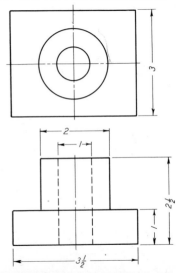

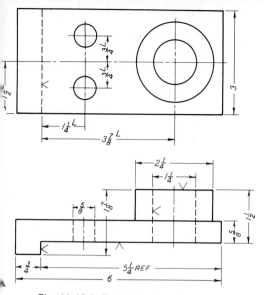

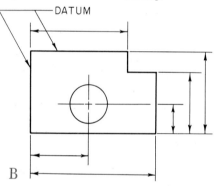

Fig. 11-15d. First and second shapes.

Fig. 11-16. Datum dimensioning.

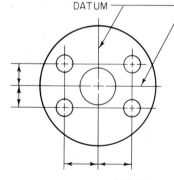

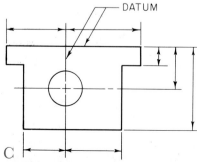

Two surfaces, two center lines, or a surface and a center line are typical datums. In Fig. 11-16 at A, two surface datums are used; at B, two center lines; and at C, a surface and a center line. A datum must be evident and accessible while the part is being made. Mating parts are parts which have contact and which must fit together; therefore, they should have the same datums.

11·17 General rules. When adding dimensions to drawings, draftsmen follow certain practices which represent good form to the extent that they have the force of rules.

1. Dimension lines should be spaced about ¼ in. apart and about ⅜ in. from the view outline (Fig. 11-4).

2. If the aligned system is used, dimensions must read in line with the dimension line and from the lower or right-hand side of the sheet (Fig. 11-12a).

3. If the unidirectional system is used, all dimensions must read from the bottom of the sheet (Fig. 11-12c).

4. On machine drawings, detail dimensions up to 72 in. should be given in inches. Above this, feet and inches

are generally used except for gear drawings, bore of cylinders, length of wheel bases, and so forth. Aircraft and automotive drawings use inches.

5. When all the dimensions are in inches, the symbol is generally omitted.

6. On architectural and structural drawings, dimensions of 12 in. and over are given in feet and inches.

7. Sheet-metal drawings are usually dimensioned in inches.

8. Furniture and cabinet drawings are usually dimensioned in inches.

9. Feet and inches are designated thus: 7′–3 or 7 ft 3 in. Where the dimension is in even feet, it is indicated thus: 7′–0.

10. The same dimension is not repeated on different views.

11. Dimensions not required for making a piece should not be given. This is especially important for interchangeable manufacture where limits are used (see Art. 11·31). Figure 11-17a at A has "not required" dimensions. These have been omitted in Fig. 11-17a at B.

12. Overall dimensions should be placed outside the smaller dimensions (Figs. 11-17a and 11-17b). With the overall dimension given, one of the

Fig. 11-17a. Omit unnecessary dimensions.

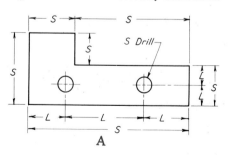

A

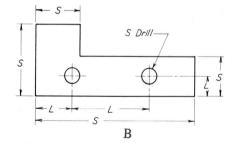

B

Fig. 11-17b. A dimension for reference should be indicated by REF.

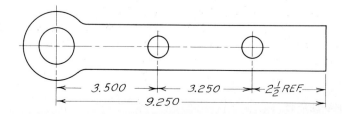

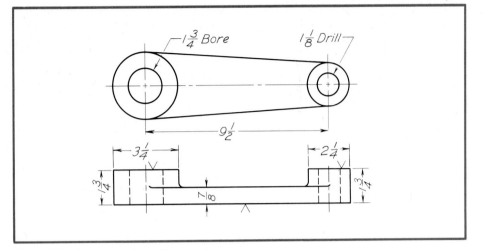

Fig. 11-17c. Center-to-center dimensions.

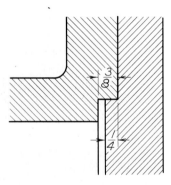

Fig. 11-17d. Dimensions within a sectioned area.

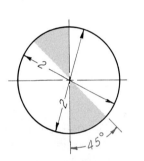

Fig. 11-17e. Avoid shaded area with aligned dimensions.

smaller distances should not be dimensioned (Fig. 11-17a at B) unless it is needed for reference, and then it should be indicated by adding REF, as in Fig. 11-17b.

13. On circular end parts the center-to-center dimension is given instead of an overall dimension (Fig. 11-17c).

14. When it is necessary to place a dimension within a sectioned area, leave a clear space for the number (Fig. 11-17d).

15. American Standard practice is to avoid placing dimensions in the area indicated by shading in Fig. 11-17e when the aligned system is used.

16. Dimensions should be given from center lines, finished surfaces, or datums where necessary.

17. Never use a center line or a line of the drawing as a dimension line.

18. Never have a dimension line as a continuation of a line of a view.

19. Never place a dimension where it is crossed by a line.

20. Always give the diameter of a circle, not the radius. The abbreviation DIA is used after the dimension except when it is obviously a diameter (D is sometimes used but is not American Standard).

21. The radius of an arc should always be given with the abbreviation R placed after the dimension.

22. In general, dimensions should not be placed inside the view outlines.

23. Extension lines should be drawn so that they do not cross each other, or dimension lines, if it can be avoided without making the drawing more complicated.

24. Do not dimension to hidden lines if it can be avoided.

25. It must be remembered that there are no absolutely hard-and-fast rules, nor any practice, not subject to possible change or modification under special conditions or requirements of a particular industry. When there is a variation of any rule, there must always be a reason which can be completely justified.

11·18 Standard details. The shape of a part, the methods of manufacture, and the purpose for which the part is to be used generally indicate the kind and accuracy of the dimensions that must be given. A knowledge of manufacturing methods, patternmaking, foundry, machine-shop procedures, forging, welding, and so forth, is very useful when you are selecting and placing dimensions. In most cases such knowledge is essential. It is also important to consider whether only one part is to be made or whether quantity-production methods are to be used. In addition, there are purchased parts, identified by name or brand, that require few, if any, dimensions. Some companies have their own standard parts for use in different machines or constructions, and these are dimensioned according to use and production methods.

There are, however, certain more or less standard details or conditions for which methods of dimensioning may be suggested.

11·19 Angles and chamfers. Angles are usually dimensioned in degrees (°), minutes (′), and seconds (″) (Fig. 11-19a at A). The abbreviation DEG may be used instead of the symbol ° when degrees only are indicated. Angular tolerance is generally bilateral (plus or

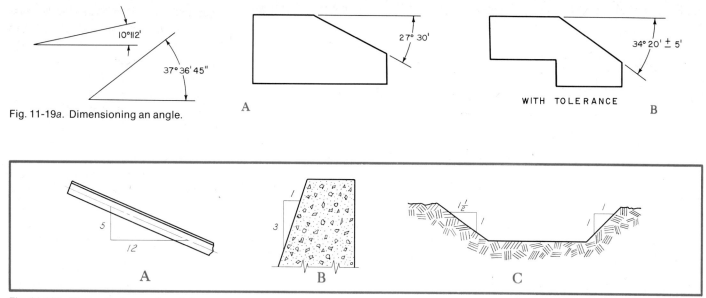

Fig. 11-19a. Dimensioning an angle.

A

B

WITH TOLERANCE

Fig. 11-19b. Dimensioning angles of slopes.

A   B   C

minus), as $\pm\frac{1}{2}°$ for degrees and $\pm5'$ for minutes (Fig. 11-19a at B). Angular tolerance is stated either on the drawing or in a space provided in the title block. Angular measurements on structural drawings are given by run and rise, using 12″ for the horizontal side of the triangle (Fig. 11-19b at A). A similar method is used for slopes, as at B and C, where one side of the triangle is made equal to 1.

Methods of dimensioning chamfers are shown in Fig. 11-19c at A and B.

11·20 Tapers may be specified by giving one diameter or width, the length, and the American Standard taper number, as in Fig. 11-20 at A. Another method is shown at B, where the length, one diameter, and the taper are given. For a close fit the taper is dimensioned as at C, where the diameter is given at a located gage line. At D one diameter and the angle are given.

11·21 Dimensioning curves. A curve composed of arcs of circles is dimensioned by the radii with centers

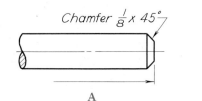

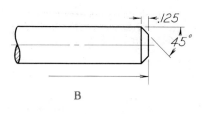

Fig. 11-19c. Dimensioning chamfers.

Fig. 11-20. Dimensioning tapers.

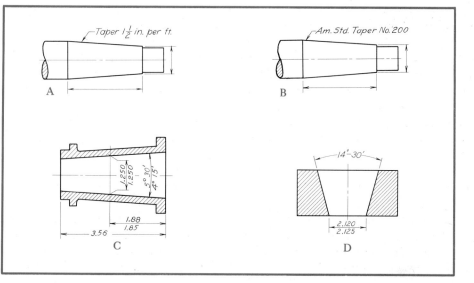

A   B

C   D

located by points of tangency (Fig. 11-21a at A and B). Noncircular or irregular curves (Fig. 11-21b) may be dimensioned as at A or from datum lines, as at B. A regular curve may be described and dimensioned by showing the construction or naming the curve, as at C, giving the basic dimensions.

11·22 Dimensioning a detail drawing. The drawing of a separate part with the dimensions, notes, and information for making the part is called a *detail drawing.* The order of dimensioning is as follows: The views of a drawing should be completed before starting to add any of the dimensions or notes. Then consider the actual shape of the part and the characteristic views. Now draw the extension lines, all of them including the lengthening of any center lines, if needed. Consider the size dimensions and the related location dimensions. Put on the dimension lines, leaders, and arrowheads. After considering any changes, put in the dimensions and add any required notes.

11·23 Dimensioning an assembly drawing. When the parts of a machine are shown together in their relative positions, the drawing is called an *assembly drawing.* The rules and methods of dimensioning apply where a complete description of size is required.

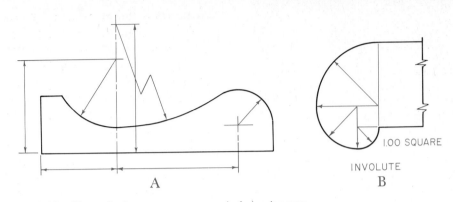

Fig. 11-21a. Dimensioning curves composed of circular arcs.

Drawings of complete machines, constructions, and so forth, are made for different uses and have to be dimensioned to serve the purpose for which they were designed.

1. If the drawing is merely to show the appearance or arrangement of parts, the dimensions may be left off.

2. When it is desired to tell the space required, give overall dimensions.

3. Where it is necessary to locate parts in relation to each other without giving all the detail dimensions, it is usual to give center-to-center distances and the dimensions needed for putting the machine or construction together or erecting it in position. For purposes indicated at 1, 2, and 3, photodrawings

may be made of the completed machine with necessary information added as in Art. 8·16.

4. In some industries assembly drawings may be completely dimensioned either with or without extra part views (Chap. 13). Such drawings serve the purpose of both detail and assembly drawings. These are often referred to as *composite drawings.*

For furniture and cabinetwork sometimes only the major dimensions are given, such as length, height, and sizes of stock. The details of joints are left to the cabinetmaker or the standard practice of the company, especially where machinery is used and construction details are standardized.

Fig. 11-21b. Dimensioning noncircular curves.

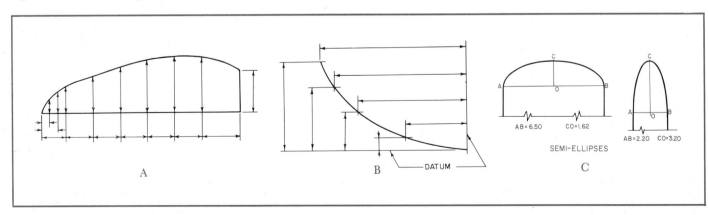

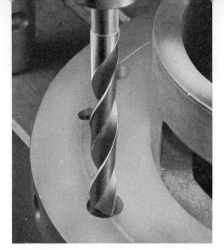

Fig. 11-24a. Drilling a hole.

Fig. 11-24b. Reaming a hole.

Fig. 11-24c. Counterboring to a specified depth. Spot facing is generally used to provide smooth spots.

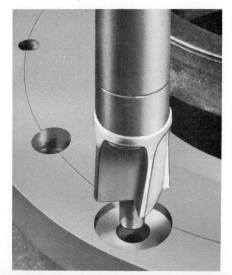

11·24 Notes for dimensions. Some of the operations for which information is given by notes are drilled holes (Fig. 11-24a), reamed holes (Fig. 11-24b), and counterboring or spot facing (Fig. 11-24c). The use of notes for specifying these and other dimensions and operations is indicated in Fig. 11-24d. In this figure, A is for a drilled hole, B is for a hole to be drilled and reamed, C and D specify counterbore, E specifies countersink for a No. 24 flat-head screw, F, G, and H are for countersunk and counterdrilled holes, I specifies a spot face to provide for a nut, and J specifies a smooth-surface spot face.

When a hole is to be made in a piece after assembly with its mating piece, the note should read as previously stated but with the addition of the words "at assembly." Because such a hole is located when it is made during assembly with its mating part, no dimensions are required for its location. Other dimensions with machining operations are suggested in Fig. 11-24e.

Fig. 11-24d. Dimensions for holes.

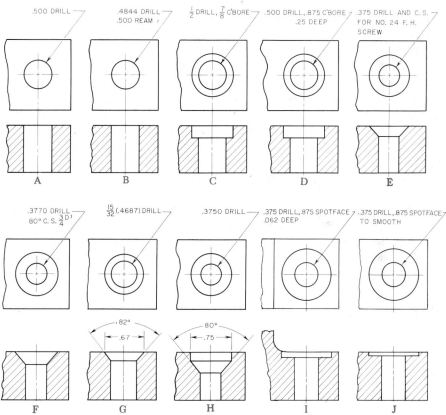

Fig. 11-24e. Operations with limits specified.

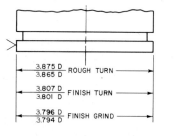

A

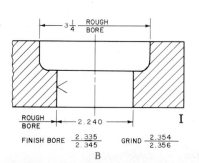

B

11·25 Abbreviations.

Many of the abbreviations used as a part of dimensioning are familiar, such as the few examples from American Standards which follow:

Allowance	ALLOW
Alloy	ALY
Aluminum	AL
Babbitt	BAB
Bevel	BEV
Cast iron	CI
Center line	CL or ℄
Chamfer	CHAM
Cold-rolled steel	CRS
Countersink	CSK
Degree	(°) DEG
Diameter	DIA
Dimension	DIM.
Key	K
Keyseat	KST
Keyway	KWY
Left	L
Left hand	LH
Limit	LIM
Material	MATL
Maximum	MAX
National	NATL
Not to scale	NTS
Outside diameter	OD
Pattern	PATT
Radial	RAD
Radius	R
Require	REQ
Revise	REV
Right hand	RH
Screw	SCR
Spherical	SPHER
Spot faced	SF
Square	SQ
Stock	STK
Surface	SUR
Tabulate	TAB
Thread	THD
Tolerance	TOL
United States Gage	USG
United States Standard	USS
Wrought Iron	WI

For a complete list refer to the last *American Standard Abbreviations for Use on Drawings,* ASA Z32.13-1950, or a later revision.

11·26 Sketching and measuring.

Sketching as a means of shape description and study was considered in Chap. 6. When sketches that are to be used in making drawings are made from machine or furniture parts, it is necessary to define the size, the material, the kinds of surfaces (either finished or rough), the limits of accuracy, and all other information that might have any future value.

11·27 After sketching the views

of an object or part of an object, add all necessary dimension lines in exactly the same way as for views made with instruments. The piece should now be examined and the kind of material noted, together with the kinds of finish and location of all finished surfaces. When everything else is done, it is time to measure the piece and fill in the figures to tell the size. For this purpose various measuring tools will be needed. A 2-ft rule, a steel scale, and a pair of calipers will be sufficient for most purposes.

11·28 Other machinists' tools

are often necessary or convenient for checking measurements on a workpiece with dimensions on a drawing. The student should know something about the tools that are available and how to use them.

The flat scale or the steel scale and straightedge can be used in many ways, as suggested in Fig. 11-28a. The distances can be read directly.

Whenever possible, take measurements from finished surfaces. Outside and inside calipers, with their use illustrated, are shown in Fig. 11-28b. The distance between the points is read by applying the calipers to a scale.

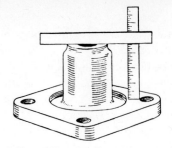

Fig. 11-28a. Using the flat scale to make a measurement.

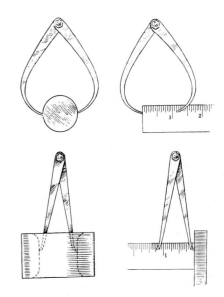

Fig. 11-28b. Using the outside and inside calipers.

Fig. 11-28c. Using a filler at A and a transfer caliper at B.

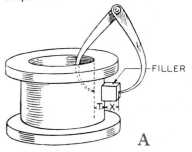

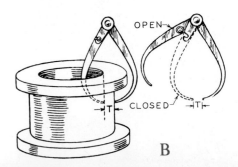

When the calipers cannot be removed from a thickness, the plain calipers may be used by inserting an extra piece or filler (Fig. 11-28c at A); the transfer calipers at B may also be used. The distance *X* must be subtracted from the total distance to obtain the desired thickness *T* when a filler is used. The transfer calipers are provided with a false leg, set so that the calipers may be opened and then brought back to the same position after being removed from the casting.

All measurements of wood construction can generally be obtained with sufficient accuracy by using the 2-ft or the 6-ft rule. Other tools that are useful, if at hand, include the steel square, try square, combination square, surface gage, depth gage, radius and screw-thread gages, and protractor.

When a pictorial sketch is dimensioned, the only additional consideration is to use care to see that all extension lines are either in or perpendicular to the particular plane on which the dimension is being given. (Refer to Art. 6·14.)

11·29 For accurate measurements vernier calipers (Fig. 11-29a) and micrometer calipers (Fig. 11-29b) are used. Photographic and electrical methods have been developed to make extremely accurate measurements where necessary in connection with certain kinds of operations and parts of equipment or machines.

11·30 Interchangeable manufacture. When large quantities of parts are made to be assembled with other parts, as on an assembly line, it is necessary to make the parts so that any part will fit into place without further machine or hand work. This requires specified allowances for size so that mating parts will fit together. Mating parts are parts which have contact and which must fit together to meet the re-

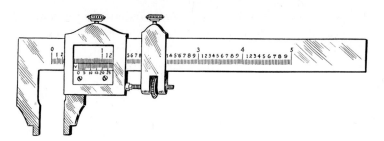

Fig. 11-29a. The vernier caliper.

quirements for which they are to be used. A rod or shaft and the hole in which it turns are mating parts. The diameter of the rod would be limited, and so would the diameter of the hole.

11·31 Limit dimensioning. When parts must have accurate measurements, the dimensions are given in decimals rather than fractions. Micrometers (Fig. 11-29b) and various kinds of gages and measuring devices, such as the gage blocks illustrated in Fig. 11-1, are used to check accuracy.

Since absolute accuracy cannot be expected, a workman is required to keep within a fixed limit of accuracy. The number of hundredths, thousandths, or ten-thousandths of an inch that are allowed as a variation from absolute measurements is called the *tolerance.* The tolerance may be specified by a note on the drawing or in a space provided in the title block, as: "Dimension Tolerance 0.01 Unless Otherwise Specified." Limiting dimensions, or limits to specify the maximum and minimum dimensions permitted, are used to show the necessary degree of accuracy. This is illustrated at A in Fig. 11-31a. Note that the maximum limiting dimension is placed above the dimension line for the shaft (external dimension) and that the minimum limiting dimension for the hole in the ring is placed above the dimension line.

At B and C in Fig. 11-31a the basic sizes are given, and the tolerance specified, plus or minus, is shown. Consec-

Fig. 11-29b. The micrometer caliper.

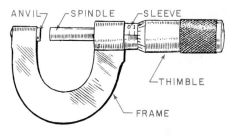

Fig. 11-31a. Limit dimensions.

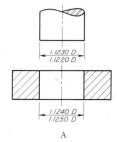

A

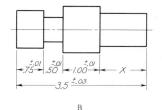

B

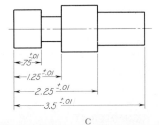

C

utive dimensions are shown at B, where the dimension designated by *X* could have some variation. This dimension would not be given unless required for reference, in which case it would be followed by the abbreviation REF. Progressive dimensions are shown at C, where they are all given from a single surface (sometimes called *base-line dimensioning*).

Accurate or limiting dimensions should not be called for unless necessary, for they greatly increase the cost. The detail drawing in Fig. 11-31*b* has limits for only two dimensions; all others are nominal dimensions, with variations permissible according to the purpose for which the part is to be used.

11·32 Precision, or exactness. For precise information on dimensioning for accuracy of measurements and positions, the latest edition of ASA Y14.5 should be studied and used as a reference. Articles 11·33 to 11·38 are extracted from the American Standard Drafting Manual *Dimensioning and Notes* (ASA Y14.5-1957) with the permission of the publisher, The American Society of Mechanical Engineers, 345 East 47th St., New York, N.Y., 10017.

Fig. 11-31*b*. A detail drawing with limits.

11·33 Expressing size and position.

Definitions relating to size. The following five terms have been defined to provide a common interpretation in respect to their use in this standard.

Size. Size is a designation of magnitude. When a value is assigned to a dimension it is referred to hereinafter as the size of that dimension. *Note: It is recognized that the words "dimension" and "size" are both used to convey the meaning of magnitude.*

Nominal size. The nominal size is the designation which is used for the purpose of general identification. Example: ½ in. pipe.

Basic size. The basic size is that size from which the limits of size are derived by the application of allowances and tolerances.

Design size. The design size is that size from which the limits of size are derived by the application of tolerances. When there is no allowance the design size is the same as the basic size.

Actual size. An actual size is a measured size.

Limits of size. The limits of size (commonly referred to simply as "Limits") are the applicable maximum and minimum sizes.

Position. Dimensions that establish position generally require more analysis than dimensions that only state sizes. Either linear or angular expressions may locate features with respect to one another (point-to-point), or from a datum. Point-to-point distances may be adequate for describing simple parts. Dimensions from a datum may be necessary if a part with more than one critical dimension must mate with another part.

Locating round holes. Figs. ... [11-33*a* through 11-33*f*] illustrate the positioning of round holes by giving distances, or distances and directions, to the hole centers. These methods can also be used to locate round pins and other features of symmetrical contour. Allowable variations for any of the positioning dimensions illustrated may be specified by giving a tolerance with each distance or angle, by stating limits of dimensions or angles, or by ... true position expressions. ...

11·34 Tolerance. A tolerance represents the total amount by which a given dimension may vary. A tolerance should be expressed in the same form as its dimension; the tolerance of a decimal dimension should be expressed by a decimal to the same number of places, and the tolerance of a dimension written as a common fraction should be expressed as a common fraction. An exception to this is a close tolerance on an angle which may be expressed by a decimal representing a linear distance. ...

In a "chain" of dimensions with tolerances, overall variations in position that may occur are equal to the sums of the tolerances on the intermediate distances. The datum dimensioning method ... [of Fig. 11-33*f*] avoids overall accumulations, but the tolerance on the distance between two features equals the sum of the tolerances on two dimensions from the datum. Where

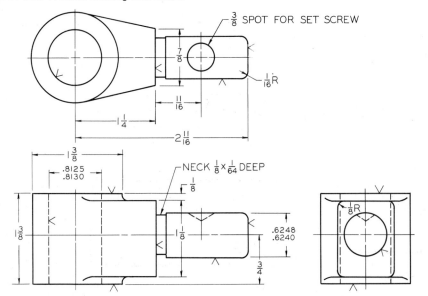

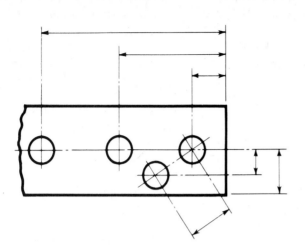

Fig. 11-33a. Locating by linear distances. (ASA)

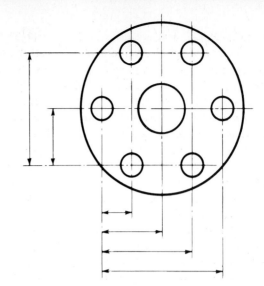

Fig. 11-33b. Locating holes by rectangular coordinates. (ASA)

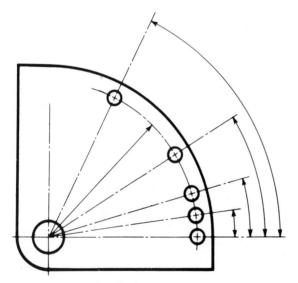

Fig. 11-33c. Locating holes on a circle by polar coordinates. (ASA)

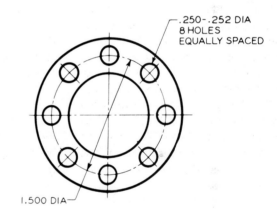

.250-.252 DIA
8 HOLES
EQUALLY SPACED

1.500 DIA

Fig. 11-33d. Locating holes on a circle by radius or diameter and "equally spaced." (ASA)

Fig. 11-33e. "Equally spaced" holes in a line. (ASA)

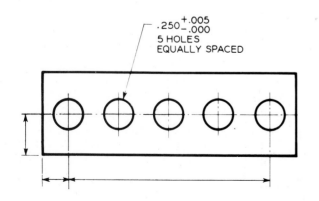

.250 $^{+.005}_{-.000}$
5 HOLES
EQUALLY SPACED

Fig. 11-33f. Dimensions for datum lines. (ASA)

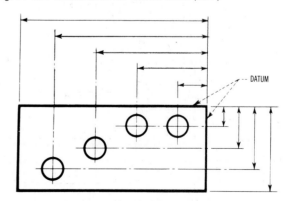

DATUM

the distance between two points must be controlled closely, the distance between the two points should be dimensioned directly, with a tolerance. ... [Fig. 11-34a] illustrates a series of "chain" dimensions where tolerances accumulate between points X and Y; datum dimensions in ... [Fig. 11-34b] show the same accumulation with larger tolerances; ... [Fig. 11-34c] shows how to avoid accumulation without the use of extremely small tolerances.

Unilateral tolerance system. A unilateral system of tolerances allows variations in only one direction from a design size. This way of stating a tolerance is often helpful where a critical size is approached as material is removed during manufacture. See Fig. ... [11-34d]. For example, close-fitting holes and shafts are often given unilateral tolerances.

Bilateral tolerance system. A bilateral system of tolerances allows variations in both directions from a design size. Bilateral variations are generally given with locating dimensions, or with any dimension that can be allowed to vary in either direction. See Fig. ... [11-34d].

11·35 Limit system. A limit system indicates only the largest and smallest permissible dimensions. See Figs. ... [11-35a] and ... [11-35b]. The tolerance is the difference between the limits.

Expressing allowable variations. Various expressions are used to state the amounts of variation permitted for the dimensions indicated on drawings.

The expressions recommended in this Standard are listed and described as follows:

(a) Two tolerance numerals are specified, one plus and one minus. This form of expression is necessary if the plus variation differs from the minus variation. It may be used in preference to (b) where the plus and minus variations are equal. See Fig. ... [11-34d]. Note: Two variations in the same direction should never be specified.

(b) A combined plus and minus sign is followed by a single tolerance numeral. This method is very generally followed if the plus variation is equal to the minus variation. See Fig. ... [11-35c].

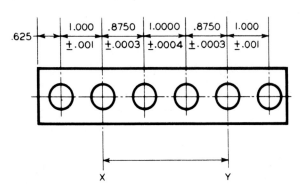

Fig. 11-34a. Point-to-point, or chain, dimensioning. *(ASA)*

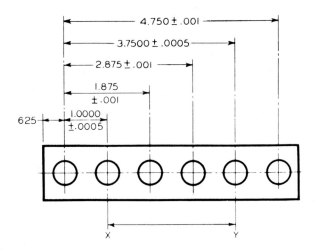

Fig. 11-34b. Datum dimensioning. *(ASA)*

Fig. 11-34c. Dimensioning to prevent tolerance accumulation between X and Y. *(ASA)*

Fig. 11-34d. Giving a tolerance by a plus figure and a minus figure. *(ASA)*

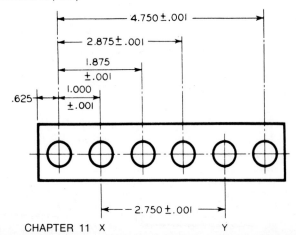

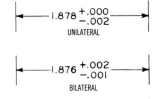

(c) The maximum and minimum limits of size are specified. The numerals should be arranged in one of two ways, but not both on the same drawing.

(1) The high limit is always placed above the low limit where dimensions are given directly, and the low limit always precedes the high limit where dimensions are given in note form. See Fig. ... [11-35a].

(2) For location dimensions given directly (not by note), the high limit numeral (maximum dimension) is placed above and the low limit numeral (minimum dimension) is placed below. For size dimensions given directly, the numeral representing the maximum material condition is placed above and the numeral representing the minimum material condition is placed below. Where the limits are given in note form, the numeral that otherwise would be above shall precede the other. See Fig. ... [11-35b].

(d) It is not always necessary to state both limits.

(1) A unilateral variation is sometimes expressed without stating that the variation in the other direction is zero. See Fig. ... [11-35d at A].

(2) MIN or MAX is often placed after a numeral where the other limit is not important. Depths of holes, lengths of threads, chamfers, etc., are often limited in this way. See Fig. ... [11-35d at B].

(e) Other expressions allowing variations are described under Positional Tolerances, ... [Art. 11·38]; Positional

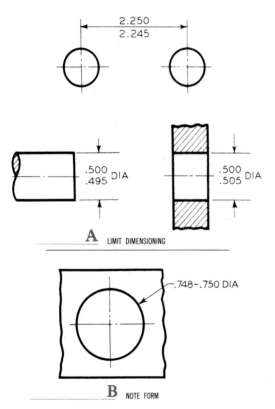

Fig. 11-35a. Specifying limits: first method. (ASA)

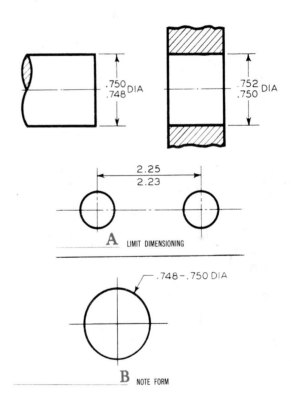

Fig. 11-35b. Specifying limits: second method. (ASA)

Fig. 11-35c. Using a combined plus and minus sign. (ASA)

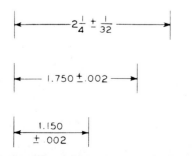

Fig. 11-35d. Expressing a single tolerance or limit. (ASA)

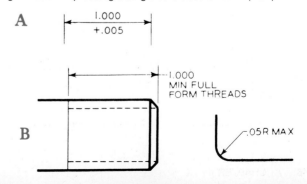

Tolerances at Maximum Material Condition, . . . [Art. 11·37].

(f) The above recommendations refer to linear tolerances, but the forms of expression are also used for angular tolerances. Angular tolerances may be in degrees, minutes and seconds, or in decimals.

11·36 Placing tolerance and limit numerals. A numeral indicating a tolerance should be placed to the right of the dimension numeral, and in line with it. An accepted alternative method places the tolerance numeral below the dimension numeral, with the dimension line between. Fig. . . . [11-36] shows both arrangements.

11·37 Dimensioning for fits. For interchangeable manufacture, the tolerances on dimensions must be such that an acceptable fit will result from assembly of parts having any combination of actual sizes that are within the tolerances. See Fig. . . . [11-37a].

Fig. . . . [11-37b] shows a method of dimensioning mating parts that must fit one another, when they do not need to be interchangeable. The size of one

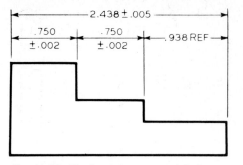

Fig. 11-36. Placing tolerance and limit numerals. Note the reference dimensions. *(ASA)*

part need not be held to a close tolerance, because it is to be modified at assembly to the size that is necessary for the desired fit.

"Hole basis" and "shaft basis." To specify the dimensions and tolerances of an internal and an external cylindrical surface so that they will fit together as desired, it is necessary to begin calculations by assuming either the minimum hole size or the maximum shaft size.

A basic hole system is a system of fits in which the design size of the hole is the basic size and the allowance is applied to the shaft.

A basic shaft system is a system of fits in which the design size of the shaft is the basic size and the allowance is applied to the hole.

NOTE: For further information on limits and fits, see ASA B4.1-1955 or subsequent revision thereof.

"Basic hole" system. Limits for a fit in the basic hole system are determined by (1) specifying the minimum hole size, (2) determining the maximum shaft size by subtracting the desired allowance (minimum clearance) from the minimum hole size for a clearance fit, or adding the desired allowance (maximum interference) for an interference fit, and (3) adjusting the hole and shaft tolerances to obtain the desired maximum clearance or minimum interference. See Fig. . . . [11-37c]. Tooling economies can often be realized by calculating from the basic hole size, providing the size selected can be produced by a standard tool (reamer, broach, etc.) or gaged with a standard plug gage.

"Basic shaft" system. Limits for a fit in the basic shaft system are determined by (1) specifying the maximum shaft size, (2) determining the mini-

Fig. 11-37a. Indicating dimensions of surfaces that are to fit closely. *(ASA)*

Fig. 11-37b. Dimensioning noninterchangeable parts that are to fit closely. *(ASA)*

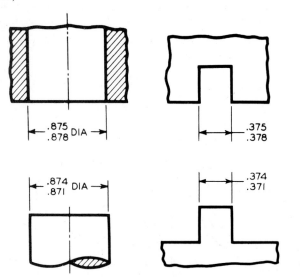

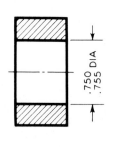

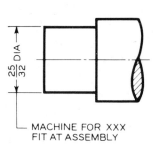

— MACHINE FOR XXX
FIT AT ASSEMBLY

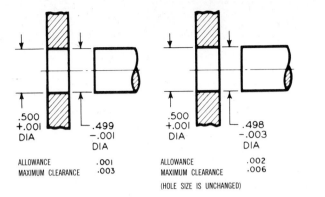

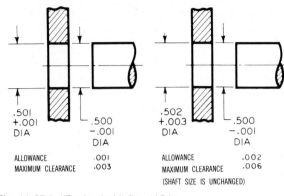

.500
+.001
DIA

.499
−.001
DIA

.500
+.001
DIA

.498
−.003
DIA

ALLOWANCE   .001
MAXIMUM CLEARANCE .003

ALLOWANCE   .002
MAXIMUM CLEARANCE .006
(HOLE SIZE IS UNCHANGED)

Fig. 11-37c. "Basic hole" fits. (ASA)

.501
+.001
DIA

.500
−.001
DIA

.502
+.003
DIA

.500
−.001
DIA

ALLOWANCE   .001
MAXIMUM CLEARANCE .003

ALLOWANCE   .002
MAXIMUM CLEARANCE .006
(SHAFT SIZE IS UNCHANGED)

Fig. 11-37d. "Basic shaft" fits. (ASA)

mum hole size by adding the desired allowance (minimum clearance) to the maximum shaft size for a clearance fit, or subtracting for an interference fit, and (3) adjusting hole and shaft tolerances to obtain the desired maximum clearance or minimum interference. See Fig. ... [11-37d]. The "basic shaft" method is recommended only if there is a particular reason for it, for example, where a standard size of shafting can be used.

11·38 Positional tolerances. Figs. ... [11-33a] through ... [11-33f] illustrate the locating of holes or other features by means of rectangular or polar coordinates. In the past, these coordinates have been shown with individual tolerances predominantly. The engineering intent can often be expressed more precisely if locations are given as True Positions, with tolerances to state how far *actual positions* can be displaced from True Positions. Positional tolerancing may be applied for the location of features by stating in the note the allowable tolerance.

Features such as holes and bosses may be allowed to vary from the specified position in any direction from the true position axis while other features such as slots may be allowed to vary from the specified position on either side of the true position plane. There-

fore, there are two methods for applying positional tolerancing. See Fig. ... [11-38].

The foregoing Arts. 11·33 to 11·38 cover a limited part of the dimensioning standards. Further study may be pursued in the latest revised edition of American Standard ASA Y14.5.

11·39 Precision requirements extend beyond those mentioned in this chapter. Reference to American Standard ASA Y14.5 will present tolerances for contours, straightness, forms, parallelism, squareness, angularity, symmetry, concentricity, roundness, etc.

11·40 Surface texture. In addition to size, it is sometimes necessary to indicate the condition of the surfaces of material. Absolute smoothness is not possible. Surfaces have irregulari-

ties, and standards have been developed for establishing classifications for roughness, waviness, and lay, as well as symbols for indicating such conditions.

The subject is contained in the American Standard ASA B46.1-1962, to which reference is made for study and information. An idea of surface texture is indicated by the paragraphs which follow, extracted from *Surface Texture* (ASA B46.1-1962) with the permission of the publisher, The American Society of Mechanical Engineers, United Engineering Center, 345 East 47th St., New York, N.Y., 10017.

Surfaces, in general, are very complex in character. This standard deals only with the height, width, and direction of surface irregularities, since these are of practical importance in specific applications.

Fig. 11-38. True-position dimensioning. (ASA)

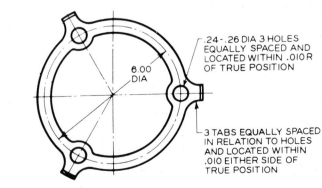

.24 - .26 DIA 3 HOLES EQUALLY SPACED AND LOCATED WITHIN .010 R OF TRUE POSITION

6.00 DIA

3 TABS EQUALLY SPACED IN RELATION TO HOLES AND LOCATED WITHIN .010 EITHER SIDE OF TRUE POSITION

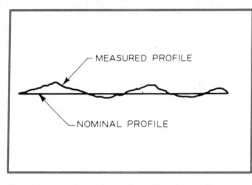

Fig. 11-41a. An enlarged profile shows that a surface is not as it appears. (ASA)

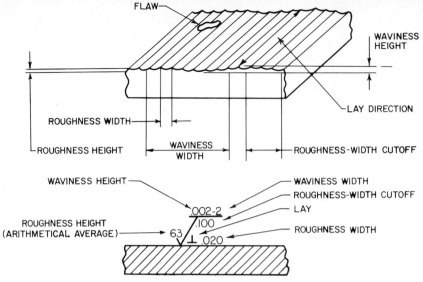

Fig. 11-41b. Relation of symbols to surface characteristics. Refer to Fig. 11-42c. (ASA)

11·41 Classification of terms and ratings related to surfaces. The terms and ratings in this standard relate to surfaces produced by such means as machining, abrading, extruding, casting, molding, forging, rolling, coating, plating, blasting, or burnishing, etc.

Surface texture. Repetitive or random deviations from the nominal surface which form the pattern of the surface. Surface texture includes roughness, waviness, lay and flaws.

Profile. The profile is the contour of a surface in a plane perpendicular to the surface, unless some other angle is specified.

Measured profile. The measured profile is a representation of the profile obtained by instrumental or other means. See Figure ... [11-41a].

Microinch. A microinch is one millionth of an inch (0.000001 inch). For written specifications or reference to surface roughness requirements, microinches may be abbreviated as MU in.

Roughness. Roughness consists of the finer irregularities in the surface texture usually including those irregularities which result from the inherent action of the production process. These are considered to include traverse feed marks and other irregularities within the limits of the roughness-width cutoff. See Figure ... [11-41b].

Roughness height. For the purpose of this standard, roughness height is rated as the arithmetical average deviation expressed in microinches measured normal to the center line. The preferred series of roughness height values is given in Table 1.

Table 1
Preferred Series Roughness Height Values (Microinches)

	5	20	80	320
	6	25	100	400
1	8	32	125	500
2	10	40	160	600
3	13	50	200	800
4	16	63	250	1000

Roughness width. Roughness width is the distance parallel to the nominal surface between successive peaks or ridges which constitute the predominant pattern of the roughness. Roughness width is rated in inches.

Roughness-width cutoff. The greatest spacing of repetitive surface irregularities to be included in the measurement of average roughness height. Roughness-width cutoff is rated in inches. Standard values are given in Table 2. Roughness-width cutoff must always be greater than the roughness width in order to obtain the total roughness height rating.

Table 2
Standard Roughness-Width Cutoff Values (Inches)
When no value is specified, the value 0.030 is assumed.

0.003	0.010	0.030	0.100	0.300	1.000

Waviness. Waviness is the usually widely-spaced component of surface texture and is generally of wider spacing than the roughness-width cutoff. Waviness may result from such factors as machine or work deflections, vibration, chatter, heat treatment or warping strains. Roughness may be considered as superposed on a "wavy" surface.

Waviness height. Waviness height is rated in inches as the peak to valley distance. The preferred series of maximum waviness height is given in Table 3.

Table 3
Preferred Series Waviness Height Values (Inches)

0.00002	0.00008	0.0003	0.001	0.005	0.015
0.00003	0.0001	0.0005	0.002	0.008	0.020
0.00005	0.0002	0.0008	0.003	0.010	0.030

Waviness width. Waviness width is rated in inches as the spacing of successive wave peaks or successive wave valleys. When specified, the values shall be the maximum permissible.

Lay. The direction of the predominant surface pattern, ordinarily determined by the production method used. Lay symbols shall be as specified in ... [Art. 11·42] and shown in Figure ... [11-42*d*].

Flaws. Flaws are irregularities which occur at one place or at relatively infrequent or widely varying intervals in a surface. Flaws include such defects as cracks, blow holes, checks, ridges, scratches, etc. Unless otherwise specified, the effect of flaws shall not be included in the roughness height measurements.

Contact area. Contact area is the area of the surface required to effect contact with its mating surface. Unless otherwise specified, contact area shall be distributed over the surface with approximate uniformity. Contact area shall be specified as shown in Figure ... [11-42*c* at E].

11·42 Designation of surface characteristics. Where no surface control is specified, it is to be assumed that the surface produced by the operation will be satisfactory. If the surface is critical, the quality of surface desired should be indicated.

Surface symbol. The symbol used to designate surface irregularities is the check mark with horizontal extension as shown in Figure ... [11-42*a*]. The point of the symbol shall be on the line indicating the surface, on the extension line or on a leader pointing to the surface. The long leg and extension shall be to the right as the drawing is read. Where roughness height only is indicated, it shall be permissible to omit the horizontal extension. For typical applications of the symbol on a drawing, see Figure ... [11-42*b*].

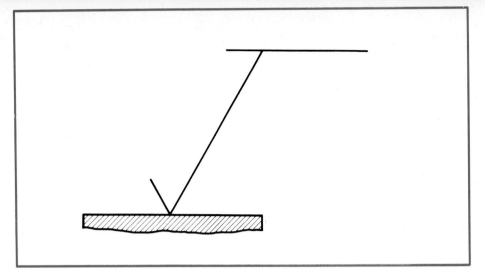

Fig. 11-42*a*. The surface symbol. *(ASA)*

Where the symbol is used with a dimension, it affects all surfaces defined by the dimension. Areas of transition, such as chamfers and fillets, shall conform with the roughest adjacent finished area unless otherwise indicated.

Surface roughness symbols, unless otherwise specified, shall apply to the completed surface. Drawings or specifications for plated or coated parts shall definitely indicate whether the surface roughness symbols apply before plating, whether the surface roughness symbols apply after plating, or whether the surface roughness symbols apply both before and after plating.

Fig. 11-42*b*. The surface symbol on a drawing. *(ASA)*

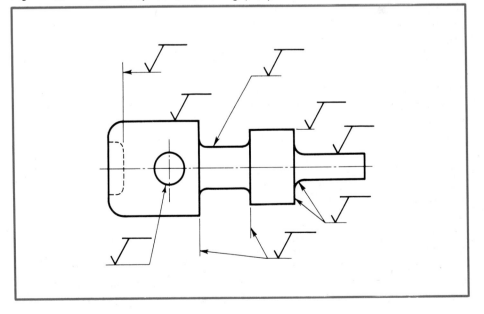

Application of symbols and ratings. Figure . . . [11-42c] illustrates the specification of roughness, waviness and lay by insertion of the ratings in appropriate portions of the symbol. Only those ratings required to specify adequately the desired surface shall be shown in the symbol.

Symbols indicating direction of lay. Symbols for lay are shown in Figure . . . [11-42d].

Roughness and waviness ratings, unless otherwise specified, shall apply in a direction which gives the maximum reading; normally across the lay.

This is the end of the material extracted (and adjusted) from ASA *Surface Texture,* ASA B46.1-1962. It is intended to suggest the consideration which may be given to surface quality. For further study the complete standard should be used.

11·43 Problem suggestions. Group 11, page 472. Two lists are presented. List 1 includes basic and in general more elementary problems than List 2. Selections should be made according to the purpose of the course. List 2 may be used for additional assignments, or selections may be used for advanced students. Additional problems can be assigned from other groups. Review of Chap. 11 in connection with the problems in Group 13 should be assigned. A few problems should be dimensioned with two-place decimals.

List 1: Problems 11·1, 11·2, 11·3, 11·4, 11·5, 11·6, 11·7, 11·8, 11·9, 11·10, 11·13, 11·14, 11·17, 11·18, 11·21, 11·23, 11·27, 11·31.
List 2: Problems 11·11, 11·12, 11·15, 11·16, 11·19, 11·20, 11·22, 11·24, 11·25, 11·28, 11·29, 11·45, 11·46.

Fig. 11-42c. Applications of symbols and ratings. *(ASA)*

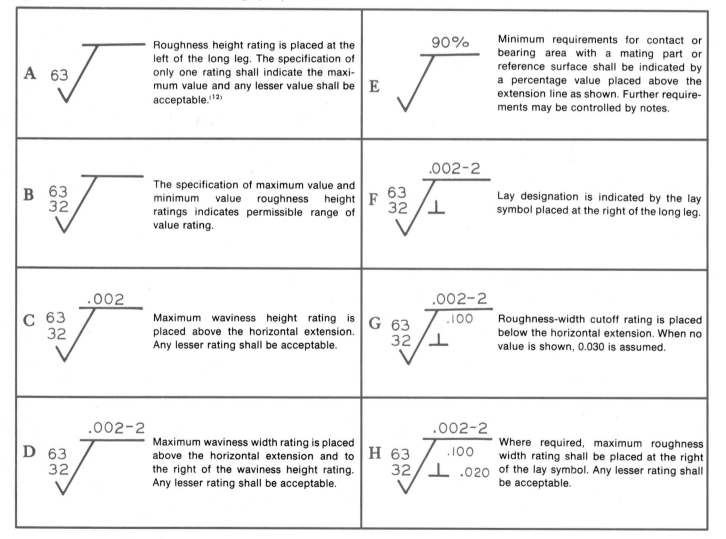

A 63	Roughness height rating is placed at the left of the long leg. The specification of only one rating shall indicate the maximum value and any lesser value shall be acceptable.[12]
B 63 / 32	The specification of maximum value and minimum value roughness height ratings indicates permissible range of value rating.
C 63 / 32 .002	Maximum waviness height rating is placed above the horizontal extension. Any lesser rating shall be acceptable.
D 63 / 32 .002-2	Maximum waviness width rating is placed above the horizontal extension and to the right of the waviness height rating. Any lesser rating shall be acceptable.
E 90%	Minimum requirements for contact or bearing area with a mating part or reference surface shall be indicated by a percentage value placed above the extension line as shown. Further requirements may be controlled by notes.
F 63 / 32 ⊥ .002-2	Lay designation is indicated by the lay symbol placed at the right of the long leg.
G 63 / 32 ⊥ .002-2 .100	Roughness-width cutoff rating is placed below the horizontal extension. When no value is shown, 0.030 is assumed.
H 63 / 32 ⊥ .020 .002-2 .100	Where required, maximum roughness width rating shall be placed at the right of the lay symbol. Any lesser rating shall be acceptable.

Fig. 11-42d. Lay symbols. *(ASA)*

Lay Symbol	Designation	Example
||	Lay parallel to the line representing the surface to which the symbol is applied.	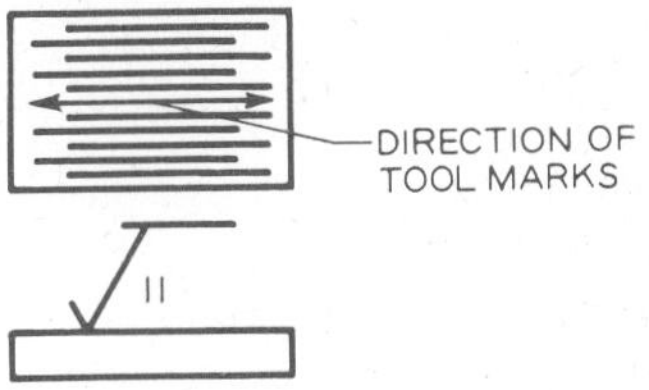 DIRECTION OF TOOL MARKS
⊥	Lay perpendicular to the line representing the surface to which the symbol is applied.	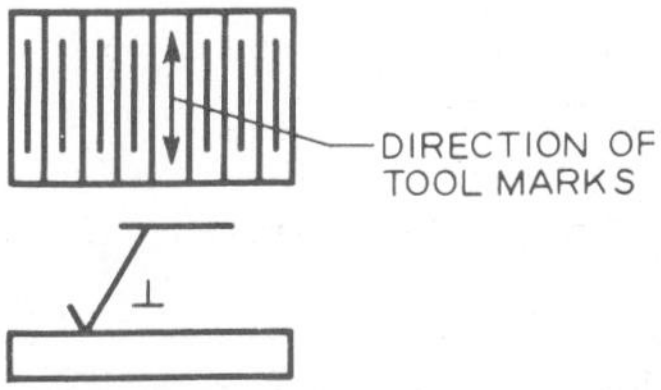 DIRECTION OF TOOL MARKS
X	Lay angular in both directions to line representing the surface to which symbol is applied.	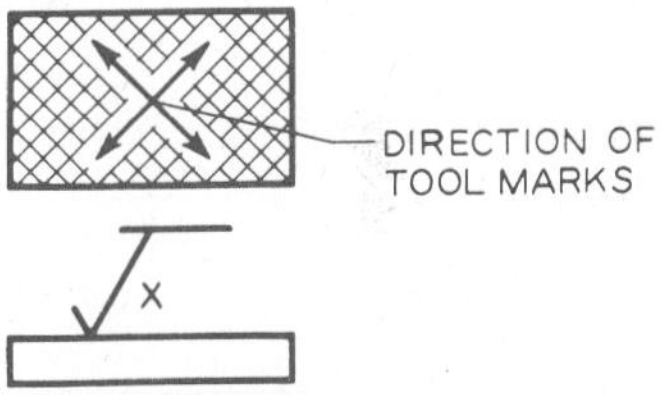 DIRECTION OF TOOL MARKS
M	Lay multidirectional.	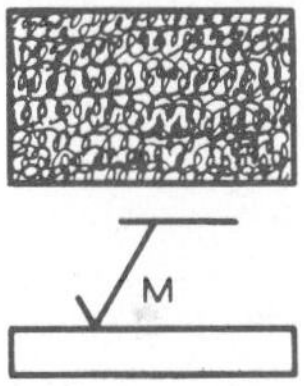
C	Lay approximately circular relative to the center of the surface to which the symbol is applied.	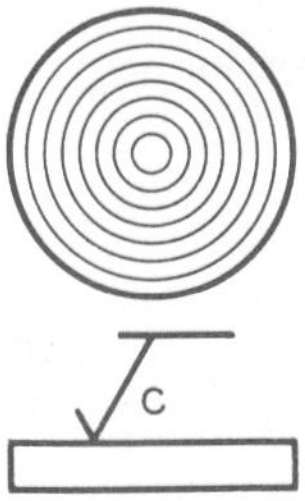
R	Lay approximately radial relative to the center of the surface to which the symbol is applied.	

12

Screws, bolts, and other fastenings

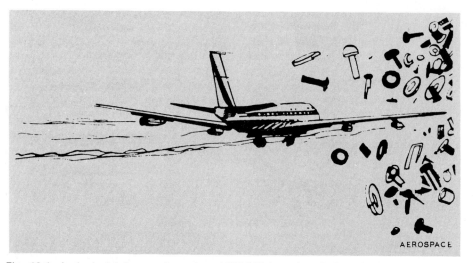

Fig. 12-1. A single jet transport requires 1,225,000 fastening devices, including 1,000,000 rivets, 140,000 lock bolts, and 60,000 structural bolts and other fastenings.

12•1 Standard fastenings. In all fields of engineering and industry, separate parts have to be held together. This may require permanent fastenings, removable fastenings, or adjustable fastenings. There are many ways of fastening or joining parts together. These include screws, bolts and nuts, rivets, welding, brazing, soldering, adhesive binders, collars, clutches, keys, tight fits, and many special fasteners.

Screws and rivets hold parts together on machines and devices of all kinds: the radio, air conditioning and heating apparatus, the Diesel locomotive, the automobile, and the airplane (Fig. 12-1).

12•2 The screw. The screw is very old, but its origin is unknown. Archimedes (287–212 B.C.) is credited with first applying the principle of the screw to practical use in his device for raising water. The same principle is used today in the screw conveyor for moving flour and sugar in commercial bakeries, for raising wheat to grain elevators, and for many other purposes.

Screws are used in so many ways that it is necessary to know the different forms (Fig. 12-2a) and the purposes for which they are made and to be able to draw and to specify them. The most familiar occurrence of screw threads is on the ordinary wood screw (Fig. 12-2b) and the common bolt (Fig. 12-2c). Wood-screw threads have a space between them to allow for part of the difference in the strength of wood and metal. Screws are made of metals, wood, nylon, rubber and other materials to suit the purposes for which they are to be used.

Fig. 12-2a. Some kinds of threaded fastenings.

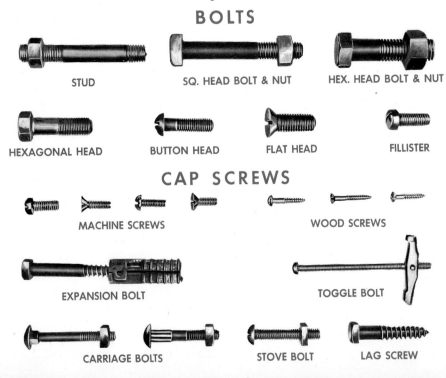

BOLTS

STUD   SQ. HEAD BOLT & NUT   HEX. HEAD BOLT & NUT

HEXAGONAL HEAD   BUTTON HEAD   FLAT HEAD   FILLISTER

CAP SCREWS

MACHINE SCREWS   WOOD SCREWS

EXPANSION BOLT   TOGGLE BOLT

CARRIAGE BOLTS   STOVE BOLT   LAG SCREW

12·3 Screw-thread standards. The first screws were made to suit a particular purpose and without any thought of how anyone else might make one of the same diameter. With industrial development, it became necessary to provide for uniformity in the form and number of threads per inch on screws of any given diameter.

Screw-thread standards in the United States were developed from a system presented by William Sellers in a report to the Franklin Institute in Philadelphia in 1864. Screw-thread standards in England came from a paper presented to the Institution of Civil Engineers in 1841 by Sir Joseph Whitworth. These two standards were not interchangeable.

Work on standards has continued with the growth of industry and the need for uniformity and interchangeable manufacture. In 1948 the Unified Thread Standards were agreed upon by standardization committees of Canada, the United Kingdom, and the United States. The Unified Standards are now the basic American Standards and are described in the *American Standard Unified Screw Threads for Screws, Bolts, Nuts and Other Threaded Parts* (ASA B1.1-1960)[1] and in Handbook H-28, *Federal Screw Thread Specifications.*[2]

12·4 Some screw-thread terms which should be known are illustrated in Fig. 12-4a. The Unified and American (National) screw-thread profile shown in Fig. 12-4b is the form used for general fastening purposes. Other forms of threads are used to meet various requirements, and some of these are

[1] American Standards Association, 10 East 40th St., New York, N.Y., 10016.

[2] U.S. Government Printing Office, Washington, D.C., 20402.

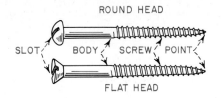

Fig. 12-2b. Wood screws.

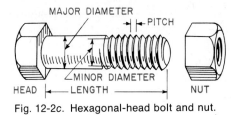

Fig. 12-2c. Hexagonal-head bolt and nut.

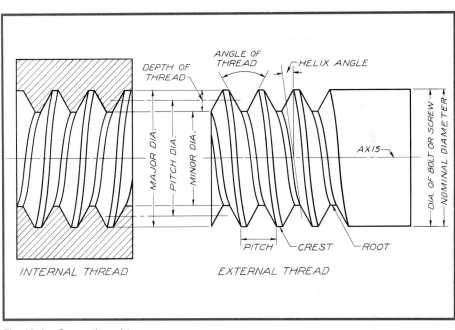

Fig. 12-4a. Screw-thread terms.

Fig. 12-4b. Unified screw-thread profiles.

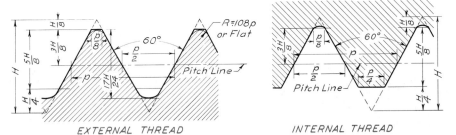

illustrated in Fig. 12-4c. The sharp V is seldom used. The square thread and similar forms (worm thread and acme thread) are designed to transmit motion or power and to hold the forces in line with the axis. The knuckle thread is familiar on electric-light sockets, and so forth, and as a "cast" thread. The Dardelet thread is a self-locking thread designed by a French military officer. The former British Standard (Whitworth) has rounded crests and roots and a 55° angle. The former United States Standard had flat crests and roots and a 60° angle. The buttress thread takes pressure in one direction only: against the surface at an angle of 7° with a perpendicular to the axis.

12•5 To draw a true representation of a screw thread, it is necessary to draw the projection of a helix (Fig. 12-5a). (A helix is a curve generated by a point moving uniformly around a

Fig. 12-4c. Some of the various screw-thread profiles.

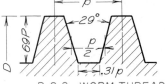

AMERICAN NATIONAL UNIFIED

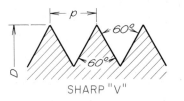

SHARP "V"

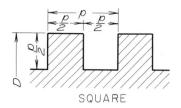

SQUARE

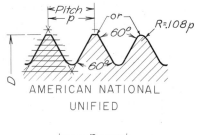

B. & S. WORM THREAD

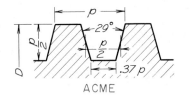

ACME

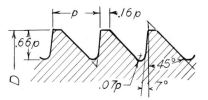

KNUCKLE

DARDELET

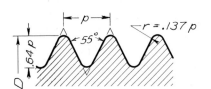

BRITISH STANDARD (WHITWORTH)

BUTTRESS

Fig. 12-5a. Picture of a helix at A and projection of a helix at B.

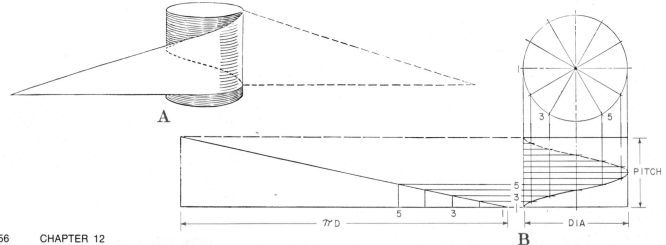

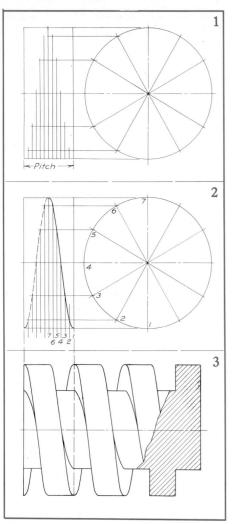

Fig. 12-5*b*. Helix and square thread.

cylinder and uniformly parallel to the axis of the cylinder.) The hypotenuse of a right triangle will form one turn of a helix if wrapped around a cylinder if the base of the triangle is equal to the circumference of the cylinder (Fig. 12-5*a* at A). The altitude will be the pitch of the helix. A right triangle and the projections of the corresponding helix are shown in Fig. 12-5*a* at B.

The method of drawing the projections of a helix is shown in Fig. 12-5*b* in Spaces 1 and 2. Draw two projections of a cylinder (Space 1). Divide the circumference into a number of equal parts and the pitch into the same number of equal parts. From each point in the circumference draw lines parallel to the axis to meet lines perpendicular to the axis drawn through the corresponding divisions of the pitch (Space 2). A smooth curve drawn through the points thus found will give the projection of the helix.

The application of the helix is shown in Space 3, which is the actual projection of a square thread. Such drawings are seldom made, since they require too much time and are no better, practically, than the conventional representations commonly used (see Art. 12·8).

12·6 Single and multiple threads. "A screw thread is a ridge of uniform section in the form of a helix on the external or internal surface of a cylin-

der, or in the form of a conical spiral on the external or internal surface of a cone or frustum of a cone."[3]

The *pitch* of a thread, *p*, is the distance from a point on the thread form to the corresponding point on the next form, measured parallel to the axis (Fig. 12-6). The *lead, L,* is the distance a threaded part would move parallel to the axis during one complete rotation in relation to a fixed mating part (the distance a screw would enter a threaded hole).

Most screws have single threads (Fig. 12-6 at A) and are so understood if not otherwise specified. A single thread has a single ridge in the form of a helix, and the pitch and the lead are the same. A double thread (Fig. 12-6 at B) has two ridges in the form of helixes, and the lead is twice the pitch. A triple thread (Fig. 12-6 at C) has three ridges, and the lead is three times the pitch. The number of threads per inch is 1 in. divided by the pitch. The number of turns per inch is one divided by the lead. This is the number of turns for the screws to move 1 in. through a threaded hole.

12·7 Right- and left-hand threads. Threads are always right hand unless marked otherwise. A right-hand thread is one which turns in a clockwise direc-

[3] *Nomenclature, Definitions and Letter Symbols for Screw Threads* (ASA B1.7-1953), American Standards Association, 10 East 40th St., New York, N.Y., 10016.

Fig. 12-6. Single, double, and triple threads.

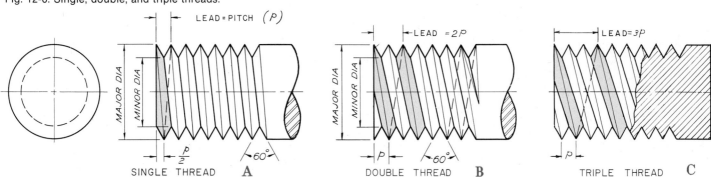

tion to enter a threaded part when viewed from the outside end (Fig. 12-7a at A). A left-hand thread is one which turns in a counterclockwise direction when viewed from the outside end (Fig. 12-7a at B). Left-hand threads are always indicated by the initials LH. A turnbuckle (Fig. 12-7b) is an example of right- and left-hand threads.

12·8 Representations of American Standard and Unified screw threads on drawings. The same symbols are used for coarse or fine threads and for right-hand or left-hand threads, with notes to give the necessary information.

Three types of representation are provided by the ASA:

1. Detailed representation approximates the actual appearance of threads (Fig. 12-8a). The pitch is not often drawn to scale but is approximated for convenience in drawing. The helixes are

Fig. 12-7a. A right-hand screw thread at A and left-hand screw thread at B.

drawn as straight lines. The threads are drawn as sharp Vs. In general, this representation would not be used for diameters of less than 1 in. It is a somewhat realistic (or pictorial) representation but is not usual practice on working drawings except where it might be needed for clearness. The order of drawing the detailed representation of screw threads is shown in Art. 12·9.

2. The schematic representation omits drawing the Vs (Fig. 12-8b). The

crest and root lines are spaced by eye (estimating the pitch) to look good for the given diameter. The crest and root lines may be perpendicular to the axis or slanted to approximate the helix angle (Fig. 12-4a). American Standards shows thin crest lines and thick root lines, but all lines are often drawn the same to save time, especially on regular pencil working drawings. The order of drawing the schematic representation of screw threads is shown in Art. 12·10.

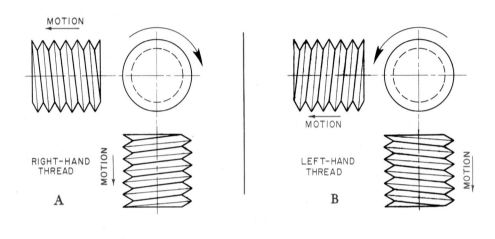

Fig. 12-7b. A turnbuckle uses right-hand and left-hand screw threads.

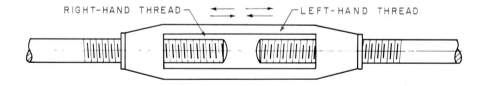

Fig. 12-8a. Detailed representations of screw threads.

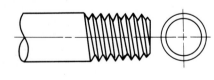

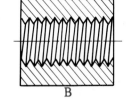

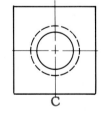

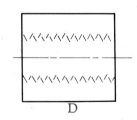

A   B   C   D

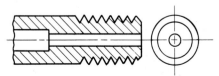

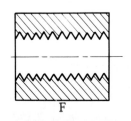

E   F

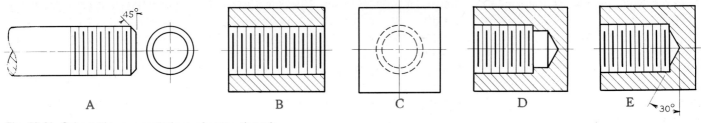

Fig. 12-8*b*. Schematic representations of screw threads.

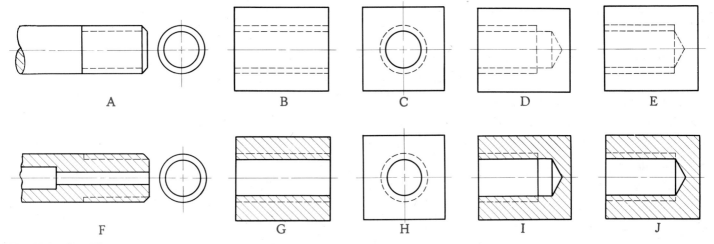

Fig. 12-8*c*. Simplified representations of screw threads.

3. The simplified representation (Fig. 12-8*c*) is the most generally used method of drawing screw threads. It is easily and quickly drawn and, in most cases, serves as well as any method. The crest and root lines are not drawn. The depth of thread is shown by a dash line parallel to the axis, located by eye to look good. The order of drawing the simplified representation of screw threads is shown in Art. 12·11.

12·9 To draw the detailed representation of screw threads. The detailed representation uses the sharp-V profile to approximate the American Standard and Unified threads. Straight lines are used to represent the helixes of the crest and root lines. The order of drawing the V-form thread is shown in Fig. 12-9*a*. The pitch is seldom drawn to

Fig. 12-9*a*. To draw the detailed representation of screw threads.

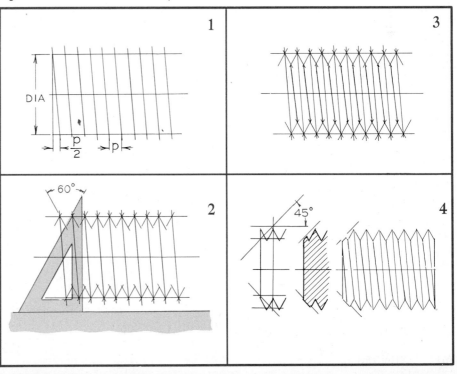

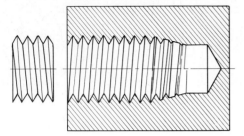

Fig. 12-9b. Internal threads in section (threaded hole).

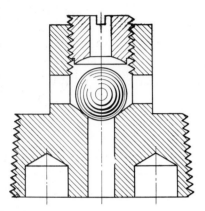

Fig. 12-9c. Threads in section on assembled pieces.

scale; generally it is approximated and drawn to look good. In Space 1, Fig. 12-9a, lay off the pitch, *p,* and the half pitch, *p/2,* as shown. Adjust the triangle to the slope and draw the crest lines (if a drafting machine is used, set the ruling arm to the slope of the crest line). In Space 2 draw one side of the V for the threads with the 30°–60° triangle (if a drafting machine is used, set the ruling arm for the 30° angle). Then reverse the triangle, or ruling arm, and complete the Vs. In Space 3 set the triangle, or the ruling arm of the drafting machine, to the slope of the root lines and draw as shown. Notice that the root lines are not parallel to the crest lines because the root diameter is less than the major diameter. In Space 4 draw 45° chamfer lines as shown by the construction in red.

The sectional view of a threaded hole with a right-hand thread is shown in Fig. 12-9b. Notice that the slope of the thread lines is opposite to that of a right-hand external thread, as they must match the far side of the screw.

The realistic, or V-form, thread representation (Fig. 12-9c) is sometimes useful to provide clarity where two or more threaded pieces are shown in section.

12·10 To draw the schematic representation of screw threads (Fig. 12-10a). At A the outside diameter of the screw thread is laid off. At B a method of construction is shown for the thread depth and the chamfer. At C the thin crest lines are drawn perpendicular to the axis. At D the thick root lines are drawn parallel to the crest lines.

The crest and root lines may be drawn at a slope (Fig. 12-10b at A) where single threads are suggested by a slope of half the pitch. On pencil drawings the crest and root lines are generally drawn the same width (Fig. 12-10b at B). On most drawings schematic representations are drawn to look good, with no attempt to lay off the pitch to scale.

Fig. 12-10a. To draw the schematic representation of screw threads.

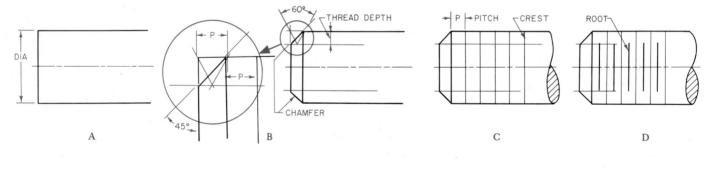

Fig. 12-10b. Slope-line representation at A and uniform-width lines at B.

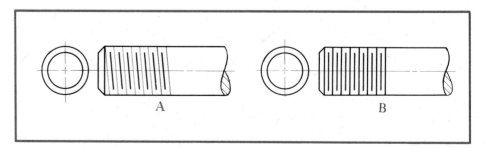

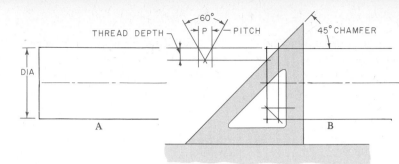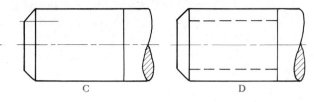

Fig. 12-11. To draw the simplified representation of screw threads.

Fig. 12-12. To draw square threads.

Fig. 12-13. To draw acme threads.

12·11 To draw the simplified representation of screw threads (Fig. 12-11). At A the outside diameter of the screw is laid off. At B a method of construction is shown for the screw-thread depth and the chamfer. At C the chamfer has been drawn and the length of the thread is indicated. At D dash lines have been drawn to complete the simplified representation of the threads.

12·12 To draw square screw threads (Fig. 12-12). The depth of the square thread is one-half the pitch. In Space 1 lay off the diameter; the pitch, *p*, one-half pitch spaces; and the depth of thread lines. In Space 2 draw the crest lines. In Space 3 draw the root lines as shown. In Space 4 the internal square thread is drawn in section.

12·13 To draw acme screw threads (Fig. 12-13). The depth of the acme thread is one-half the pitch. The stages in drawing acme threads are shown in Space 1. The pitch diameter is midway between the outside diameter and the root diameter and locates the pitch line. On the pitch line lay off one-half pitch spaces and draw the thread profile. Draw the crest lines; then, draw the root lines to complete the view. The construction is enlarged in Space 2.

A sectional view of an internal acme thread is shown in Space 3. Other representations sometimes used for internal threads by hidden lines and in sections are shown in Space 4.

1

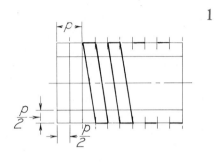

2

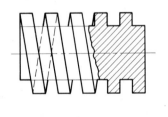

3

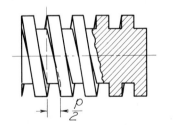

4

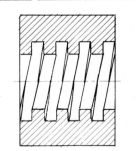

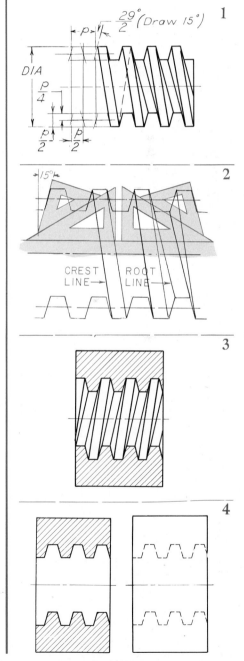
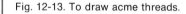

12·14 Thread series for Unified and American National screw threads. The number of threads per inch for a given diameter varies according to the purpose for which the screw is used. Several *series* of threads are provided in ASA B1.1. Letter symbols are used to designate the different series.

Coarse-thread series (UNC or NC). The pitch is relatively large for a specific diameter and is used for general engineering purposes.

Fine-thread series (UNF or NF). The pitch is smaller (greater number of threads per inch) for a specific diameter than for the coarse-thread series. It is used where a finer thread is required, as in the automotive, aircraft, and similar industries.

Extra-fine-thread series (UNEF). The pitch is smaller than for the fine-thread series. It is used where the depth of thread must be kept very small, as on aircraft equipment or thin-walled tubes.

Three series provide the same number of threads per inch regardless of diameter. These are:

Eight-thread series (8UN or 8N). This series uses 8 threads per inch for all diameters.

Twelve-thread series (12UN or 12N). This series uses 12 threads per inch for all diameters.

Sixteen-thread series (16UN or 16N). This series uses 16 threads per inch for all diameters.

Special threads (UNS, UN, or NS). These are nonstandard, or special, combinations of diameter and pitch.

American National Standard thread series have been largely replaced by the Unified standard since the agreement of 1948 (Art. 12·3). The letter symbols for the American National series are listed for reference and identification.

Coarse-thread series (NC). This series is used for bulk production of screws, bolts, nuts, and general use.

Fine-thread series (NF). This series has smaller pitch than NC for same diameter and is used where the coarse series is not suitable.

Extra-fine-thread series (NEF). This series is used where a smaller pitch than NF is desired, as on thin-walled tubes.

The symbol NS is used to specify special threads.

Eight-thread series (8N) is a uniform-pitch series for large diameters.

Twelve-thread series (12N) is a uniform-pitch series where a medium-fine pitch is required for large diameters.

Sixteen-thread series (16N) is a uniform-pitch series where still smaller pitch is required.

12·15 Classes of fits for Unified and American National screw threads. The amounts of tolerance and allowance specified to meet requirements for screw-thread fits are provided by *screw-thread classes*. Specific requirements can be met by the selection of series and class. In brief, the classes for Unified threads are: *Classes 1A, 2A, and 3A* for external threads only; *Classes 1B, 2B, and 3B* for internal threads only.

Classes 1A and 1B replace American National Class 1 for new designs. These classes have a large allowance (loose fit) and are intended for purposes where quick and easy assembly is required.

Classes 2A and 2B are the thread standards most used for general purposes, such as the production of bolts, screws, nuts, and similar threaded items.

Classes 3A and 3B provide for more accurate work, where closer tolerances are desired than in Classes 2A and 2B.

Classes 2 and 3 are American National standard. Description and tabular information are given in Appendix 1 of ASA B1.1, from which the following is quoted: "Gaging practice for minimum Class 3 external threads is the same as for Class 3A threads; that for minimum Class 2 external threads is the same as for Class 2A; and that for maximum Classes 2 and 3 internal threads is the same as for Classes 2B or 3B."

12·16 Screw-thread specifications. Screw threads are specified by diameter (nominal, or major, diameter), number of threads per inch, length of thread, initial letters of the series, and class of fit. Threads are understood to be single right hand. If threads are to be left hand, the letters LH should follow the class symbol. For double or triple threads, the word "double" or "triple" should be given.

Some examples follow:

$1\frac{1}{4}-7$UNC-1A ($1\frac{1}{4}$ diameter, 7 threads per inch, Unified threads, coarse threads, series 1, external).

$\frac{1}{2}-13$UNC-2A ($\frac{1}{2}$ diameter, 13 threads per inch, Unified threads, coarse threads, series 2, external).

$\frac{7}{8}-14$UNF-2B ($\frac{7}{8}$ diameter, 14 threads per inch, Unified threads, fine threads, series 2, internal).

$1\frac{5}{8}-18$UNEF-3B$-$LH ($1\frac{5}{8}$ diameter, 18 threads per inch, Unified threads, extra-fine threads, series 3, internal, left-hand).

Tapped (threaded) holes are specified by a note giving the diameter of the tap drill ($\frac{27}{64}''$); depth of hole ($1\frac{3}{8}''$); thread information ($\frac{1}{2}$ diameter, American National threads, Class 2); and length of thread ($1''$), as:

$$\frac{27}{64} \text{ DRILL} \times 1\frac{3}{8} \text{ DEEP}$$
$$\frac{1}{2}-13\text{NC}-2 \times 1 \text{ DEEP}$$

For complete information, *American Standard Unified* and *American National Screw Threads for Screws, Bolts, Nuts and Other Threads* (ASA B1.1) should be consulted.

12·17 Threaded fastenings are made in many forms for different uses. Enough information is included in the following articles to enable the student to identify and draw the threaded fasteners in most common use on machines, engineering and other projects, and constructions. These include: square- and hexagonal-head bolts, square and hexagonal nuts, studs, machine screws, cap screws and setscrews, etc. Tables of dimensions for drawing purposes for bolts, nuts, and some of the other generally used threaded fasteners are given in the Appendix.

Certain bolt and nut dimensions have been designated as Unified Standard for use in the United States, Great Britain, and Canada. For complete information, the latest American Standards Association standard (ASA B18.2) should be consulted.

12·18 American Standard square and hexagon bolts and nuts are of such importance that the student should learn the principal terms used (Fig. 12-18a) and be able to draw the necessary views from the instructions which follow. In general, bolts and nuts may be regular or heavy and square or hexagon. Regular bolts and nuts are used for the general run of work. Heavy bolts and nuts are somewhat larger than regular and are used where a larger bearing surface is required or where a relatively larger hole is required in the part being held. Regular forms include square bolts, hexagon bolts, semifinished hexagon bolts, square nuts, hexagon nuts, and semifinished hexagon nuts. Heavy forms include hexagon bolts and nuts, semifinished hexagon bolts and nuts, finished hexagon bolts, and square nuts.

Regular bolts and nuts are not finished on any surface. Semifinished bolts and nuts are processed to have a flat bearing surface. "Finished bolts and nuts" refers to the quality of manufacture and the closeness of tolerance and does not mean that the surfaces are completely machined. Semifinished boltheads and nuts (Fig. 12-18b) have a washer-faced bearing surface or have chamfered corners with a diameter equal to the distance across the flats. The thickness of the washer face is approximately 1/64 in.

Fig. 12-18a. Bolt and nut terms.

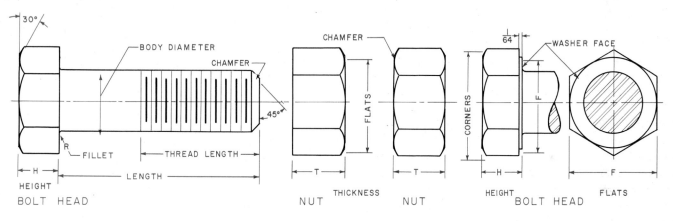

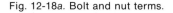

Fig. 12-18b. Semifinished boltheads and nuts.

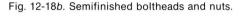

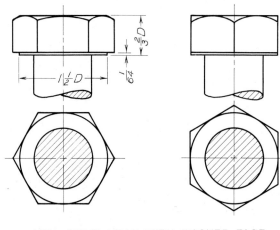

HEX. BOLT HEAD WITH WASHER FACE

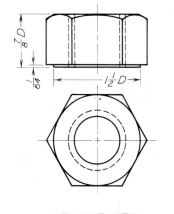

HEX. NUT WITH WASHER FACE

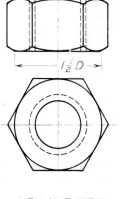

HEX. NUT WITH CHAMFER FACE

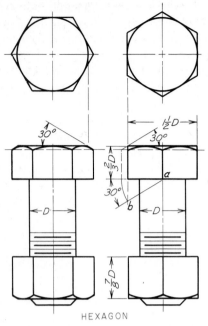

Fig. 12-19a. Regular hexagonal bolthead and nut.

12·19 Regular boltheads and nuts. For drawing purposes the dimensions may be obtained from the proportions given in Figs. 12-19a and 12-19b or from the Appendix. The chamfer angle may be drawn at 30° for either the hexagon or the square forms. (The standard indicates 25° for the square form.) Radii for the arcs may be found by trial to suit the conditions. Note that one-half the distance across corners, ab, may be found by the construction shown.

12·20 Heavy hexagonal boltheads and nuts. For drawing purposes the dimensions may be obtained from the proportions given in Fig. 12-20 or from the Appendix. Also see Appendix V-1962 of ASA B18.2-1960. The standard for heavy square bolts has been removed.

A new standard covers hexagonal structural bolts, which are made of high-strength steel. These are used for structural-steel joints. Dimensions for drawing are given in the Appendix.

12·21 To draw a regular square bolthead across flats (Fig. 12-21). (Square boltheads are not made in heavy sizes.) For regular sizes the width across flats $= W = 1\frac{1}{2}D$ where D is the major diameter of the bolt. The height

Fig. 12-21. To draw a regular square bolthead across flats.

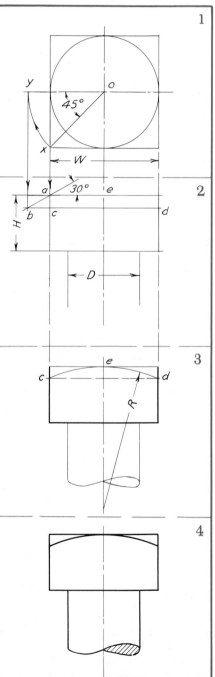

Fig. 12-19b. Regular square bolthead and nut.

Fig. 12-20. Heavy hexagonal bolthead and nut.

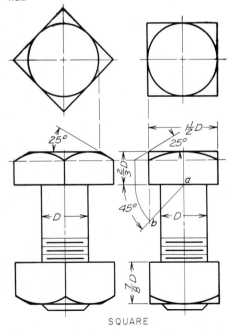

SQUARE   HEXAGON

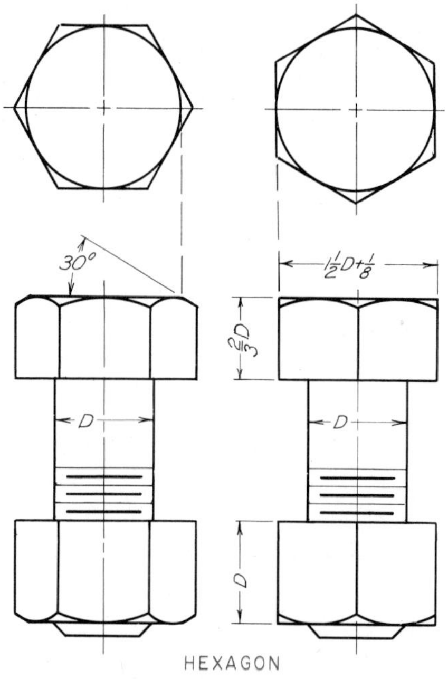

of the head $= H = \frac{2}{3}D$. In Space 1 draw the center line and start the top view by drawing the chamfer circle with a diameter equal to the distance across the flats. Draw a square about this circle. In Space 2 draw a horizontal line representing the bearing surface of the head and lay off the height of the head, H. Draw the top line of the head and project down from Space 1 to obtain the vertical edges. Draw ox in the top view (Space 1), revolve to y, and project down to Space 2. From a in Space 2 draw the 30° chamfer line ab and project across to c and d. In Space 3 the chamfer arc is drawn through c, e, and d by radius R. Radius R can be found by trial, or $R = W$ may be used. Complete the view as in Space 4.

12·22 To draw a regular square bolt-head across corners (Fig. 12-22). (Square boltheads are not made in heavy sizes.) For regular sizes, $W = 1\frac{1}{2}D$ and $H = \frac{2}{3}D$. In Space 1 draw the center line and start the top view by drawing the chamfer circle with a diameter equal to the distance across the flats. About this circle, draw a square with the 45° triangle, as shown. Draw a horizontal line in Space 2 representing the bearing surface of the head and lay off the height of the head, H. Draw the top line of the head and project the vertical edges from Space 1. Project the diameter of the chamfer circle from the top view and draw 30° chamfer lines as shown (Space 2). Project point x down to obtain points f and g in Spaces 2 and 3 and draw line bcd. Then draw the chamfer arcs through bfc and cgd by radius R. Radius R can be found easily by trial, or $R = yo = \frac{1}{2}$ distance across corners may be used. Now, complete the view as in Space 4. You can use the same method to draw a nut except that $T = \frac{7}{8}D$ for regular nuts, and $T = D$ for heavy nuts.

Boltheads and nuts are usually drawn across corners on all views of design drawings, regardless of projection. This is done to show the largest space required in order to permit turning space, or clearance. It also prevents hexagon heads and nuts being confused with square heads and nuts.

Fig. 12-22. To draw a regular square bolt-head across corners.

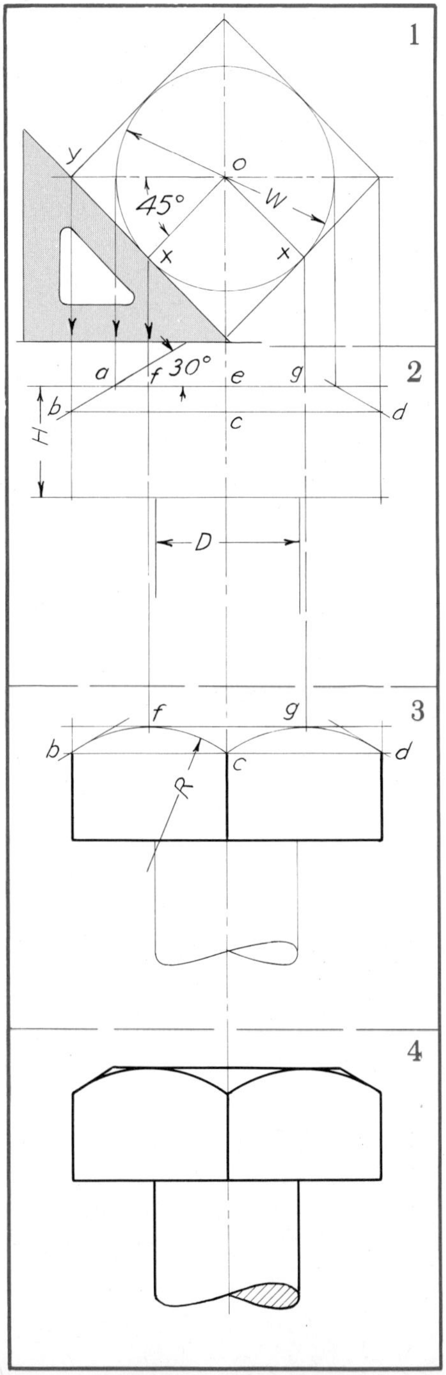

12·23 To draw a hexagon bolthead across corners (Fig. 12-23a). Start the top view as in Space 1 by drawing the chamfer circle with a diameter equal to W, the distance across the flats. For a head across corners, draw a

Fig. 12-23a. To draw a regular hexagonal bolthead across corners.

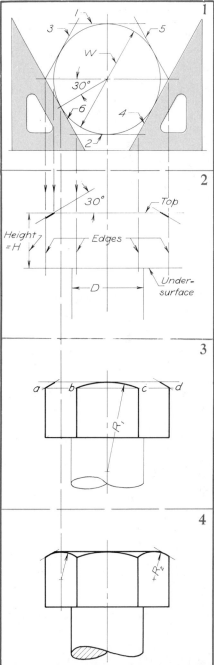

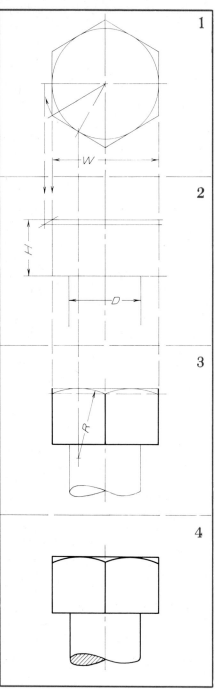

Fig. 12-23b. To draw a regular hexagonal bolthead across flats.

Fig. 12-24. Notes for bolts, studs, and threaded holes.

hexagon as indicated by the lines 1, 2, 3, 4, 5, 6. For the front view (Space 2) draw a horizontal line representing the bearing or undersurface of the head. Lay off the height of the head and the top surface. Then project from the top view and draw the chamfer line.

Draw line *abcd* (Space 3) to locate the chamfer intersections. Radius R_1 can be found by trial so that the arc will pass through points *b* and *c* and be tangent to the top line. Complete the front view as in Space 4 by drawing arcs with radii R_2 (tangent to top line and through points *a* and *b* at the left, and *c* and *d* at the right, by trial).

To draw a hexagon bolthead across flats, proceed as illustrated in Fig. 12-23b. You can draw hexagon nuts with the same construction, but note the difference between the height of the head and thickness of the nut.

12·24 Boltheads and nuts have dimensions so well standardized that they are seldom dimensioned on drawings. For a standard bolt the necessary information is given in a note, as in Fig. 12-24 at A, which specifies 1″ diameter, 8 threads per inch, Unified coarse-thread series, Class 2A fit, 2¾″ long, regular hex-head bolt. A bolt may hold

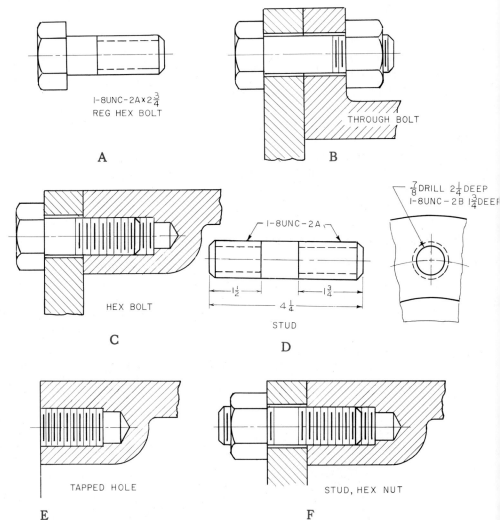

Fig. 12-24. Notes for bolts, studs, and threaded holes.

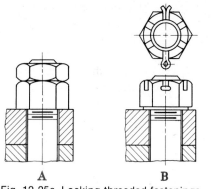

A   B   C   D

Fig. 12-25a. Locking threaded fastenings.

HEXAGONAL   FILLISTER   FLAT

BUTTON   FLUTED SOCKET   HEXAGONAL SOCKET

Fig. 12-26. Cap screws.

a part in place by passing through another part and using a nut, as at B, or by passing through a part and screwing into a threaded hole, as at C.

A stud or stud bolt (Fig. 12-24 at D) has threads on both ends and is used where a bolt is not suitable and for parts which must be removed often. The length of thread from each end is given by dimensions as shown. A tapped (threaded) hole is dimensioned as at E. One end of a stud is screwed permanently into place as at F, and a nut is screwed onto the projecting end. Under certain conditions a stud may be passed through two parts with a nut on each end.

Fig. 12-25b. Chemical methods of locking a fastener.

12•25 Lock nuts and various devices are used to prevent nuts, or bolts and screws, from working loose. Many special devices are available.

Some forms of lock nuts are shown in Fig. 12-25a. There are many special forms designed to provide positive locking.

A new self-locking fastener, the Jay-Lock (Fig. 12-25b), consists of an epoxy chemical locking agent which combines with a hardening agent. When bolts or screws are engaged, it provides a strong, vibrationproof band.

12•26 Cap screws (Fig. 12-26) are used for fastening two pieces together by passing through a clearance hole in one and screwing into a tapped hole in the other. In most cases the clearance hole need not be shown on the drawing. Cap screws have a naturally bright finish in keeping with the machined parts with which they are used. Coarse, fine, or 8 threads may be on cap screws with Class 3A on the socket-head type and Class 2A on the others.

Dimensions of American Standard cap screws are in the Appendix.

12•27 Machine screws (Fig. 12-27) are used where small diameters are required. Sizes below ¼ in. in diameter are specified by number. They may screw into a tapped hole or extend through a clearance hole and into a nut (square nuts are used). The finish is bright. The ends are flat, as illustrated. Machine screws up to 2 in. long are threaded full length. Coarse or fine threads and Class 2 may be used on machine screws.

Fig. 12-27. Machine screws.

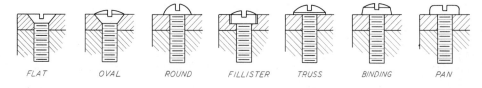

FLAT   OVAL   ROUND   FILLISTER   TRUSS   BINDING   PAN

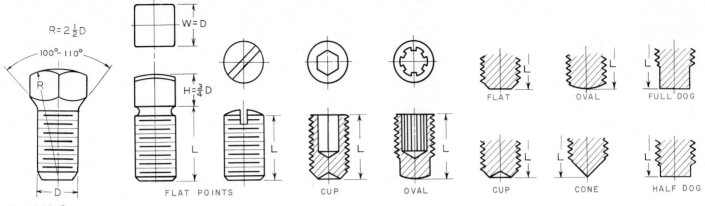

Fig. 12-28. Setscrews.

12·28 Setscrews (Fig. 12-28) are used for holding two parts in a desired position relative to each other by screwing through a threaded hole in one piece and bearing against the other. There are two general types: square head and headless. The square-head setscrews are a source of accidents when used on rotating parts and violate safety codes. Headless setscrews may have either a slot or a socket. Any of the points may be used on any setscrew.

12·29 Wood screws (Fig. 12-29) are made of steel, brass, or aluminum and are finished in various ways. Steel screws may be bright (natural finish),

blued, galvanized, or copper plated; both steel and brass screws are sometimes nickel plated. Round-head screws are set with the head above the wood; flat-head screws are set flush, or countersunk. Wood screws may be drawn as illustrated. They are specified by number, length, style of head, and finish. Length of flat-head screws is measured overall; round-head screws, from under head to point; oval-head screws, from largest diameter of countersink to point. For sizes and dimensions see the Appendix.

12·30 Some miscellaneous threaded fastenings are shown in Fig. 12-30. The names indicate the purposes for which they are used. Screw hooks and screw eyes are specified by diameter and overall length.

A lag screw, or lag bolt, is used for fastening machinery to wood supports and for heavy wood constructions when a regular bolt cannot be used. It is similar to a regular bolt but has wood-screw threads. Lag bolts are specified by the diameter and the length from under the head to the point. The pro-

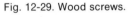

Fig. 12-29. Wood screws.

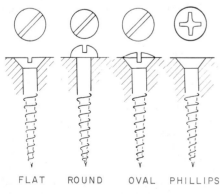

Fig. 12-30. Miscellaneous threaded fastenings.

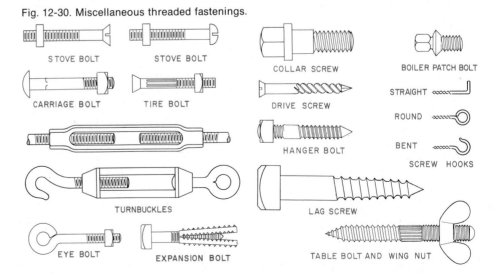

portions of the head are the same as the proportions found on regular boltheads.

12•31 Materials for threaded fastenings include steel, brass, bronze, aluminum, cast iron, wood, and nylon. Nylon screws and bolts (Fig. 12-31) are made in various bright colors, such as red, blue-green, yellow, white, etc.

12•32 Keys (Fig. 12-32) are used to secure pulleys, gears, cranks, and similar parts to a shaft. The form of the key is selected to suit the duty that it must perform. This ranges from the saddle key for light duty to special forms, such as two square keys, for heavy duty. The common sunk key may have a breadth of about one-fourth the shaft diameter and a thickness of from five-eighths the breadth to the full breadth. The Woodruff key is much used in machine-tool work. It is made in standard sizes and is specified by number (see Appendix). Special forms of pins have been developed to take the place of keys for some purposes. These pins require only a drilled hole instead of the machining which is necessary in order to make keys.

12•33 Rivets. Sheet-metal plates, structural-steel shapes, boilers, tanks, and many other classes of work are put together with rivets as permanent fastenings. Rivets are rods of metal with a preformed head on one end. The rivet, heated red hot, is placed through the parts to be joined and held in place while a head is formed on the projecting end. The rivet is said to be "driven."

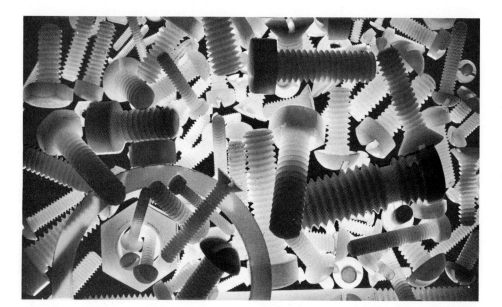

Fig. 12-31. Nylon bolts and screws are made in many colors. *(Anti-Corrosive Metal Products Company, Inc.)*

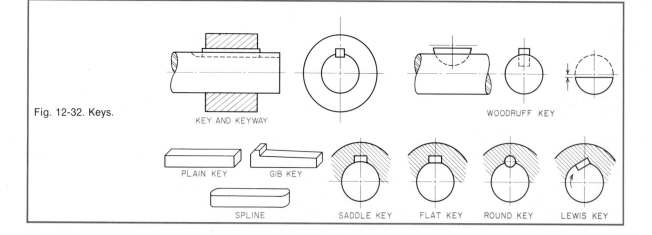

Fig. 12-32. Keys.

KEY AND KEYWAY
WOODRUFF KEY
PLAIN KEY
GIB KEY
SPLINE
SADDLE KEY
FLAT KEY
ROUND KEY
LEWIS KEY

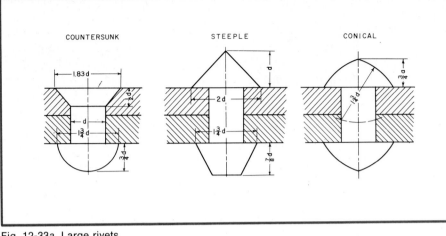

Fig. 12-33a. Large rivets.

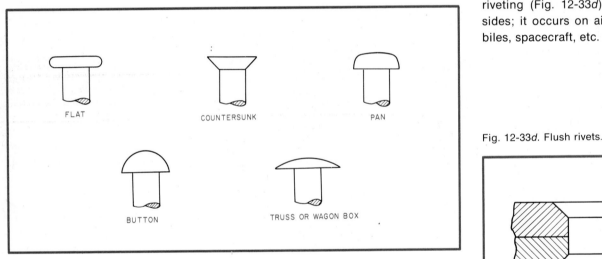

Fig. 12-33b. Small rivets.

Large rivets (Fig. 12-33a) have nominal diameters ranging in size from ½ to 1¾ in. Small rivets (Fig. 12-33b) range from ¹⁄₁₆ or ³⁄₃₂ to ⁷⁄₁₆ in. in diameter.

There are many forms of "blind" rivets for use where one side of the plates cannot be reached or where the space is too small to use a regular rivet. One type is the du Pont explosive rivet (Fig. 12-33c), which has a small explosive charge in the cavity when inserted. After the charge is exploded, a head is formed. This makes blind riveting possible, since the head can be formed inside closed or inaccessible places.

Sometimes it is desirable to have clear surfaces on plates which are fastened together. This requires flush riveting (Fig. 12-33d) on one or both sides; it occurs on airplanes, automobiles, spacecraft, etc.

Fig. 12-33d. Flush rivets.

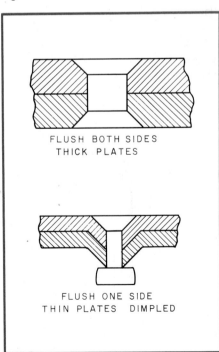

Fig. 12-33c. Explosive rivet. *(Explosives Department, E. I. du Pont de Nemours & Company)*

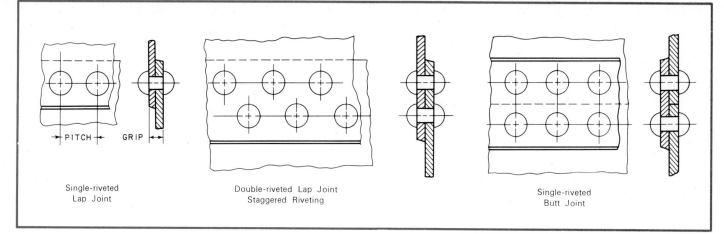

Fig. 12-33e. Riveted joints.

Riveted joints (Fig. 12-33e), used for joining plates, may have lap joints or butt joints and may have single or multiple riveting. (See Appendix for American Standard rivet dimensions.)

For some purposes, such as tanks, steel buildings, etc., high-strength structural bolts are coming into use. Welding is also in wide use.

12·34 Problem suggestions. Group 12, page 478. Two lists are presented. List 1 includes basic problems. Selections from List 2 may be used for additional assignments, or selections may be made for more advanced students. Review of Chap. 12 should be assigned in connection with the problems in Group 13.

List 1: Problems 12·5, 12·6, 12·7, 12·8, 12·9, 12·15, 12·17, 12·21, 12·22, 12·26, 12·29.

List 2: Problems 12·1, 12·3, 12·4, 12·14, 12·16, 12·18, 12·19, 12·20, 12·23, 12·24, 12·25, 12·27, 12·28, 12·30, 12·31, 12·32, 12·33.

13
Working drawings

13·1 Drafting practice. A working drawing is one that gives all the information necessary for making a single part or a complete machine or structure. The drawing completely describes shape and size and gives specifications for the kinds of material to be used, the methods of finish, and the accuracy required. A picture and the working drawing of a simple machine part are shown in Fig. 13-1.

13·2 Working drawings are based upon orthographic projection (Chap. 5), with dimensions and notes added as described in Chap. 11. The automotive and aerospace industries use the uni-directional placing of dimensions. It is also used to a considerable extent in this book, as industry in general is fast adapting this practice.

Such drawings must conform in style with good practice as followed in the office where they are made. There must be contrast, which is obtained by giving proper values to the various lines that compose the views. Figures that are easy to read, uniform lettering, and the use of standard terms are essential. When completed, a working drawing must be thoroughly checked for errors and improvements (Art. 13·25) before the drawing is submitted for approval.

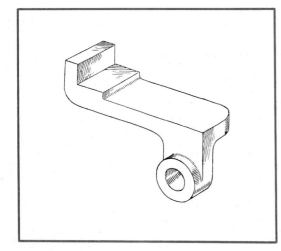

Fig. 13-1. A working drawing of a machine part.

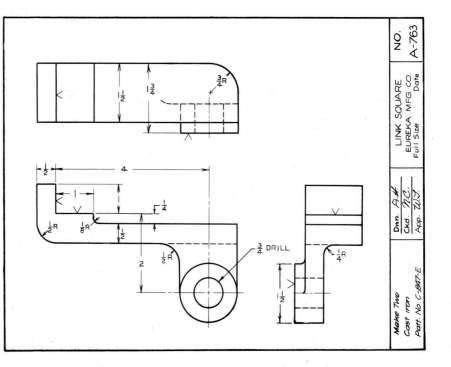

13·3 Making drawings for industrial use. In the language of drawing, an object is described by telling its shape and its size. All drawings, whether for steam or gas engines, machines, buildings, airplanes, automobiles, missiles, or satellites, are made on the same principles.

Sometimes an unfavorable comparison is made between a student's drawing and a "real drawing." The finished appearance of a real drawing, as made by a draftsman or engineer, is due to a thorough knowledge of engineering drafting and its use in industry. The correct order of going about the work and some of the procedures that draftsmen usually follow are described in this chapter. The student must become thoroughly familiar with this practice if his drawings are to have the style and good form that are so necessary.

Good pencil work is essential. This requires neatness, few erasures, and dense, sharp lines on tracing cloth, tracing paper, or film. Blueprints, diazotype, or other reproductions are then made to provide necessary copies. Most drawings used to be made with ink on tracing cloth, but present practice is to use a pencil for all except some special purposes.

13·4 Detail drawings. The drawing of a single piece that gives all the information necessary for making it is called a *detail drawing,* as for the simple part in Fig. 13-4a. A detail working drawing must be a complete and accurate description of the piece, with carefully selected views and well-located dimensions (Fig. 13-4b).

When a large number of machines are to be manufactured, it is usual to make a detail drawing for each part on a separate sheet, especially when some of the parts may be used on other machines. When several parts are used on a single machine, it is common practice in some industries to detail a number

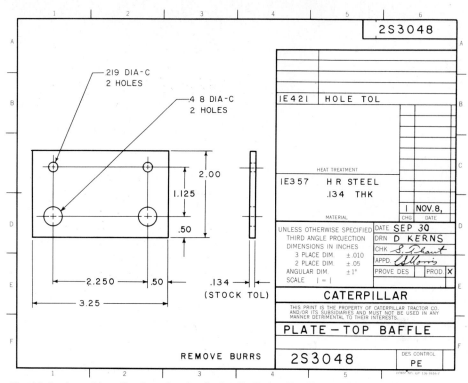

Fig. 13-4a. A working drawing of a simple detail. *(Caterpillar Tractor Company)*

Fig. 13-4b. A one-view working drawing. The one view and the extra section provide a complete description.

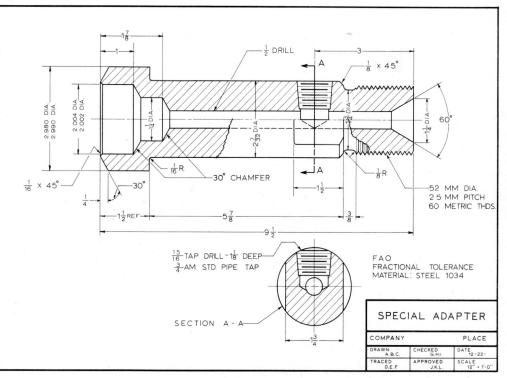

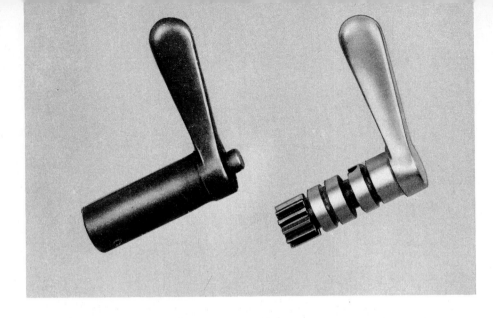

Fig. 13-4c. Index-plunger operating handle; forging and finished part. *(The Hartford Special Machinery Company)*

Fig. 13-4d. Working drawing of part shown in Fig. 13-4c. *(The Hartford Special Machinery Company)*

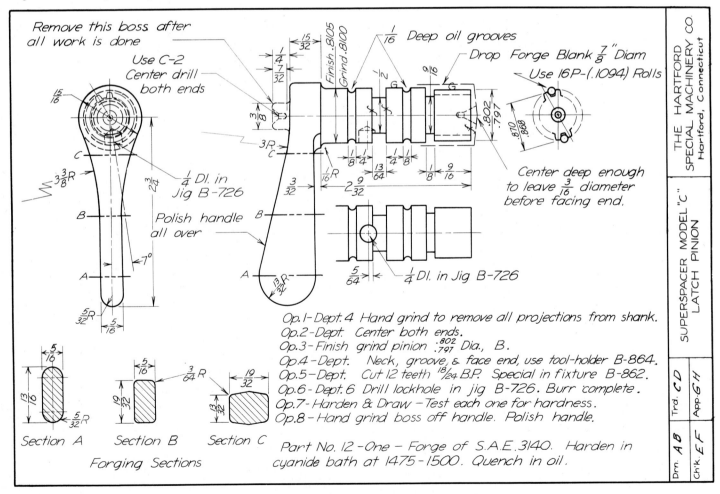

Remove this boss after all work is done

Use C-2 Center drill both ends

$\frac{1}{4}$ Dl. in Jig B-726

Polish handle all over

Finish .8105
Grind .8100

$\frac{1}{16}$ Deep oil grooves

Drop Forge Blank $\frac{7}{8}$" Diam

Use 16P-(.1094) Rolls

Center deep enough to leave $\frac{3}{16}$ diameter before facing end.

$\frac{1}{4}$ Dl. in Jig B-726

Op.1- Dept. 4 Hand grind to remove all projections from shank.
Op.2- Dept. Center both ends.
Op.3- Finish grind pinion $\frac{.802}{.797}$ Dia., B.
Op.4- Dept. Neck, groove, & face end, use tool-holder B-864.
Op.5- Dept. Cut 12 teeth $\frac{18}{24}$ B.P. Special in fixture B-862.
Op.6- Dept. 6 Drill lockhole in jig B-726. Burr complete.
Op.7- Harden & Draw -Test each one for hardness.
Op.8- Hand grind boss off handle. Polish handle.

Part No. 12 -One - Forge of S.A.E. 3140. Harden in cyanide bath at 1475-1500. Quench in oil.

Section A   Section B   Section C

Forging Sections

THE HARTFORD SPECIAL MACHINERY CO.
Hartford, Connecticut

SUPERSPACER MODEL "C" LATCH PINION

Drn. *AB*   Trd. *CD*
Chk. *EF*   App. *GH*

of parts on one drawing. Sometimes separate detail drawings are made for the use of different workmen, such as the patternmaker, hammersmith, machinist, or welder. Such drawings have only the dimensions and information needed by the workmen for whom the drawing is made. Figure 13-4c shows a forging as formed and after it has been machined. The working drawing of the superspacer latch pinion made by the Hartford Special Machinery Company is shown in Fig. 13-4d. Notice how the parts to be removed after all work is done are shown; also, notice the detailed list of machine operations. Figure 13-4e shows a combination drawing, or two-part detail drawing, for an oil-pump drive gear. The right-hand half gives the dimensions for the forging, and the left-hand half gives the machin-

Fig. 13-4e. A two-part detail drawing showing separate information for forging and machining. (Caterpillar Tractor Company)

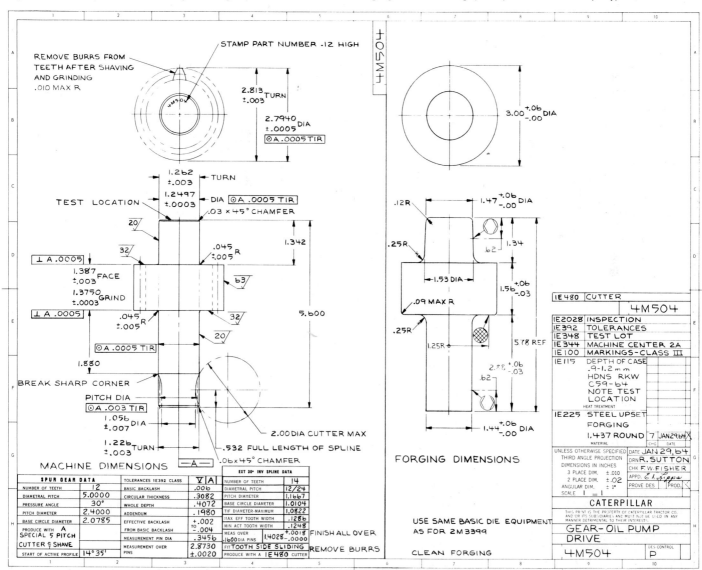

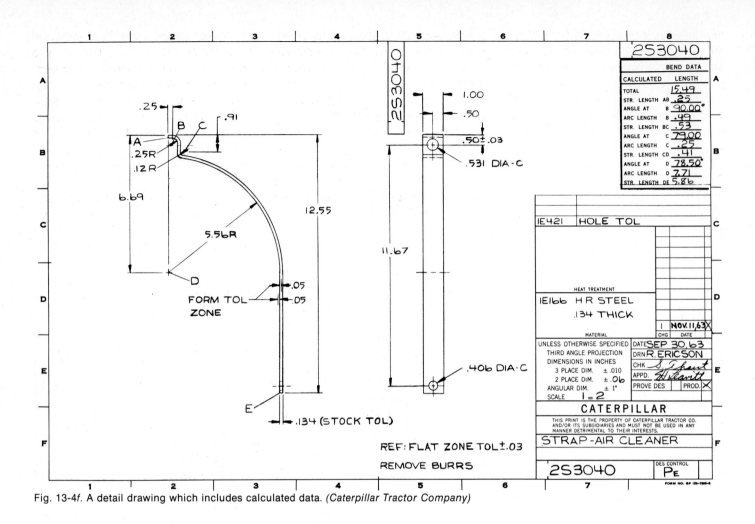

Fig. 13-4f. A detail drawing which includes calculated data. *(Caterpillar Tractor Company)*

Fig. 13-4g. A standard shown blank at A and filled in at B.

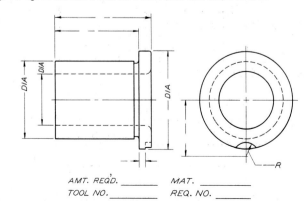

ing dimensions and information. A detail drawing may contain calculated data, as shown for the air cleaner strap in Fig. 13-4f.

Standard detail drawings are often made for parts which have the same shape but not the same dimensions. When such parts are often used, the views are drawn with blank spaces for dimensions and notes (Fig. 13-4g at A) to be filled in with the required information (as at B). Of course, the views will not be to scale, except perhaps for one size. A similar kind of drawing is sometimes used with letters used for dimensions. A table is placed on the drawing to give the dimensions for different sizes of the part. Either all or part of the dimensions may be used on a tabulated drawing (see Fig. 16-9).

13·5 Assembly drawings. A drawing of a completely assembled construction is called an *assembly drawing*. Such drawings vary greatly in respect to completeness of detail and dimensioning. Their particular value is in showing the way in which the parts go together, to show the appearance of the construction as a whole, and to give dimensions necessary for installation, space necessary, foundation, electrical or hydraulic connections, and so forth. When complete information is given, assembly drawings may be used for working drawings. This is possible when there is little or no complex detail; Fig. 13-5a shows such a drawing. Furniture and other wood construction can often be shown in assembly working drawings by adding necessary enlarged details or partial views.

Fig. 13-5a. An assembly working drawing for a belt tightener.

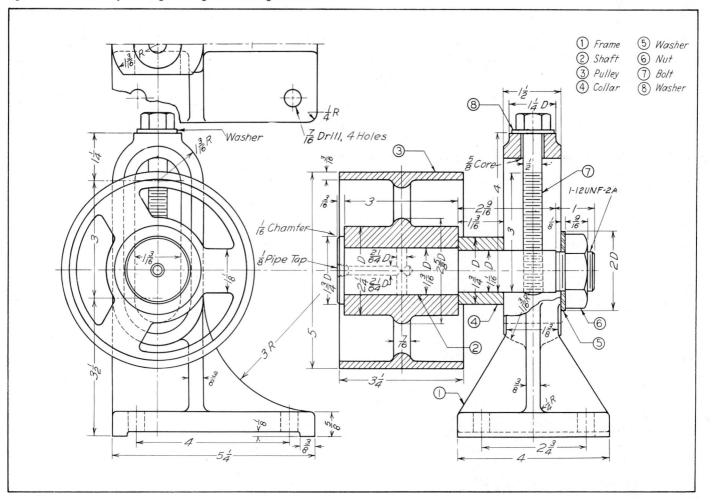

Assembly drawings of machines are generally made to small scale. They have selected dimensions to tell overall distances, important center-to-center distances, and local dimensions. All, or almost all, hidden lines may be left out; and if drawn to a very small scale, unnecessary detail may be omitted (Fig. 13-5b is an example). Either exterior or sectional views may be used. When the general appearance is the main purpose of the drawing, only one or two views need be used. Because of the size of some assembled constructions, it may be necessary to draw different views of the assembly on separate sheets. The same scale should be used on all sheets.

Photoprint assembly drawings described in Fig. 8-16a provide a clear and easily understood method of showing the appearance and operating parts of a complete machine. A special assembly drawing (Fig. 13-5c) is made for reference to identify parts to be used for assembly. Note the tabular list in the upper right-hand corner. Note also

Fig. 13-5b. An outline assembly drawing. *(Lufkin Foundry and Machine Company)*

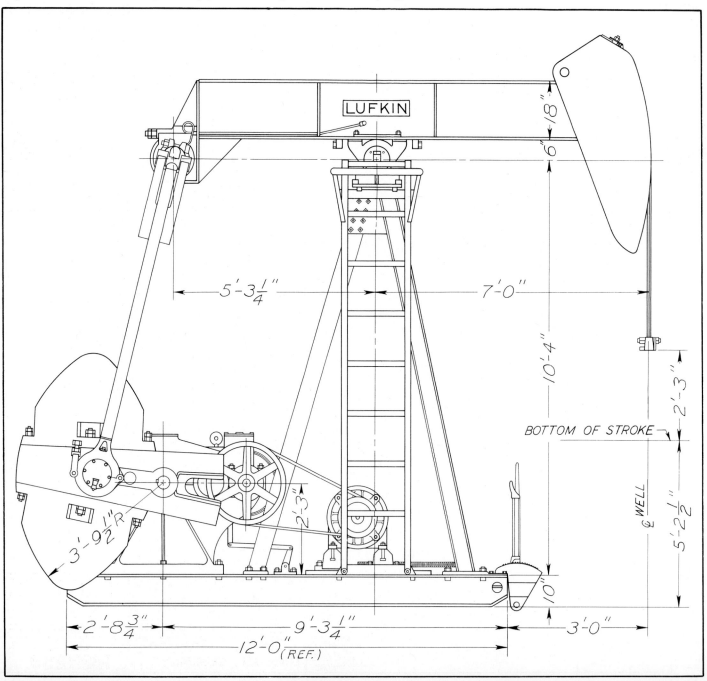

the selection of dimensions given on the drawing.

Many other kinds of assembly drawings are made for special purposes, such as: part assemblies for a group of parts, drawings for use in assembling or erecting a machine, drawings to give directions for maintenance and operations, and so forth. A most important kind of assembly drawing is the *design layout,* from which the detail drawings are made.

13·6 Choice of views. A drawing can be used more easily if the draftsman makes the proper selection of views. For the complete description of an object, at least two views are generally required. Although a drawing is not a picture, it is always advisable to select the views that require the least effort to read. Each view must have a part in the description; otherwise, it is not needed and should not be drawn. In some cases one view is all that is

necessary, provided a note is added or the shape and size are standard or evident. Complex pieces may require more than three views, some of which may be partial views, auxiliary views, and sectional views. The reason for making the drawing must always be kept in mind when a question arises. The final test of the value of a drawing is its clearness and exactness in giving the complete information necessary for the intended purpose.

Fig. 13-5c. A reference assembly drawing. *(Link-Belt Company)*

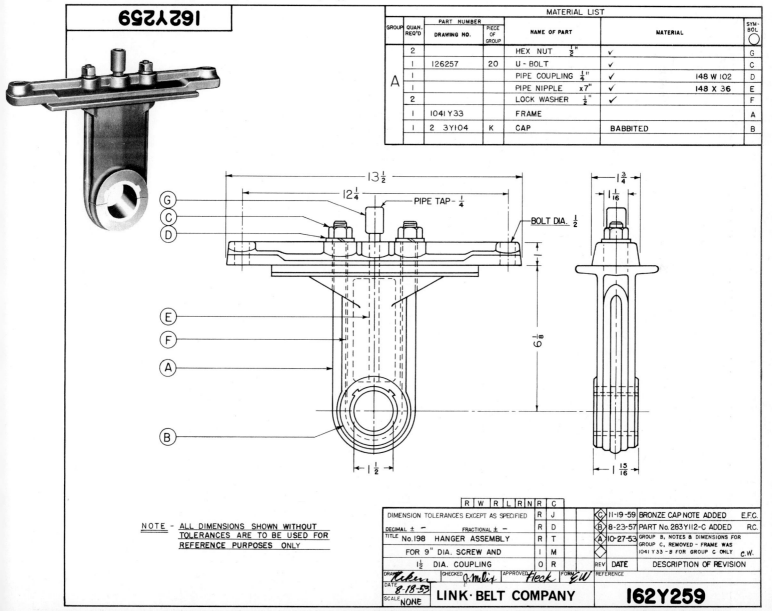

13·7 Choice of scale. The choice of scale for a detail drawing is governed by three things: (1) the size necessary for showing all details clearly, (2) the size necessary for carrying all dimensions without crowding, and (3) the size of paper used. In most cases it is desirable to make detail drawings to full size. Other scales commonly used are half, quarter, and eighth (see Art. 2·23). Such scales as $2'' = 1'$, $4'' = 1'$, and $9'' = 1'$ are to be avoided. If a part is very small, it is sometimes drawn to an enlarged scale, perhaps twice full size or more.

When a number of details are drawn on one sheet, they should, if possible, be made to the same scale. If different scales are used, they should be noted near each drawing. A detail, or part detail, drawn to a larger scale may often be used to advantage on drawings. This will save the making of separate detail drawings. General assembly drawings can be made to the scale that will show the desired amount of detail and work up well on the size of sheet used. Sheet-metal pattern drawings for practical use are always made full size, although practice models may be constructed from small-scale layouts.

Complete assemblies generally use a small scale, often fixed by the standard size of sheet selected by the company for assemblies. Part assemblies use a scale selected to suit the purpose, such as: to show how the parts are put together, to identify the parts, to explain an operation, or to give other information.

13·8 Placing views. It is sometimes necessary to work out the location of the views in the space available. The experienced draftsman generally can "spot" the views with little or no computation. When the views have to be placed in a definite working space, the space required for each view and their relative positions are considered, and the total room required is compared with the size of the drawing sheet.

Consider the guide yoke shown in the picture in Fig. 13-8. Three views are to be drawn in a working space 15" wide and 10½" high. The top view will require 2½" in a vertical direction and the front view 3⅞". Allowing, say, 1½" between views, the total is 7⅞". Subtracting 7⅞" from 10½" (the height of the space), we have left 2⅝" to be di-

Fig. 13-8. Placing the views in the working space.

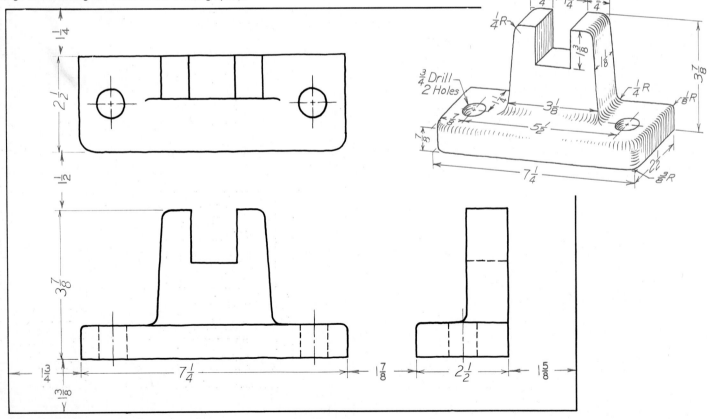

vided between top and bottom. In the layout sketch (Fig. 13-8), the base line of the front view has been placed 1⅜" up, which leaves 1¼" above the top line of the top view. The sum of the horizontal dimensions of the front and side views is 9¾". Allowing 1⅞" between views, there is left 3⅜" for the two side spaces. In Fig. 13-8 the left space is 1¾" and the right is 1⅝". It is not necessary to make spaces exactly alike between views or around them.

13•9 Order of working. After shape and size description, the most important thing is to develop good form. A systematic method of working will help to achieve the desired results. (Refer to Art. 2·10 for the kinds of lines to use, to Chap. 10 for the representation of sectional views, and to Chap. 11 for dimensioning.) The order of making the different parts of a drawing is the first item. A drawing is started by drawing the center and base lines as in Space 1 of Fig. 13-9. These form the skeleton for the views. Then block in the views as in Space 2. Next, draw the arcs and complete the views as in Space 3. The views should be carried along together. Do not attempt to finish one view before making another. Learn the following order and follow it as nearly as possible on every drawing:

1. Determine what views are required.
2. Plan the arrangement of views.
3. Determine the scale to use.
4. Lay off the sheet to proper size and block in the title space or record strip, if required.
5. Draw the primary center and base lines.
6. Lay off the principal measurements.
7. Block in the views by drawing the preliminary and final blocking-in lines.

Fig. 13-9. The order of procedure in making a working drawing.

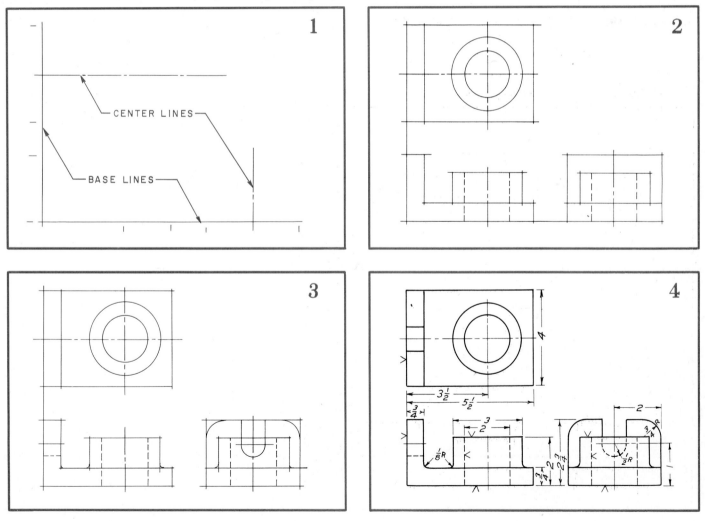

8. Lay off the detail measurements.
9. Draw the center lines for details.
10. Draw all complete circles and the preliminary and final lines for details.
11. Draw part circles, fillets, and rounded corners.
12. Draw such lines as could not be drawn previously.
13. Draw all extension and dimension lines.
14. Put on arrowheads.
15. Put in dimensions and notes.
16. Draw section lines, if needed.
17. Letter in the title.
18. Check the drawing carefully.

13•10 Titles. Every sketch and drawing must have some kind of title; the form, completeness, and location vary. On working drawings the title is usually boxed in the lower right-hand corner (Fig. 13-10a at A, B, and C) or included in the record strip extending across the bottom or end of the sheet (Fig. 13-10a at D) as far as needed.

The title gives as much as is necessary of the following information:

1. The name of the construction, machine, or project.
2. The name of the part or parts shown, or simple details.
3. Manufacturer, company or firm name, and address.
4. Date, usually date of completion.
5. Scale or scales.
6. Heat treatment, working tolerances, etc.
7. Numbers of the drawing of the shop order or customer's order, according to the system used.
8. Drafting-room record: names or initials, with dates of draftsman, tracer and checker, and approval of chief draftsman, engineer, etc.
9. A revision block or space for recording changes, when required, should be placed above or at the left of the title block.

A form for a basic layout of a title block (Fig. 13-10b) is extracted from the American Drafting Standards Manual *Section, Size and Format* (ASA Y14.1-1957) with the permission of the publisher, The American Society of Mechanical Engineering, 345 East 47th Street, New York, N.Y. The arrangement, size, and content may vary.

In large drafting rooms the title is generally printed on the paper, cloth, or film, leaving spaces to be filled in. Separate printed adhesive titles are used by many firms.

13•11 List of material or parts list. It is necessary, or desirable, to include on most drawings a list of parts, the

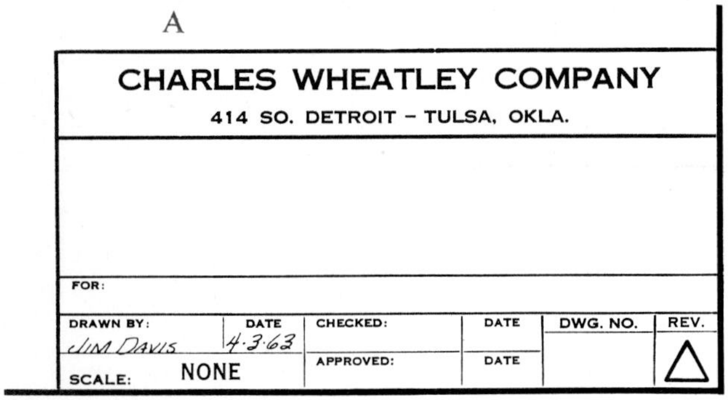

Fig. 13-10a. Titles. Boxed titles at A, B, and C. A strip title at D.

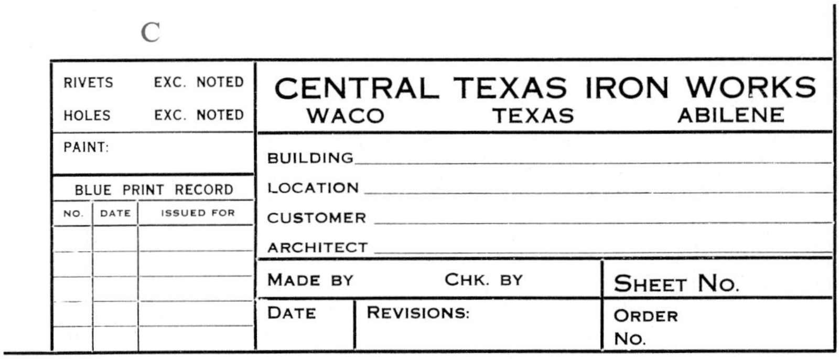

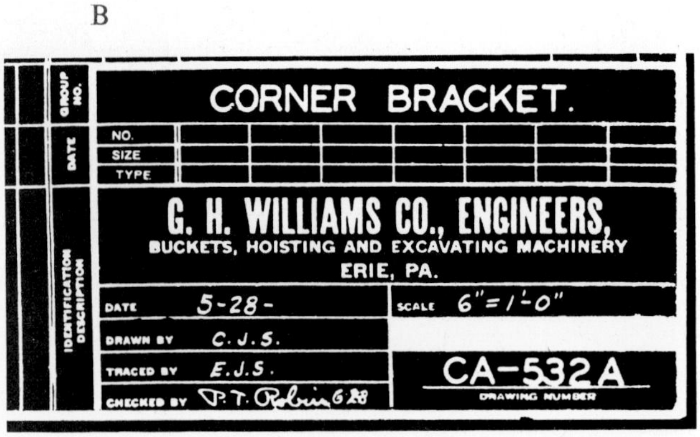

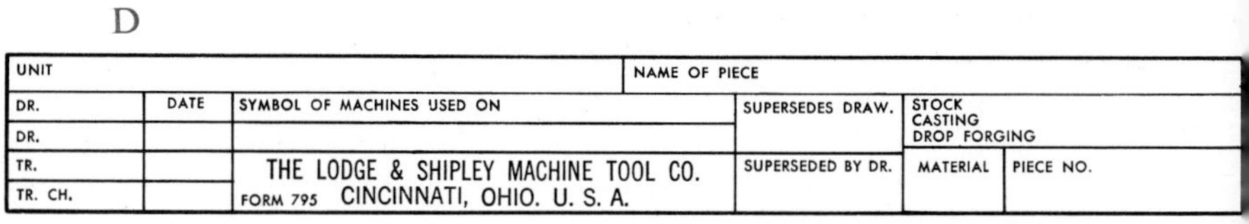

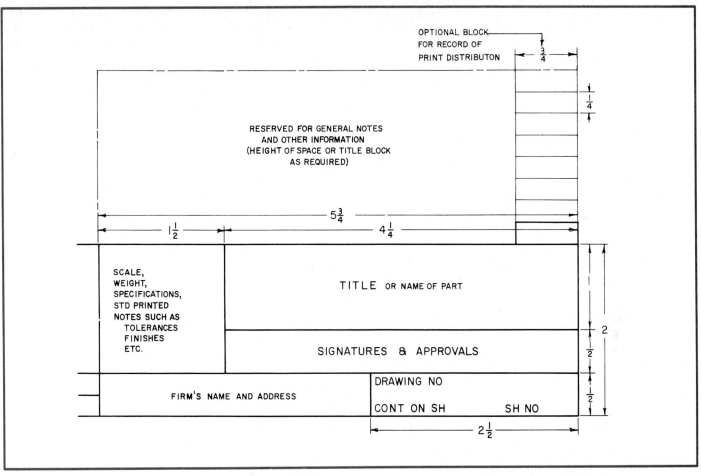

Fig. 13-10b. Basic layout for a title block. *(From American Standard ASA Y14.1-1957)*

In the figure:

OPTIONAL BLOCK
FOR RECORD OF
PRINT DISTRIBUTON

RESERVED FOR GENERAL NOTES
AND OTHER INFORMATION
(HEIGHT OF SPACE OR TITLE BLOCK
AS REQUIRED)

SCALE,
WEIGHT,
SPECIFICATIONS,
STD PRINTED
NOTES SUCH AS
TOLERANCES
FINISHES
ETC.

TITLE OR NAME OF PART

SIGNATURES & APPROVALS

FIRM'S NAME AND ADDRESS

DRAWING NO

CONT ON SH   SH NO

$5\frac{3}{4}$ $1\frac{1}{2}$ $4\frac{1}{4}$ $2\frac{1}{2}$ $\frac{3}{4}$ $\frac{1}{4}$ 2 $\frac{2}{2}$

materials of which they are made, identification numbers, or other information. Such drawings may include assembly drawings of various kinds, or detail drawings, where a number of parts are shown on the same sheet.

The names of parts, material, number required, part numbers, and so forth, may be given in notes near the views of each part. The preferred method is to place part numbers near the views with a leader and then collect all the necessary information in tabulated lists called a *list of material* or *parts list* (Fig. 13-11a). This list is sometimes placed above the title, but American Standards recommends placing it in the upper right corner of the sheet.

Fig. 13-11a. A bill of material.

BILL OF MATERIAL FOR IDLER PULLEY			
NAME	REQ.	MAT'L	NOTES
IDLER PULLEY	I	C.I.	
IDLER PULLEY FRAME	I	C.I.	
IDLER PULLEY BUSHING	I	BRO.	
IDLER PULLEY SHAFT	I	C.R.S.	
$\frac{5}{8}$ SAE HEX NUT	I		$\frac{3}{8}$ HIGH PURCHASED
WOODRUFF KEY 405	I		PURCHASED
$\frac{1}{8}$ OILER	I		PURCHASED

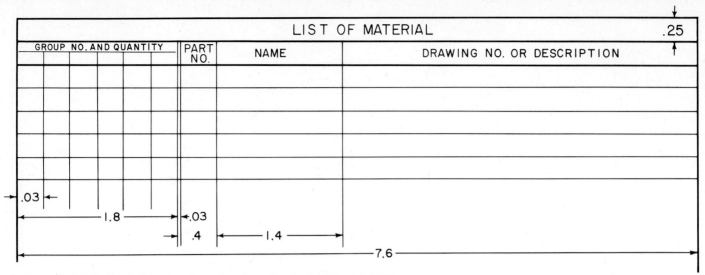

Fig. 13-11*b*. A list-of-material form. *(From American Standard ASA Y14.1-1957)*

Sometimes it may be lettered or typewritten on a separate sheet titled "Parts List for Drawing No. 00" in order to identify it. The American Standards (ASA Y14.1) presents the form shown in Fig. 13-11*b*. The column widths may be varied to suit the data to be entered therein.

13•12 Grouping and placing parts. When a number of details are used for one machine only, they are often grouped on a single sheet or set of sheets. A convenient arrangement is to group the forging details together, the casting details together, the brass details together, and similarly, other materials. In general, it is well to show parts in the position that they will occupy in the assembled machine, with related parts near each other. Long pieces, however, such as shafts and bolts, are drawn with their long dimensions parallel to the long dimension of the sheet.

13•13 Adapting principles in the drafting room. The principles of shape description by means of views have been explained. They form the basis

for working drawings. In the actual use of mechanical drawing, it is sometimes necessary, or desirable, to violate these rules. The reason for each violation must be thoroughly understood, as well as the method of making the necessary changes in the drawing.

When exact projections of exterior, or sectional, views result in complicated or misleading views, they are modified. Such violations are called *conventional representations* and are used to make drawings easier to read (Chap. 10). Rules and standards must be considered as guides to be followed when they serve the purpose best. They are not fixed and unchangeable laws.

13•14 Rough and finished castings. Castings are made by pouring molten metal, such as cast iron, brass, aluminum, etc., into molds formed in sand. Wooden patterns are used to form the molds. The surfaces of the cooled metal, when removed from each mold, have been roughened by contact with the sand. Sometimes the casting can be used in this form, but more often some of the surfaces must be finished, or made smooth, and brought to size

by machining. Round surfaces are finished on a lathe or similar machine. Flat surfaces are finished on a shaper, planer, milling machine, or similar machine. Finished surfaces must always be indicated on a drawing, and when necessary, the smoothness and the degree of accuracy must be specified.

13•15 Fillets and rounds. Sharp corners and edges are generally undesirable. Rounded corners and edges not only look better but are also stronger. For this reason, interior corners are filled in with fillets, and exterior corners are rounded.

13•16 Pulleys and flywheels. Included under this general class are pulleys that carry belts, flywheels for storing energy, and handwheels for adjustment. Each has a rim, arms, and a hub.

Belt pulleys (Fig. 13-16*a*) are made of cast iron, steel, plastic, wood, paper, and so forth. The face of a belt pulley is generally crowned (made higher in the center). The crown tends to keep the belt centered. Some rim sections are shown in Fig. 13-16*b*. Flanges may

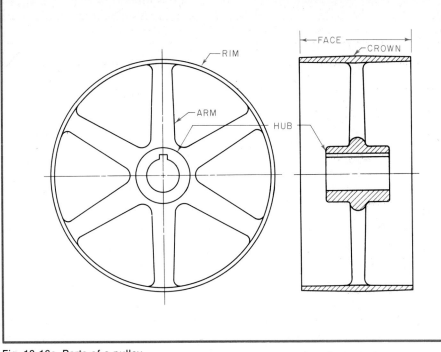

Fig. 13-16a. Parts of a pulley.

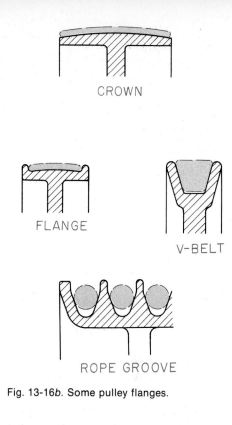

CROWN

FLANGE

V-BELT

ROPE GROOVE

Fig. 13-16b. Some pulley flanges.

be used on small belt pulleys to keep the belt in place. For V-belts, specially shaped pulleys are used, as illustrated. For rope or cable driving, such as elevators or cable cars, grooved pulleys are used.

Flywheels have heavy rims which store up or give out energy when the speed changes. The rim of a flywheel is, therefore, thick in proportion to its width in order to concentrate weight. Flywheels (Fig. 13-16c) are made in many forms for use on steam engines, gas engines, presses, and other machinery where their regulating action is needed.

13·17 Bearings are supports for moving parts of machines. They may be either flat or round. The runner of a sled or an ice skate is essentially a flat bearing. A typewriter carriage slides on flat bearing surfaces known as

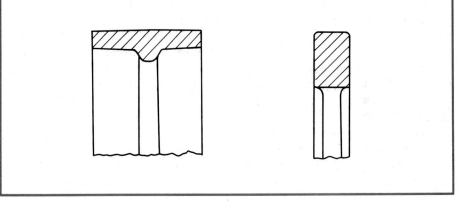

Fig. 13-16c. Flywheel rims.

slides, or *ways.* The wheels of roller skates are built around ball bearings that roll around a round shaft. Sometimes cylindrical rollers are used instead of steel balls. Plain ball or roller bearings are designed for use under load and speed conditions.

Plain round bearings are usually lined with babbitt metal (a mixture of the three metals: copper, antimony, and tin) or some other substance that slides easily against the shaft. Bearings are often oiled or greased by means of grooves that help the parts rub easily together. A hole through a piece of metal is the simplest type of bearing. It may or may not be bushed, lined, or oiled.

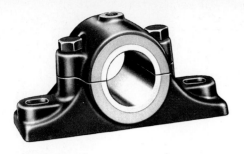

There are many types of journal bearings. They may be solid or split, babbitted or bushed. They may have ball or roller bearings and many other features. A split bronze-bushed journal bearing is shown in Figs. 13-17a and 13-17b.

13·18 Shafting drawings are of two general kinds. Transmission or lineshaft drawings are made to show the location of pulleys, gears, bearings, keyways, and so forth. The diameter and the length of the shaft must be shown, together with the locating di-

Fig. 13-17a. A split bronze-bushed journal bearing. *(Dodge Manufacturing Corporation)*

Fig. 13-17b. Drawing of the split bronze-bushed journal bearing shown in Fig. 13-17a. *(Adapted from details of Dodge Manufacturing Corp.)*

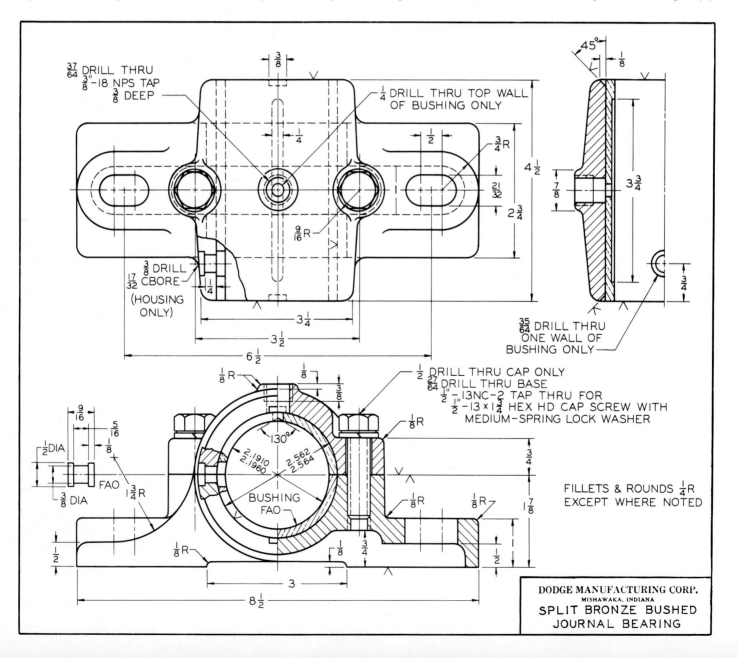

mensions and notes specifying the sizes and kinds of the various features. Shafting is made of either hot-rolled or cold-rolled steel.

Drawings for machine shafts are made in the same way as other machine parts (Fig. 13-18). Complete information must be given by dimensions and notes. Shafts are made of steel of a grade suited to the purpose for which the shafts are used, and they are machined to size.

13·19 Shaft couplings. For joining shafting end to end, couplings of various types are used. Two forms of sleeve couplings are illustrated in Figs. 13-19a and 13-19b. Many other designs are made for use under different conditions of load and speed or where the axes are not parallel or in line.

13·20 Pipe used to convey fluids is made of various materials: lead, brass, copper, aluminum, steel, wrought iron, cast iron, wood, concrete, and so forth. For steam, gas, and similar purposes, standard pipe of steel or iron is commonly used. Such pipe is specified by the nominal inside diameter, which differs from the actual diameter. The dimensions for pipe in general use (formerly known as *Standard)* are given in the Appendix.

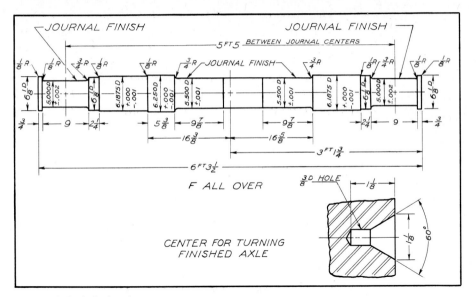

Fig. 13-18. A shaft drawing.

This former standard was used for ordinary pressures of around 125 lb per sq in. In addition, *extra heavy* (X) pipe was made with thicker walls for heavier pressures but with the same outside diameter as the standard pipe. This reduced the inside diameter for the same nominal size. *Double extra heavy* (XX) pipe used the same outside diameter, but the inside diameter was smaller; it was used for still higher pressures. Large pipe, over 12 in. in

diameter, was called *OD pipe* and was specified by the outside diameter and thickness of the material from which it was made.

Present practice is covered in the published American Standard *Wrought-steel and Wrought-iron Pipe* (ASA B36.10-1959). This gives wall thicknesses and weights for different schedule numbers and replaces the former standard and the extra heavy (X) and double extra heavy (XX) standards.

Fig. 13-19a. A sleeve coupling.

Fig. 13-19b. A split coupling.

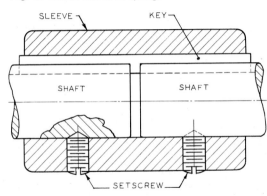

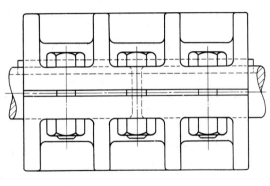

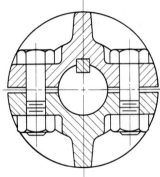

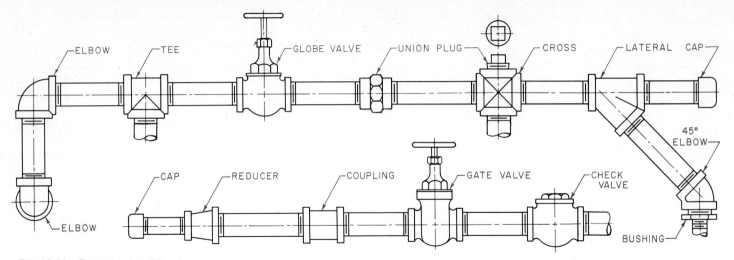

Fig. 13-21a. Screwed pipe fittings.

13·21 Pipe joints and fittings. Ordinary small pipe is "made up," or joined together, with "fittings." Several screwed fittings are shown and named in Fig. 13-21a. The American Standard pipe thread (Fig. 13-21b) is used on screwed pipe and fittings. Note the taper, which provides for a tight joint; there is also a straight pipe thread. The latest American Standard should be consulted for complete information on pipe, pipe thread, and pipe fittings.

Pipe and fittings with beveled ends (Fig. 13-21c) are joined together by welding. Flanged pipe and fittings (Fig. 13-21d) are used for larger sizes of pipe for many purposes. The flanges are bolted together. Other methods are used for joining plastic pipe, tubing, wood pipe, cast-iron pipe, and so forth. Cast-iron pipe may be bolted together by end flanges, or it may be joined by bell-and-spigot ends, as shown in Fig. 13-21e.

Fig. 13-21b. American Standard pipe thread.

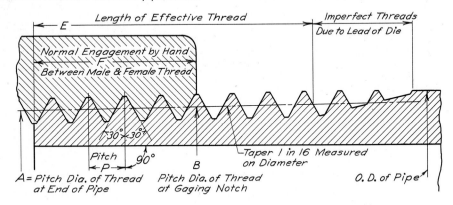

$$A = D - (0.05D + 1.1)P$$
$$B = A + 0.0625 F$$
$$E = (0.80D + 6.8)P$$
$$\text{Depth of Thread} = 0.80P$$

Fig. 13-21c. Welded pipe fittings.

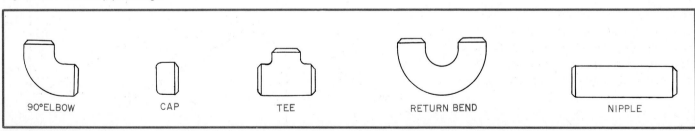

90°ELBOW   CAP   TEE   RETURN BEND   NIPPLE

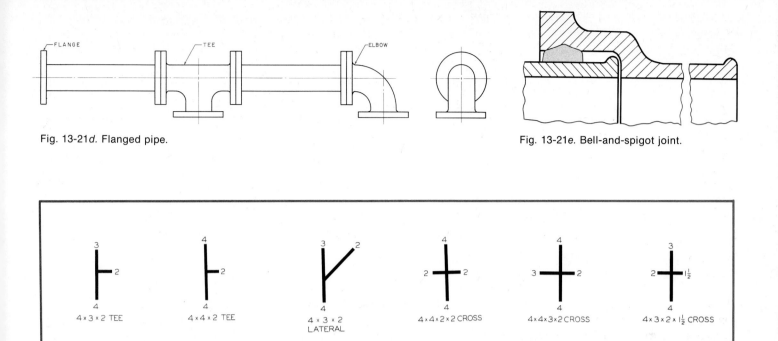

Fig. 13-21d. Flanged pipe.

Fig. 13-21e. Bell-and-spigot joint.

Fig. 13-22. How sizes of pipe fittings are specified.

13·22 Sizes of pipe fittings are specified by the nominal size of pipe with which they are used (Fig. 13-22). The size of the "run" is given first for a tee, or a cross, and then the side outlets. Reducing fittings are used to join different sizes of pipe. The size is specified by giving the largest run opening first and then the opposite end of the run.

13·23 Piping drawings. Drawings for piping layouts may use the representations of Art. 13·21 with dimensions and notes added to specify lengths, sizes, kinds, and locations. Simple single-line layouts (Fig. 13-23a) with standard symbols for valves, fittings, etc., are preferred. See latest edition of American Standard *Graphical Symbols for Pipe Fitting* (ASA Z32.2.3). Pictorial representations of piping, either single line (Fig. 13-23b)

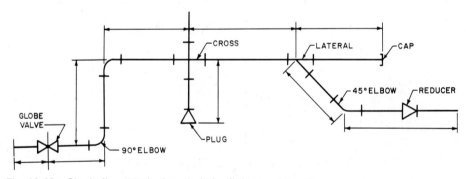

Fig. 13-23a. Single-line standard symbols for fittings, valves, etc.

Fig. 13-23b. Single-line pictorial drawings using standard symbols.

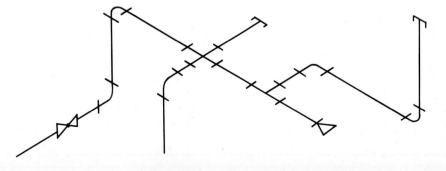

or realistic (Fig. 13-23c), are effective in showing a piping layout. Regular orthographic working drawings are used for steam-plant layouts. A piece of such a drawing for the exhaust lines of a steam plant is shown in Fig. 13-23d.

13·24 Notes and specifications. Information that cannot be represented graphically must be given in the form

Fig. 13-23c. Pictorial drawings show the positions in space of piping layout. *(Courtesy of Jenkins Bros., manufacturers of valves)*

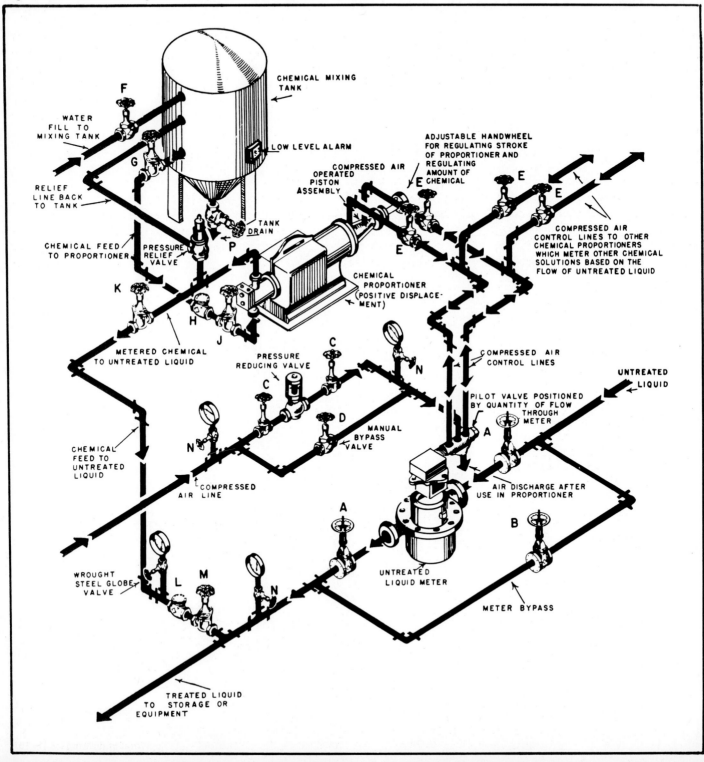

of lettered notes and symbols. Trade information that is understood generally by those on the job is often given in this way. Such notes include the following items: number required, material, kind of finish, kind of fit, method of machining, kinds of screw threads, kinds of bolts and nuts, sizes of wire, and thickness of sheet metal.

The materials in general use are wood, plastic, cast iron, wrought iron, steel, brass, aluminum, and various alloys. All parts to go together must be of the proper size so that they will fit. Some pieces may be left rough, partly finished, or completely finished. The wood used for making furniture is first shaped with woodworking tools and machines. Many metals, such as cast iron, brass, aluminum, and so forth, are given the required form by molding, casting, and machining. First, a wooden pattern of the shape and size

required is made and placed in sand to make an impression, or mold, into which the molten metal is poured. Wrought iron and steel are made into shapes by rolling or forging in the rolling mill or blacksmith shop. Some kinds of steel may be cast.

There are many interesting ways of forming metals for special purposes and many special alloys that cannot be described in a drawing book, but the student will learn much by observing the shapes of parts of machinery and the materials of which they are made.

After a part is cast or forged, it must be machined on all surfaces that are to fit other surfaces. Round surfaces are generally formed on a lathe. Flat surfaces are finished or smoothed on a planer, milling machine, or shaper. Drill presses, boring mills, or lathes are used for making holes. Extra metal is allowed for surfaces that are to be

finished. To specify such surfaces, the V-symbol is placed on the lines which represent the edges of surfaces to be finished. If the entire piece is to be finished, a note such as "Finish All Over" (or "FAO") may be used and all other marks omitted.

Specifications as to methods of machining, finish, and other treatment are given in the form of notes, such as "Spot face," "Grind," "Polish," "Knurl," "Core," "Drill," "Ream," "Countersink," "Harden," "Caseharden," "Blue," and "Temper." It is often necessary to add notes in regard to assembling, order of doing work, or other special directions.

13•25 Checking a drawing. After a drawing has been completed, it must be very carefully examined before it is used. This is called *checking the drawing.* It is very important work and should

Fig. 13-23d. Part of a piping drawing for a steam plant.

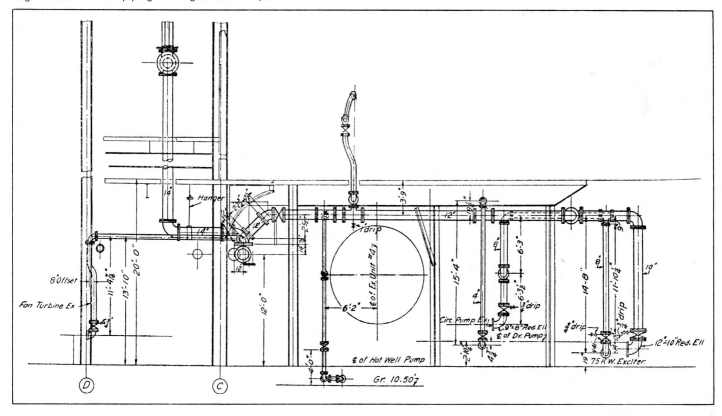

be done by someone who has not worked on the drawing.

Thorough checking requires a definite order of procedure and consideration of the following items:

1. See that the views completely describe the shape of each piece.
2. See that there are no unnecessary views.
3. See that the scale is sufficiently large to show all detail clearly.
4. See that all views are to scale and that correct dimensions are given.
5. See that there will be no interferences during assembly or operation and that necessary clearances are provided.
6. See that sufficient dimensions are given to define the sizes of all parts completely and that no unnecessary or duplicate dimensions are given.
7. See that all necessary location or positioning dimensions are given with necessary precision.
8. See that necessary tolerances, limits and fits, and other precision information is given.
9. See that the kind of material and the number required of each part are specified.
10. See that the kind of finish is specified, that all finished surfaces are marked, and that finish is not called for where not needed.
11. See that standard parts and stock items, such as bolts, screws, pins, keys or other fastenings, handles, catches, etc., are used where suitable.
12. See that all necessary explanatory notes are given and properly placed.

Each draftsman is expected to inspect his own work for errors or omissions before the drawings are turned over to the checker.

13·26 Problem suggestions. Group 13, page 482. Three lists are presented. List 1 includes more elementary problems. Selections of two or three problems should be made from List 1 for a brief course. Selections of a few drawings from List 2 may be used for alternative or additional problems. Selections from List 3 may be made for advanced students or for those taking a more extensive course. Review of Chaps. 9 to 12 should be assigned in connection with these problems. It will add interest and value to this chapter if a few parts of machines are available which can be sketched, measured, drawn, and traced.

WORKING DRAWINGS

List 1: Problems 13·3, 13·4, 13·6, 13·8, 13·14, 13·16, 13·17, 13·19, 13·21, 13·27.
List 2: Problems 13·5, 13·9, 13·12, 13·15, 13·20, 13·23, 13·29.
List 3: Problems 13·7, 13·10, 13·11, 13·13, 13·18, 13·22, 13·23, 13·24, 13·25, 13·28, 13·30, 13·31, 13·32.

WOOD PROJECTS

List 1: Problems 13·33, 13·35, 13·36, 13·38, 13·40, 13·43, 13·44.
List 2: Problems 13·34, 13·37, 13·39, 13·41, 13·42, 13·48.
List 3: Problems 13·45, 13·46, 13·47, 13·50, 13·51, 13·52, 13·53, 13·54.

ASSEMBLY AND DETAIL DRAWINGS

List 1: Problems 13·56, 13·58, 13·61, 13·62, 13·66, 13·69.
List 2: Problems 13·55, 13·59, 13·63, 13·68, 13·70, 13·71.
List 3: Problems 13·57, 13·60, 13·64, 13·65, 13·67, 13·72, 13·73, 13·74, 13·75, 13·76, 13·77, 13·78.

14

Pictorial drawing

14·1 Pictorial drawing. From within the home (Fig. 14-1a) to outer space (Fig. 14-1b), pictorial drawings can show and describe anything which can be built or imagined. Pictorial drawings have become an essential part of the graphic language in engineering of all kinds, in architecture, in science, in electronics, in technical illustration, and in almost every profession.

On working drawings the shape description is always done by the exact method of separate views, or orthographic projection, as you have studied in previous chapters. In addition to a knowledge of this system of drawing, one should be able to make a pictorial view, either freehand or with instruments. The person who quickly and skillfully makes a pictorial sketch or drawing finds this ability very helpful in design work. Pictorial sketches help in reading and visualizing a drawing. They also show the appearance of an object to persons who cannot read orthographic projection. Notes, reports, and published articles are more helpful if they contain pictorial draw-

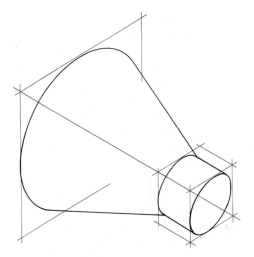

Fig. 14-1a. The plan tells the carpenter how to build the kitchen, but the picture shows the housewife how it looks.

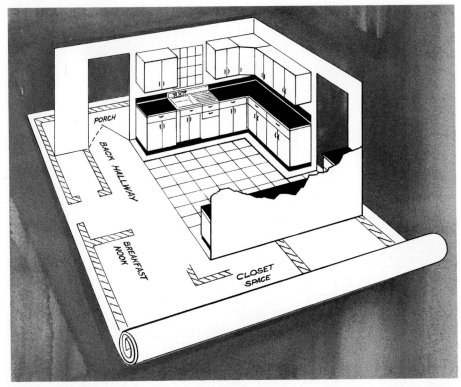

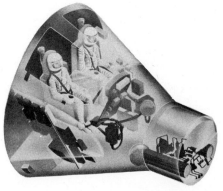

Fig. 14-1b. The Gemini spacecraft. Sketches, drawings, and pictures are important in developing the means of exploring space. *(NASA, McDonnell Aircraft Corporation)*

ings. In the study of drawing, one of the best exercises is to translate orthographic drawings into pictorial drawings.

Pictorial drawings are used often to show exploded views on production drawings (Chap. 15), to illustrate parts lists, and to explain the operation of machines, apparatus, and equipment and for many other purposes.

14·2 Pictorial views. Those familiar with the subject often make sketches in perspective. These show the object as it would actually appear to the eye (Fig. 14-2, Spaces 1 and 2). An easier way, although the result is not so pleasing in appearance as a well-made perspective, is to use one of the pictorial methods of projection, such as isometric drawing (Space 3) and oblique projection (Space 4). These all show three faces in one view. Their advantage is that the principal lines can be measured directly. Although similar in effect, these three methods should not be confused. Cabinet drawing (Space 5) is a form of oblique drawing with distances parallel to oblique axis reduced one-half.

Fig. 14-2. Some kinds of pictorial drawing.

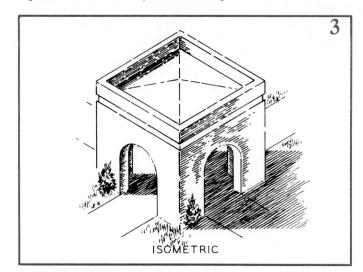

ISOMETRIC

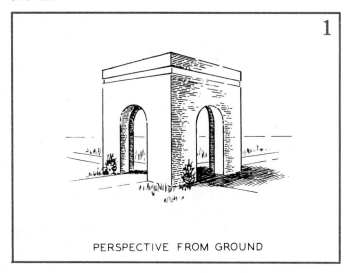

PERSPECTIVE FROM GROUND

OBLIQUE

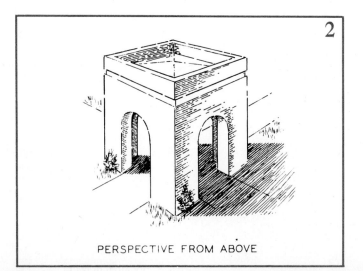

PERSPECTIVE FROM ABOVE

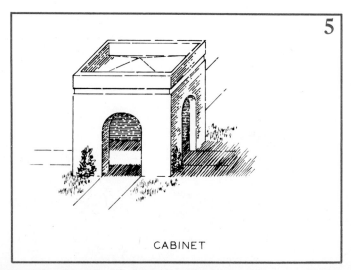

CABINET

14·3 Isometric projection and isometric drawing. An isometric projection may be obtained by revolution (Fig. 14-3a). Three views of a cube in the usual position are shown in Space 1.

Space 2: Revolve the cube from the position of Space 1 through 45° about a vertical axis. The front and side views will now show as two equal rectangles.

Space 3: Revolve the cube forward about an axis perpendicular to the profile plane from the position of Space

2 until the body diagonal,[1] *OB,* of the cube is horizontal (perpendicular to the frontal plane), as shown. The front view will be an isometric projection of the cube. The cube has been tilted up on a corner, and the diagonal of the base of the cube has been revolved through 35°–16′. The front view (isometric projection) shows the three

---

[1] The body diagonal is the longest line that can be drawn in a cube. In Space 2 a line from the upper front corner to the lower back corner is a body diagonal.

---

faces equal in shape and size. In this position it is evident that the edges do not show in their true length but are all of equal length. Thus, 1″ on the cube in Space 1 is .8165″ on the isometric projection.

In Space 4 of Fig. 14-3a an isometric drawing of the same cube is shown. It has the same shape as the isometric projection, but the edges are drawn their true length instead of the shortened length. This variation in size does not affect the pictorial value of the view for shape description, but it does simplify the drawing of the view because all measurements are made with the regular scale. This makes it possible to draw a pictorial view at once without projecting from other views or using a special scale. A special scale can be constructed as shown in Space 3, beneath the side views, if desired.

Isometric projection by auxiliary views is illustrated in Fig. 14-3b. The first auxiliary is in the direction of the diagonal of the top surface of the cube. The second auxiliary is in the direction of the body diagonal, as indicated in the first auxiliary view.

14·4 An isometric drawing (Fig. 14-4). Orthographic views of a filler block are shown in Space 1. An iso-

Fig. 14-3a. Isometric projection and isometric drawing.

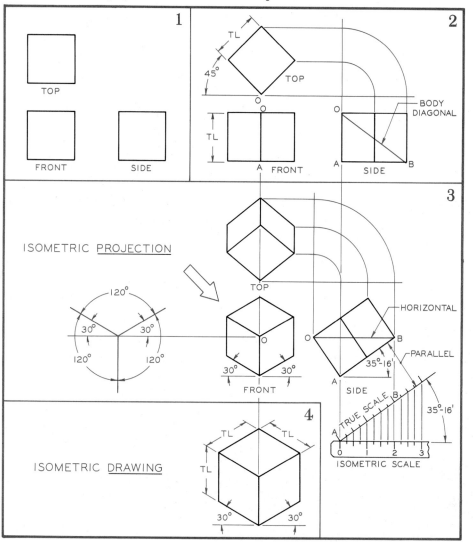

Fig. 14-3b. Isometric by double auxiliary.

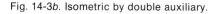
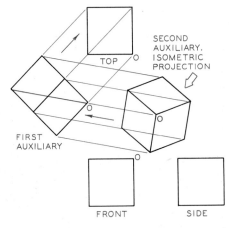

metric drawing is built upon a skeleton of three lines representing the edges of a cube. These three lines form three equal angles of 120° and are called *isometric axes* (Fig. 14-4, Space 2). One, *OA*, is drawn vertically; the other two, *OB* and *OC*, are drawn with the 30°–60° triangle as shown in Space 2. The intersection of these lines represents the upper front corner, *O*, of the block. Measuring the width, *W*, the depth, *D*, and the height, *H*, of the block on the three axes and drawing lines through the points parallel to the axes will give the isometric drawing of the block, as in Space 3. To locate the rectangular hole, Space 3, lay off 1″ along *OC* to *c* and from *c* lay off 2″ to *c¹*. Through *c* and *c¹* draw lines parallel to *OB*. In like manner locate *b* and *b¹* on axis *OB* and draw lines parallel to *OC*. Draw a vertical line from corner 3. Brighten the drawing to complete it, as in Space 4.

The purpose of a pictorial drawing, in general, is to show how something

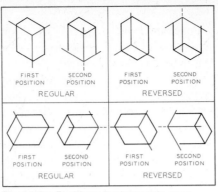

Fig. 14-5a. Positions for isometric axes.

looks. Hidden lines are not "part of the picture"; therefore, they are omitted except in some particular case when a certain feature might be indicated for explanation.

14•5 Position for the isometric axes. The axes may be arranged in different ways provided their relative positions are not changed (120° with each other). Several positions shown and identified in Fig. 14-5a will be applied later in this chapter.

The arrangement of the axes in Fig. 14-4 is the first position and is based upon the three edges of the cube which meet at the upper front corner. It is

Fig. 14-5b. An isometric drawing. Axes in second position.

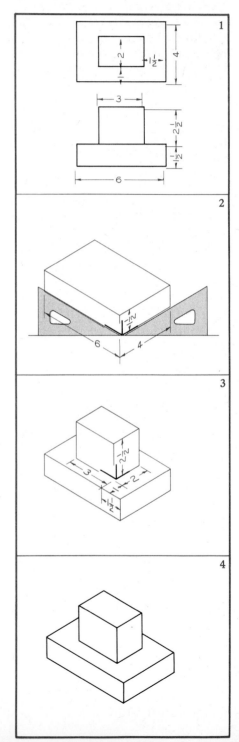

Fig. 14-4. An isometric drawing. Axes in first position.

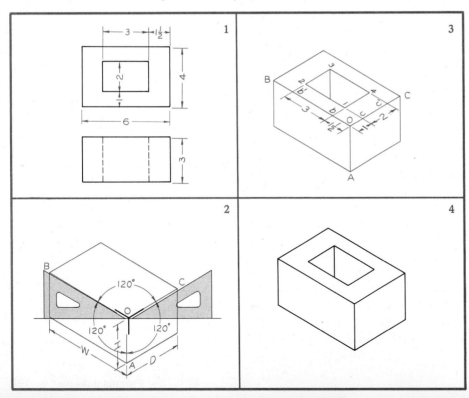

often more convenient to place the axes in the second position, which starts at the lower corner (Fig. 14-5b).

Any line of an object parallel to one of the edges of a cube is drawn parallel to an isometric axis and is called an *isometric line*. The first rule of isometric drawing is:

Measurements can be made only on isometric lines.

Fig. 14-6a. Construction for nonisometric lines.

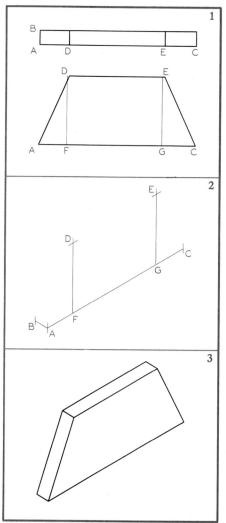

The second rule is:

Remember the isometric cube.

14·6 Nonisometric lines. Lines not parallel to any of the isometric axes are called *nonisometric lines.* Such lines will not show in their true length and cannot be measured; they must be drawn by locating their two ends.

Angles between lines on isometric drawings do not show in their true size and cannot be measured in degrees. All the angles of a cube are right angles, but in the isometric drawing some would measure 120° and some 60°. In the drawing of angles other than 90° the lines forming them must be transferred from the orthographic views as shown in Fig. 14-6a. To make an isometric drawing of the packing block shown in Space 1, first drop the perpendiculars on the front view from the points *D* and *E,* giving the construction lines *DF* and *EG.* Then draw the two isometric axes, *AB* and *AC,* as in Space 2, and transfer the distances *AF* and *CG* from Space 1 to Space 2; use the dividers. Draw vertical construction lines at *F* and *G* equal in length to lines *DF* and *EG* taken from the front view in Space 1 to locate points *D* and *E.* The nonisometric lines *AD* and *CE* can then be drawn and the isometric view finished as in Space 3. The isometric representations of the angles will be as shown at *DAF* and *ECG.* Any angle or any nonisometric line may be located on an isometric drawing by locating end points of the line.

For an angle given in degrees (Fig. 14-6b), lay out the angle *AOB,* making *AO* any convenient length. Draw *AB* perpendicular to *AO* to form a right triangle. To lay out the angle on the front face of the cube: Lay off O_1A_1 on the isometric view equal to *AO* of the true angle and draw A_1B_1 parallel to O_1O_2 and equal to *AB* taken from the true

angle. Draw O_1B_1, and $A_1O_1B_1$ is the isometric angle. To lay out the angle on the top face: Lay off $O_2A_2 = OA$, $A_2B_2 = AB$ parallel to O_2C, and draw O_2B_2. $A_2O_2B_2$ is the isometric angle.

Lines which are parallel on an object or construction always show parallel regardless of the point of view. If we remember this, it will often save time in making isometric and oblique drawings.

Figure 14-6c shows a line, *AB,* making an angle with the three regular planes. Locate the end points *A* and *B* by measurements parallel to the isometric axes taken from the orthographic views.

Fig. 14-6b. Angles parallel to isometric planes.

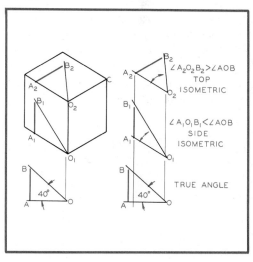

Fig. 14-6c. An angle inclined to *H, F,* and *P.*

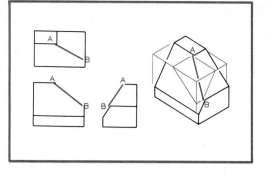

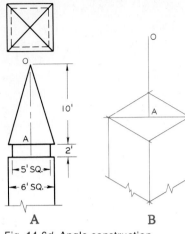

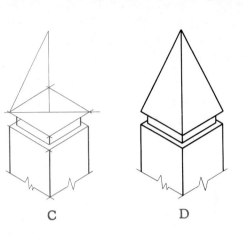

A   **B**   **C**   **D**

Fig. 14-6d. Angle construction.

the left or right surfaces of the object may be drawn in the same way, as shown at E, F, G, and H in Fig. 14-7a, Space 2.

The construction for quarter rounds is the same as for one-quarter of a circle. This is illustrated in Spaces 3

Fig. 14-7b. Construction for isometric drawing of a cylinder.

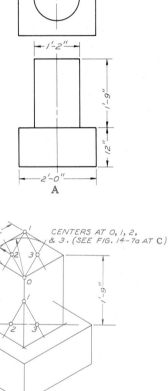

A

B

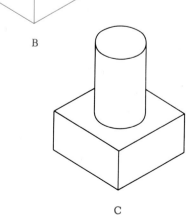

C

Figure 14-6d has four nonisometric lines. The method for making the isometric drawing of the tower is shown in stages at A, B, and C, where the apex is located by erecting a vertical line, OA, equal to the height.

14·7 Isometric circles. Circles will appear as ellipses, but instead of a true ellipse being drawn, a four-centered approximation can be used. To draw an isometric circle, first make the isometric

drawing of the square that will contain it (Fig. 14-7a, Space 1 at B). From the points of tangency, T, draw perpendiculars as indicated at B. Their intersections will give four centers from which arcs may be drawn tangent to the sides of the isometric square. Two of these centers will fall on the intersections of the perpendiculars, as shown at C, and two at the corners, as shown at D. Thus, the entire construction may be made with the 60° triangle. Circles on

Fig. 14-7a. Construction for isometric circles and arcs.

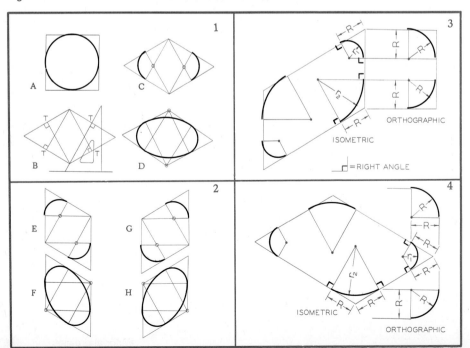

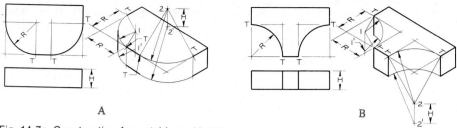

Fig. 14-7c. Construction for outside and inside arcs.

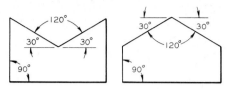

Fig. 14-8. A simple isometric template.

and 4 of Fig. 14-7a. Note that the radius is measured along the tangent lines from the corner in each case and that the actual perpendiculars are then drawn to locate the centers for the isometric arcs. It will be observed that r_1 and r_2 are found in the same way as the short and long radii of a complete isometric circle.

When an arc is more or less than a quarter circle, it is sometimes possible to draw all or part of a complete isometric circle and use as much of it as is needed. In other cases it may be necessary, or desirable, to plot points as shown in Fig. 14-7d.

Figure 14-7b shows the construction for an isometric drawing of a cylinder. First, draw a square prism with sides equal to the diameter of the cylinder, as at B. Now, locate the tangent points

and the centers for the isometric circles in the two bases of the cylinder. Refer to Space 1 of Fig. 14-7a. Draw the visible arcs and complete the drawing, as at C.

Figure 14-7c shows the construction tor an outside corner arc at A and for an inside corner arc at B. Note the tangent points, T, and the centers 1 and 1^1 and 2 and 2^1.

The latch at A in Fig. 14-7d has arcs tangent to an acute angle and to an obtuse angle. When arcs tangent to the sides of such angles are drawn on an isometric view, the approximation used for arcs tangent to right angles is not suitable. In such cases the curve should be plotted.

To make an isometric drawing of the latch, block in the isometric form as at B. Locate the tangent points, T_1 and T_2, for the arc of radius R by distances

transferred from the orthographic view at A to the isometric view at B. Next, as shown at D, locate points on the isometric arc (curve) by plotting points (as 1 and 2) by transferring distances from the orthographic view to the isometric view.

14·8 Isometric templates are made in a variety of forms. They are convenient and timesaving when many isometric drawings have to be made. They have openings for drawing ellipses and 30°, 60°, and 90° guiding edges. Simple homemade guides (Fig. 14-8) are convenient. Ellipse templates (Art. 4·44) are very convenient for drawing true ellipses on isometric drawings. If available, they give a better appearance and save the extra time required to draw approximate ellipses.

Fig. 14-7d. Construction for arcs in acute and obtuse angles.

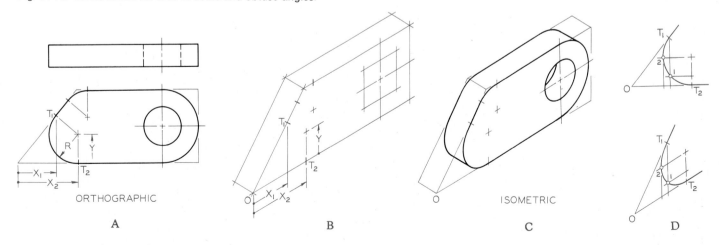

14·9 Isometric curves. Curves and true isometric arcs of circles are drawn by plotting a series of points. This is illustrated in Fig. 14-9. First, draw the orthographic view (Space 1) and locate a number of points by drawing lines as shown. Draw these same lines in iso-metric as illustrated for a vertical plane (Space 2) and a horizontal plane (Space 3). Then plot points by transferring distances from the orthographic to the isometric view. Draw a smooth curve through the points on the isometric view.

Fig. 14-9. To plot curves on an isometric drawing.

Fig. 14-10. Steps in making an isometric drawing.

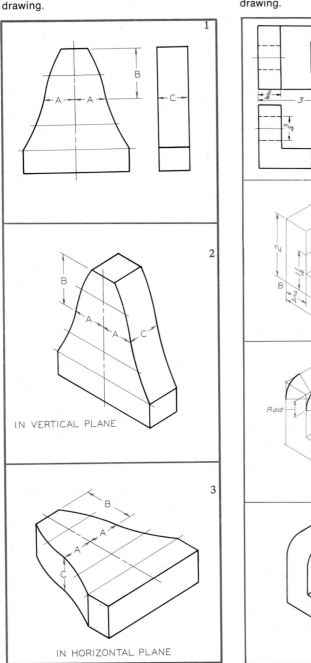

IN VERTICAL PLANE

IN HORIZONTAL PLANE

14·10 Making an isometric drawing. Make an isometric drawing of the guide shown in Fig. 14-10, Space 1.

1. Draw the axes *AB, AC,* and *AD* in second position (Fig. 14-10, Space 2).

Measure from *A* the length 3″ on *AB.*

Measure from *A* the width 2″ from *AC.*

Measure from *A* the thickness ⅝″ on *AD.*

Through these points draw iso-metric lines, blocking in the vase.

2. Block in the upright part, making two measurements of only 2″ and ¾″.

3. Locate the center of the hole and draw center lines as shown. Block in a ¾″ isometric square and draw the hole as an approximate ellipse (Art. 14·7). At the upper corners measure the ½″ radius on each line, as in Space 3. Draw real perpendiculars to find the centers of the quarter circles.

4. Complete as in Space 4.

14·11 Isometric sections. Isometric drawings are generally made as outside views, but sometimes a sectional view is needed. The section is taken on an isometric plane, that is, on a plane parallel to one of the faces of the cube. Figure 14-11a shows isometric full sections taken on a different plane for each of three objects (Spaces 1, 2, and 3). Note the thin red lines indicating the part that has been cut away. Isometric half sections are illustrated in Fig. 14-11b. The construction lines of Space 1 are for the object shown in Space 2. The construction lines of Space 3 are for the object shown in Space 4. Note the outlines of the cut surfaces in Spaces 1 and 3. The "cut method" is to draw the complete outside view and the isometric cutting plane. The part of the view that has been cut away is then removed. A second method is to draw the section on the isometric cutting plane and then to work from it to complete the view.

Fig. 14-11a. Some isometric sections.

Fig. 14-11b. Some isometric half sections.

14·12 Reversed axes. Sometimes it is desirable to represent a part as viewed from below. This is done by reversing the axes as in Fig. 14-12. Draw the orthographic views as in Space 1; then, draw the axes in reversed position as in Space 2. Lay off the measurements and complete the view as in Space 3.

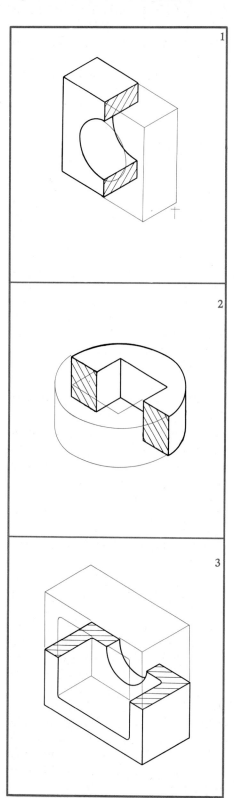

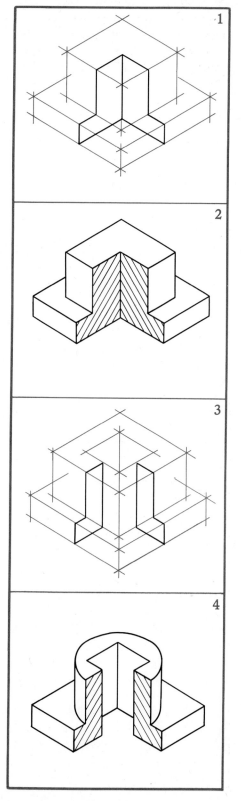

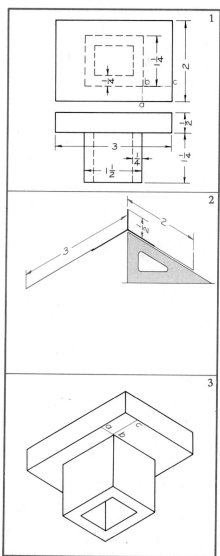

Fig. 14-12. Steps in making an isometric drawing with reversed axes.

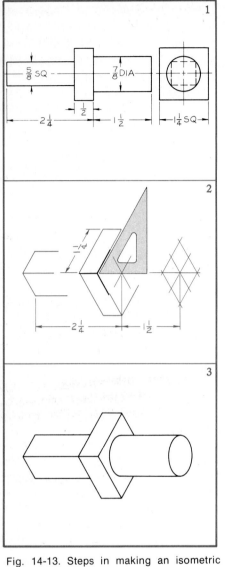

Fig. 14-13. Steps in making an isometric drawing with the long axis horizontal.

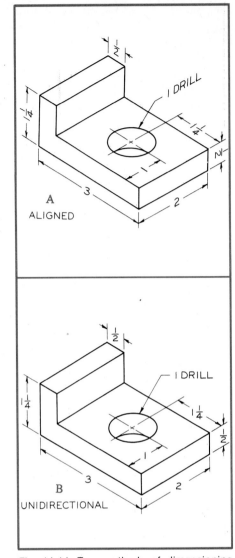

Fig. 14-14. Two methods of dimensioning isometric views.

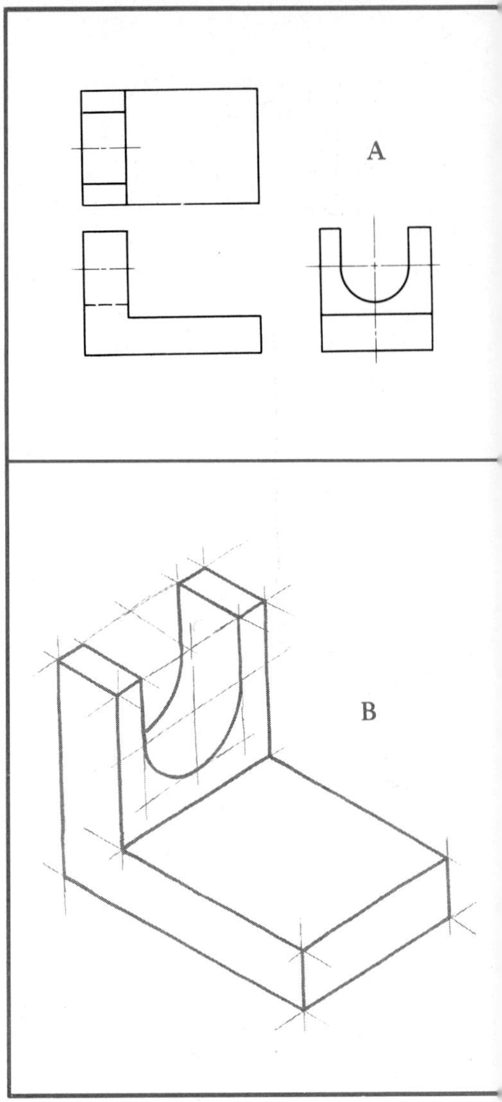

Fig. 14-15. An isometric sketch.

14·13 Long axis horizontal. Long pieces may be drawn with one axis horizontal, as in Fig. 14-13. For the object shown in Space 1, draw the axes as shown by the heavy lines in Space 2. Lay off the measurements given in Space 2 that are parallel to the axes and proceed in the usual way to complete the view as in Space 3. Except for the positions of the axes the view is drawn in the same way as any other isometric view.

14·14 Dimensioning isometric drawings. There are two general methods of placing dimensions on isometric drawings. The older method is to place dimensions in the isometric planes, or extensions of them, and to adjust letters and numerals for isometric shapes as at A in Fig. 14-14. A simpler method (at B), which is often satisfactory uses the unidirectional system with numerals and lettering reading from the bottom of the sheet. See also Art. 6·14.

14·15 Isometric sketching. Freehand isometric sketches are of great help in reading orthographic views and in explaining objects or parts of constructions. Isometric sketching paper with lightly ruled, tinted lines for the directions of the axes furnishes a convenient aid in making isometric sketches, (Art. 6·2). In Fig. 14-15 the orthographic views of a yoke bracket are shown at A and an isometric sketch is shown at B. The principles of isometric

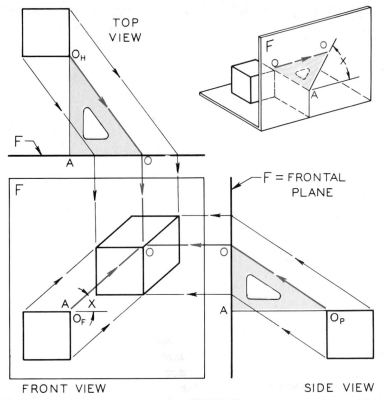

TOP VIEW

O_H

F

A O

F = FRONTAL PLANE

F

O

O

A X

O_F

O

A

O_P

FRONT VIEW

SIDE VIEW

Fig. 14-16. An oblique drawing is obtained by projectors at an angle with the picture plane.

drawing form the basis of isometric sketching, but since sketches are not made to scale, their appearance may be improved by "flattening." This can be done by giving the axes an angle less than 30° with the horizontal and by slightly converging the lines, as well as shortening the lengths, to avoid distortion and to give the effect of perspective. This is sometimes called *faked perspective.*

Always block in construction squares before sketching circles or arcs. Remember that the long axes of ellipses representing circles on the top face are horizontal. Dimensioning a pictorial sketch is illustrated in Arts. 6·14 and 14·14.

14·16 Oblique projection and oblique drawing (Fig. 14-16). An isometric projection is obtained by projectors perpendicular to the picture plane from an object placed in a special revolved position (Art. 14·3). An oblique projection is obtained by projectors at an angle (not 90°) with the picture plane and parallel to each other. We do not

have a distinction between oblique projection and oblique drawing. If the projectors make an angle of 45°, the oblique projection is called a *cavalier projection;* however, the general term is *oblique drawing.*

Note the three orthographic views of the cube in Fig. 14-16, where one oblique projector is shown for point *O.* This projector is the hypotenuse of a 45° triangle, and parallel projectors from the cube to the frontal plane will give the oblique projection of the cube. Reference to the pictorial sketch will show that angle *X* can be any desired amount by revolving the triangle about side *OA.*

14·17 Oblique drawing. In this form of pictorial drawing (Fig. 14-17*a*), the object is placed with one surface parallel to the picture plane (the frontal plane) instead of at an angle as in isometric drawing. The picture is then obtained by projection lines which make an angle with the picture plane instead of being perpendicular to it. These are called *oblique projecting lines.* Oblique drawings are constructed in the same manner as isometric drawings, that is, on three axes; however, two of the axes always make right angles with each other.

The same methods and rules that were used in isometric drawing apply to oblique drawing, but compared with isometric, oblique drawing has the distinct advantage of showing one face without distortion. Thus objects with irregular outlines can be drawn by this method much more easily and effec-

Fig. 14-17*a*. The oblique axes and oblique drawings.

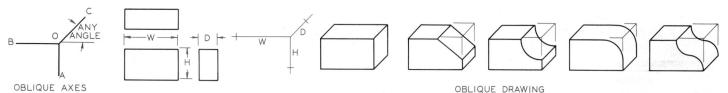

OBLIQUE AXES

OBLIQUE DRAWING

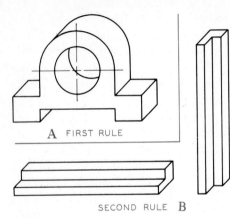

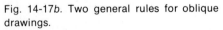

A FIRST RULE

SECOND RULE B

Fig. 14-17b. Two general rules for oblique drawings.

tively than in isometric. Some draftsmen prefer it for practically all pictorial work.

The first rule in oblique drawing is:

Place the object so that the irregular outline or contour faces the front (Fig. 14-17b at A).

The second rule is:

Place the object so that the longest dimension is parallel to the picture plane (Fig. 14-17b at B).

14•18 Positions for the oblique axes (Fig. 14-18). Two of the axes, AO and OB, are drawn at right angles. The oblique axis, OC, may be drawn at any angle: to the right or left and up or down as illustrated.

14•19 Angles and inclined surfaces on oblique drawings. Angles parallel to the picture plane show in true size. Other angles can be laid off by locating the ends of the inclined line of the angle.

A plate with the corners cut off at angles is shown in Fig. 14-19a at A. An oblique drawing with the angles parallel to the picture plane is shown at B. At C the angles are parallel to the profile plane and at D they are parallel to the horizontal plane. In each case the angle is laid off by measurements parallel to oblique axes, as shown by the red lines.

Planes at angles are drawn by locating the lines which enclose them, as illustrated in Fig. 14-19b.

14•20 Oblique circles. On the front face, circles and curves show in their true shape (Fig. 14-20a, Space 1). On other faces you can approximate circles and arcs, as in isometric, by drawing perpendiculars from the tangent points to locate centers c_1 and c_2. In Space 1 a circle is shown as it would be drawn on a front plane, a side plane, and a top plane. In Space 2 a circle is shown as it would appear on three faces

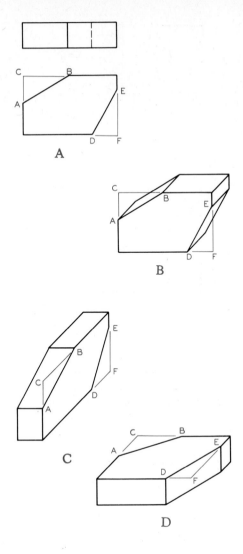

Fig. 14-19a. Angles on oblique drawings.

Fig. 14-18. Positions for oblique axes.

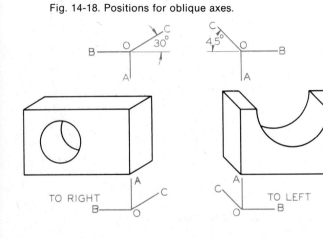

TO RIGHT

TO LEFT

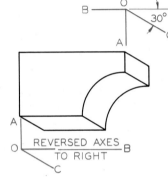

REVERSED AXES
TO RIGHT

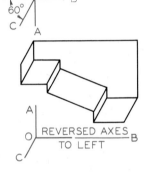

REVERSED AXES
TO LEFT

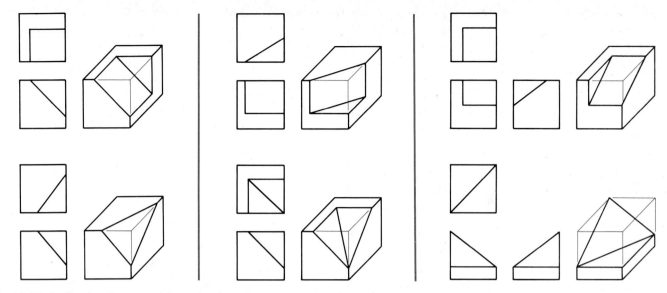

Fig. 14-19b. Inclined surfaces on oblique drawings.

of a cube with the construction for locating the centers of the arcs. In Space 3 the oblique drawing shown has some arcs in a horizontal plane. In Space 4 the oblique drawing shown has some arcs in a side plane.

Fig. 14-20a. Circles parallel to the picture plane are circles; on other planes, ellipses.

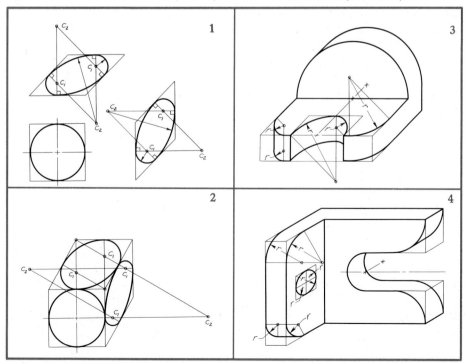

Circles not parallel to the picture plane when drawn by the approximate method indicated are not pleasing but are satisfactory for some purposes. Ellipse templates, when available, give much better results; of course, the ellipse can be plotted if desired (Fig. 14-20b).

Fig. 14-20b. To plot oblique circles.

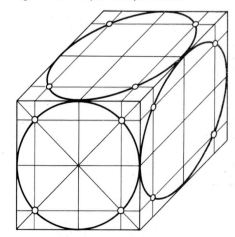

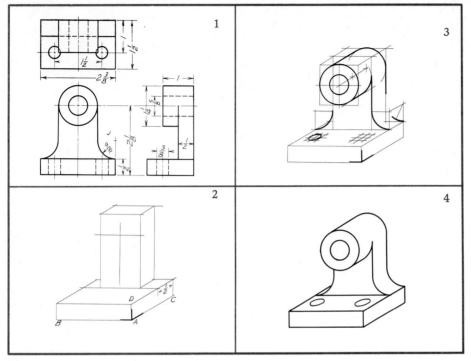

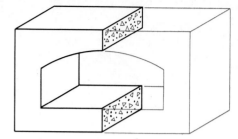

Fig. 14-22a. An oblique section.

Fig. 14-21a. Steps in making an oblique drawing.

14·21 Making an oblique drawing. Make an oblique drawing of the bearing of Fig. 14-21a, Space 1. Observe that all but two small circles can be shown in their true shape.

1. Draw the axes AB, AC, and AD for the base in second position and measure on them the length, width, and thickness of the base, as in Space 2.

Draw the base; on it block in the upright, omitting the projecting boss, as shown in the figure.

2. Block in the boss as in Space 3 and find the centers of all circles and arcs.

3. Draw the circles and circle arcs.

4. Finish the drawing as in Space 4. Figure 14-21b is a drawing for study.

14·22 Oblique sections (Figs. 14-22a and 14-22b). Oblique drawings are generally made as outside views, but sometimes a sectional view is necessary. The section is taken on a plane parallel to one of the faces of an oblique cube. Figure 14-22a shows an oblique full section and Fig. 14-22b shows an oblique half section. Note the thin red lines which indicate the part which has been cut away.

14·23 Cabinet and other oblique drawings. Variations in the angles which the oblique projectors make with the picture plane permit oblique drawings to be made with variations in the length of measurements parallel to the oblique axis. The usual angle which the oblique projectors make with the picture plane is 45° (Fig. 14-23a).

Fig. 14-21b. An oblique drawing for study.

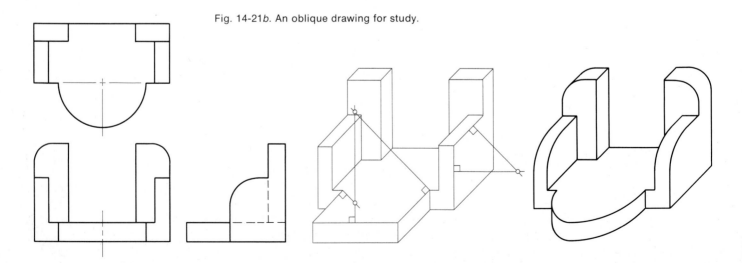

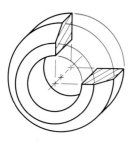

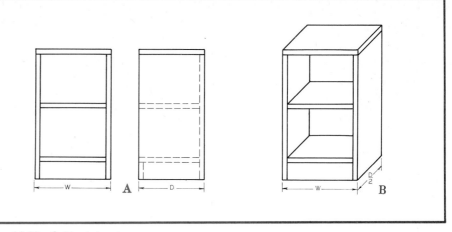

Fig. 14-23c. Cabinet drawing.

Fig. 14-22b. An oblique half section.

Fig. 14-23a. The projectors are parallel to the hypotenuse of a 45° triangle, so full measurements are made on the oblique axis. This is cavalier projection.

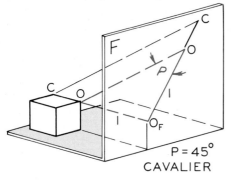

P = 45°
CAVALIER

Fig. 14-23b. The projectors make an angle of 63°–26′. One side of the right triangle shown is one-half the length of the other, so half measurements are made on the oblique axis. This is cabinet projection.

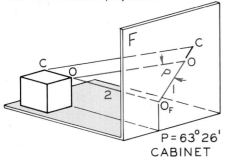

P = 63°26′
CABINET

This is cavalier projection and provides for full measurements parallel to the oblique axis.

When the projectors make an angle of 63°26′, the measurements parallel to the oblique axis will be one-half of the full measurements (Fig. 14-23b). This is called *cabinet drawing*. The oblique axis may be placed in the same positions as for any oblique drawing. All measurements parallel to the oblique axis are reduced to one-half size. Note the right triangles with sides having a ratio of 1 to 2.

The views of a simple case are shown in Fig. 14-23c at A, and a cabinet drawing is shown at B. Cabinet drawings are often used for representing furniture and similar projects.

The appearance of an oblique drawing can be changed by the proportion of the full measurements used on the oblique axis. All measurements parallel to the oblique axis must be in the same proportion to the full measurements (Fig. 14-23d).

14·24 Isometric sketching. Freehand isometric sketches are important for working out ideas, reading orthographic views and explaining shapes and positions of parts and projects.

Fig. 14-23d. Measurements parallel to the oblique axis in proportion to the full measurements.

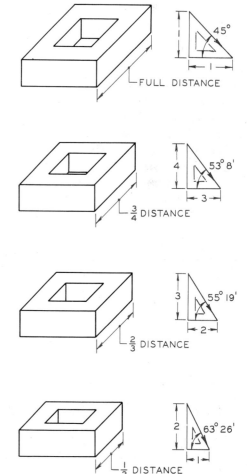

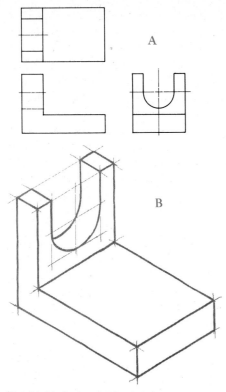

Fig. 14-24. An isometric sketch.

Fig. 14-25. An oblique sketch.

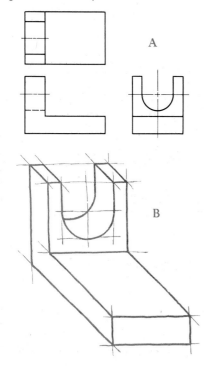

Fig. 14-26a. Looking straight down the expressway. Note that the sides of the highway appear to converge to a point in the distance. This is the effect in one-point, or parallel, perspective.

Isometric ruled paper with light tinted lines for the directions of the axes is a convenient aid in making isometric sketches. In Fig. 14-24 the orthographic views of a yoke bracket are shown at A and an isometric sketch is shown at B. The principles of isometric drawing provide the basis for isometric sketching. While sketches are not made to scale they should be made in proportion to avoid giving a false impression. The appearance can be improved by "flattening the axes." This can be done by giving the axes an angle less than 30° with the horizontal and by slightly converging the lines, as well as shortening the lengths, to avoid distortion and give the effect of perspective. This is sometimes called *fake perspective*.

Always block in construction squares before sketching circles or arcs. Remember that the long axes of ellipses representing circles on the top face are horizontal.

Dimensioning a pictorial sketch is illustrated in Art. 6·14. Refer to Chap. 6 where several isometric sketches are shown.

14·25 Oblique sketching. In Fig. 14-25 the orthographic views of a yoke bracket are shown at A and an oblique sketch is shown at B. The principles of oblique drawing provide the basis of oblique sketching, but the appearance can often be improved by reducing the measurements parallel to the oblique axis. Always block in construction lines before sketching circles, arcs, and other curves (see Fig. 14-20a and Art. 6·4).

14·26 Perspective drawing is the representation of an object as it appears to the eye from a particular position. Perspective effect will be noted on most photographs (Figs. 14-26a and 14-26b).

Fig. 14-26b. When a building is viewed at an angle, two sides can be seen. The top and ground lines of each side appear to converge toward points. This is the effect in two-point, or angular, perspective.

14·27 Definitions of terms. The projectors for orthographic views are perpendicular to the plane of projection and are parallel to each other. The projectors for a perspective view converge at a single point, the eye of the observer, and are called visual rays. They may be thought of as lines drawn from points on the object to the eye, as indicated in Fig. 14-27 where other terms are illustrated. The *picture plane* (PP) is the plane upon which the view (picture) is drawn. The *station point* (SP) is the position of the observer when looking at the object. The *horizontal plane* passes through the observer's eye and intersects the picture plane in the horizon. The *ground plane* (GP) upon which the observer stands and upon which the object rests intersects the picture plane in the *ground line* (GL). The *center of vision* (CV) is the point in which the axis of vision (visual ray from the eye perpendicular to the picture plane) pierces the picture plane. Note that the eye level may be at any level on, above, or below the ground. If viewed from a high elevation, an aerial view would be obtained. If on the ground, a ground or "worm's eye" view would be obtained. In Fig. 14-27 the perspective of a card has been drawn on the picture plane.

Fig. 14-27. Some perspective terms.

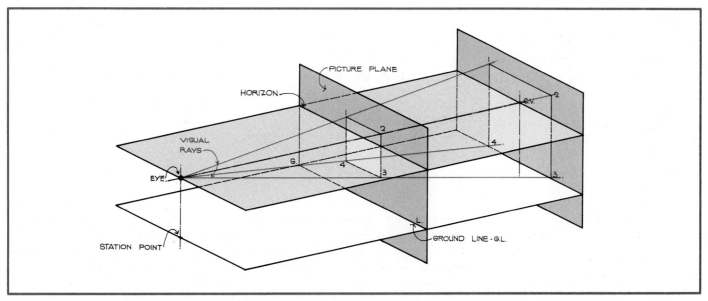

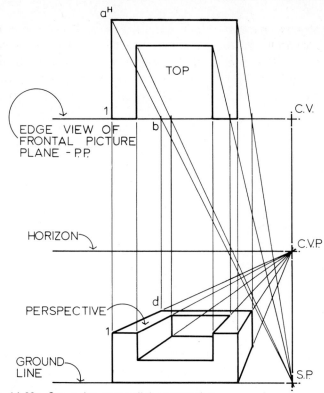

Fig. 14-28a. One-point, or parallel, perspective.

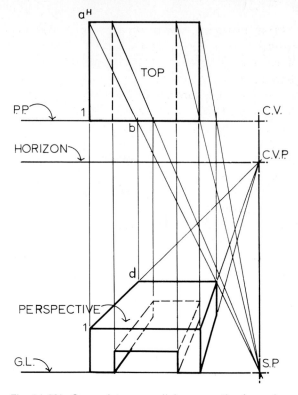

Fig. 14-28b. One-point, or parallel, perspective from above.

14•28 One-point perspective, or parallel perspective, is illustrated in Fig. 14-28a. One face of the object is generally placed in the picture plane and will remain in true size and shape. Decide on the scale to be used and draw the top view. Assume the position of the station point (SP). The center of vision point (CVP) will always be on the horizon. To draw the perspective, draw a line (visual ray) from SP to point a^H in the top view to intersect the picture plane in point b. Next, draw a visual ray from CVP to point 1 in the front view. Project point b vertically from the top view to intersect the visual ray from point 1 in the front at point d, as shown. Other points needed to draw the picture are found in the same manner.

The station point is generally placed a short distance to one side of the object; but if it is placed too far away, an unpleasant picture will result. Note the effect of a high center of vision in Fig.

14-28b. One-point perspective is useful for some purposes such as architectural interiors, as suggested by the photograph in Fig. 14-28c, but for most purposes one-point perspective does not give as pleasing results as two-point perspective, described in Art. 14·29.

Fig. 14-28c. The interior of a shop building shows one-point perspective effect. *(National Tube Division, United States Steel Corporation)*

14·29 Two-point perspective is illustrated in Fig. 14-29a by the drawing of the simple bookend. To make the drawing, draw the line representing the top view of the picture plane (PP). Then draw the top view (or plan) at an angle selected to give the desired view. Select a station point (SP) at a position in front of the picture plane. Here the PP is in contact with the nearest corner of the bookend. The side view is drawn at the same scale as the top view, and the ground line is drawn at the base of the bookend. Select and draw a line repre-

senting the horizon at a desired distance above the ground line (GL). There are two vanishing points. The right vanishing point (RVP) is located by drawing a line from SP and parallel to the right side of the object to intersect the picture plane at the top view of RVP^H. The top view of the left vanishing point

Fig. 14-29a. Two-point, or angular, perspective showing how it is drawn.

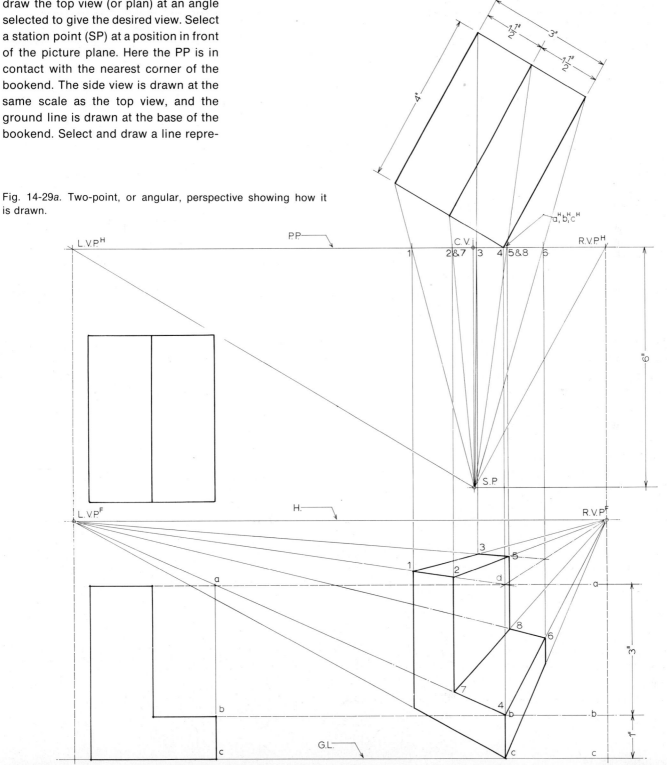

LVP^H is located in like manner. Then project down to the horizon line to locate RVP^F and LVP^F. Note the point *a* in space, as indicated in the side view. The top view of points *a, b,* and *c* are at the same point. To locate point *a* in the perspective, project down from the top view and over from the side view; then, continue down and project over from the side view to locate points *b* and *c*. Now, draw lines from *a, b,* and *c* to the RVP^F and LVP^F. Draw the visual rays from SP to each point in the top view. From their intersections with the pic-

ture plane, project down to locate points 1 to 8 on the perspective. Join the points to complete the perspective as shown.

Figure 14-29*b* shows a perspective of a bookend which is the same as Fig. 14-29*a* except that it has an inclined surface. It is drawn in the same way as

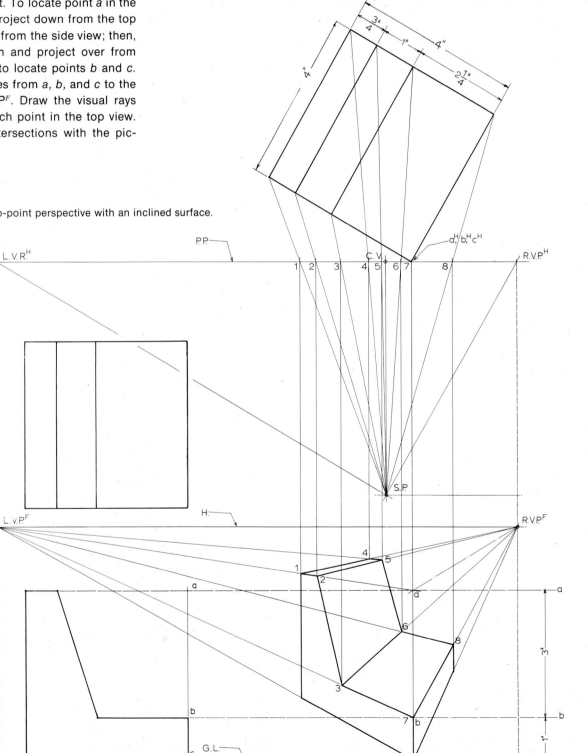

Fig. 14-29*b*. Two-point perspective with an inclined surface.

Fig. 14-29a by locating two points on each of the inclined lines (2-3 and 5-6) and joining them, as shown.

Figure 14-29c shows a perspective of a bookend which is the same as Fig. 14-29a except that it has two circular surfaces. Note that points on the circular edges are numbered and located on the perspective.

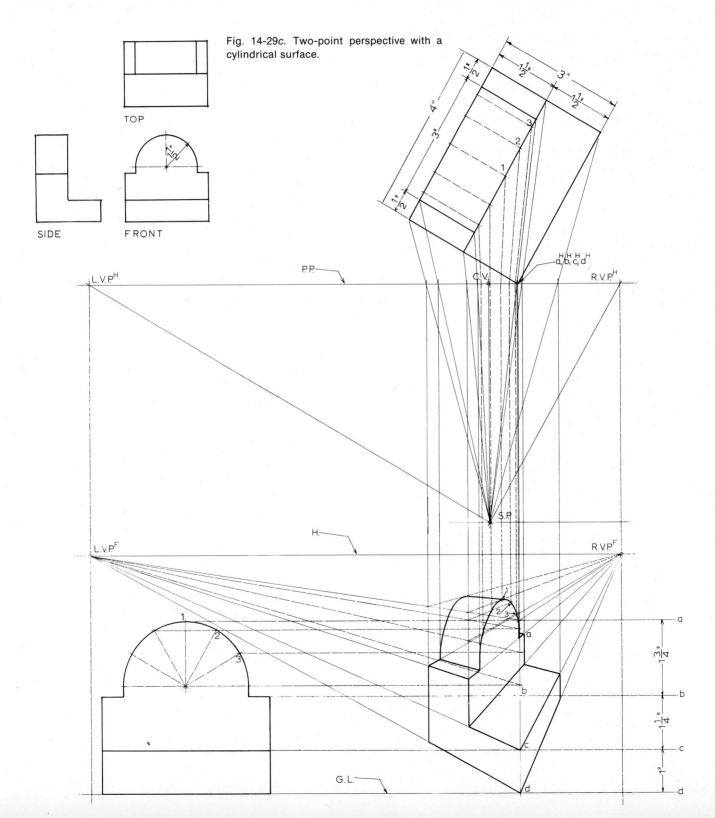

Fig. 14-29c. Two-point perspective with a cylindrical surface.

After acquiring experience, only the perspective of the enclosing construction square may be drawn, in which the curved surface may be sketched.

14•30 Perspective sketching. The principles of perspective as used in perspective drawing provide the basis for perspective sketching. A sketch made in perspective gives a better and more pleasing picture than an isometric or oblique sketch. The principles of mechanical perspective studied in Arts. 14·26 to 14·29 will simplify the making of perspective sketches.

The perspective sketch in Fig. 14-30a will be recognized as a one-point perspective. The front face of the chest is parallel to the picture plane, and the horizontal lines on that face, or parallel to it, remain horizontal. The receding lines meet at the one vanishing point.

The perspective in Fig. 14-30b will be recognized as a two-point or angular perspective. The table is turned at an angle to the picture plane. The vertical lines remain vertical. The two sets of horizontal lines each converge toward the two vanishing points on the horizon, the horizontal line at eye level.

14•31 Making a perspective sketch from the object. In sketching from the object, place it below the level of the eye, unless it is very large, in order to show the outline of shape to the best advantage. Start by drawing a line for the nearest vertical corner. From this sketch lightly the directions of the principal lines, running them past the limits of the figure. Test the directions and proportionate lengths with a pencil as follows. With the drawing board or sketch pad held perpendicular to the line of sight from the eye to the object, hold the pencil at arm's length parallel to the board and rotate the arm until the pencil appears to coincide with the line on the model. Then move the pencil parallel to this position back to the board. This gives the direction of the line. To estimate the apparent lengths, hold the pencil in the same way and mark with the thumb (as in Fig. 14-31) the length of the pencil that covers the line. Rotate the arm with the thumb held in position until the pencil coincides with another line and estimate the proportion of this measurement to the second line.

Fig. 14-30a. One-point perspective sketch.

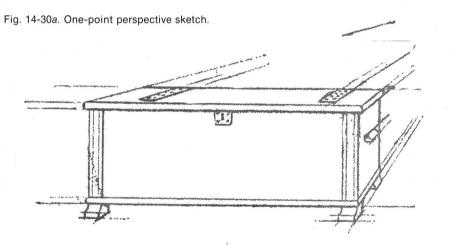

Fig. 14-30b. Two-point perspective sketch.

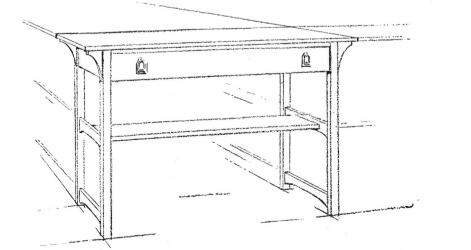

Fig. 14-31. Estimating proportions.

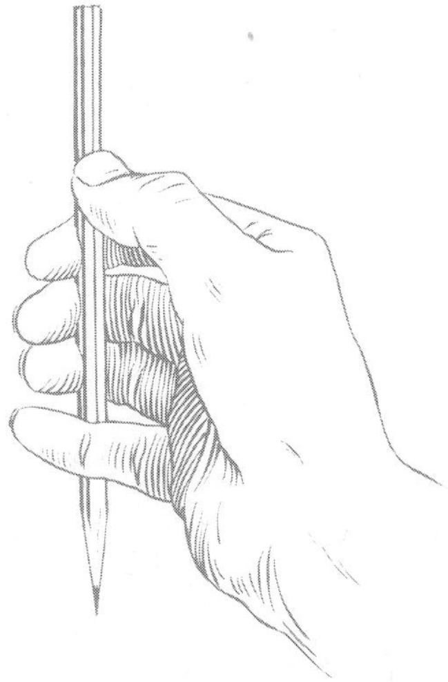

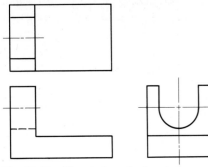

Fig. 14-32a. Views of a yoke bracket.

Block in the enclosing squares for all circles and circle arcs. Work with light, free sketch lines, and do not erase any lines until the whole sketch is blocked in. Draw the main outlines first, then add details. Finally, brighten the sketch with heavier lines.

14·32 Making a perspective sketch from the views. Orthographic views of a yoke bracket are shown in Fig. 14-32a and are sketched in angular perspective in Fig. 14-32b.

To make a sketch or drawing in angular perspective when the orthographic views are given instead of the object itself, the method generally used is what is known as the *cone of rays method.* In this method the plan is first drawn with its front corner against a line representing the picture plane as shown in Fig. 14-32b. Think of this as the top view of the object with the picture plane standing up against the front edge. Imagine the observer standing out in front of the plane at the point SP, look-

Fig. 14-32b. Making a perspective sketch of a yoke bracket.

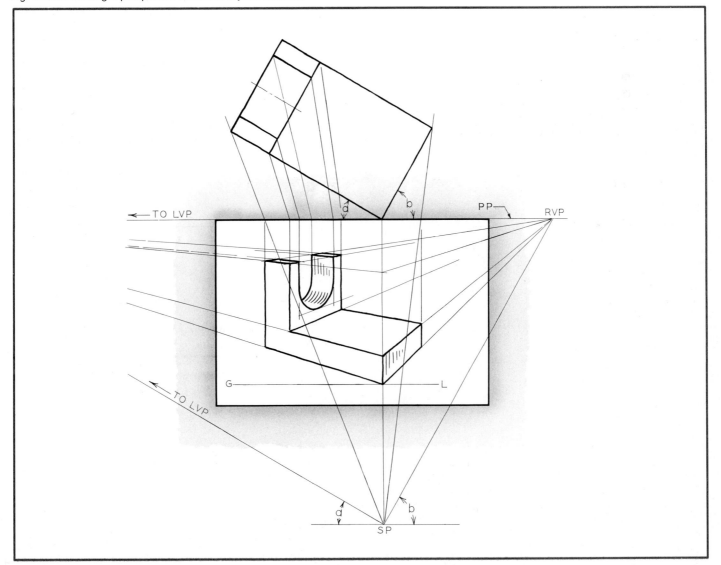

ing at the object through the plane. There will be a ray of light from each point of the object to the observer's eye. The picture as seen from this point will be the intersection of all these rays with the picture plane PP. (To avoid distortion, the station point SP is taken at a distance from the picture plane at least twice the width or height of the object.) Thus, if lines are drawn from the point SP to the different points on the plan, their intersections with PP will give the widths of the picture. Remember that so far we are looking down on the edge of the picture plane and that

the picture is all in the line PP. A horizontal line on the picture plane at a height above the ground equal to the height of the observer's eye will be the horizon. From SP, lines drawn parallel to the lines of the plan will pierce the picture plane on the horizon, giving the vanishing points RVP and LVP. Now imagine the picture plane to be detached, moved forward and then laid down into the plane of the paper. In the figure this has been done for convenience so that the horizon of the picture plane coincides with the line PP. This means practically that the line GL, which

is the bottom edge of the picture plane, was drawn as far below PP as the height of the observer's eye. At the intersection of GL and a perpendicular from the front corner of the plan draw a vertical line representing the front edge of the object and lines to RVP and LVP for the lower horizontal edges. Perpendiculars dropped from the intersection of the rays with the picture plane will give the length and width of the object. Vertical measurements must all be made on the vertical line in the picture plane and vanished back to meet the location of the point to be measured. A study of

Fig. 14-32c. Two-point, or angular, perspective.

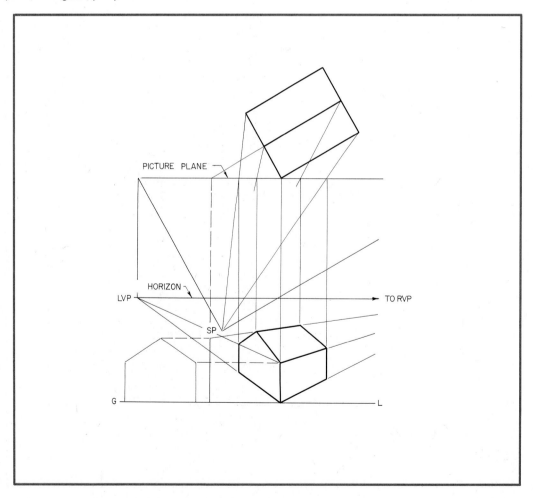

Fig. 14-32b will show the method of finishing the sketch.

Compare the views in Figs. 14-24, 14-25, and 14-32b which are all pictures of the same object (the yoke bracket of Fig. 14-32a).

A study of Figs. 14-32c and 14-32d will assist the student in making angular and parallel perspective sketches.

14·33 Problem suggestions. Group 14, page 509. Three lists are presented. List 1 includes basic and more elementary problems from which selections may be made according to the purpose of the course. Selections may be made from List 2 for additional or alternative problems. These are a little more difficult than List 1. Selections may be made from Lists 2 and 3 for more advanced students or for those taking a more extensive course. A large number of problems are listed so that they may be varied from year to year. In some courses only a small number may be used to serve the purpose.

List 1: Problems 14·1, 14·3, 14·8, 14·11, 14·13, 14·16, 14·17, 14·19, 14·20, 14·23, 14·24, 14·27, 14·30, 14·33, 14·35, 14·36, 14·37, 14·40, 14·42, 14·43, 14·45, 14·46, 14·47, 14·52, 14·54, 14·58, 14·59, 14·61; and selections from 14·67 to 14·74.

List 2: Problems 14·2, 14·5, 14·7, 14·10, 14·13, 14·15, 14·22, 14·25, 14·28, 14·29, 14·43, 14·48, 14·53, 14·60; and selections from 14·75 to 14·82.

List 3: Problems 14·28, 14·31, 14·32, 14·34, 14·38, 14·40, 14·44, 14·49, 14·50, 14·51, 14·54, 14·55, 14·56, 14·60, 14·62; and selections from 14·83 to 14·90.

Fig. 14-32d. One-point, or parallel, perspective.

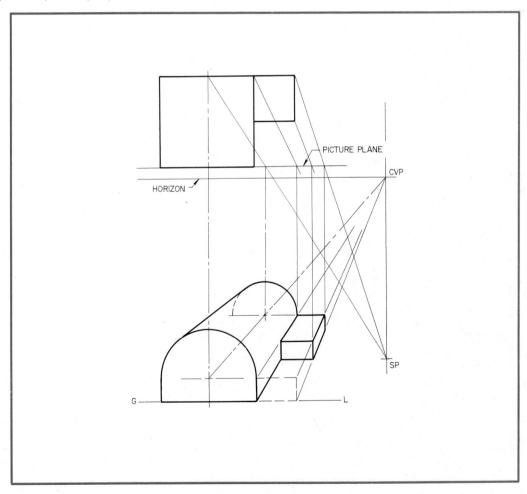

15
Technical illustrations

THE TECHNICAL MANUALS REQUIRED FOR THE OPERATION AND MAINTENANCE OF A SUPERSONIC BOMBER MAKE A STACK 13½ FEET HIGH.

AEROSPACE

Fig. 15-1a. Technical manuals contain many technical illustrations.

Fig. 15-1b. A technical illustration to show the orbiting geophysical observatory (OGO) in flight. The OGO is a standardized satellite on which the National Aeronautics and Space Administration will send as many as 50 different scientific experiments into orbit on a single mission. (NASA photograph)

15•1 Technical illustration has an important place in all phases of engineering and science. Technical illustrations form an essential part of the technical manuals for aircraft (Fig. 15-1a), machine tools, automobiles, tractors, air conditioners, and many other things. Technical illustrations are also made to give a "visible" description of space satellites (Fig. 15-1b). In technical illustration, pictorial drawings are used to describe parts and the methods for making them. Pictorial drawings show how the parts fit together and the steps that are followed to complete the product on the assembly line. Technical illustrations were probably used to organize and set up the assembly line itself. They are useful for many industrial, engineering, and scientific purposes.

Technical illustration drawings vary from simple sketches to rather extensive shaded drawings. They may be based upon any of the pictorial methods: isometric, perspective, oblique, and so forth. The complete project may be shown, or parts of groups of parts, and the views may be exterior, interior, sectional, cutaway, or phantom. The purpose in all cases is to provide a clear and easily understood description. Previous chapters, in particular Chap. 6, "Sketching," and Chap. 14, "Pictorial Drawing," furnish the basis for making technical illustrations. Drawings for use within a company's plant can sometimes be made by a regular draftsman with artistic talent, but for most purposes the special requirements of such drawings call for work by a professional technical illustrator.

An important kind of technical illustration is the *production illustration* (Fig. 15-1c), which shows preliminary attachment details of assembly being explained at the Boeing Company. Technical illustration has been used for many years for illustrated parts lists, operation and service manuals, process manuals, and similar purposes. The aircraft industry in particular has found production illustration especially valuable. In aircraft construction, pictorial drawings are used when the plane is first designed, at many stages of its manufacture, and as it is completed on the assembly line. When the plane is delivered to the customer, the industry supplies illustrated service, repair, and operation manuals.

The technical illustrator and the commercial artist have several things in common. For example, both must have the ability to draw pictures. The technical illustrator must have a technical or engineering mind to go along with his drawing abilities as draftsman and artist.

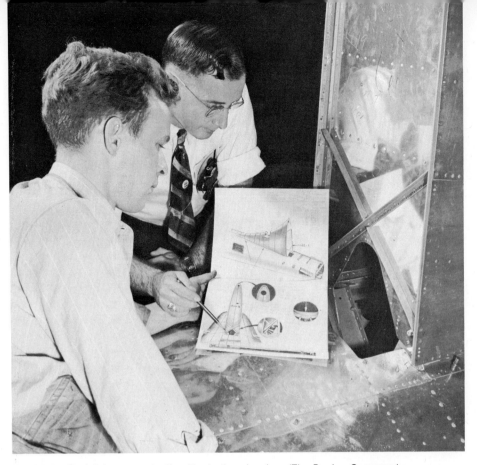

Fig. 15-1c. Explaining a production illustration drawing. *(The Boeing Company)*

15·2 Definition. 👉 *A technical illustration, in general, means a pictorial drawing made to provide technical information by visible methods.* It is made for a definite useful purpose which must be served clearly and quickly. It must show shapes and relative positions needed for the purpose without anything which might prevent a correct understanding. Sufficient shading to bring out the shape may be used, but none for artistic effect, as a technical illustration is for *use;* it is not a work of art. It must, however, be well done or it will be no better than illegible handwriting.

In addition to pictorials, technical illustrations include graphic charts (Chap. 24), schematics (Fig. 24-13), flow charts (Fig. 24-15a), diagrams, and sometimes circuit layouts (Chap. 18). Dimensions are not a part of tech-

nical illustrations, as they are not working drawings used for manufacturing products.

15·3 To make a technical illustration. The steps are similar to the order of preparing other drawings, but special attention is paid to the particular purpose for which the drawing is made. A suggested list follows:

1. Become familiar with the source material, which may be orthographic views, photographs or written descriptions with sketches, or the actual project.

2. Consider the purpose of the illustration. What is it to show? Make some preliminary sketches.

3. Consider the size of the drawing necessary, or allowable, and the size to which it may be reduced for reproduction.

4. Prepare and consider a suitable layout.

5. Draw and work up the illustration carefully and accurately in pencil. An H or 2H pencil is suggested. Be careful not to groove the surface. In a clear space above the drawing, letter the word "TOP." Sometimes the pencil drawing may be finished or traced in pencil and used without inking. In such cases it is necessary to see that the drawing is clean and that the lines are black. The grade of pencil must be selected to give lines of the required quality on the surface used.

6. Indicate lettering notes and numbers in the best locations on the drawing in pencil. Consider appropriate sizes.

7. Trace on cloth or film. Tube-point pens (Art. 3·17) are favored for much of the inking. Sometimes the original

pencil drawing may be inked. Consider the kind and amount of shading to be used.

8. Add the lettering notes and numbers in ink. This may be done freehand or mechanically. In selecting the sizes of lettering, consider legibility, the importance of lettered matter, and the effect of reduction for reproduction. Some usual sizes to consider are Wrico 120, 140, 175, and 200.

9. Clean the drawing and touch up where necessary if any lines are not black or have been weakened by erasure.

10. Put on the amount of reduction and/or the size to which the drawing is to be reduced.

11. The drawing may now be mounted on suitable cardboard, using Scotch Magic Mending Tape, or two-side adhesive tape, at the four corners.

The above is the general order of working; however, different companies have standards which specify requirements in detail as to just how their technical illustrations are to be prepared.

15•4 Tools and tips. The regular drafting equipment described in Chaps. 2 and 8 provide most of the tools used by the technical illustrator. An H or 2H pencil, with the point kept well sharpened and clean, is the most useful tool. Keep all tools clean. A few other useful items include a crow quill pen, a felt-tip pen, tube-point pens (such as Wrico fountain pens), masking tape, Scotch tape, X-acto knife, paper stomps, two or three brushes, and a reducing glass.

The technical illustrator should become familiar with the use of Craftint, Zip-a-tone, Chart-Pac, screen tints, etc. He should also learn about the various methods of reproduction and the effect of reduction when his drawing is to be used in a smaller size. Lines must be firm and black. Erasures must be clean. The part of a drawing not being worked on should be kept covered with tracing paper or sheet plastic.

15•5 Lettering is an important element of technical illustration. In some cases templates or scriber guides can be used, but good freehand lettering is often necessary; it is a required skill for a technical illustrator. Chapter 3, which discusses lettering, provides the basis for developing the ability to letter.

15•6 Exploded views. Perhaps the easiest way to understand an exploded view is to take a single piece and separate it into its individual parts, as in Fig. 15-6a. Orthographic views are

Fig. 15-6a. How a view is exploded.

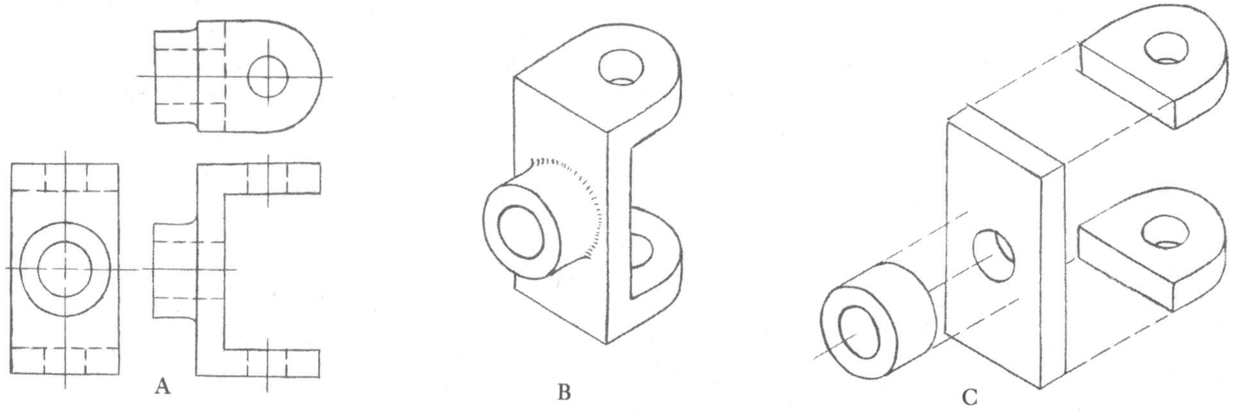

Fig. 15-6b. Exploded views.

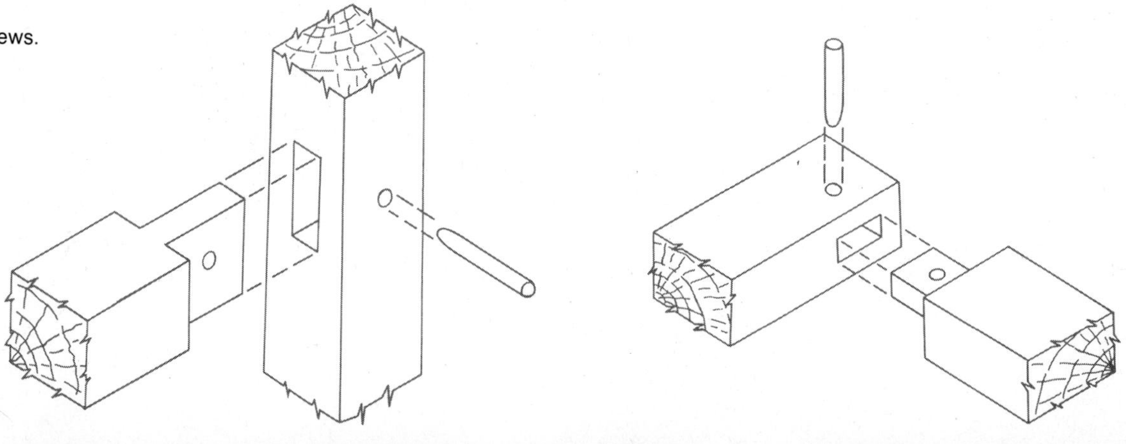

Fig. 15-6c. An exploded view.

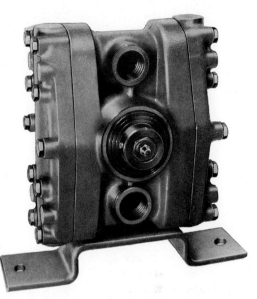

Fig. 15-6d. The exterior of a high-pressure pump. *(Industrial Division, Standard Precision, Inc.)*

shown at A and a pictorial view is shown at B. At C an "explosion" has projected the elementary parts away from each other. This illustrates the principle of exploded views.

Simple examples of exploded views are shown in Figs. 15-6b and 15-6c. All such views are based upon the same principle: projecting the parts from the positions they occupy when put together, or just pulling them apart. The exterior of a high-pressure piston pump is shown in Fig. 15-6d. An exploded illustration of the pump is shown in Fig. 15-6e. Note that all parts are easily identified.

Fig. 15-6e. An exploded view which shows and identifies the parts of a high-pressure piston pump. It is a single-piston, double-ended displacement pump with pressure capabilities up to 1000 psi and a capacity of 2 gpm at 650 psi. Psi = pounds per square inch; gpm = gallons per minute. *(Industrial Division, Standard Precision, Inc.)*

1. Pump Body (M-10091)
2. Cylinder Heads (M-10095)
3. Piston (M-10097)
4. Valve Assembly (M-10147)
5. Pump Shaft (10-10050)
6. Outer Ball Bearing (10-10050)
7. Washer (10-10050)
8. Inner Roller Bearing (10-10050)
9. Grease Zerk (1/4 – 28)
10. "O" Rings (125)
11. "O" Rings (132)
12. "O" Rings (220)
13. Back Up Ring (9)
14. Head Bolts (1/4-20 – 1 1/4)

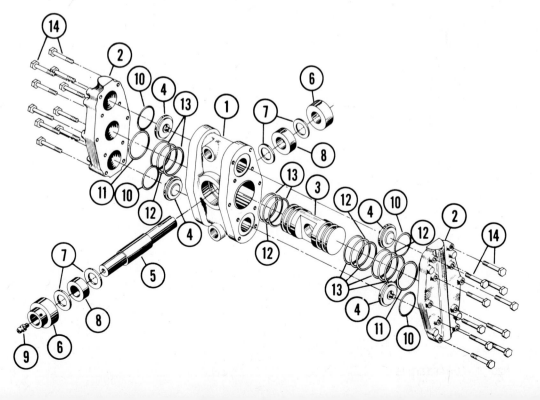

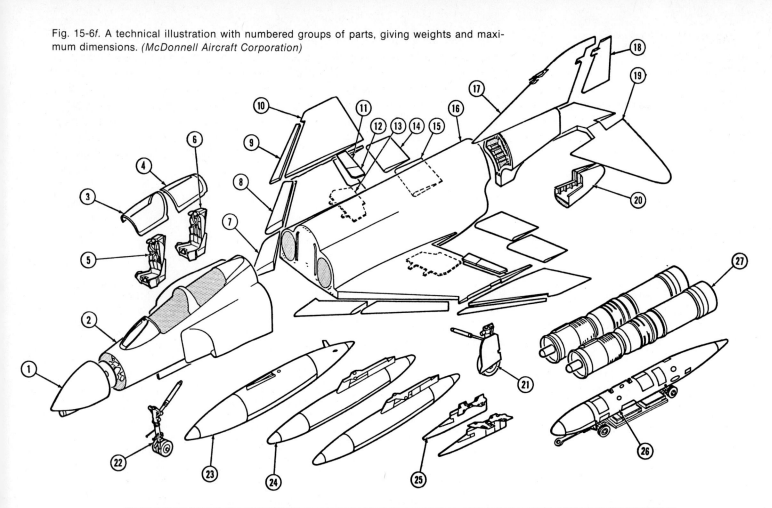

Fig. 15-6f. A technical illustration with numbered groups of parts, giving weights and maximum dimensions. *(McDonnell Aircraft Corporation)*

ITEM	COMPONENTS	UNIT WEIGHT (POUNDS)	APPROXIMATE MAXIMUM DIMENSIONS (INCHES)		
			HEIGHT	WIDTH	LENGTH
1	RADOME	180.00	40	40	56
2	FORWARD FUSELAGE LESS SEATS, CANOPIES, AND NOSE GEAR	6192.00	84	80	205
3	PILOT'S CANOPY	82.00	18	35	53
4	RIO CANOPY	76.00	18	35	53
5	PILOT'S EJECTION SEAT (MARTIN-BAKER)	145.00	56	22	36
6	RIO EJECTION SEAT (MARTIN-BAKER)	145.00	56	22	36
7	INBOARD LEADING EDGE FLAP (1)	62.00	12	22	81
8	CENTER LEADING EDGE FLAP (1)	72.00	10	16	117
9	OUTBOARD LEADING EDGE FLAP (1)	27.00	3	21	77
10	OUTER WING PANEL LESS FLAP (1)	257.00	8	132	75
11	OUTBOARD SPOILER (1)	19.00	6	16	40
12	INBOARD SPOILER (1)	12.00	6	17	23
13	SPEEDBRAKE (1)	36.00	8	29	67
14	AILERON (1)	47.00	7	48	65
15	TRAILING EDGE FLAP (1)	48.00	9	48	67
16	CENTER FUSELAGE INCLUDING INNER WING PANELS—LESS FUEL	8471.00	76	231	266
17	AFT FUSELAGE INCLUDING FIN	1214.00	154	60	175
18	RUDDER	66.00	64	4	43
19	STABILATOR	642.00	68	96	212
20	TAIL CONE	73.00	30	29	72
21	MAIN GEAR (1)	604.00	52	8	26
22	NOSE GEAR	295.00	54	20	22
23	CENTERLINE EXTERNAL FUEL TANK (1) (EMPTY)	235.00	38	40	260
24	EXTERNAL WING FUEL TANK (1) (EMPTY)—INCLUDES PYLON	331.00	37	27	240
25	WING MISSILE PYLON (1)	146.00	20	30	115
26	STARTER POD INCLUDING FUEL AND OIL	2015.00	31	29	264
27	ENGINE INCLUDING M.A.C. INSTALLED PARTS (1)	3835.00	52	52	225
	EXCLUDING: ENGINE OIL—	99.00			
	HYDRAULIC OIL—	8.00			

Weights and sizes of parts are matters of importance for aircraft. Figure 15-6f is a technical illustration with exploded groups. It shows the identification of groups, as well as the weights and sizes of groups. Such information is vital to the manufacturers of aircraft and space vehicles.

15•7 Identification illustrations. Pictorial drawings are very useful for identifying parts. They help save time when the parts are manufactured or assembled in place and are useful for illustrating operating instruction manuals and spare parts catalogs, and for many other purposes.

Identification illustrations usually take the form of exploded views. If parts are few, they can be identified by names and pointing arrows. The identification illustration in Fig. 15-7a is an example showing numbers for the parts and a tabulation below with names and quantities. The main purpose of the

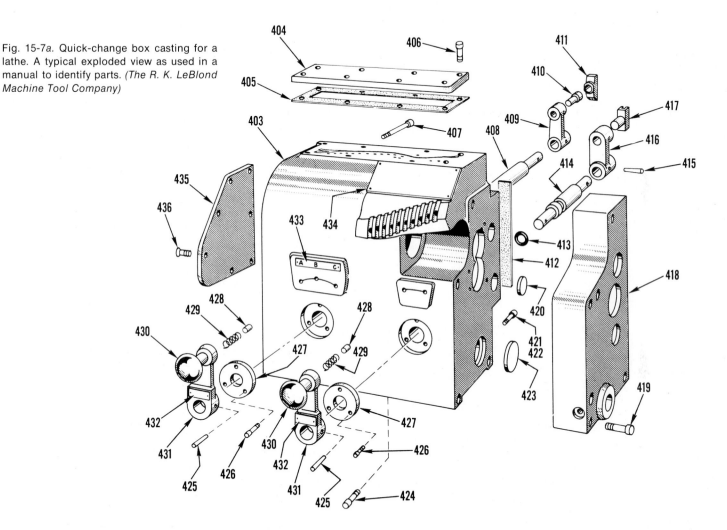

Fig. 15-7a. Quick-change box casting for a lathe. A typical exploded view as used in a manual to identify parts. (*The R. K. LeBlond Machine Tool Company*)

PART NO.	PART NAME	QTY.	PART NO.	PART NAME	QTY.	PART NO.	PART NAME	QTY.
403	QUICK CHANGE BOX	1	414	SHAFT, SHIFTER	1	425	PIN	2
404	COVER, TOP	1	415	PIN, TAPER	2	426	SCREW	6
405	GASKET, COVER	1	416	LINK, SHIFTER	1	427	COLLAR	2
406	SCREW, SOCKET HEAD CAP	8	417	SHOE, SHIFTER	1	428	PLUNGER	2
407	SCREW	2	418	COVER, SLIP GEAR	1	429	SPRING	2
408	SHAFT, SHIFTER	1	419	SCREW	4	430	KNOB	2
409	LINK, SHIFTER	1	420	PLUG	2	431	LEVER	2
410	PIN	1	421	SCREW	3	432	PLATE, FEED-THD.	1
411	SHOE, SHIFTER	1	422	SCREW	1	433	PLATE, COMPOUND	1
412	GASKET (MAKE IN PATTERN SHOP-BOX TO BED)	2	423	PLUG (NOT USED WITH SCREW REVERSE)	1	434	PLATE, ENGLISH INDEX	1
413	"O" RING	2	424	SCREW	3	435	COVER	1
						436	SCREW	7

parts breakdown drawing (Fig. 15-7b) is to identify the parts. Observe the clearness with which the parts are shown by the simple line work and the extremely few shade lines. This is, or it should be, a characteristic of all technical illustrations.

15·8 Space diagrams and installation illustrations. Pictorial drawings, by showing where parts go, save a lot of time. They are especially helpful in showing operating controls, piping installations for steam lines, oil and hydraulic systems, wiring, and other space arrangements. Such drawings vary according to the purpose for which they are used. They may be shown in detail or more or less in outline form. The purpose in general is to show the positions of the parts of the installation. A pictorial space drawing of piping is shown in Fig. 13-23c.

An installation illustration is shown in Fig. 15-8. The numbers are for identification. These would be listed in a separate assembly parts list to accompany the drawing. Note the bracket to group the parts (Nos. 8 to 18) and show where they go; also, note the long-dash lines which "connect" groups of parts to show where they go.

15·9 Rendering. For certain purposes, or where shapes are difficult to read, surface shading or rendering of some kind may be desirable. A study of rendering and of shades and shadows would be necessary to develop professional skill, but the student should learn to recognize some methods used.

For most industrial illustrations, accurate descriptions of shapes and positions are more important than fine artistic effects. Desired results can often be obtained without any shading. In general, surface shading should be limited to the least amount necessary to define the shapes illustrated.

Fig. 15-7b. This is a sample of a typical illustrated parts breakdown drawing, which is used primarily for the purpose of identifying component parts of an assembly. By referring to a tabular parts list which accompanies the drawing, a person can readily determine the proper part number and the quantity of parts used in the assembly. *(Sample supplied courtesy of the Technical Illustrators Association)*

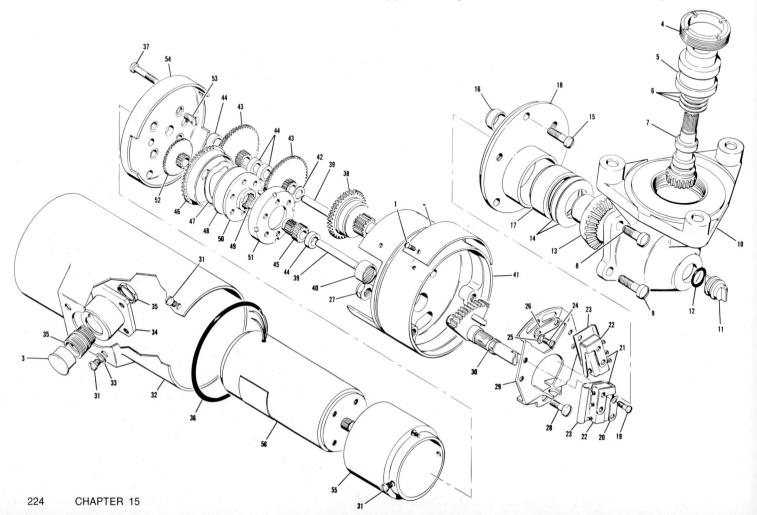

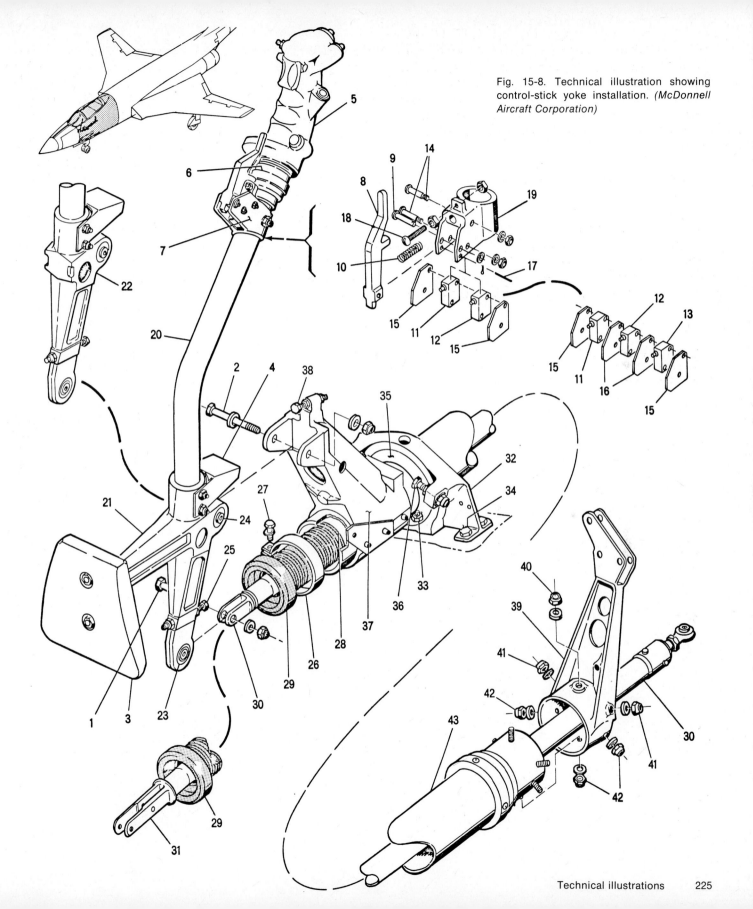

Fig. 15-8. Technical illustration showing control-stick yoke installation. *(McDonnell Aircraft Corporation)*

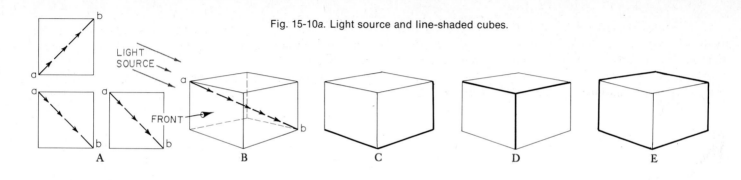

Fig. 15-10a. Light source and line-shaded cubes.

Fig. 15-10b. A maintenance manual illustration. Notice that only the necessary detail is shown and that just enough shading is used to emphasize and give form to the parts. This apparently simple form of shading is effective for many purposes but must be handled carefully. *(Sample supplied courtesy of the Technical Illustrators Association)*

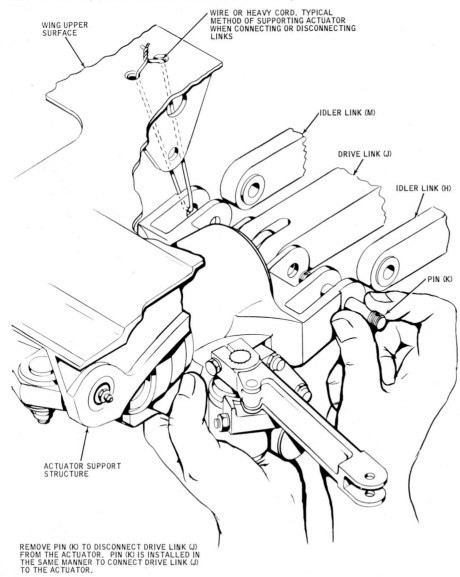

WING UPPER SURFACE

WIRE OR HEAVY CORD. TYPICAL METHOD OF SUPPORTING ACTUATOR WHEN CONNECTING OR DISCONNECTING LINKS

IDLER LINK (M)

DRIVE LINK (J)

IDLER LINK (H)

PIN (K)

ACTUATOR SUPPORT STRUCTURE

REMOVE PIN (K) TO DISCONNECT DRIVE LINK (J) FROM THE ACTUATOR. PIN (K) IS INSTALLED IN THE SAME MANNER TO CONNECT DRIVE LINK (J) TO THE ACTUATOR.

Line drawings are used most for both pictorials and schematics. In addition, there are halftone renderings, photographs, and isometric, oblique, and perspective pictorials (Chap. 14). Different ways of rendering technical illustrations include the use of screen tints, pen and ink, wash, stipple, felt-tip pen and ink, smudge, edge emphasis, and other means, which can be observed in the technical illustrations of aircraft companies, automobile manufacturers, machine-tool makers, and even in the directions which come with your TV set.

15•10 Line shading may be done mechanically, freehand, or sometimes by a combination of both. The light is generally considered to come from in back of and above the left shoulder of the observer and across the diagonal of the object, as at A and B in Fig. 15-10a. The 45° lines at A show the direction of the light to be down, back, and to the right. This is a convention used by draftsmen and renderers. At C the upper left and top edges would be in the light and drawn with thin lines. The lower right and bottom edges would be shaded and drawn with thick lines. At D the edges meeting in the center are made with thick lines to accent the shape. At E the edges meeting at the center are made with thin lines, and thick lines are used on the other edges to bring out the shape.

An example of the use of a small amount of line shading is shown and described in Fig. 15-10b.

15•11 Surface shading (Fig. 15-11). With the light rays coming in the usual conventional direction, as at A, the top and front surfaces would be lighted and the right-hand surface would be shaded, as at B. The front surface can have light shading with heavy shading on the right-hand side, as at C, or solid black may be used on the right-hand side, as at D.

15•12 Some shaded surfaces are indicated in Fig. 15-12. An unshaded view is shown at A for comparison. Ruled-surface shading is shown at B, freehand shading at C, stippled shading at D, Craftint shading at E, and Ben Day shading at F.

Stippling, at D, consists of dots; short, crooked lines; or similar treatment to produce a shaded effect. It is a good method when it is well done, but it requires considerable time. Craftint paper, at E, is made with a great variety of invisible allover dots, lines, and patterns which can be made visible by the application of a developing solution. The Ben Day process, at F, uses films to cover the surface with dots or lines.

Fig. 15-11. Some methods of rendering the faces of a cube.

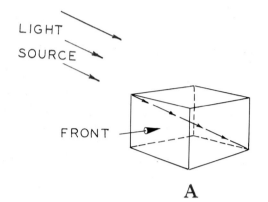

A

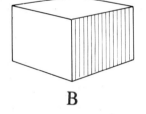

B

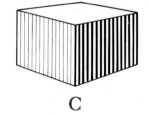

C

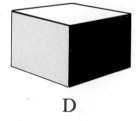

D

Fig. 15-12. Some kinds of rendering.

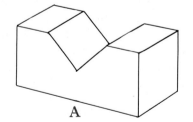

A

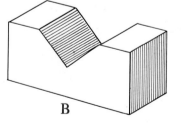

B

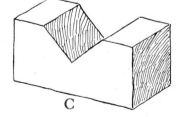

C

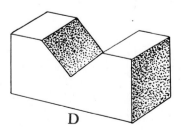

D

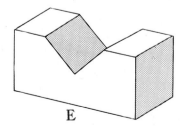

E

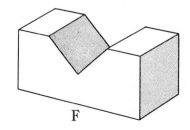

F

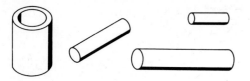

Fig. 15-14a. Simple line rendering for cylinders.

15·13 Airbrush rendering (see Fig. 19-8) produces pictures that resemble photographs. Compressed air is used to spray the solution to obtain the different shading effects in this process. Wash drawings of Sumi (Japanese ink with water added) produce similar results. In this method brushes like those used in watercolor painting are used.

15·14 Cylinder shading. Simple rendering is generally preferred for technical illustrations. Figure 15-14a suggests a few methods by which a single thick line or a small black shading band is used to emphasize the cylindrical shape.

Various methods showing more complete shading are illustrated in Fig. 15-14b. At A the shade lines follow the curvature. Lines parallel to the elements are used at B, C, and E. Stippling is used at D, and surface shading is used at F. The student should learn to recognize the methods of shading illustrated.

Fig. 15-14b. Rendering cylinders with surface shading.

Fig. 15-15a. A cutaway illustration. This is a very useful type of illustration for showing interior construction and arrangement. Notice the simple treatment used to show everything clearly. *(Sample supplied courtesy of the Technical Illustrators Association)*

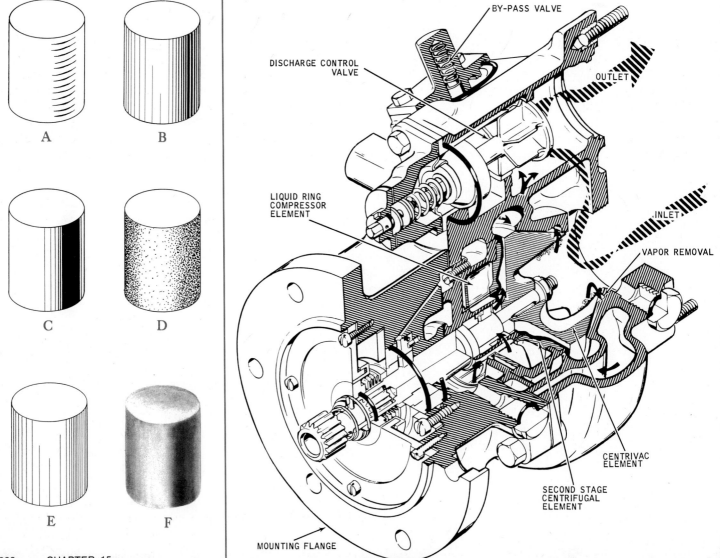

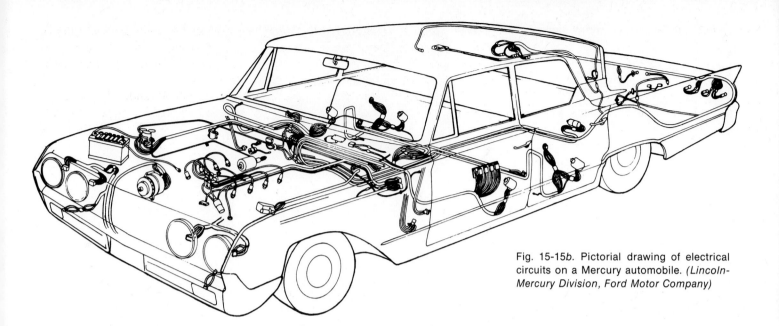

Fig. 15-15*b*. Pictorial drawing of electrical circuits on a Mercury automobile. *(Lincoln-Mercury Division, Ford Motor Company)*

15•15 Technical illustrations may be made by any pictorial or diagrammatic method and modified to suit any special purpose. A few examples are included here as suggestions.

A sectional, or cutaway, drawing is shown in Fig. 15-15*a*. Such drawings may start with a more or less complete exterior view, or the cutting planes may be outlines. (See Art. 14·11 for the construction of sectional pictorial views.) Notes and pointing arrows are carefully placed to show at a glance. The very least amount of shading is used in order to show the cutaway with the greatest clarity.

The illustration in Fig. 15-15*b* was made to show wiring circuits. The automobile is drawn with few thin lines and no shading, as its purpose is to show electrical equipment positions.

The illustration in Fig. 15-15*c* was made to show some orbiting satellites and for use in describing and explain-

Fig. 15-15*c*. Some standardized satellites include orbiting astronomical, geophysical, and solar observatories. Technical illustrations show what these satellites look like. *(NASA)*

Orbiting Astronomical Observatory (OAO)

Orbiting Geophysical Observatory (OGO)

Orbiting Solar Observatory (OSO)

Fig. 15-15*d*. Outline emphasis by a thick black or white line is an effective method of making a shape stand out. *(Rockford Clutch Division, Borg-Warner)*

ing them. The illustration in Fig. 15-15*d* is an example of emphasis by using a thick line to outline the overall shape.

15•16 Building construction illustrations. Details of the construction for buildings can be made clearly and can be easily understood by pictorial sketches or drawings. Any of the methods may be used for this purpose, but simple isometric and oblique views are about all that are necessary in most cases, as indicated in Fig. 15-16. (See also Chap. 21.)

15•17 Furniture construction illustration. Pictorial methods have been much used for furniture and are especially adapted for this purpose. Isometric is useful for showing joints and how parts go together. Study the illustrations in Probs. 13·33 to 13·54.

Fig. 15-16. Building construction details.

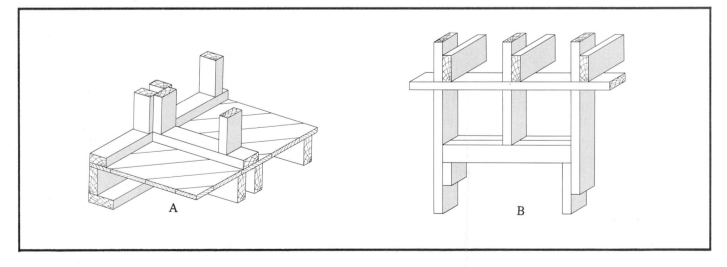

15·18 Reproduction of illustrations. Illustrations made on tracing cloth or thin paper may be reproduced the same size by making direct contact prints, as described in Arts. 8·13 and 8·14. Regular photographic paper may be used with such drawings or with photographic negatives at a reduced size. Photostats may be made in the same or a different size. Where a large number of copies are required, line cuts, halftones, or offset prints are made.

Line cuts (Fig. 15-10*b*) are photoengravings made on zinc or copper plates from black-line or pen-and-ink drawings. The drawing is generally made larger than desired and reduced when photographed on the plate. All lines, dots, figures, and lettering must be black to reproduce well. The plate is etched and used in a printing press.

Halftones (Fig. 15-1*c*) are photoengravings made by photographing through a screen formed by two glass plates. Lines are ruled at uniform distances apart and are placed so that squares are formed. In this way, a negative is made that shows the view as made up of minute dots, and from it a photographic contact print is made on a copper plate. This plate is etched and used in a printing press. The halftone process is used to make cuts from photographs, wash drawings, airbrush drawings, shaded pencil drawings, and whenever there are different shades of gray, as well as black and white, to be reproduced.

The offset process can be used to reproduce any kind of drawing by photographing the drawing on a metal plate, from which it is transferred to printing cylinders. It is a kind of mechanical lithograph. By this process solid lines, as well as all the various tones of photographs or wash drawings, are reproduced.

15·19 Problem suggestions. Group 15, page 523. Three lists are presented. List 1 includes basic principles from which selections may be made to suit the purpose of the course. Selections from Lists 2 and 3 may be made for additional problems or for more advanced students.

List 1: Problems 15·1, 15·2, 15·3, 15·5, 15·6, 15·10, 15·11.

List 2: Problems 15·4, 15·7, 15·8.

List 3: Problems 15·9, 15·12, 15·13, 15·14, 15·15, 15·16.

16

Aerospace drafting

Complexity of modern aircraft is pointed up by the fact that more than 5,000 engineers are directly involved in the design, development and production of a supersonic bomber.

Fig. 16-1a. This aircraft requires an enormous number of drawings.

Fig. 16-1b. The McDonnell F-4C Phantom, a U.S. Air Force jet aircraft. *(McDonnell Aircraft Corporation)*

16•1 The aircraft industry. Modern high-speed and supersonic aircraft include many parts made of many different materials (Fig. 16-1a). Conventional aluminum, magnesium, and steel alloys are usually strong enough for the inner, or substructure, parts; however, much of the outer structure and skins, which are subjected to high temperatures during supersonic flight, must be made of high-temperature, high-strength materials.

Figure 16-1b shows a U.S. Air Force plane, and Fig. 16-1c shows the major components of the airplane. The fuselage, or central body, contains the operating and passenger compartments (or armament and armament controls on military craft). The fuselage structure is composed of a series of shaped bulkheads and rings (riveted, machined, or welded frames) and longitudinal members which together form a rigid framework. The sheet-metal outer skins are attached with rivets or screws.

The wings are composed of ribs which form the "fore and aft" shape, or airfoil. The ribs are attached to spars (beamlike members) running inboard and outboard from the fuselage. The wing skins are attached to the ribs and spar substructure with rivets or screws. In addition to the wings, other control surfaces which are called *airfoils* (Fig. 16-1c) include ailerons, rudders, stabilizers, flaps, and tabs. A *chord line* is a straight line between the leading edge and the trailing edge of an airfoil.

The landing gear (undercarriage) is retracted and extended by hydraulic or electrical drive mechanisms. Hy-

Fig. 16-1c. An exploded view of parts of the McDonnell F-4C Phantom. *(McDonnell Aircraft Corporation)*

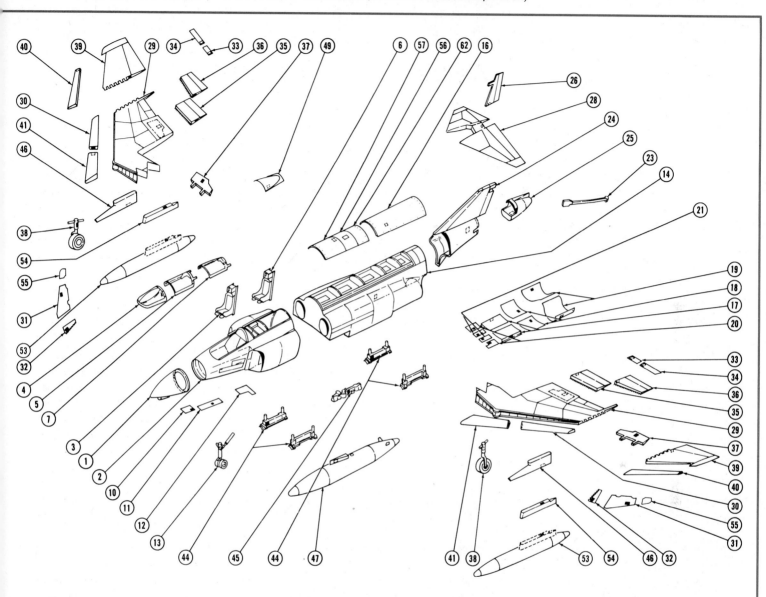

1. Radome
2. Forward fuselage
3. Pilot seat
4. Windshield
5. Forward canopy
6. Radar operation seat
7. Aft canopy
10. Nose landing gear door, forward
11. Nose landing gear door, aft
12. Hydraulic compartment access door
13. Nose landing gear shock strut

14. Center fuselage
16. Fuel tank door
17. Engine access door
18. Engine access door
19. Engine access door
20. Engine access door
21. Auxiliary engine air door
23. Arresting hook
24. Aft fuselage
25. Tail cone
26. Rudder
28. Stabilator

29. Center section wing
30. Leading edge flap
31. Main landing gear strut door
32. Main landing gear inboard door
33. Inboard spoiler
34. Outboard spoiler
35. Flap
36. Aileron
37. Speed brake
38. Main landing gear shock strut
39. Outer wing
40. Leading edge flap, outboard

41. Leading edge flap, inboard
44. Missile rack
45. Bomb rack
46. Missile pylon
47. External center-line fuel tank
49. Data link access door
53. External wing fuel tank
54. External wing fuel tank pylon
55. Landing gear door, outboard
56. Boom IFR receptacle access door
57. Fuel cell access door
62. Fuel cell access door

draulic shock absorbers are used to minimize landing shock loads.

The power plant (piston or jet engine) may be located in the fuselage or in the wings. Fuel tanks are usually located in both the fuselage and the wings.

In addition to the major structural components, an airplane includes various "systems," such as air conditioning and compartment pressurization, radar, radio, hydraulic, electrical, armament, plumbing, etc. It therefore becomes obvious that many different industries are involved in the making of an airplane. Many parts are made in different factories and shipped to the assembly plant, where they are fitted into the airplane. All this means that many kinds of drawings are required to produce the airplane. There are detail parts and assembly drawings of the airplane components as well as detail and assembly drawings of the airplane systems.

16·2 Aircraft drafting practice. Aircraft drafting has to do with the drawings made for airplanes: detail parts, subassemblies, major assemblies, installation drawings, and layouts. The aircraft draftsman should be familiar with the various materials used as well as the various processes followed in manufacturing aircraft. The fundamental principles are the same as for all other drawings, which means that a thorough knowledge of orthographic projection is a basic requirement.

The ability to make pictorial views is a valuable qualification, as they are useful for many purposes (Fig. 16-1c). Pictorial drawing has become a profession for many artist-draftsmen or technical illustrators.

The aircraft industry continuously tries to improve its methods in order to manufacture aircraft more efficiently and at lower cost. Most companies prepare carefully illustrated engineering manuals so that their employees can follow the practices best adapted to their company's product. A draftsman must be familiar with his company's manual and with the standards in general use. The SAE (Society of Automotive Engineers, Inc.) publishes a volume of *Aerospace-Automotive Drawing Standards,* which includes the authoritative standards for these industries.

16·3 Classification of aircraft drawings. In general, aircraft drawings consist of assembly and detail drawings; however, these vary in some respects from the usual machine drawings. Thus, assembly drawings may or may not contain some or all dimensions and information. They may show the whole plane, groups of parts, or just one or two parts.

One form of assembly drawing is the installation drawing. It may give information for making certain parts. Its major purpose, however, is to locate the various parts for assembling the plane. Dimensions and information that are needed to assemble the plane are found on an installation drawing. An important kind of assembly drawing is the subassembly, which applies to a group of related parts.

Some drawings take the form of diagrams for operating controls, wiring, piping, lubrication, and so on. There are also charts to cover the proper steps to be followed for proper aircraft maintenance.

Aircraft assembly and detail drawings include such a variety that only a general list can be given. The names are descriptive enough to tell the type of each drawing.

Assembly drawings
Casting and raw drawings
Casting blank drawings
Casting machining drawings
Chart drawings
Design assembly or installation
  drawings
Detailed subassembly drawings
Diagram drawings
Die-casting drawings
Electrical drawings
Equipment drawings
Extrusion drawings
Fairing drawings
Forging drawings
General arrangement drawings
Installation drawings
Layout drawings
Machining drawings
Mock-up drawings
Perspective drawings
Sheet-metal drawings
Sketches
Standard part drawings
Tabulated drawings
Tubing and cable drawings
Weld assembly drawings

16·4 A general arrangement drawing is shown in Fig. 16-4. Note that the side view shows the front of the plane toward the left-hand end of the drawing. This is the standard arrangement for either assembly or detail drawings. Parts are left-hand or right-hand according to the position that they occupy relative to the pilot seated in the cockpit of the plane.

16·5 Casting drawings. Two drawings may be made for castings, one a casting blank drawing *(rough casting)* and the other a casting machining drawing *(finished part).* They may be on one sheet, as in Fig. 16-5, or on separate sheets. In general, casting drawings should be made full size and should have the views arranged with the center lines or datum planes parallel to the main part of the casting. Auxiliary and sectional views should be used where needed to show exact information for every detail of the casting.

Study the views of the casting blank drawing at the left in Fig. 16-5 and note the information given, which refers only to the casting blank.

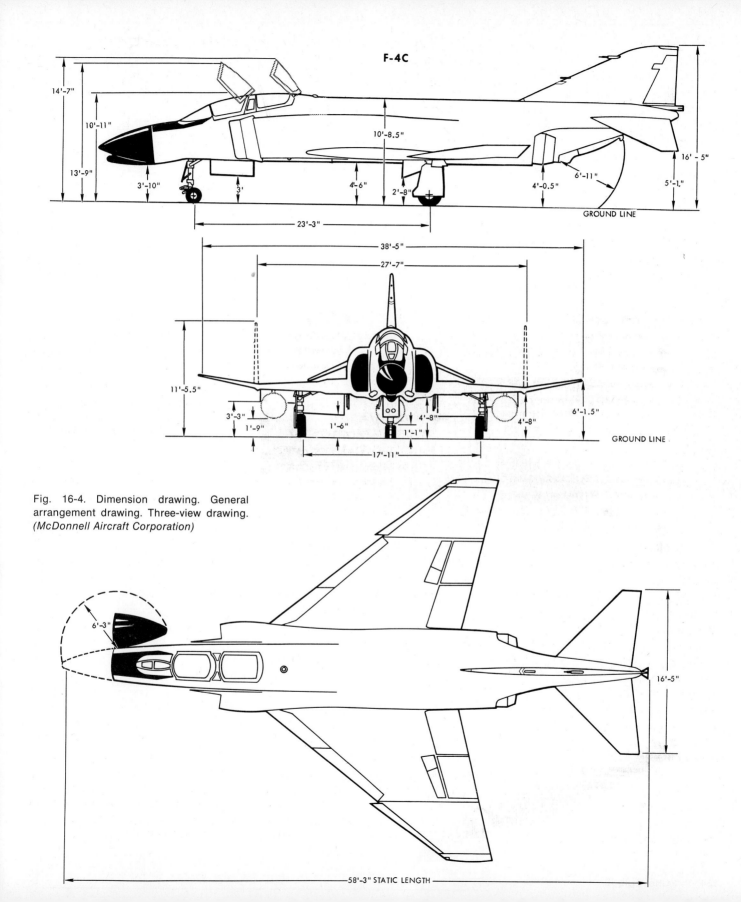

Fig. 16-4. Dimension drawing. General arrangement drawing. Three-view drawing. *(McDonnell Aircraft Corporation)*

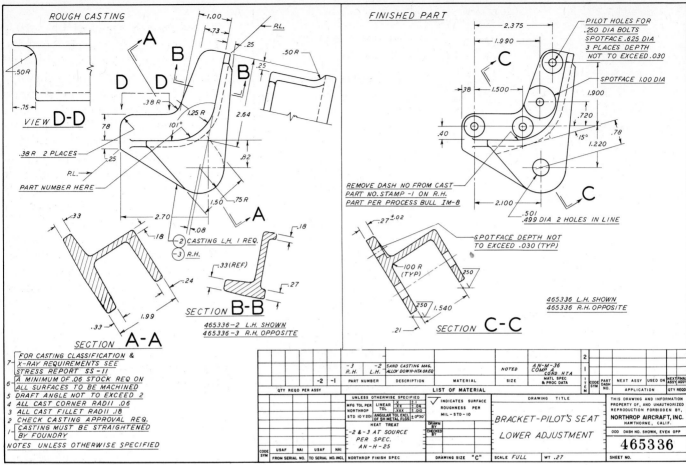

Fig. 16-5. Casting drawing, bracket. *(Northrup Aircraft, Inc.)*

Dimensions on the casting blank are coordinated with the machining drawing, which is located from the same center or base lines used to locate the machined surfaces. Study the views of the machining drawing at the right on Fig. 16-5 and note the information given for the machinist, inspector, and others for all operations such as machining, assembly of bushings, and so forth.

Fittings which may be used as "cast," or without any fabrication (machining, and so forth), may be completely detailed on a casting blank drawing.

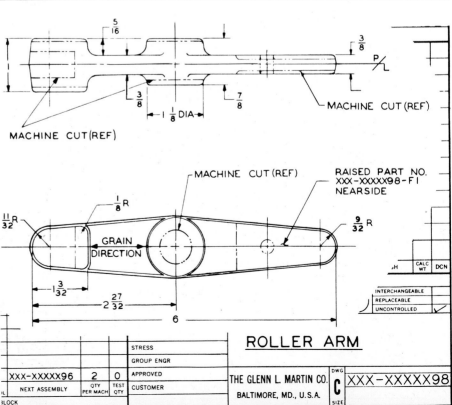

Fig. 16-6a. Forging blank drawing, roller arm. *(The Glenn L. Martin Company)*

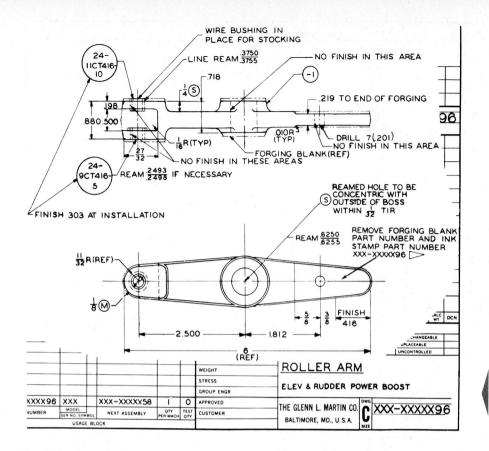

16•6 Forging drawings.

A forging blank drawing is shown in Fig. 16-6a, and a forging machining drawing for the same part *(roller arm)* is shown in Fig. 16-6b. These two drawings should be studied and compared. A single drawing may be made for fittings which may be used as forged (Fig. 16-6c).

The forging blank drawing (Fig. 16-6a) provides complete information for the diesinker, forger, inspector, and others, with complete information for the forging blank only.

The forging machining drawing (Fig. 16-6b) gives information for the machinist, inspector, and others for all operations, such as machining, assembly of bushings, bearings, and so forth.

Fig. 16-6b. Forging machining drawing, roller arm. *(The Glenn L. Martin Company)*

Fig. 16-6c. Drawing for the forging of a fitting. *(Grumman Aircraft Engineering Corporation)*

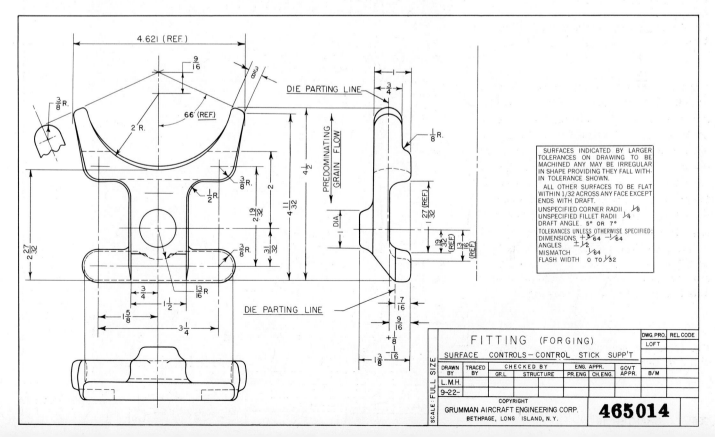

16·7 Sheet-metal drawings are based upon the principles of intersections and developments, as discussed in Chap. 20. However, it is necessary to consider the thickness of metal, bend allowances, and other factors when laying out flat patterns (developments) or sheet-metal templates. The parts shown in Figs. 16-7a and 16-7b are made of sheet metal. In Fig. 16-7b note the use of decimal fractions exclusively. Design standards are used for light-

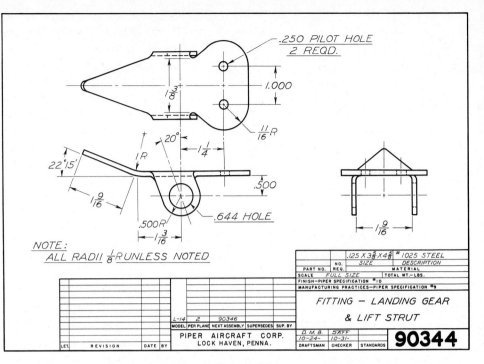

Fig. 16-7a. Sheet-metal part. *(Piper Aircraft Corporation)*

Fig. 16-7b. Sheet-metal part. *(Boeing Aircraft Company)*

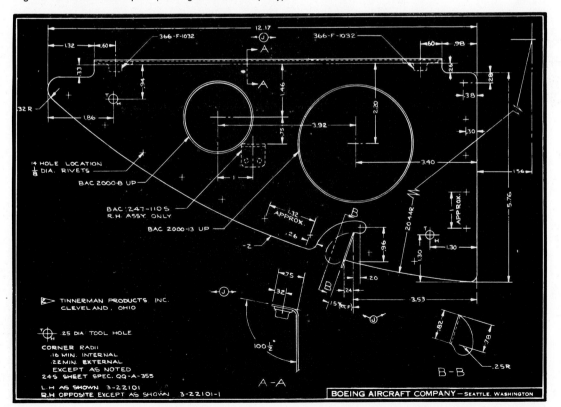

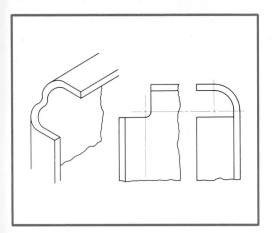

Fig. 16-7c. Bend relief.

ening holes shown, as in the note "BAC 2000-8 and -13 UP," which indicates direction of the flange.

Sheet metal is used extensively for forming parts of airplanes as well as for the curved skin covering. Many factors enter into the selection of the proper material, the design, and the forming of such parts. Only a few considerations can be indicated here because specialized knowledge and experience are necessary for a complete understanding of this part of airplane design.

Bend relief is an allowance made at the corners when plates are bent. A method of bend relief is shown in Fig. 16-7c. Allowance must be made for bends (Fig. 16-7d). The minimum bend radius depends upon the material and

the thickness. Values can be found in the engineering manuals of aircraft companies.

Joggling (Fig. 16-7e) is used when plates or structural shapes overlap in order to present an unbroken surface for the skin.

16•8 Sketching (Chap. 6) is used in many ways in connection with the design of aircraft and in making information more readable. Sketches may contain complete information for the fabrication of small parts, to forward (present) small parts, to forward small portions of information on large drawings, or for changes in manufacture of the aircraft. Sketch pads with printed forms are used for such purposes. The views may be freehand sketches or

Fig. 16-7d. Bend allowance.

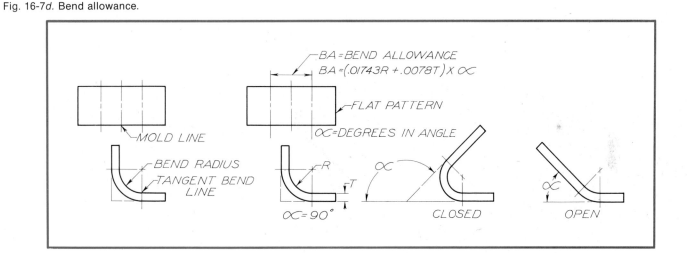

Fig. 16-7e. Joggling.

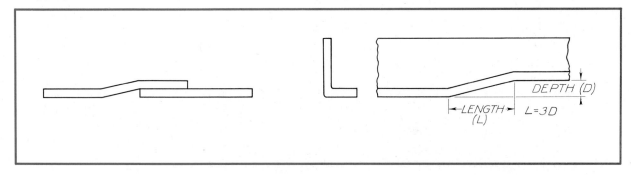

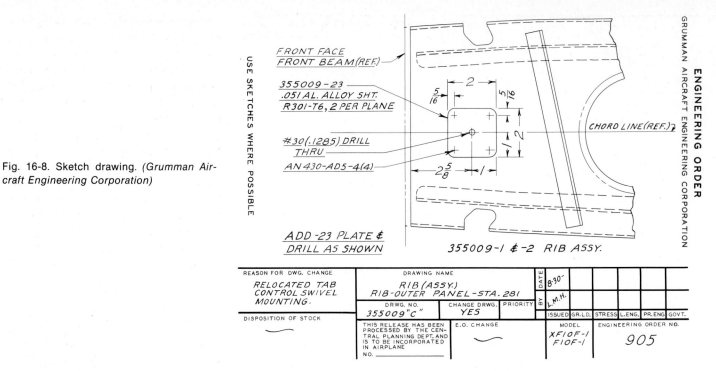

USE SKETCHES WHERE POSSIBLE

Fig. 16-8. Sketch drawing. *(Grumman Aircraft Engineering Corporation)*

Fig. 16-9. Tabulated drawing. *(Douglas Aircraft Company, Inc.)*

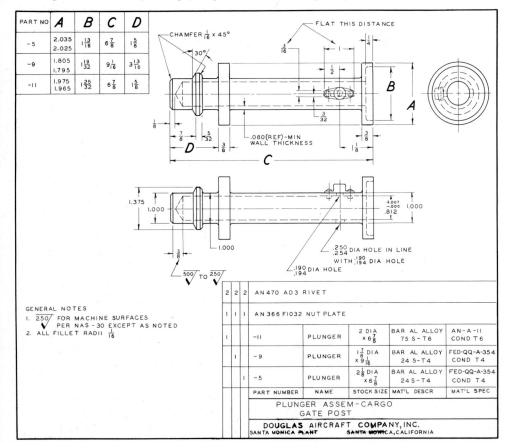

GENERAL NOTES
1. $\frac{250}{}$ FOR MACHINE SURFACES PER NAS - 30 EXCEPT AS NOTED
2. ALL FILLET RADII $\frac{1}{16}$

"drawings." Figure 16-8 illustrates a sketch-pad sheet for an addition to a rib assembly.

16·9 Tabulated drawings may be used for either assembly or detail drawings where only a few of the dimensions are different on the same basic piece, as in Fig. 16-9 for the dimensions A, B, C, and D.

16·10 Assembly drawings explain parts joined together to form a unit (Figs. 16-10a and 16-10b). They call out (specify) all the parts which are required, including such details as bolts, screws, and fasteners of any kind needed to join the parts. Clips, brackets, and so forth, may be detailed on sheet-metal assembly drawings by assigning dash numbers (Art. 16·14) to identify them. Such dash numbers for details shown on assembly drawings save the time and expense of making separate drawings for each part which is required.

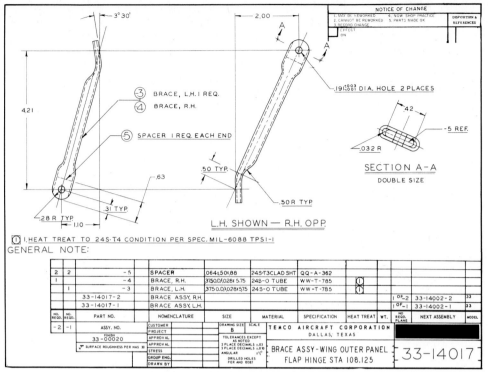

Fig. 16-10a. Brace assembly. *(Temco Aircraft Corporation)*

Fig. 16-10b. Fitting assembly. *(Temco Aircraft Corporation)*

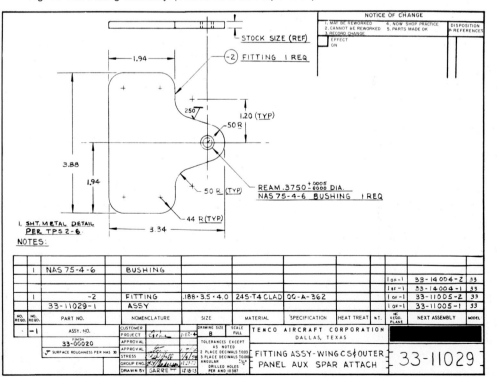

16•11 Layouts of various kinds form an important part of aircraft design and drafting from the general overall design to pencil layouts for subassemblies and groups of parts. Such drawings provide for the relations of the parts, manufacturing procedure, operating and other equipment, and so forth. Layout drawings are extremely accurate drawings and show all necessary information for making details and assembly drawings, for determining clearances, for stress analysis, for calculation of weights, for detailing shapes, for dimensioning, and for specifying various materials and treatments.

16•12 Lofting. Full-size layouts for large projects are made by *lofting,* a term that comes from the ship loft where the lines or exact shapes of ships are worked out full size. Lofting is an important kind of layout for airplane design. Accurate full-size contours and sections are developed by lofting. Curves are faired (adjusted or smoothed out) to obtain smooth surfaces, and templates are made for use where necessary.

Specialized knowledge of materials and their properties as well as experience and good judgment are necessary for this work. Such work cannot be done on drawing boards but must be laid out on special loft floors where the required areas are available.

16•13 Dimensions and notes. The usual practice is to give all dimensions in inches and to omit the inch mark except as on the three-view assembly drawing (see Fig. 16-4), where feet and inches are used.

All notes and dimensions are placed to read from the bottom of the drawing, regardless of the direction of the dimension lines, whether they are horizontal, vertical, or at an angle, as shown on the illustrations in this chapter. Dimensions less than $5/16$ are shown

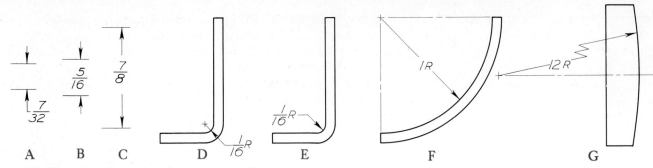

Fig. 16-13*a*. Dimensions for vertical distances and radii.

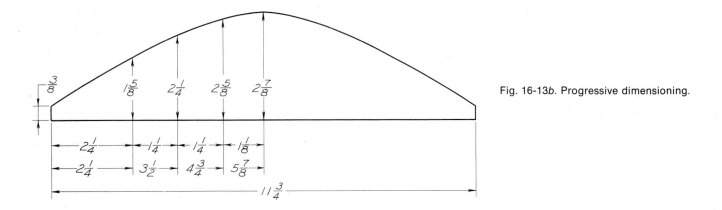

Fig. 16-13*b*. Progressive dimensioning.

Fig. 16-13*c*. Dimensioning for angles.

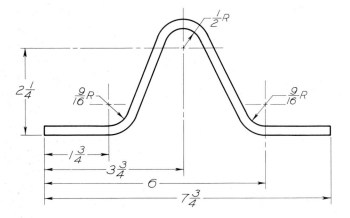

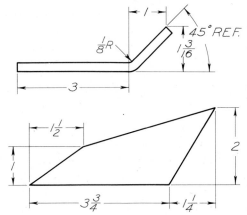

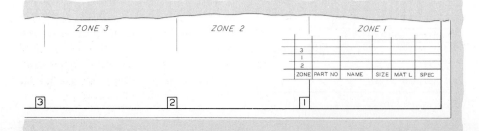

Fig. 16-13*d*. Zone marking.

as at A in Fig. 16-13a and 5/16 and larger as at B and C. Capital letters are generally used for all lettering, either vertical or inclined, according to the practice of the particular company.

Radii are given for the inside radius on all bends (Fig. 16-13a at D, E, F, and G). Progressive dimensioning is sometimes used with regular dimensioning (Fig. 16-13b). Linear dimensions are preferred to degrees for angles (Fig. 16-13c), but degrees may be given for reference.

Notes are used to give necessary information and instructions. They should not be used in place of dimensions. However, when used to specify an operation, the dimension may be included for such purposes as the diameter and depth of drilled or reamed holes. Other notes are indicated on the illustrations.

The basic principles of dimensioning as described in Chap. 11 apply, with the exceptions here noted, together with exceptions made by any special company practice.

Large drawings which have much information, such as views of several parts, extra part views, sectional views, references to other views, and so forth, are marked off in zones (vertical strips 11 in. wide) as in Fig. 16-13d. The zones are numbered in small squares along the bottom border lines, as shown. The numbers in the zone column of the title tell the zone in which the views or other items will be found and save the time which would be spent in searching for them.

16•14 Dash numbers. When two or more parts are drawn on a detail drawing or an assembly drawing, they are identified by dash numbers of the drawing. The basic number is the drawing number. This number, followed by a dash number, identifies a piece shown on that drawing. Thus 3279-3 would indicate part -3 on drawing 3279. On the drawing the -3 may be enclosed in a circle or left in the clear, but it must be placed close to the part that it identifies. Even dash numbers may be used for right-hand parts and odd dash numbers for left-hand parts, or the numbers may be followed by the letters R or L.

Particular practice in the use of dash numbers varies with different companies.

16•15 Titles and nomenclature. Titles used on aircraft drawings vary according to the practice of different companies. In general, the title may include such information as model, title of assembly or detail, drawing number, calculated weight, actual weight, dimensional limits, scale, date, identification of draftsman, tracer, checker, engineer, and so forth, and provision for a material list.

The name on an aircraft part should locate the part as to the group or subgroup to which it belongs so far as possible. Breakdown parts lists are available in company drafting rooms. In general, the name of the part (noun) is placed first, followed by the main group and subgroup, as explained in the following paragraphs which give the practice of the Aeronca Aircraft Corporation.

Drawing titles. In naming drawings, U.S. Air Force standard practice is followed. The drawing title must consist first of the basic identifying word (noun) entered on the top line of the title block, followed on the second line by a suitable description and modifying words. For example:

BRACKET—
WING AILERON HINGE

This is read: "WING AILERON HINGE BRACKET" and the title will be entered in the number book thus: Bracket—"Wing Aileron Hinge."

No basic names of more than one word can be used.

Names such as "tie rods," "push rods," and "push tubes" can be written similar to the following example:

ROD—AILERON CONTROL PUSH

The details of an assembly must be named in agreement with the name of the assembly and consistently with each other as follows:

ASSEMBLY—FLOATING INSTRUMENT PANEL BOTTOM BRACKET

BRACKET—FLOATING INSTRUMENT PANEL BOTTOM

The parts may be further identified, when there is danger of confusion of parts with similar names, by the addition of such words as "right," "left," "upper," "lower," "end," and "center" or by such words as "long," "short," "main," or "auxiliary."

The words "and" and "for" can be omitted from the title, as the title should be as concise as possible.

16•16 Standard parts. Some parts are manufactured for general use and are available in standard sizes and dimensions. Such parts are "called out," or identified, by numbers or symbols. Some companies make their own standard parts for their own use which are called out in a similar manner.

There are standard sections for various extruded shapes and tubes, standard fabrics, bolts, eyebolts, nuts, castle nuts, stop nuts, cotter pins, taper pins, turnbuckles, bushings, rivets, keys, sheet-metal screws, and so forth. Other standards include those of the American Standards Association (ASA), Society of Automotive Engineers (SAE), and other societies, and the government standards as used by the Air Force, the Army, and the Navy. Until the Armed Forces merged, government standards were designated for the Air

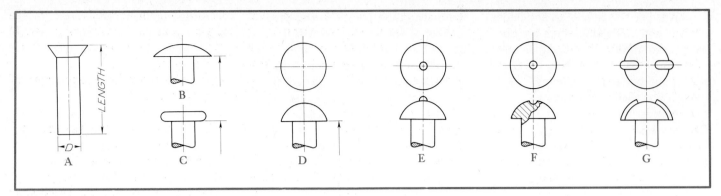

Fig. 16-17. Aircraft rivets.

Corps (AC) and jointly for the Army and Navy (AN). Recently a new set of standards has been organized for all the services. The new standards, known as *Military Standards* or *Mil Standards,* are replacing the AC and AN numbers. Some AC and AN Standards will continue until the new Mil Standards are complete. Books of standards are used for reference when drawings are made in aircraft drafting rooms.

16·17 Aircraft rivets. Some aircraft rivets are illustrated in Fig. 16-17. For complete dimensions and information, access should be had to AN Standard sheets. A countersunk head (AN425)

is shown at A, a brazier head (AN455) at B, a flat head (AN442) at C, and a round head (AN430) at D. Identification markings indicate the material: Type A (aluminum, 3S) without marking is shown at D; Type D (aluminum alloy, 17S) with raised dot is shown at E, Type AD (aluminum alloy, A17S) with depression is shown at F, and Type DD (aluminum alloy, 24S) is shown at G.

Codes are used for calling out rivets, as, for example, AN425AD4-8. AN425 means Army-Navy Standard countersunk head, AD means A17S material, 4 means the diameter in thirty-seconds of an inch, and 8 means the length in sixteenths of an inch.

16·18 Aircraft bolts. An AN aircraft bolt is shown in Fig. 16-18, with some

D	Threads per in.	E	F
No. 10			
0.189	32	$7/16$	0.375
$1/4$	28	$1/2$	0.4375
$5/16$	24	$37/64$	0.500
$3/8$	24	$21/32$	0.5625
$7/16$	20	$23/32$	0.625
$1/2$	20	$7/8$	0.750
$9/16$	18	$1 1/64$	0.875
$5/8$	18	$1 3/32$	0.9375
$3/4$	16	$1 5/64$	1.0625
$7/8$	14	$1 7/16$	1.250
1	14	$1 21/32$	1.4375

For bolthead, $H = \frac{1}{2}D + \frac{1}{32}''$. For nut, $H = \frac{3}{4}D$.

dimensions in the table. Sheets of AN standards are used in aircraft plants to give all dimensions and other information for each diameter of bolt. Identification marks, three of which are shown, are used on the head: for aluminum alloy specification QQ-A-351, the head is left unmarked, as at B; for aluminum alloy QQ-A-354, the head is marked as at C; for steel, the head is marked as at D.

Fig. 16-18. Aircraft bolt.

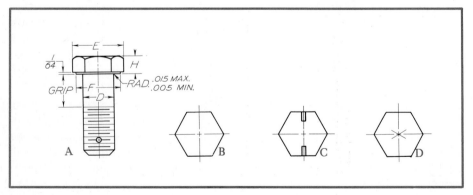

Code symbols are used to call out bolts, as, for example, AN4-7. AN means steel, Army-Navy Standard; 4 means the diameter in sixteenths of an inch or $4/16 = 1/4$ diameter; 7 means the length in eighths of an inch, or $7/8$ in. long. For aluminum alloy, the dash is replaced by a letter (or letters) to indicate the alloy, as in AN4D7. If the hole for a pin at the end of a bolt is to be omitted, the letter A is added, as in AN4D7A.

The length of bolts is given by the number of eighths up to $7/8$ in. in diameter; for 1 in. or more, it is given in inches and eighths. Thus 1 in. is given as 10, or 1 in. and no eighths; $1 1/8$ in. is given as 11, or 1 in. and one-eighth.

For other aircraft threaded fastenings, clevis bolts, eyebolts, special lock nuts, and so forth, reference should be made to the latest AN Standard sheets which are on hand in the company drafting room.

16•19 A checklist of procedures used as a guide for group drawing checkers by the Grumman Aircraft Engineering Corporation includes the following items for consideration. It may also be utilized by the man on the drawing board in the final analysis of a completed drawing.

Drawing arrangement
Selection of sheet size
Placement of notes, stamps, etc.
Drawing appearance
  General simplicity and neatness—useless waste of time in unnecessary detail
  Lettering—$5/32$ high
Part numbering and unnecessary notes regarding same
Title block and bill of materials
Model block
General make-up of drawing—call-outs, drill notes, sections, views, etc.
Applicable stamps
Applicable notes
  General
  Commercial articles
  Interchangeability and replaceability
  Tool engineering information
Zoning (where applicable)

Drawing number on roll sizes (reverse side, opposite corners along margin)
Installations, for proper next assembly call-out(s)
Assemblies (major)—for applicable installations
Special drawings
  Participating and/or licensee contractor's drawings
  Altered government standards
  Specification control drawings
  Altered commercial and/or patented articles
  Matched parts

16•20. Problem suggestions. Group 16, page 523. Three lists are represented. List 1 is elementary. Selections from Lists 2 and 3 may be made for more advanced students according to the purpose of the course.

List 1: Problems 16·1, 16·3, 16·5, 16·8, 16·9, 16·12.
List 2: Problems 16·2, 16·4, 16·7.
List 3: Problems 16·6, 16·11, 16·13, 16·14, 16·15.

17
Welding drawings

17•1 Welding is being used for an ever-increasing variety of mechanical and structural purposes, such as building up and fastening parts together. Welding has become common practice for steel buildings (Fig. 17-1). Standard steel shapes, plates, and bars may be welded together to make machine frames, bases, jigs and fixtures, and so forth. The greater strength of steel in tension is often an advantage that permits a design of less weight and complication for parts that were formerly made of cast iron. Sheet-metal work can be simplified by welding instead of riveting the joints.

The aircraft, automotive, and ship-building industries have developed welding as a major fabricating method for steel, aluminum, and magnesium.

17•2 Welding processes. The two basic processes are *fusion welding* and *resistance welding.* Fusion welding makes use of welding material in the form of a wire or rod which is added to the weld. These filler rods combine with the metal being welded. Gas or a carbon arc is used to create the heat so that the metals flow together. Resistance welding uses an electric current to generate welding heat by the resistance of the parts to an electric current. The parts are welded by pressure. Welding processes include forge welding, resistance welding, arc welding, gas welding, thermit welding, induction welding, flow welding, cold welding, and soldering and brazing. There are many welding books that can be used for reference or study.

17•3 Welding drawings make use of ideographic (picture-writing) symbols to give the necessary welding information (Art. 17·5). These symbols have been developed by the American Welding Society and provide a flexible means of giving specifications, type, location, and size of weld, as well as various combinations to suit any condition. Every drafting room should be provided with one or more copies of the latest edition of *Welding Symbols and Instructions for Their Use.* These symbols have been adopted as American Standard.

Compare the photograph and drawing of a casting for a sheave housing in Fig. 17-3a with the same part which was made by welding, shown in Fig. 17-3b.

Fig. 17-1. Welding steel on a building. *(Courtesy Engineering News-Record)*

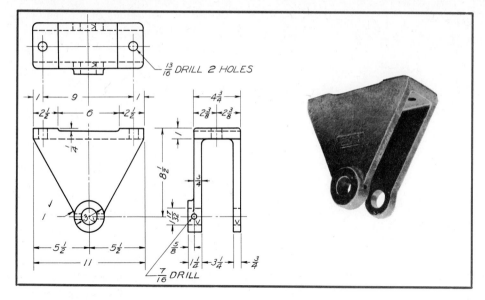

Fig. 17-3a. Cast-sheave housing. *(Wellman Engineering Company and Lincoln Electric Company)*

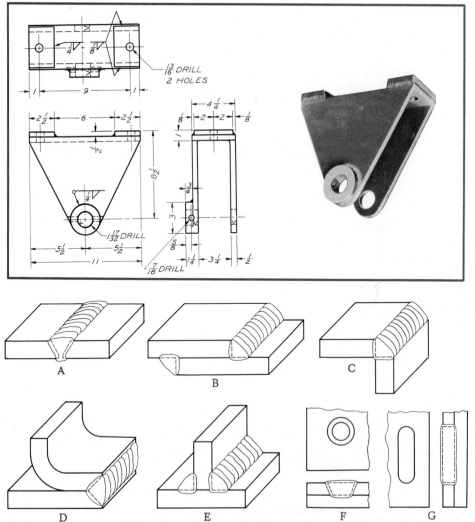

Fig. 17-3b. Welded-sheave housing. *(Wellman Engineering Company and Lincoln Electric Company)*

17•4 Types of joints are shown and named in Fig. 17-4a. Many variations in the kinds of welds are used in making these joints. These are further influenced by the preparation of the parts, as illustrated for the few joints which are named in Fig. 17-4b. The preparation of the groove is shown by the hidden lines at A to I, inclusive. The size of the root opening is shown by R and the amount of the angle by A at J and K. The size of weld, or the leg of a fillet weld, is indicated by S at L.

Many combinations and varieties of joints are used to meet the great number of different conditions that occur in welding practice. Knowledge of conditions and experience are necessary to make a proper selection of the types and sizes of welds.

Fig. 17-4a. Basic types of joints. (A) Butt joint (V-groove weld). (B) Lap joint (fillet weld). (C) Corner joint (fillet weld). (D) Edge joint (V-groove weld). (E) T-joint (fillet weld). (F) Plug weld. (G) Slot weld.

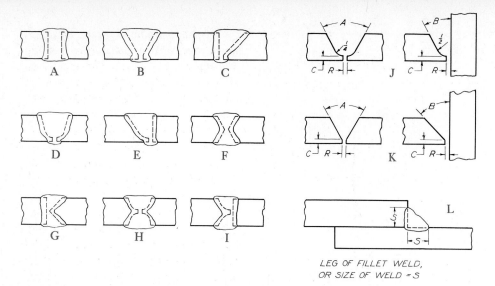

Fig. 17-4b. Groove joints. (A) Square groove. (B) Single V-groove. (C) Single bevel groove. (D) Single U-groove. (E) Single J-groove. (F) Double V-groove. (G) Double bevel groove. (H) Double U-groove. (I) Double J-groove. (J) $A = 45°$ min, $C = \frac{1}{16}''$ to $\frac{3}{16}''$, $R = 0''$ to $\frac{9}{16}''$, $B = 35°$, 25°. (K) $A = 60°$ min, $C = 0''$ to $\frac{1}{8}''$, $R = \frac{1}{8}''$ to $\frac{1}{4}''$, $B = 45°$ min.

placed on both sides of the reference line. The arrow is drawn to point with a definite break toward the member to be grooved when the bevel or J-groove weld symbol is used (Fig. 17-5d). At A, the meaning is not clear. At B, the arrow clearly indicates that the vertical member is to be grooved on the arrow side, as at C. At D, the symbol clearly indicates the desired welds, as at E.

The tail of the arrow is used for specification reference, as at A in Fig. 17-5e, where A2 placed in the tail signifies the specification described in connection with that figure and shown at B. Also, see Fig. 17-5b, where the letter T is placed in the tail of the arrow to refer to a specification. The tail of the arrow may be omitted when a specification reference is not needed, as in drawings where standard company specifications are used.

17•5 Basic arc- and gas- (fusion-) welding symbols of the American Welding Society are given in Fig. 17-5a, which shows both basic and supplementary symbols. Separate symbols may be selected to describe any desired weld, since these symbols may be assembled to describe either the most simple or the most complicated joints.

The standard location of information on welding symbols is shown on Fig. 17-5b. The notes indicate how symbols and data are placed in relation to the reference line. The perpendicular leg of the fillet, bevel, and J-groove weld symbol is always placed to the left.

The words "near side" and "far side," formerly used, have been replaced by the words "arrow side" and "other side" (Fig. 17-5c). The symbol is shown at the left and the desired weld at the right (at A to E). Note that the weld symbol for the arrow side is placed on the side of the reference line toward the reader; for the other side it is placed on the side of the reference line away from the reader; for both sides it is

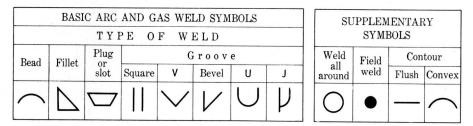

Fig. 17-5a. Arc- and gas-welding symbols.

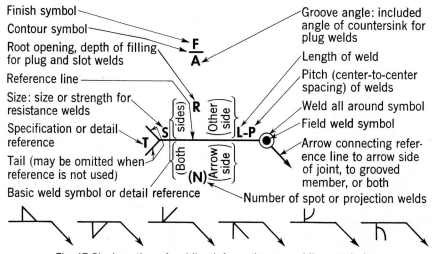

Fig. 17-5b. Location of welding information on welding symbols.

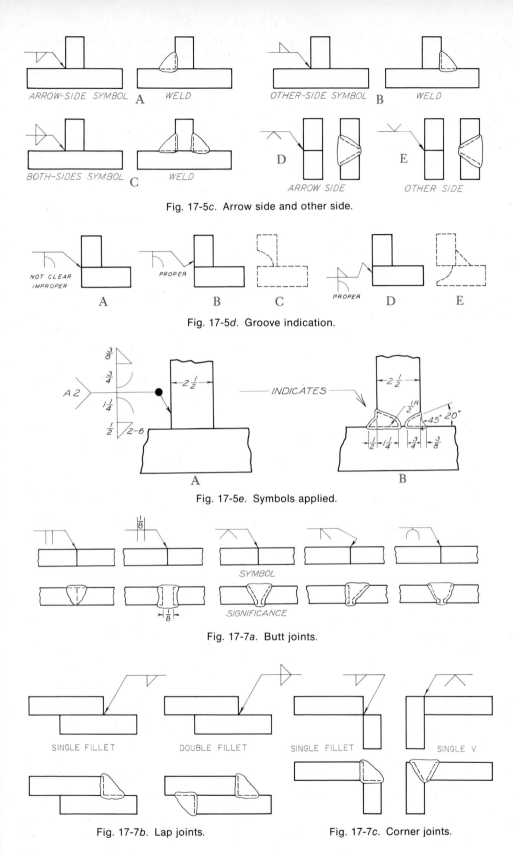

Fig. 17-5c. Arrow side and other side.

Fig. 17-5d. Groove indication.

Fig. 17-5e. Symbols applied.

Fig. 17-7a. Butt joints.

SINGLE FILLET   DOUBLE FILLET   SINGLE FILLET   SINGLE V

Fig. 17-7b. Lap joints.

Fig. 17-7c. Corner joints.

17·6 An example of the way in which the symbols are used to give welding information is illustrated in Fig. 17-5e at A and B. This joint is described as follows: double-filleted-welded, partially grooved, double-J tee joint with incomplete penetration [type of joint shown by the drawing]. Grooves of standard proportion (which are ½ in. R, 20° included angle, edges in contact before welding) ¾ in. deep for other- (or far-) side weld and 1¼ in. deep for arrow- (or near-) side fillet weld with increments 2 in. long, spaced 6 in. center to center. All fillets standard 45° fillets. All welding done in field in accordance with welding specification number A2 (which requires that the weld be made by manual d-c shielded metal-arc process, using high-grade, covered, mild-steel electrode and that the root be unchipped and welds be unpeened but that the joint be preheated before welding).

17·7 Meaning of symbols. Some symbols used to indicate various welded joints and their meanings are shown in Figs. 17-7a to 17-7c. In each case the symbol is shown on the top row and the preparation of the joint before welding is shown by hidden lines on the bottom row.

Welding symbols are shown on a machine drawing in Fig. 17-3b and on a structural drawing, Fig. 17-7d, page 250.

17·8 "Resistance welding[1] differs from other forms of welding in that no extraneous materials, such as fluxes[2] or filler rods are used. . . ." The welding heat is generated by the resistance of the parts to the electric current. For

[1] *Resistance Welding Manual,* Resistance Welder Manufacturers' Association, Philadelphia, Pa.

[2] *Fluxes* are fusible materials or gases that are used to cleanse metals for welding by dissolving oxides. They also are used to prevent the possible formation of oxides and to release gases during the welding process.

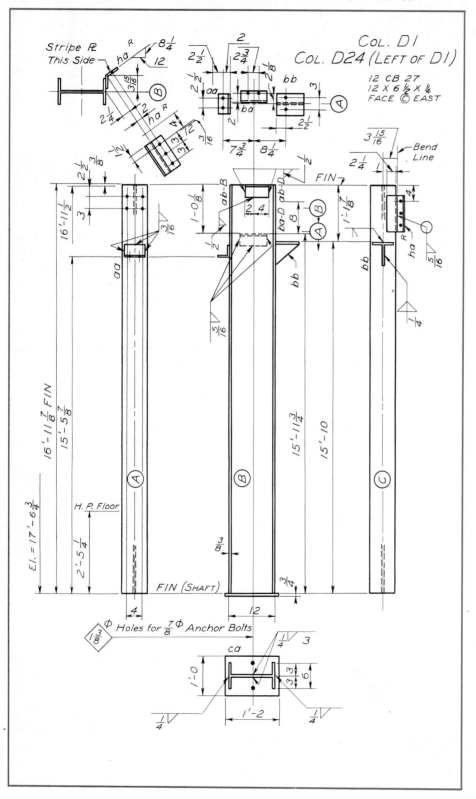

contact welding, the parts are placed together, electric current is passed through, and pressure is applied to force the parts together to produce a forge weld. For flash welding, the parts are placed either in very light contact or with a very small air gap; the electric current "flashes," or arcs, and melts the ends of the parts.

17·9 Resistance welds. There are two major classes of resistance welds: spot welding (including spot, projection, seam, cross-wire, and contact welding) and butt welding (including butt-flash, push-butt, percussive, and contact welding).

A few definitions formulated by the Nomenclature Committee of the Resistance Welder Manufacturers' Association are as follows:

Spot welding. A resistance process wherein the fusion is confined to a relatively small portion of the area of the lapped parts to be joined by the shape or contour of one or both welding electrodes (Fig. 17-9a at A).

Projection welding. A resistance-welding process wherein localization of heat between two or more surfaces or between the end of one member and the surface of another is effected by projections (Fig. 17-9a at B and C).

Butt-seam welding. A welding process with the pieces positioned edge to edge (Fig. 17-9a at D).

Lap-seam welding. A seam-welding process wherein overlapping or tangent spot welds are made progressively (Fig. 17-9a at E).

Flash-butt welding. A resistance butt-welding process wherein the necessary heat is derived from an arc or series of arcs established between the parts being welded prior to the application of the weld consummating (completion) pressure. The pressure is applied when the heat thus obtained has produced proper welding conditions (Fig. 17-9a at F).

Upset-butt welding. A resistance-welding process wherein the current is applied after the parts to be welded are brought into contact and wherein the heat is derived from the flow of current (Fig. 17-9a at G).

Basic resistance-welding symbols are given in Fig. 17-9b. The basic reference line and arrow are used as with arc- and gas-welding symbols, but in general there is no arrow side or other side. Figure 17-5b covers both resistance welds and gas welds.

The spot-welding symbol is shown in Fig. 17-9c in the top row. The second row shows a plan view. The third row shows a section through the weld. At A the minimum diameter of each weld is specified as 0.30 in. At B the minimum shearing strength of each weld is specified as 800 lb. At C and D are two methods of specifying that the welds start 1 in. from the left end and are spaced 2 in. center to center.

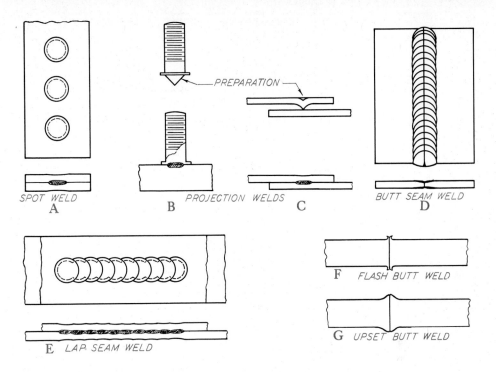

Fig. 17-9a. Resistance welds.

BASIC RESISTANCE WELD SYMBOLS			
TYPE OF WELD			
Spot	Projection	Seam	Flash or upset
✳	✕	⟋⟍⟋⟍	❘

SUPPLEMENTARY SYMBOLS			
Weld all around	Field weld	Contour	
		Flush	Convex
◯	●	─	⌒

Fig. 17-9b. Resistance-welding symbols.

Fig. 17-9c. Spot-welding symbols.

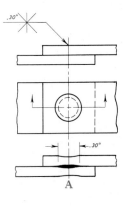
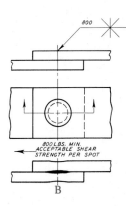
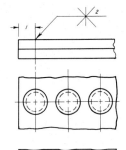

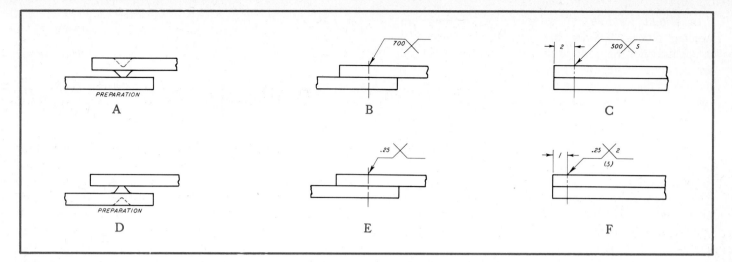

Fig. 17-9d. Projection-welding symbols.

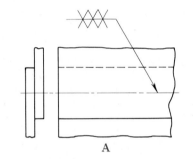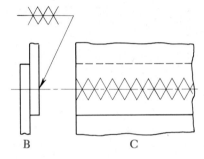

Fig. 17-9e. Seam-welding symbols.

The projection-welding symbol is shown in Fig. 17-9d, with the preparation at A and D. At A the embossment (projection) is on the arrow-side member, in which case the symbol is placed as at B and C. At B the "700" means that the acceptable shear strength per weld is to be not less than 700 lb. At C the minimum shear strength per weld is 500 lb, and the welds are to be spaced 5 in. center to center. At D the embossment (projection) is on the other-side member. At E the minimum diameter of the weld is 0.25 in. At F the minimum diameter of the weld is 0.25 in., spaced 2 in. center to center. There are five welds. The symbol for seam welding is shown in Fig. 17-9e; here the arrow is used at A and B, and the alternative method of placing the symbol on the view is shown at C.

17•10 Problem suggestions. Group 17, page 527. Three lists are presented. The more elementary problems are included in List 1. Other problems may be assigned from Lists 2 and 3 for advanced students. Reference books on welding, if available, are very desirable and helpful.

List 1: Problems 17·1, 17·2, 17·3, 17·4, 17·5, 17·8.

List 2: Problems 17·6, 17·7, 17·9.

List 3: Problems 17·10, 17·11, 17·12.

18
Electrical and electronics drafting

18•1 Electrical and electronic drafting. Drawings for electrical machines, details, fixtures, apparatus, and related construction are based upon the same basic principles of orthographic projection and dimensioning as for all other drafting. However, electrical and electronic drafting has to do with drawings which show circuits, or wiring diagrams. These circuits must be planned by the electrical design engineer (Fig. 18-1a). Sketches form an important part of the design studies from which draftsmen work.

Various types of diagrams and a great number of graphic symbols are used to show the different parts or components of a system, where they are located, and how they are connected to serve the required purpose. This is illustrated by the simple one-tube coil-condenser tuned radio receiver of Fig. 18-1b, where the parts are named. If you are interested, you will find that you can actually build this set by some further study and investigation. The completed radio will appear as shown in the picture. As a help in becoming familiar with the symbols, this figure shows the various parts of the receiver in their approximate positions. Wiring diagrams, however, do not always indicate the positions of the parts. Such diagrams are made only to show the

Fig. 18-1a. Electrical design engineers in a production conference.

Fig. 18-1b. A schematic diagram (lower right) and a picture (above) of a simple radio receiver.

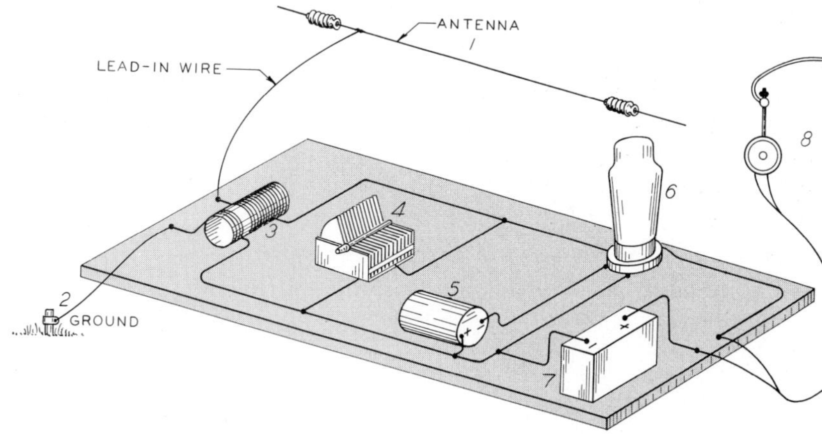

Picture	Symbol	Part
1	1A	Antenna (aerial)
2	2A	Ground connection
3	3A	Antenna coil
4	4A	Variable condenser
5	5A	A battery
6	6A	Triode vacuum tube 1H4G
7	7A	B battery
8	8A	Earphones

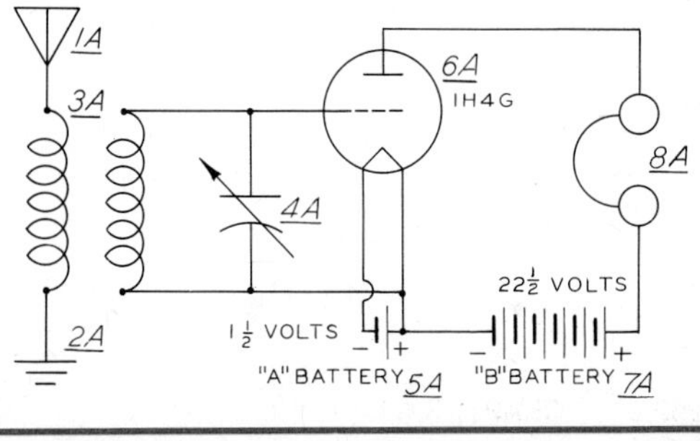

parts which make up the set and the connections.

Electrical drafting requires a basic knowledge and understanding of electricity in addition to the ability to make drawings; therefore, one should seek to learn about electricity and how it behaves, as well as about the materials, tools, and processes used in electrical work. Electricity and electronics comprise important fields of knowledge which require a great amount of study. This chapter will serve as an introduction to electrical symbols, wiring diagrams, and circuits as elements of electrical and electronic drafting.

Students who have had a basic course in electricity will find it of special value in understanding and making electrical drawings. Others are advised to read and study a book on the subject, such as *Understanding Electricity and Electronics,* by Buban and Schmitt (McGraw-Hill Book Company). A few paragraphs on electricity in general follow.

18•2 Electricity. The source of electrical energy is the tiny atom. In the natural condition, all atoms are made up of several kinds of particles. One of these particles, the electron, is most important in the study of electricity and electronics.

The electrons within an atom rotate about the center, or nucleus, of the atom in definite paths, or orbits (Fig. 18-2). All electrons in all atoms are alike; each possesses what is called a *negative charge* of electricity. Atoms differ from one another in the number of electrons and other particles which they contain. When all the atoms that make up a substance are alike, the substance is called an *element*. Copper, gold, and lead are common elements. When different kinds of atoms are joined together, they form a *compound*. Water, acids, and salt are common compounds. The smallest amount of a compound that retains all the properties of the compound is known as a *molecule*.

18•3 Voltage and current. Under certain conditions, electrons can be made to leave their "parent" atoms. This happens, for example, when a length of wire is connected across the terminals of a battery. The battery produces an electrical pressure called *electromotive force,* or *voltage.* The voltage causes a steady stream of electrons to flow through the wire. If a light bulb is connected into the wire (Fig. 18-3a), electrons will move through the lamp filament. As a result, the energy of the moving electrons is changed into heat energy as the filament becomes white hot. The glow of the filament produces the light.

The electron pathway formed by the battery, the wire, and the lamp filament is a simple form of electrical circuit. In other circuits electrical energy is changed into other kinds of energy, such as magnetism, sound, and light.

A direct current (d-c) is a flow of electrons through a circuit in one direction only (Fig. 18-3b). An alter-

Fig. 18-2. Inside the atom. In this atom of oxygen gas eight electrons whirl about the nucleus. *(From Understanding Electricity and Electronics, by Peter Buban and Marshall L. Schmitt, McGraw-Hill Book Company)*

Fig. 18-3a. A simple electric circuit.

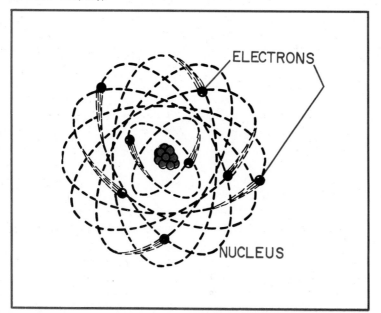

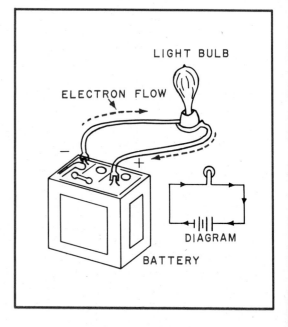

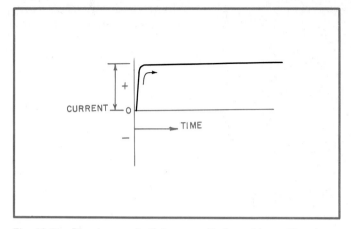

Fig. 18-3b. Direct current attains magnitude and keeps it as long as the circuit is complete.

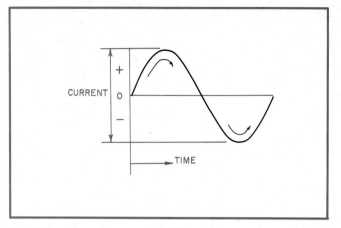

Fig. 18-3c. Alternating current builds up from zero to a maximum in a positive direction, falls to zero, and then builds to a maximum in a negative direction and falls back to zero.

nating current (a-c) is a flow of electrons in one direction during a fixed period of time and then in the opposite direction during a like period of time (Fig. 18-3c). This is called a *cycle*. The number of times this cycle is repeated in one second is called the *frequency* of the alternating current, such as 60 cycle.

18•4 Resistance. Electrons can move through some materials more easily than through others. Electrical current will flow more easily through a copper wire than through a steel wire of the same size. The steel offers more resistance. Materials with a small resistance to the flow of electrons are called *conductors.* Silver is the best-known conductor, but it is too expensive for general use. Copper and aluminum are good conductors and are the most widely used. Materials through which electrons will not flow easily are called *insulators.* The most commonly used insulating materials are glass, porcelain, plastics, and rubber compounds.

18•5 Electricity and electronics. Electricity, in general, has to do with the application of the energy of electrons moving through conductors or wires. Common examples include house wiring systems, generators, and transformers.

Electronics has to do with electrons moving through metallic conductors and through other conductors such as gases, a vacuum, and materials known as *semiconductors.* The most common semiconductor devices are transistors and diodes made of germanium or silicon. Both electricity and electronics are concerned with the flow of electrons through circuits designed for a definite purpose.

18•6 Basic electrical units are volts to measure voltage, ohms to measure resistance, amperes to measure current, and watts to measure power. The value of a unit used to show an electrical quantity is often given by a prefix, such as: kilovolts (kv) where 1 kilovolt equals 1000 volts; 1 milliampere (ma) equals 0.001 ampere; 1 kilowatt (kw) equals

1000 watts; 1 kilohm (k) equals 1000 ohms. For other combined forms of units, consult an electrical handbook or text.

18•7 Basic formulas. There is a definite relation between the values of voltage, current, and resistance in a circuit. This relation is known as *Ohm's law,* in which E = volts (pressure), I = amperes (current), and R = ohms (resistance). It may be expressed as $E = I \times R; I = \dfrac{E}{R}; R = \dfrac{E}{I}.$

There is also a relationship between the power or wattage rating of a circuit and the values of voltage, current, and circuit. In the formulas P equals power in watts. $W = P = E \times I; P = I^2/R; P = E^2/R.$ One electrical horsepower:

HP = 746 watts

Mechanical horsepower:

HP = 33,000 foot-pounds per minute
= work required to raise a weight of 33,000 pounds in 1 minute
= 550 foot-pounds per second

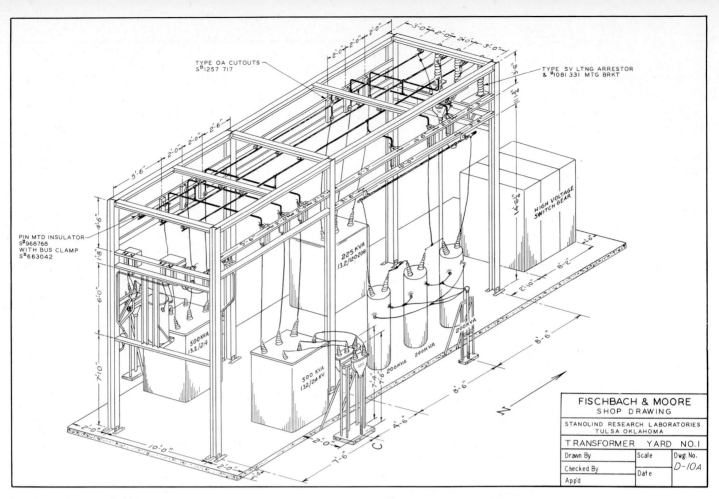

Fig. 18-8a. Pictorial drawing of a transformer yard.

18•8 Pictorial drawings (Chap. 14) are often useful for explaining electrical devices, electrical installations, and other features. The isometric drawing of the transformer yard (Fig. 18-8a) shows the relation of the electrical equipment to the supporting structure. Such a drawing is useful during assembly and erection as well as for record and reference. Details and specifications for insulators, bus clamps, cutouts, mounting brackets, lightning arresters, and so forth, are carried on other drawings to avoid complication.

One of the primary purposes of such erection drawings is to show the location at which the conduits (such as at C) are to be brought up (stubbed out) out of the concrete slab or ground. The

dimensions are important in order to have the connections for the equipment at the proper places, since conduit is installed in almost all cases before equipment is received and installed.

Another use of pictorial drawing in electrical work is illustrated in the isometric drawing of Fig. 18-8b, which shows the arrangement of part of a bus duct system. This drawing is one of many bus ducts that carry electricity to various parts of the Republic National Bank Building in Dallas, Texas. The purpose of this drawing is to take actual field measurements and convert them into an itemized schedule of component parts to be manufactured. At the same time the drawing serves as an assembly drawing for their actual identifi-

cation for installation in the building. It is necessary to show the various elbows and offsets (items 1, 5, 6, 8, and 10) in the drawing so that a suitable path for the ducts can be found around job conditions of beams, columns, shafts, or other obstacles. The insert in Fig. 18-8b is a photograph of a duct.

18•9 Graphic symbols are used on electrical and electronic diagrams to represent the component devices and operations in a circuit. The American Standard Association, Inc., 10 East 40th St., New York, is the national center for the procedure and development of American Standards by the members, including such organizations as The American Society of Mechanical

Engineers (ASME), the Electronic Industries Association (EIA), The Institute of Electronic Engineers, Inc. (IEE), The National Electrical Manufacturers Association (NEMA), and hundreds of others.

Some of the great number of American Standard symbols for use on electrical and electronic diagrams are shown in Fig. 18-9a. A complete set of symbols is given in *American Standard Graphic Symbols for Electrical and Electronic Diagrams* (ASA Y32.2-1962) and in *Military Standards* (MIL-STD-15A). Standards are subject to changes

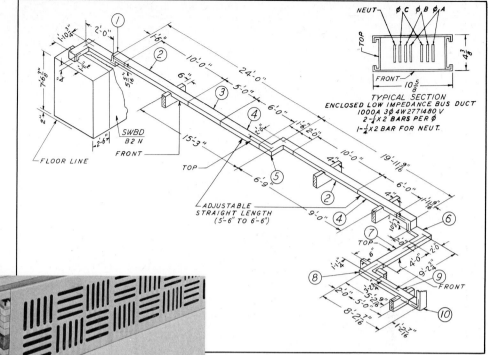

Fig. 18-8*b*. Isometric drawing of a part of a duct system. *(Photograph courtesy Westinghouse Electric and Manufacturing Company)*

Fig. 18-9a. A few electrical symbols from *American Standard Graphic Symbols for Electrical and Electronics Diagrams*, ASA Y32.2-1962, with the permission of The Institute of Electrical and Electronics Engineers, Inc.

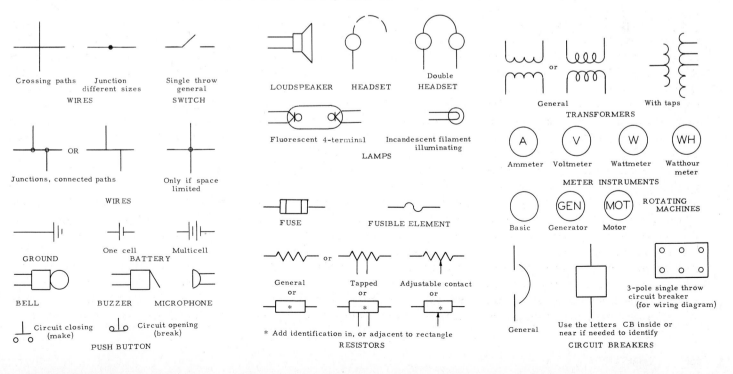

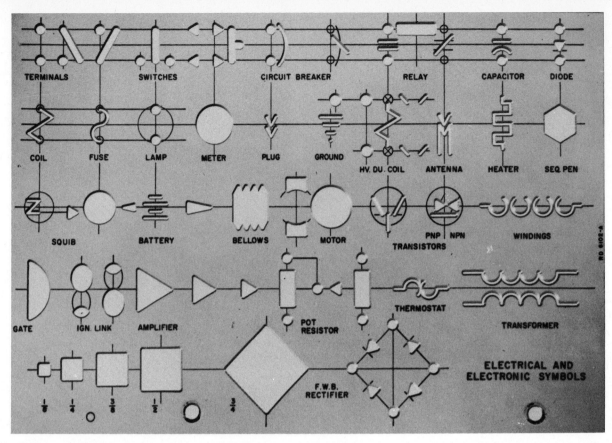

Fig. 18-9*b*. Template for drawing electrical and electronic symbols. *(RapiDesign, Inc.)*

and additions, and revisions are issued as needed; thus, the latest issue should be used. (Additional symbols are shown in Fig. 18-12.)

Graphic symbols are not drawn to scale, but the size of a given symbol should not be changed on a diagram. A variety of templates are available for drawing uniform symbols quickly and easily (Fig. 18-9*b*). (See also Arts. 2·37 and 3·19.) Grooved templates similar to those used with scriber guides for lettering (Art. 3·19) are available for drawing electrical symbols.

18•10 Basic electric circuits include series circuits, parallel circuits, and combinations of series and parallel circuits. These terms are explained in following paragraphs.

Series circuits are those where the current flows from the source (battery, generator, and so forth) through one resistance (lamp, motor, and so forth) after another, as shown in Figs. 18-10*a* to 18-10*c*. In Fig. 18-10*a* a bell (A) is operated from a battery (C) when the circuit is closed by the normally open (NO) type of pushbutton (B). In Fig. 18-10*b* a buzzer (A) is operated by the current from the transformer (C). What is item B, and what function does it have in this circuit? In Fig. 18-10*c* four lamps (C, D, E, and F) are operated from a generator (A) when the fused switch (B) is closed. All the lights must

Fig. 18-10*a*. A series-circuit diagram.

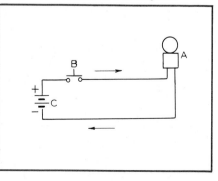

Fig. 18-10*b*. A series-circuit diagram.

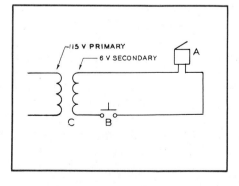

be on, for if any one is not, the circuit will be open. Remember the Christmas tree light strings that went out completely when just one lamp burned out? This was a series string of lights.

Parallel circuits provide for the current to flow through more than one path. Three separate branches or paths (C, D, and E) with lamps are shown in Fig. 18-10d. Each lamp is independent of the others. If one lamp is burned out, the others will continue to operate. With a parallel string of lights on your Christmas tree, the remaining lights continue to burn if some are missing, loose, or burned out.

A siren is shown in Fig. 18-10e. It may be activated by any one of the pushbuttons A, B, C, or D, which are all in parallel. An application of this would be in an alarm system to give warning of an attempted holdup in a store. The pushbuttons, connected in parallel, would be located under counters and in the cashier's cage.

Observe that the symbol for the siren is the same as for a loudspeaker (Fig. 18-9a) but that here it is accompanied by a note "Siren" to identify it.

Combination series and parallel circuits provide many different arrangements combining both series and parallel connections. In Fig. 18-10f lamps C and D are in series and lamps E and F are in parallel. Both lamps C and D must be on if switch A is closed, since they are in series. When switches A and B are closed, all the lamps (C, D, E, and F) are lighted. Lamps E and F will operate independently. If one fails, the other will remain lighted because they are in parallel; however, because lamps C and D are in series, as we have learned from the example of the Christmas tree lights, when one fails, the others will not light.

18•11 Electrical instruments of many kinds have been developed for measuring purposes. Two principal

ones are the ammeter and the voltmeter. The ammeter is an instrument which measures electric current in amperes. To measure the amount of current flowing through a resistance, the ammeter is connected directly in series with the resistance which is to be measured (motor, electrical appliance, and so forth), as indicated in Fig. 18-11a.

The voltmeter is an instrument which measures the electromotive force (pressure) in volts. A voltmeter is connected in parallel with that part of a circuit across which the voltage is to be measured, as indicated in Fig. 18-11b.

Fig. 18-10c. A series-circuit diagram.

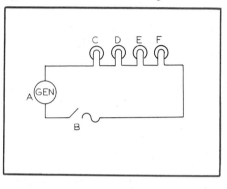

Fig. 18-10d. A parallel-circuit diagram.

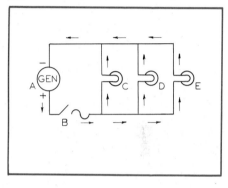

Fig. 18-10e. A parallel-circuit diagram.

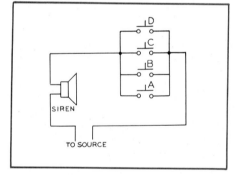

Fig. 18-10f. A combination series and parallel circuit.

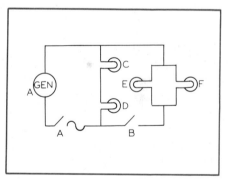

Fig. 18-11a. Ammeter connection.

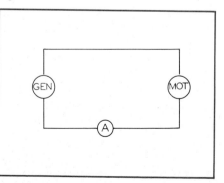

Fig. 18-11b. Voltmeter connection.

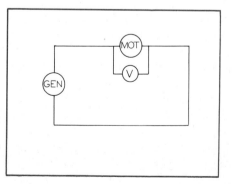

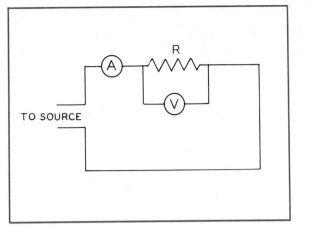

Fig. 18-11c. Ammeter and voltmeter connection.

Fig. 18-12. Some electrical symbols from *American Standard Graphic Symbols for Electrical and Electronics Diagrams*, ASA Y32.2-1962, with the permission of The Institute of Electrical and Electronics Engineers, Inc.

Figure 18-11c shows both an ammeter and a voltmeter connected in a circuit to measure the current flowing through the resistance (R) and the voltage flowing across the resistance. The amperes and the volts are then measured.

18•12 Drafting practices for using graphic symbols. The small selection of graphic symbols in Fig. 18-12 and the following quotations for using graphic symbols are quoted from *American Standard Graphic Symbols for Electrical and Electronics Diagrams* (ASA Y32.2) by permission of The Institute of Electrical and Electronic Engineers, Inc.

"Graphic symbols for electrical engineering are a shorthand used to show graphically the functioning or interconnections of a circuit. A graphic symbol represents the function of a part in the circuit. Graphic symbols are used on single-line (one-line) diagrams, on schematic or elementary diagrams or as applicable on connection or wiring diagrams. Graphic symbols are correlated with parts lists, descriptions or instructions by means of designations."

"DRAFTING PRACTICES APPLICABLE TO GRAPHIC SYMBOLS

1. A symbol shall be considered as the aggregate of all its parts.
2. The orientation of a symbol on a drawing, including a mirror image, does not alter the meaning . . . .
3. The width of a line does not affect the meaning of the symbol. In specific cases a wider line may be used for emphasis.
4. The symbols shown in this standard are in their correct relative size. This relationship shall be maintained as nearly as possible on any particular drawing, regardless of the size of the symbol used.
5. A symbol may be drawn to any proportional size that suits a particular drawing, depending on reduction or enlargement anticipated. If essential for purposes of contrast, some symbols may be drawn relatively smaller than the other symbols on a diagram.
6. The arrowhead of a symbol may be closed ⟶ or open ⟶ unless otherwise noted in this standard.
7. The standard symbol for a TERMINAL (o) may be added to each point of attachment to connecting lines to any one of the graphic symbols. Such added terminal symbols should not be considered as part of the individual graphic symbol unless the terminal symbol is included in the symbol shown in this standard.
8. For simplification of a diagram parts of a symbol for a device, such as a relay or contactor, may be separated. If this is done provide suitable designations to show proper correlation of the parts.
9. In general, the angle at which a connecting line is brought to a graphic symbol has no particular significance unless otherwise noted in this standard.
10. Associated or future paths and equipment shall be shown by lines composed of short dashes: – – –.
11. Details of type, impedance, rating, etc., may be added, when required, adjacent to any symbol. If used, abbreviations should be from the American Standard Abbreviations for Use on Drawings (Z32.13-1950). Letter combinations used as parts of graphic symbols are not abbreviations."

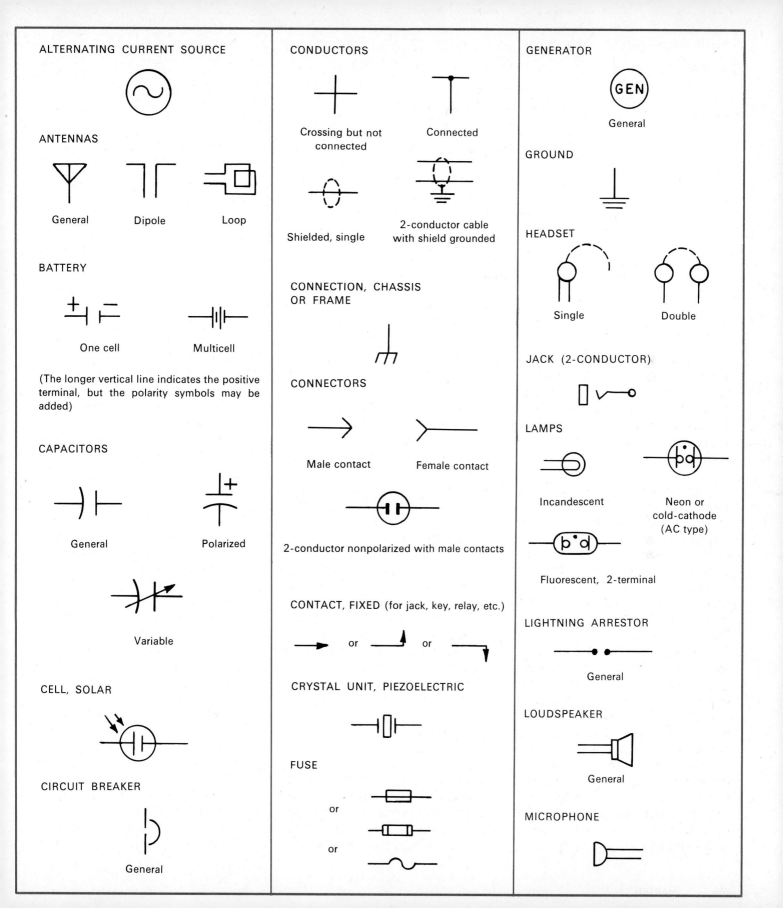

ALTERNATING CURRENT SOURCE

ANTENNAS

General   Dipole   Loop

BATTERY

One cell   Multicell

(The longer vertical line indicates the positive terminal, but the polarity symbols may be added)

CAPACITORS

General   Polarized

Variable

CELL, SOLAR

CIRCUIT BREAKER

General

CONDUCTORS

Crossing but not connected   Connected

Shielded, single   2-conductor cable with shield grounded

CONNECTION, CHASSIS OR FRAME

CONNECTORS

Male contact   Female contact

2-conductor nonpolarized with male contacts

CONTACT, FIXED (for jack, key, relay, etc.)

or   or

CRYSTAL UNIT, PIEZOELECTRIC

FUSE

or

or

GENERATOR

General

GROUND

HEADSET

Single   Double

JACK (2-CONDUCTOR)

LAMPS

Incandescent   Neon or cold-cathode (AC type)

Fluorescent, 2-terminal

LIGHTNING ARRESTOR

General

LOUDSPEAKER

General

MICROPHONE

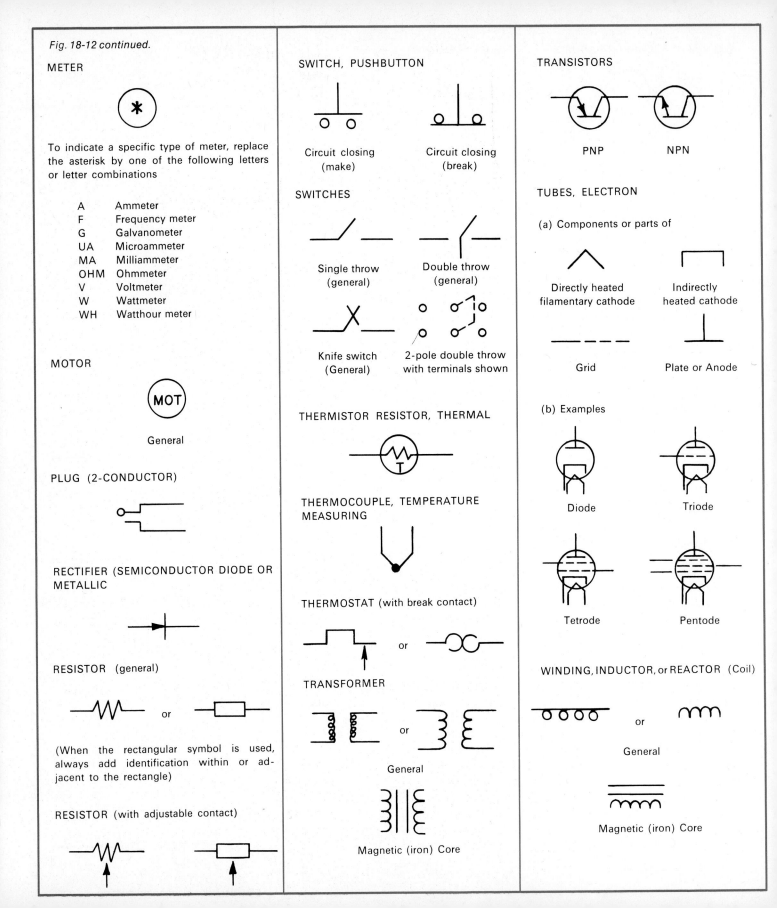

Fig. 18-12 continued.

METER

To indicate a specific type of meter, replace the asterisk by one of the following letters or letter combinations

A	Ammeter
F	Frequency meter
G	Galvanometer
UA	Microammeter
MA	Milliammeter
OHM	Ohmmeter
V	Voltmeter
W	Wattmeter
WH	Watthour meter

MOTOR

General

PLUG (2-CONDUCTOR)

RECTIFIER (SEMICONDUCTOR DIODE OR METALLIC

RESISTOR (general)

or

(When the rectangular symbol is used, always add identification within or adjacent to the rectangle)

RESISTOR (with adjustable contact)

SWITCH, PUSHBUTTON

Circuit closing (make)   Circuit closing (break)

SWITCHES

Single throw (general)   Double throw (general)

Knife switch (General)   2-pole double throw with terminals shown

THERMISTOR RESISTOR, THERMAL

THERMOCOUPLE, TEMPERATURE MEASURING

THERMOSTAT (with break contact)

or

TRANSFORMER

or

General

Magnetic (iron) Core

TRANSISTORS

PNP   NPN

TUBES, ELECTRON

(a) Components or parts of

Directly heated filamentary cathode   Indirectly heated cathode

Grid   Plate or Anode

(b) Examples

Diode   Triode

Tetrode   Pentode

WINDING, INDUCTOR, or REACTOR (Coil)

or

General

Magnetic (iron) Core

BATTERY   ELECTRON TUBE   NEON BULB   SWITCH (ROTARY)

BINDING POST   FUSE   POTENTIOMETER (CONTROL)   SWITCH (TOGGLE)

CERAMIC   MICA CAPACITOR   INDUCTOR (COIL)   RECEPTACLE   TRANSFORMER (ADJUSTABLE CORE)

PAPER

ELECTROLYTIC CAPACITOR   PHONE JACK   RECTIFIER (DIODE)   TRANSFORMER (IRON CORE)

VARIABLE CAPACITOR   METER   RESISTOR   TRANSISTOR

PIEZOELECTRIC CRYSTAL   MICROPHONE   SPEAKER

Fig. 18-13. Some electrical and electronic components, with their names and appearance. *(Heath Company, a subsidiary of Daystrom, Inc.)*

18·13 Circuit components. Figure 18-13 illustrates and names some of the most commonly used electrical and electronic components. The appearance of components should be associated with the symbols by which they are represented on circuit diagrams. Some knowledge of the operation and purpose of the components is most desirable.

18·14 Electrical diagrams are of many kinds to suit the purposes for which they are used. The following definitions adopted as American Standard and Arts. 18·14 to 18·19 are extracted from the *American Standard Drafting Manual, Electrical Diagrams* (ASA Y14-15-1960) with the permission of the publisher, The American Society of Mechanical Engineers, 345 East 47th St., New York, N.Y., 10017.

Single-line (one-line) diagram. "A diagram which shows, by means of single lines and graphic symbols, the course of an electric circuit or system of circuits and the component devices or parts used therein."

Schematic, or elementary, diagram. "A diagram which shows, by means of graphic symbols, the electrical connections and functions of a specific circuit arrangement. The schematic diagram facilitates tracing the circuit and its

functions without regard to the actual physical size, shape or location of the component device or parts."

Connection or wiring diagram. "A diagram which shows the connections of an installation or its component devices or parts. It may cover internal or external connections, or both, and contains such detail as is needed to make or trace connections that are involved. The connection diagram usually shows general physical arrangement of the component devices or parts."

Interconnection diagram. "A form of connection or wiring diagram which shows only external connections between unit assemblies or equipment. The internal connections of the unit assemblies or equipment are usually omitted."

18·15 Line conventions and lettering. "The selection of line thickness as well as letter size should take into account size reduction or enlargement when it is felt that legibility will be affected. Line conventions, relative thickness and suggested applications for use on electrical diagrams are shown in ... [Fig. 18-15].

Fig. 18-15. Line conventions for electrical diagrams.

LINE APPLICATION	LINE THICKNESS
FOR GENERAL USE	MEDIUM
MECHANICAL CONNECTION, SHIELDING, & FUTURE CIRCUITS LINE	MEDIUM
BRACKET-CONNECTING DASH LINE	MEDIUM
USE OF THESE LINE THICKNESSES OPTIONAL	
BRACKETS, LEADER LINES, ETC.	THIN
BOUNDARY OF MECHANICAL GROUPING	THIN
FOR EMPHASIS	THICK

"A line of medium thickness is recommended for general use on electrical diagrams. A thin line may be used for brackets, leader lines, etc. When emphasis of special features such as main or transmission paths is essential, a line thickness sufficient to provide the desired contrast may be used. Line thickness and lettering used with electrical diagrams shall, in general, conform with American Standard Y14.2 [latest issue] and local requirements to facilitate microfilming.

18•16 Symbols and layouts. "Graphical symbols may be drawn to any proportional size that suits a particular diagram, provided the selection of size takes into account the anticipated reduction or enlargement. For most electrical diagrams intended for manufacturing purposes, or for ultimate use in a reduced form (2½ to 1 max), it is recommended that symbols be drawn approximately 1½ times the size of those shown in American Standard Y32.2-1962."

Abbreviations for use with electrical diagrams are given in *American Standard Abbreviations for Use on Drawings ASA Z32.13* (latest issue).

"*Layout of Electrical Diagrams.* The layout of electrical diagrams shall be such that the main features are prominently shown. The parts of the diagram should be spaced to provide an even balance between blank spaces and lines. Sufficient blank area should be provided in the vicinity of symbols to avoid crowding of notes or reference information. Large spaces, however, should be avoided, except that space provision may be made for anticipated future circuits if deemed necessary."

18•17 Single-line diagrams. "The single-line diagram conveys basic information about the operation of a circuit or a system of circuits, but omits much of the detailed information usu-

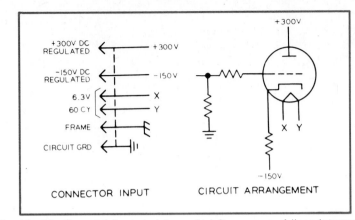

Fig. 18-18a. Identification of interrupted lines. At left, a group of lines interrupted on the diagram. At right, single lines interrupted on the diagram.

ally shown on schematic or connection diagrams. This form of presentation lends itself to simplified diagrams of complex circuits and to diagrammatic representation of communication or power systems in which a single line represents a multiconductor communication or power circuit."

In general, the practices established in Art. 18·18 apply equally well to the preparation of single-line diagrams.

18•18 Schematic diagrams. "The following sub-paragraphs contain general information for use in the preparation of schematic diagrams.

"*Layout.* The schematic diagram shall use a layout which follows the circuit, signal or transmission path either from input to output, source to load or in the order of functional sequence. Long interconnecting lines between parts of the circuit should be avoided.

"*Connecting lines.* Connecting lines should preferably be drawn horizontally or vertically and with as few bends and crossovers as possible. Connection of four or more lines at one point shall be avoided when it is equally convenient to use an alternative arrangement. When connecting lines are drawn parallel the spacing between lines after reduction shall be a minimum of $1/16$ inch. Parallel lines should be arranged

in groups, preferably three, with approximately double spacing between groups of lines. In grouping parallel lines, functional relation of the lines should be considered. Primary power and synchro circuits are examples of the application of this practice.

"*Interrupted single lines.* For single interrupted lines, the line identification may also serve to indicate destination as shown in ... [Fig. 18-18a] for the power and filament circuit paths. In identification practice for single interrupted lines shall be the same as for grouped and bracketed lines described in the following paragraph.

"*Interrupted grouped lines.* When interrupted lines are grouped and bracketed, and depending on whether the lines are horizontal or vertical, line identifications shall be indicated as shown in ... [Fig. 18-18b]. Bracket destinations or connections may be indicated either by means of notations outside the brackets as shown in ... [Fig. 18-18b] or as shown in ... [Fig. 18-18c] by means of a dash line. When the dash line is used to connect brackets it shall be drawn so that it will not be mistaken for a continuation of one of the bracketed lines. The dash line shall originate in one bracket and terminate in no more than two brackets." When drawing schematics, carefully observe the above.

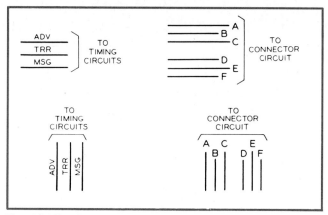

Fig. 18-18b. Typical arrangement of line identifications and destinations.

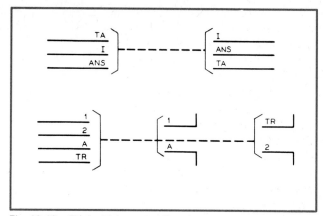

Fig. 18-18c. Typical interrupted lines interconnected by dashed lines. The dashed line shows the interrupted paths that are to be connected. Individual line identifications indicate matching connections.

18·19 Schematic diagrams for electronics and communications. "The following sub-paragraphs contain detailed information which is specifically applicable to schematic diagrams of the type used with electronic and communication equipment. This material is to be used as a supplement to the general standards of . . . [Art. 18·18].

"*Layout.* In general, schematic diagrams should be arranged so that they can be read functionally from left to right. Complex diagrams should generally be arranged to read from upper left to lower right and may be laid out in two or more layers. Each layer should be read from left to right. The overall result shall be a circuit layout which follows the signal, or transmission path,

from input to output, or in the order of functional sequence. Where practical, terminations for external connections should be located at the outer edges of the circuit layout.

"*Ground symbols.* The ground symbol $\perp$ shall be used only when the circuit ground is at a potential level equivalent to that of earth potential. The symbol $\not\!\!\!/\!/$ shall be used when an earth potential does not result from connecting to the structure which houses or supports the circuit parts."

18·20 Some electrical circuits. In Fig. 18-20a the bell (C) and the buzzer (E) are operated independently from the same battery (A) by the pushbuttons (B and D).

In Fig. 18-20b the current is from an outside source. The three-way switches (X and Y) are used so that the light at L may be turned off or on by either of the switches. Switch X might be at the garage and switch Y at the house. Each switch has three terminals. If either switch is opened, the light will be turned off, but the light may be turned on by the switch at the opposite end.

A circuit diagram is shown in Fig. 18-20c for an annunciator (an arrangement for signaling from different places to a station or post). It provides for ringing a buzzer in the annunciator when any of the buttons is pressed. Each button releases or allows a tab to drop down to identify the place where the button is pressed. Trace the circuits

Fig. 18-20a. Bell and buzzer circuit.

Fig. 18-20b. Three-way switch diagram.

Fig. 18-20c. Annunciator diagram.

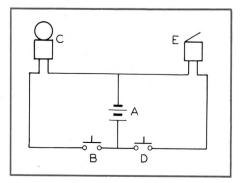

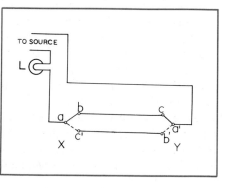

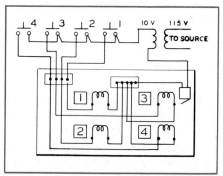

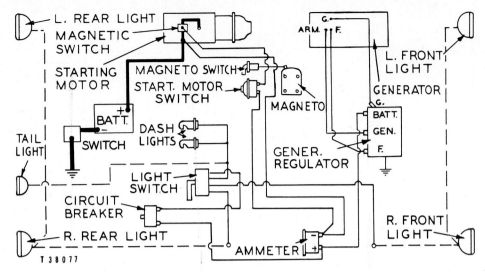

Fig. 18-20d. Wiring diagram for a Caterpillar Tractor. (Caterpillar Tractor Company)

which are operated by each of the buttons. The source of the current is from the secondary of a step-down transformer.

An electrical diagram for a Caterpillar tractor is shown in Fig. 18-20d. It is sometimes necessary to disturb the electrical system for servicing; checking wiring for loose or dirty connections, worn insulation, or broken wires; reconditioning or replacing parts; etc. In such cases a wiring diagram makes it possible to put things back together without difficulty. The short dash lines on the diagram indicate the connections for groups that are available as attachments.

Some single-line graphic symbols are shown in Fig. 18-20e. A single-line, or one-line, diagram is shown in Fig. 18-20f. Such a diagram shows the component parts or devices of a circuit or circuit system using single lines and graphic symbols. The single lines represent two or more conductors. The diagram gives the necessary basic information about the operation of the circuit but not the detailed information of a schematic diagram. A single-line diagram is a simplified representation and is useful in the fields of communications and electrical power transmission (Fig. 18-20f). The highest voltage is

usually placed at the top or left side of the diagram. The lower-voltage lines are placed in the order of their value below or on the right side of the diagram. Information concerning line location, component ratings, types of equipment, etc., is given at appropriate places on the diagram.

A motor-starter wiring diagram is shown at A in Fig. 18-20g, and a schematic, or one-line, diagram is shown at B for the same circuit. A motor starter is required for the following purposes:

1. To give the proper protection against burnouts caused by sustained overloads. This is known as *thermal overload protection*, a protection not afforded by ordinary fuses.
2. To provide for remote control by manual start-stop buttons or automatic devices, such as thermostats, pressurestats, limit switches, and so forth.
3. To furnish provisions for sequence control. This is illustrated in Fig. 18-20h.

Figure 18-20h illustrates a wiring diagram at A and a schematic, or one-line, diagram at B for the same circuit. This figure shows the sequence control

for a conveyor system consisting of three separate motors. Notice that a thin line (light-value line) is used to indicate the pilot circuit (low voltage) in contrast to a thick line (heavy-value line) to indicate the line-voltage part of the circuit. The low voltage is obtained from the step-down transformer (SDT). A transformer is an electrical device which changes the voltage of alternating current, the type used in most electrical systems. In this case, the step-down transformer changes the current from a higher voltage to a lower voltage.

In Fig. 18-20h at A (upper rectangle) start button B_1 will start the No. 1 conveyor motor at (1), but start button B_2 will not start the No. 2 conveyor motor at (2) unless conveyor motor No. 1 has started. Likewise, start button B_3 starts conveyor motor No. 3 at (3) only after conveyor motor No. 2 has started. The conveyor system may be completely stopped by the fused disconnect switch (FDS) by stop button b_1 or by its overload (O.L.). The stop button b_2 or the No. 2 motor overload will stop both conveyors Nos. 2 and 3. The stop button b_3, or overload, will only stop the No. 3 conveyor. The fuse, F, is for protection of the low-voltage control circuit.

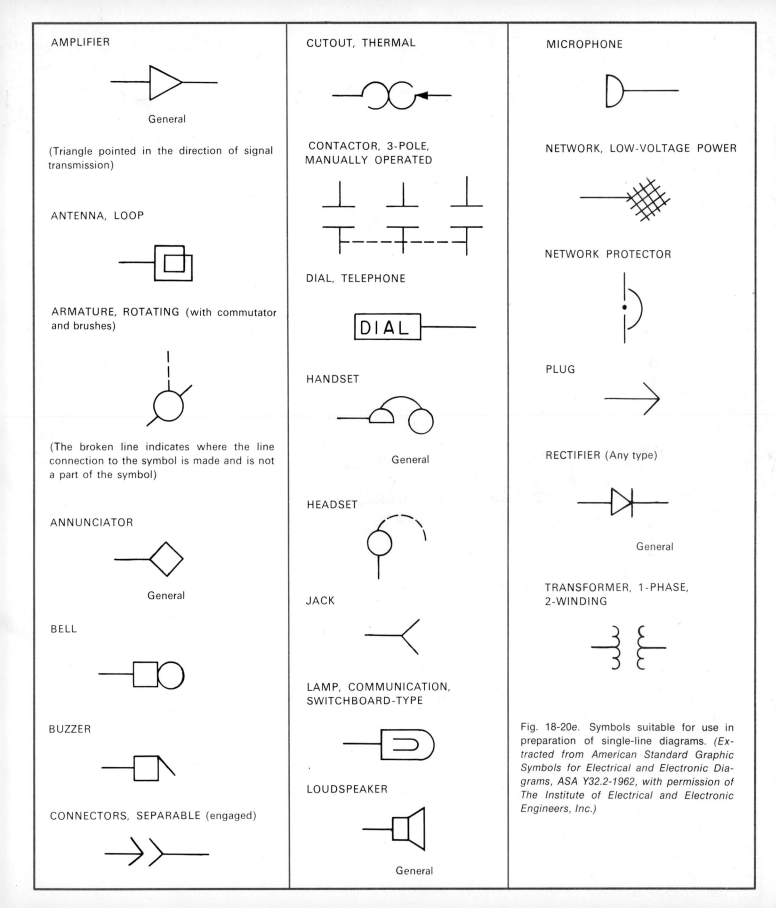

AMPLIFIER

General

(Triangle pointed in the direction of signal transmission)

ANTENNA, LOOP

ARMATURE, ROTATING (with commutator and brushes)

(The broken line indicates where the line connection to the symbol is made and is not a part of the symbol)

ANNUNCIATOR

General

BELL

BUZZER

CONNECTORS, SEPARABLE (engaged)

CUTOUT, THERMAL

CONTACTOR, 3-POLE, MANUALLY OPERATED

DIAL, TELEPHONE

DIAL

HANDSET

General

HEADSET

JACK

LAMP, COMMUNICATION, SWITCHBOARD-TYPE

LOUDSPEAKER

General

MICROPHONE

NETWORK, LOW-VOLTAGE POWER

NETWORK PROTECTOR

PLUG

RECTIFIER (Any type)

General

TRANSFORMER, 1-PHASE, 2-WINDING

Fig. 18-20e. Symbols suitable for use in preparation of single-line diagrams. (Extracted from American Standard Graphic Symbols for Electrical and Electronic Diagrams, ASA Y32.2-1962, with permission of The Institute of Electrical and Electronic Engineers, Inc.)

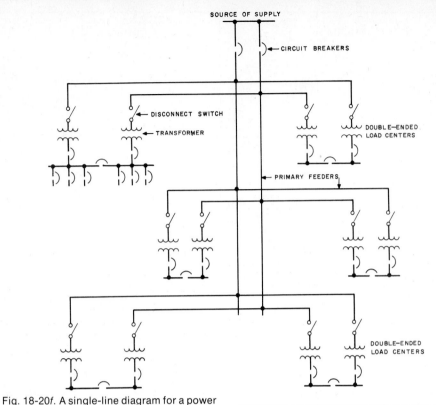

Fig. 18-20f. A single-line diagram for a power distribution system.

In Fig. 18-20h at B (lower rectangle) the same circuit is shown by a one-line diagram. The fuse, F, is for the protection of the low-voltage control circuit.

18·21 Color codes. A color-code system is a convenient way of presenting information when preparing circuit diagrams and for use on the actual wiring of the circuit. In electrical and electronic work a color code is used to indicate certain characteristics of components, such as capacitors and resistors, to identify wire leads, and to show wire connections. A particular color-code scheme may be a part of the diagram on which it is used (Fig.

Fig. 18-20h. A three-way conveyor system.

Fig. 18-20g. A single-phase starter.

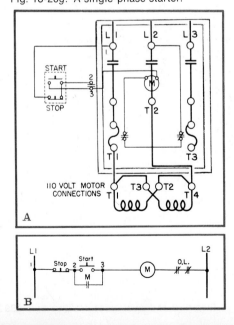

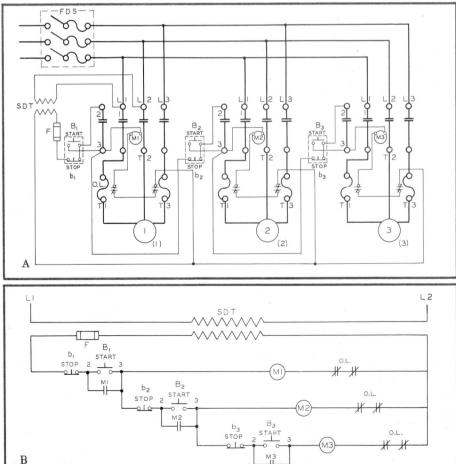

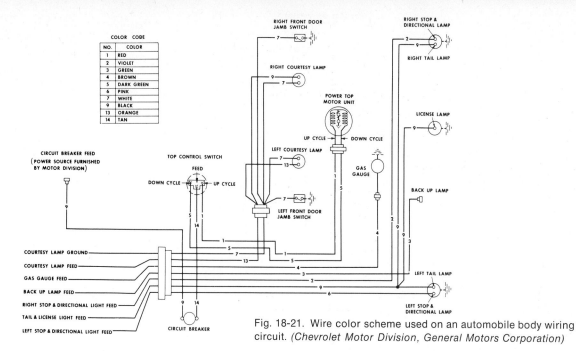

Fig. 18-21. Wire color scheme used on an automobile body wiring circuit. *(Chevrolet Motor Division, General Motors Corporation)*

18-21). When using a color code, the Electronic Industries Association (EIA) standards should be consulted, as well as any others which may apply. Note the different code used in Fig. 18-21; it is not the same as the EIA standard in the table which follows:

EIA Standard Color Code

Color	Abbre-viation	Number
Black	BLK	0
Brown	BRN	1
Red	RED	2
Orange	ORN	3
Yellow	YEL	4
Green	GRN	5
Blue	BLU	6
Violet	VIO	7
Gray	GRA	8
White	WHT	9

Color codes are used to give specific information on resistors, capacitors, chassis hooks, and component-lead wire insulation and other purposes. Such uses are covered in published standards and in textbooks.

18•22 Pictorial diagrams. Figure 18-22a presents one kind of "picture" showing the components of a circuit, where and how they are located on a chassis or panel, and how they are connected. Pictorial diagrams are

Fig. 18-22a. Pictorial diagram of a battery eliminator circuit. *(Heath Company, a subsidiary of Daystrom, Inc.)*

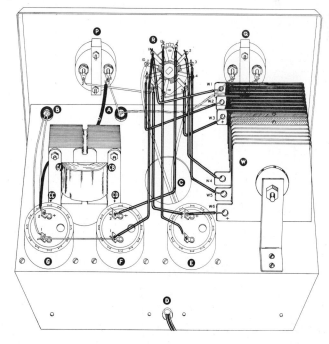

Fig. 18-22*b*. Pictorial diagram of electrical wiring on a Comet automobile. *(Lincoln-Mercury Division, Ford Motor Company)*

drawn to scale so that everything will show in proportion. Components may or may not be identified by name and rating. Wires are usually drawn in straight lines, in full view where possible, and with as few "crossovers" as possible. Such diagrams are easy to read and are widely used as guides in assembly-line production, maintenance, and service.

Another kind of pictorial diagram is illustrated by the pictorial view of some of the wiring on a Comet automobile shown in Fig. 18-22*b*. Such drawings of the electrical circuits are used to show the location of the wiring, for servicing, for indicating possible trouble in wiring or connections, and for other purposes.

18·23 Block diagrams. A block diagram (Fig. 18-23) is usually composed of squares or rectangles, or "blocks," joined by single lines and

Fig. 18-23. Block diagram of 20,000-watt broadcast transmitter. *(Gates Radio Company, a subsidiary of Harris-Intertype Corporation)*

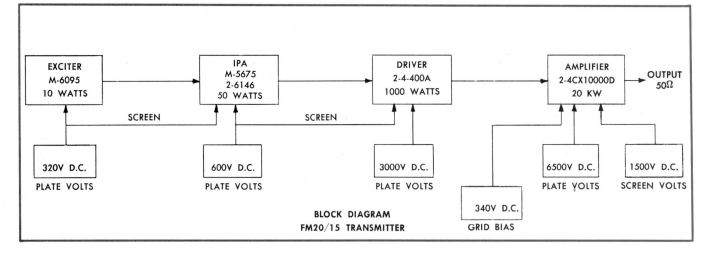

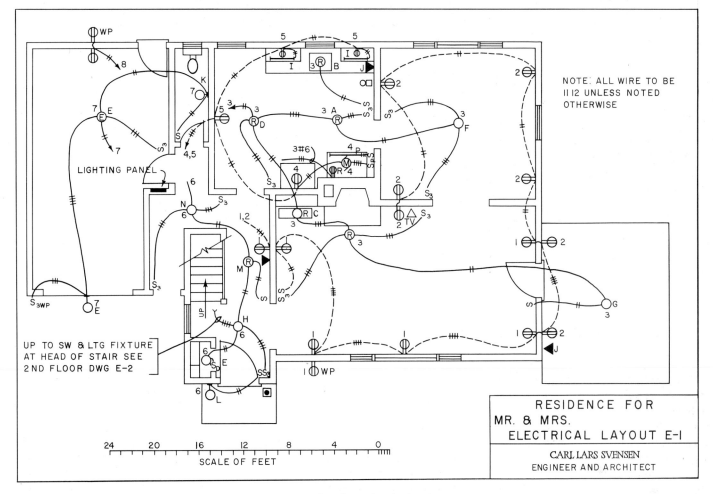

NOTE: ALL WIRE TO BE # 12 UNLESS NOTED OTHERWISE

LIGHTING PANEL

UP TO SW & LTG FIXTURE AT HEAD OF STAIR SEE 2ND FLOOR DWG E-2

| 24 | 20 | 16 | 12 | 8 | 4 | 0 |

SCALE OF FEET

RESIDENCE FOR MR. & MRS.
ELECTRICAL LAYOUT E-1

CARL LARS SVENSEN
ENGINEER AND ARCHITECT

Fig. 18-24a. Architectural floor-plan layout diagram showing first-floor electrical system.

arranged to show the relation between the various component groups or stages in the operation of a circuit. Arrowheads at the terminal ends of the lines show the direction of the signal path from input to output, reading the diagram from left to right.

Engineers often draw or sketch block diagrams as a first step in designing new equipment. Block diagrams are also used in catalogs, descriptive fold-

ers, and advertisements for electrical equipment.

18·24 Electrical layouts for buildings. The usual architect's indication of electrical outlets and switch locations is shown in Fig. 21-34. This plan only indicates the location of lights, base plugs, and desired switching arrangements. To provide a satisfactory and adequately wired electrical system

upon completion of the structure, it is necessary to have a complete and detailed set of electrical drawings and specifications prepared by someone who knows the engineering requirements. Such an electrical layout drawing is shown in Fig. 18-24a, which indicates the circuit arrangements, and so forth, for the first floor of a two-story residence. A schedule of the symbols used is shown in Fig. 18-24b.

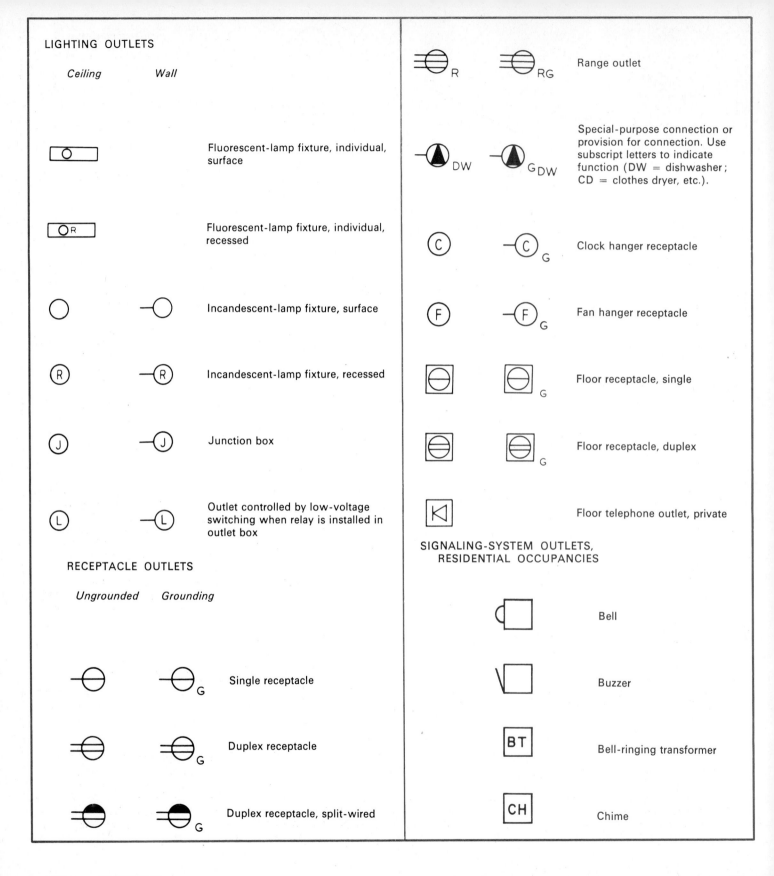

LIGHTING OUTLETS

Ceiling   *Wall*

Fluorescent-lamp fixture, individual, surface

Fluorescent-lamp fixture, individual, recessed

Incandescent-lamp fixture, surface

Incandescent-lamp fixture, recessed

Junction box

Outlet controlled by low-voltage switching when relay is installed in outlet box

RECEPTACLE OUTLETS

Ungrounded   *Grounding*

Single receptacle

Duplex receptacle

Duplex receptacle, split-wired

Range outlet

Special-purpose connection or provision for connection. Use subscript letters to indicate function (DW = dishwasher; CD = clothes dryer, etc.).

Clock hanger receptacle

Fan hanger receptacle

Floor receptacle, single

Floor receptacle, duplex

Floor telephone outlet, private

SIGNALING-SYSTEM OUTLETS, RESIDENTIAL OCCUPANCIES

Bell

Buzzer

Bell-ringing transformer

Chime

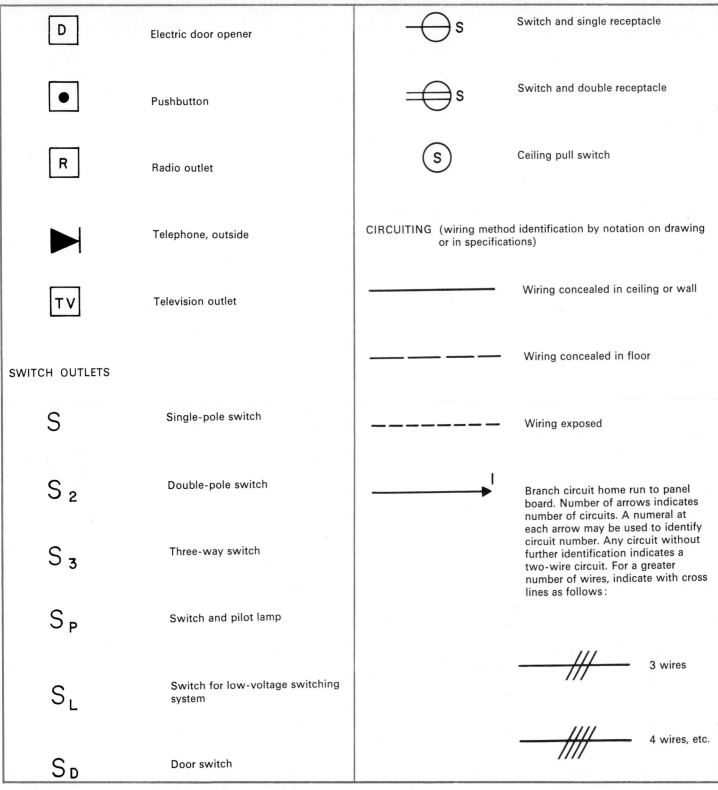

D (boxed)	Electric door opener	
● (boxed)	Pushbutton	
R (boxed)	Radio outlet	
▶	Telephone, outside	
TV (boxed)	Television outlet	

SWITCH OUTLETS

S	Single-pole switch
S_2	Double-pole switch
S_3	Three-way switch
S_P	Switch and pilot lamp
S_L	Switch for low-voltage switching system
S_D	Door switch

Switch and single receptacle

Switch and double receptacle

Ⓢ   Ceiling pull switch

CIRCUITING (wiring method identification by notation on drawing or in specifications)

Wiring concealed in ceiling or wall

Wiring concealed in floor

Wiring exposed

Branch circuit home run to panel board. Number of arrows indicates number of circuits. A numeral at each arrow may be used to identify circuit number. Any circuit without further identification indicates a two-wire circuit. For a greater number of wires, indicate with cross lines as follows:

///   3 wires

////   4 wires, etc.

Fig. 18-24b. Electrical wiring symbols used on architectural layout drawings. *(Extracted from American Standard Graphic Wiring Symbols for Architectural and Electrical Layout Drawings, ASA Y32.9-1962, with permission of The Institute of Electrical and Electronics Engineers, Inc.)*

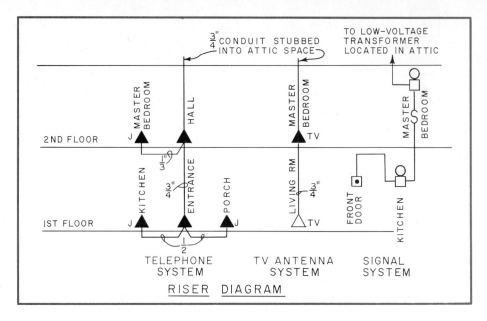

Fig. 18-24c. Riser diagram for a residence.

FIXTURE SCHEDULE

TYPE	FIXTURE DESCRIPTION	LAMP	REMARKS
A	Marco #J1-95P	150W	Recessed
B	Marco #J8-106P	100W	Recessed
C	Industrial Fluorescent	30W Fluorescent	Recessed (See Arch. Detail #10)
D	Marco #J121P	150W R40	Recessed
E	Porcelain Keyless Socket	60W	
F	Lightolier #7936	150W	
G	Lightolier #6464	150W	
H	Lightolier #4085	12-6W(656)	
I	Fluorescent Strip	30W Fluorescent	Built in under kitchen cabinet with switch
K	Lightolier #4305	2-60W	With convenience outlet
L	Marco #924SC	75W	
M	Marco #J1-96P	100W	Recessed
N	Lightolier #4321	2-60W	
P	Fluorescent Strip	30W	Built in ventahood

Fig. 18-24d. Schedule of fixtures prepared in connection with layout diagram of Fig. 18-24a.

The two floors are indicated in Fig. 18-24c, which is a riser diagram. Riser diagrams are used to show the interconnection between the various outlets of a system. The precise locations of the outlets are given on the electrical layouts, but not the interconnections. This is to avoid crowding.

The specifications will indicate the quality and type of materials and the quality of workmanship that will be acceptable.

The schedule of fixtures given in Fig. 18-24d illustrates the required information for the residence shown in Fig. 18-24a.

18•25 The interconnection diagram (Fig. 18-25) is a form of connection, or wiring, diagram which shows the electrical connections between the different assemblies, panels, or units of an electrical or electronics system. Generally, the internal connections within the various units are not shown.

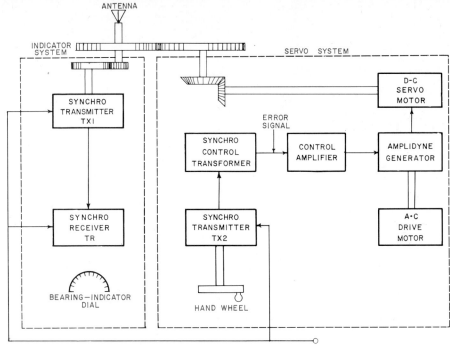

Fig. 18-25. Interconnection diagram showing the different units of a typical d-c servo system used for rotating a search radar system.

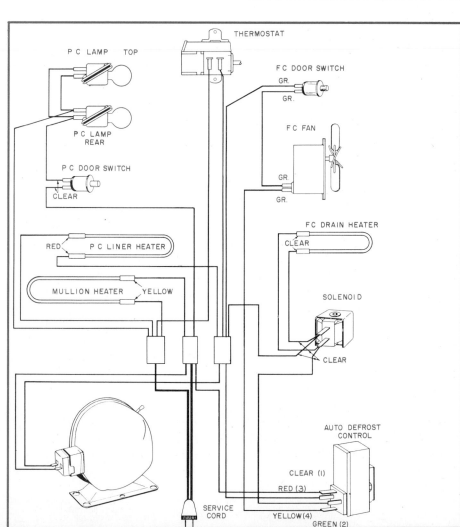

Fig. 18-26. Connection or wiring diagram for a refrigerator. (Kelvinator Division, American Motors Corporation)

The units are identified by name, and they are represented on the diagram by rectangles.

18•26 Connection or wiring diagrams. Figure 18-26 shows wiring connections in a simplified way so that the connections of the circuit system may be easily followed ,or traced. Internal or external connections, or both, may be shown. The components are named and are drawn in pictorial form. Auxiliary devices such as terminal blocks, strips, and fuse mountings are shown. Color coding is important for servicing and is indicated on Fig. 18-26.

Such diagrams furnish information needed for manufacture, installation, and maintenance and for use with schematic diagrams.

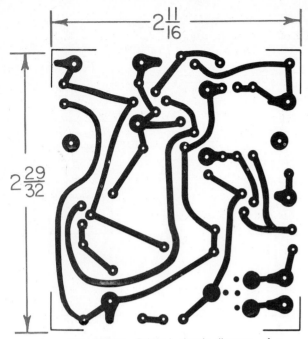

Fig. 18-27a. Printed circuit diagram of a transistor monitor amplifier. *(Gates Radio Company, a subsidiary of Harris-Intertype Corporation)*

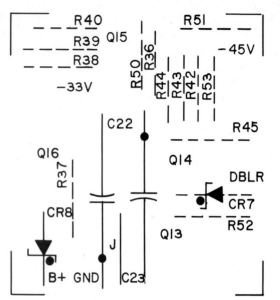

Fig. 18-27b. Component identification overlay used with the printed circuit diagram shown in Fig. 18-27a. *(Gates Radio Company, a subsidiary of Harris-Intertype Corporation)*

Fig. 18-28a. A chassis layout diagram used in the manufacture of an electronic assembly. *(Zenith Radio Corporation)*

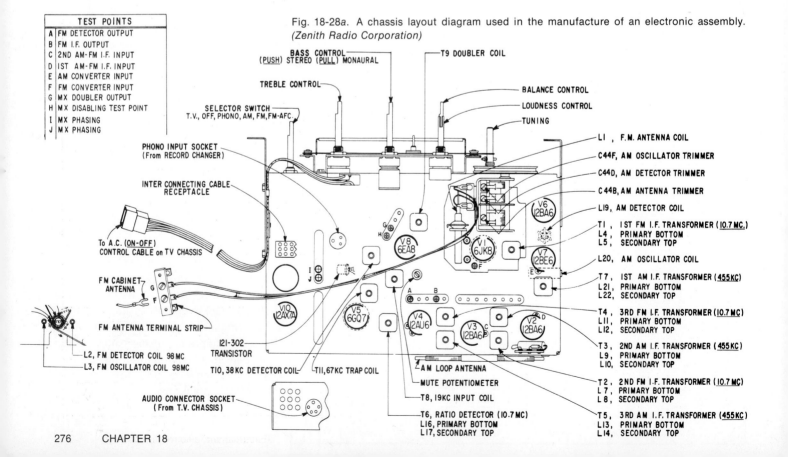

TEST POINTS	
A	FM DETECTOR OUTPUT
B	FM I.F. OUTPUT
C	2ND AM-FM I.F. INPUT
D	IST AM-FM I.F. INPUT
E	AM CONVERTER INPUT
F	FM CONVERTER INPUT
G	MX DOUBLER OUTPUT
H	MX DISABLING TEST POINT
I	MX PHASING
J	MX PHASING

18•27 Printed circuit drawings consist of accurately drawn layouts of the required pattern. The drawing is made actual size or to an enlarged scale which can be reduced to the desired size by photography. The lines (conductors) on the pattern should be at least 1/32 in. wide and should be spaced at least 1/32 in. apart. The circuit layout pattern is transferred to a copper-clad insulating base by photographic or other means. Etching is used to remove the copper from all except the required circuits (Fig. 18-27a). There are a great many ways of preparing printed circuits.

The components may be located on the printed circuit board by the use of symbols or other markings. This information is transferred to the printed circuit diagram from a component identification overlay (Fig. 18-27b).

18•28 Chassis layout drawings are mechanical layouts which are useful in the manufacture, assembly, and maintenance of all kinds of electrical and electronic products. Figure 18-28a is an example of one kind of chassis layout diagram. It shows the locations and sizes of holes or openings used for mounting the components.

Another kind of chassis layout is the parts-placement drawing (Fig. 18-28b). It shows the relative positions and sizes of the components, in outline, and identifies them in the same way as they are identified on the related schematic diagram.

Fig. 18-28b. Parts-placement diagram showing locations of electron tubes, transistors, and associated components upon chassis of a high-fidelity record player and stereo FM receiver combination. *(Zenith Radio Corporation)*

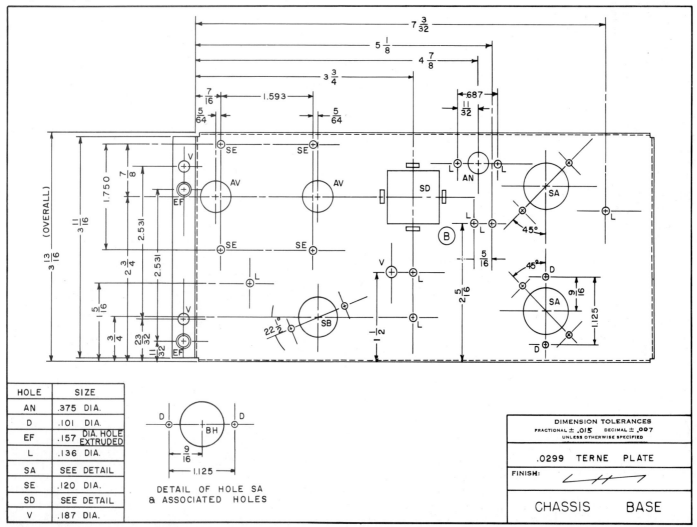

HOLE	SIZE
AN	.375 DIA.
D	.101 DIA.
EF	.157 DIA. HOLE EXTRUDED
L	.136 DIA.
SA	SEE DETAIL
SE	.120 DIA.
SD	SEE DETAIL
V	.187 DIA.

DETAIL OF HOLE SA & ASSOCIATED HOLES

DIMENSION TOLERANCES
FRACTIONAL ± .015   DECIMAL ± .007
UNLESS OTHERWISE SPECIFIED

.0299 TERNE PLATE

FINISH:

CHASSIS BASE

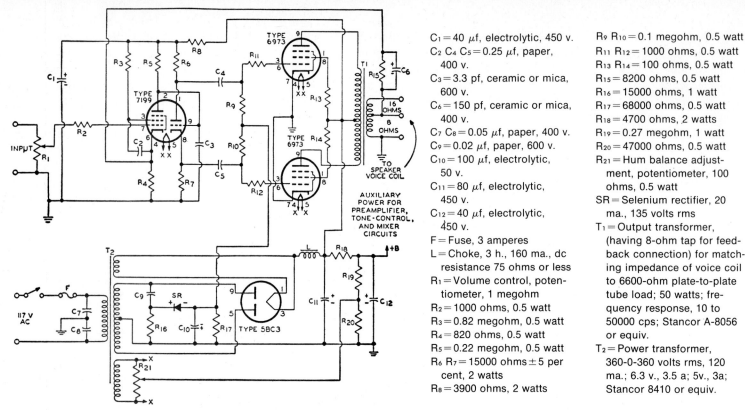

C₁ = 40 μf, electrolytic, 450 v.
C₂ C₄ C₅ = 0.25 μf, paper, 400 v.
C₃ = 3.3 pf, ceramic or mica, 600 v.
C₆ = 150 pf, ceramic or mica, 400 v.
C₇ C₈ = 0.05 μf, paper, 400 v.
C₉ = 0.02 μf, paper, 600 v.
C₁₀ = 100 μf, electrolytic, 50 v.
C₁₁ = 80 μf, electrolytic, 450 v.
C₁₂ = 40 μf, electrolytic, 450 v.
F = Fuse, 3 amperes
L = Choke, 3 h., 160 ma., dc resistance 75 ohms or less
R₁ = Volume control, potentiometer, 1 megohm
R₂ = 1000 ohms, 0.5 watt
R₃ = 0.82 megohm, 0.5 watt
R₄ = 820 ohms, 0.5 watt
R₅ = 0.22 megohm, 0.5 watt
R₆ R₇ = 15000 ohms ±5 per cent, 2 watts
R₈ = 3900 ohms, 2 watts

R₉ R₁₀ = 0.1 megohm, 0.5 watt
R₁₁ R₁₂ = 1000 ohms, 0.5 watt
R₁₃ R₁₄ = 100 ohms, 0.5 watt
R₁₅ = 8200 ohms, 0.5 watt
R₁₆ = 15000 ohms, 1 watt
R₁₇ = 68000 ohms, 0.5 watt
R₁₈ = 4700 ohms, 2 watts
R₁₉ = 0.27 megohm, 1 watt
R₂₀ = 47000 ohms, 0.5 watt
R₂₁ = Hum balance adjustment, potentiometer, 100 ohms, 0.5 watt
SR = Selenium rectifier, 20 ma., 135 volts rms
T₁ = Output transformer, (having 8-ohm tap for feedback connection) for matching impedance of voice coil to 6600-ohm plate-to-plate tube load; 50 watts; frequency response, 10 to 50000 cps; Stancor A-8056 or equiv.
T₂ = Power transformer, 360-0-360 volts rms, 120 ma.; 6.3 v., 3.5 a; 5v., 3a; Stancor 8410 or equiv.

Fig. 18-28c. A circuit diagram of a high-fidelity audio amplifier. *(Reprinted from RCA Receiving Tube Manual RC-23, courtesy of RCA, copyright proprietor)*

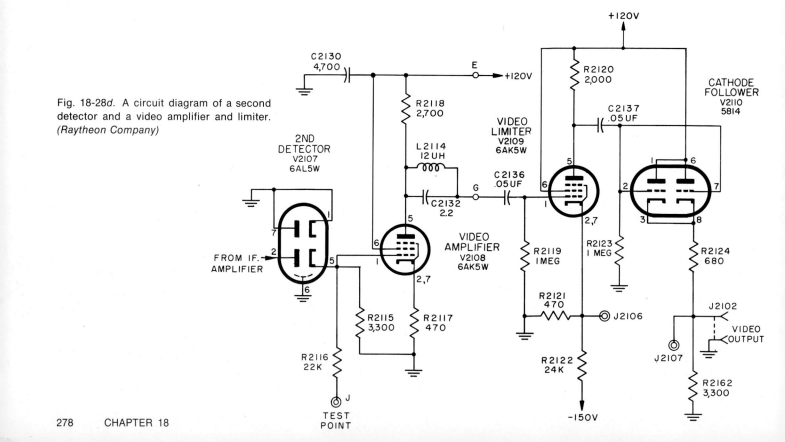

Fig. 18-28d. A circuit diagram of a second detector and a video amplifier and limiter. *(Raytheon Company)*

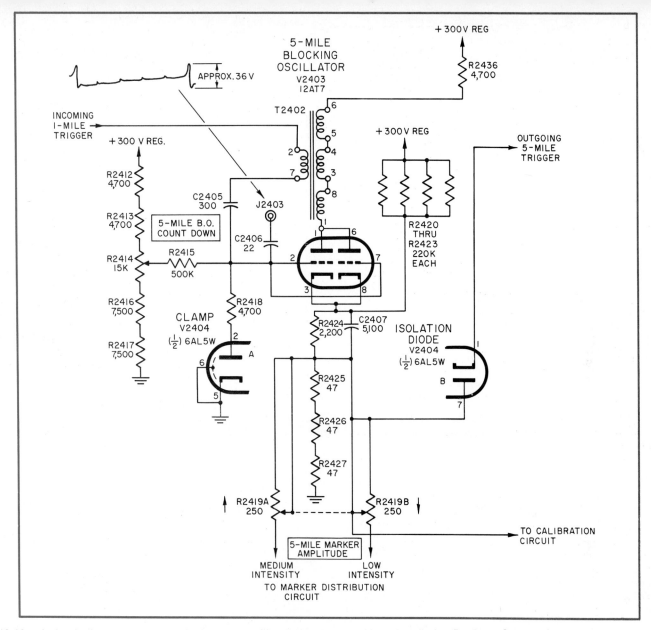

Fig. 18-28e. A circuit diagram of a count-down-block oscillator with clamp and isolation diode. *(Raytheon Company)*

The circuit diagram for a high-fidelity audio amplifier shown in Fig. 18-28c shows conventional tubes and electrical components. It illustrates one of the important applications of RCA receiving tubes.

The schematic diagrams in Figs. 18-28d and 18-28e represent parts of a storm-detector radar (AN/CP8-9) manufactured by the Raytheon Company for the U.S. Army Signal Corps. The circuit names are given in the legends for the illustrations (Figs. 18-28d and 18-28e).

18·29 Problem suggestions. Group 18, page 527. Three lists are presented. List 1 includes elementary problems. List 2 has somewhat more advanced problems for students who are interested and have studied electricity. The problems in List 3 are for those students who have made a hobby of radio and radar.

List 1: Problems 18·1, 18·2, 18·4, 18·5, 18·8, 18·9, 18·11, 18·14, 18·17, 18·22, 18·23, 18·25.

List 2: Problems 18·3, 18·6, 18·7, 18·10, 18·15, 18·18, 18·24, 18·26.

List 3: Problems 18·12, 18·13, 18·16, 18·19, 18·20, 18·21, 18·27, 18·28, 18·29.

19
Cams and gears

19•1 Cams and gears are machine parts that frequently occur on working drawings. The theory and specification of cams and gears are important divisions of the study of mechanism to which the student is referred. The student should know how to represent them on drawings as indicated in this chapter.

19•2 Cams. A cam is a machine element used to obtain an irregular or special motion not easily obtained by other means. Its shape is derived from the motion required of it. *Plate cams* are illustrated in Figs. 19-2a and 19-2b. As the cam in Fig. 19-2b revolves, it moves the *follower* up and down for one-half revolution and allows it to remain at rest for the remaining one-half revolution. *The cylindrical cam* in Fig. 19-2c revolves and moves the follower back and forth parallel to the axis of the shaft. Some cam terms are given in Fig. 19-2d, which illustrates how the cams act.

Fig. 19-2a. Cam installation using the McGill cam follower. The small gear at the lower left-hand corner meshes with a large gear (covered with a guard) secured to a shaft. The cam shown at the center is secured to the same shaft. As the cam revolves, it moves the cam follower (a hollow cylinder) attached to the link and gives it a variable motion. The link is pivoted near the upper right-hand corner in the illustration. *(McGill Manufacturing Company, Inc.)*

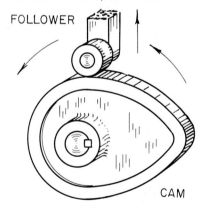

Fig. 19-2b. A plate cam with roll follower. Moves the follower up and down.

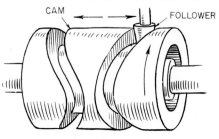

Fig. 19-2c. A cylindrical cam with roll follower. Moves the follower back and forth.

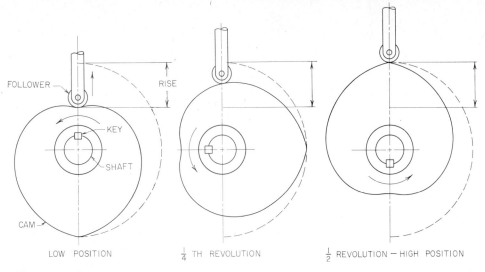

FOLLOWER

RISE

KEY

SHAFT

CAM

LOW POSITION $\frac{1}{4}$ TH REVOLUTION $\frac{1}{2}$ REVOLUTION — HIGH POSITION

Fig. 19-2d. Cam terms and action. The cam is turned by the revolving shaft and raises and lowers the follower.

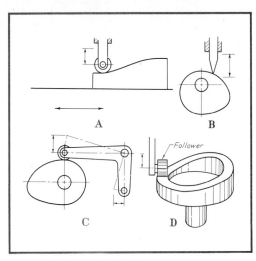

Follower

A   B

C   D

Fig. 19-3b. Some kinds of cams.

19•3 Kinds of cams. A cam for operating the valve of an automobile engine is illustrated in Fig. 19-3a. This cam has a *flat follower* which rests against the face of the cam. *The slider cam* in Fig. 19-3b at A moves the follower up and down as the cam moves back and forth. A cam with a *point follower,* off center, is shown at B. A lever cam is shown at C and a cylindrical cam of the edge type is shown at D. Plate and grooved cams are illustrated in Fig. 19-3c. The roll of the follower is guided by the groove, which has a width equal to the diameter of the roller. A grooved cam being ma-

Fig. 19-3a. Automobile valve cam. *(Oldsmobile Division of General Motors Corporation)*

Fig. 19-3c. Plate and grooved cams. *(The Rowbottom Machine Company)*

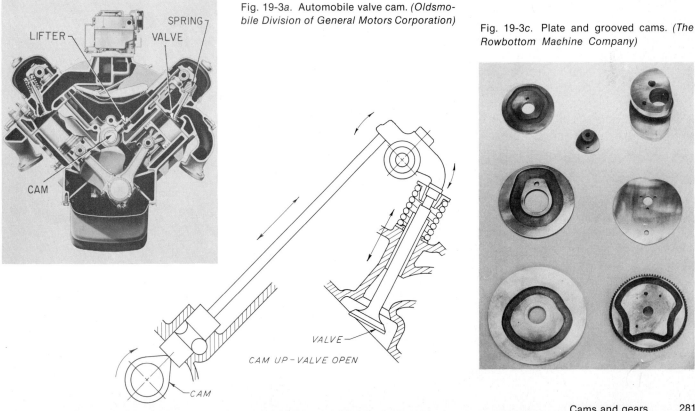

LIFTER   SPRING

VALVE

CAM

VALVE

CAM UP – VALVE OPEN

CAM

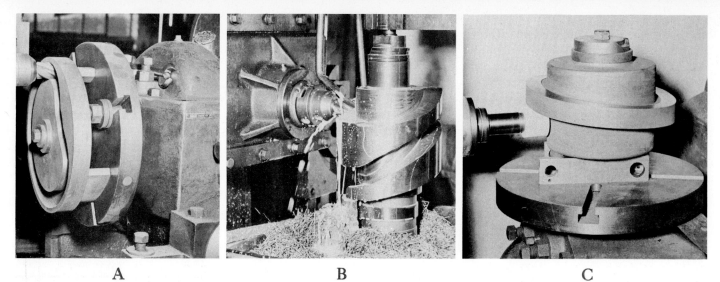

Fig. 19-3d. Machining cams. *(The Rowbottom Machine Company)*

chined is shown in Fig. 19-3d at A, and forms of cylindrical cams are shown at B and C.

19·4 To draw a cam outline. Given point *O*, the center of the shaft, and point *A*, the lowest position of the center of the roller (Fig. 19-4 at A), it is required to raise the center of the roller 1.875″ with uniform motion during 120° of a revolution of the shaft; to remain at rest (*dwell*) for 30°; to drop 1.250″ during 90°; to remain at rest for 30°; and to drop 0.625″ during the remaining 90°. The shaft revolves uniformly.

The *cam displacement diagram* at B in Fig. 19-4 indicates the desired motion. The horizontal line represents one

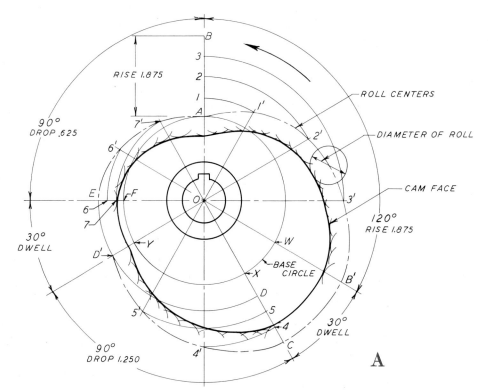

Fig. 19-4. To lay out and draw a plate cam.

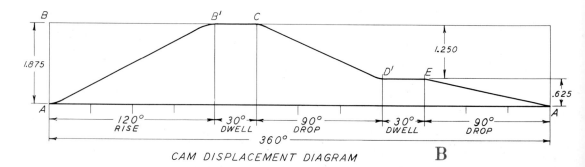

CAM DISPLACEMENT DIAGRAM

revolution of the base circle, 360°, and is divided in parts proportional to the number of degrees for each action. Vertical distances show the actual rise and fall.

To draw the cam shown at A in Fig. 19-4, divide the rise, *AB*, into a number of equal parts (four parts are used for clearness, but to obtain a more accurate solution more parts would be used). Divide the arc *AW* (120°) into the same number of equal parts as the rise and draw radial lines from *O*. With center *O* draw arcs with radii *O1*, *O2*, *O3*, and *OB* to locate points 1′, 2′, 3′, and *B′* on the line of roller centers. Using an irregular curve, draw a smooth curve through these points.

Draw arc *B′C* (30°) with radius *OB′*. This will allow the follower to be at rest, for it will be at a constant distance from *O*.

Lay off *CD* = 1.250″ and divide it into a number of equal parts (three are shown). Divide arc *XY* (90°) into the same number of equal parts (three) and draw radial lines from *O*. Draw arcs with center *O* and radii *O4*, *O5*, and *OD* to locate points 4′, 5′, and *D′*. Draw a smooth curve through points 4′, 5′, and *D′*.

Draw arc *D′E* (30°) with radius *OD* to provide for the 30° dwell.

The distance *EF* will be 0.625″ (the remaining part of the drop to the base circle). Divide *EF* into a number of equal parts (three are shown). Divide arc *FA* into the same number of equal parts (three) and draw radial lines. Draw arcs with radii *O6* and *O7* to locate points 6′ and 7′. Using an irregular curve, draw a smooth curve through points *E*, 6′, 7′, and *A*.

With centers on the line of roll centers, draw successive arcs with the radius of the roll as indicated. Then, using an irregular curve, draw a smooth curve tangent to the arcs which have been drawn, as shown by the cam face line in Fig. 19-4.

19•5 Motion. The motion of the follower of a cam may be uniform, harmonic, or uniformly accelerated. At A in Fig. 19-5 the thin line *AC* represents uniform motion. Equal distances on the rise are made for equal distances on the travel (equal intervals of time). To avoid a sudden jar at the beginning and end of motion, arcs are used to modify the motion, as shown by the heavy line. Harmonic motion, shown at B, is smoother. Draw a semicircle with the rise as a diameter. Divide it into a number of equal parts and the travel into the same number of equal parts. Project across and up to locate the points as shown and draw a smooth curve through them. Uniformly accelerated motion, represented at C, is still smoother. The rise is divided into parts proportional to 1, 3, 5...5, 3, 1. The travel is divided into the same number of parts (equal parts). Project across and up to locate the points to draw a smooth curve through, as shown.

Fig. 19-5. Some kinds of motion.

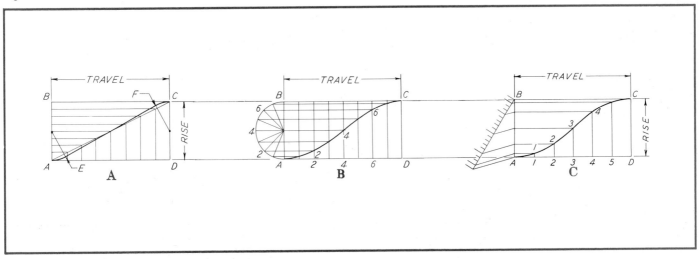

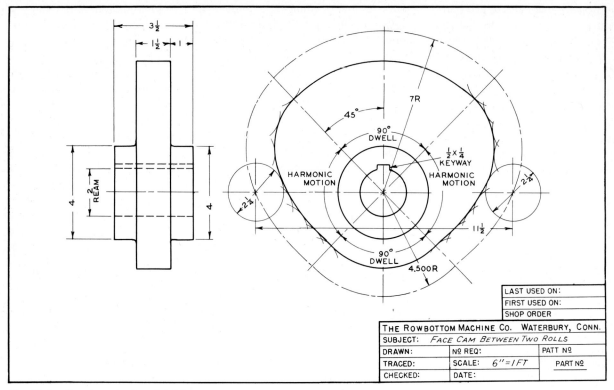

Fig. 19-6a. Drawing of a face (plate) cam.

Fig. 19-6b. Drawing of a barrel (cylindrical) cam.

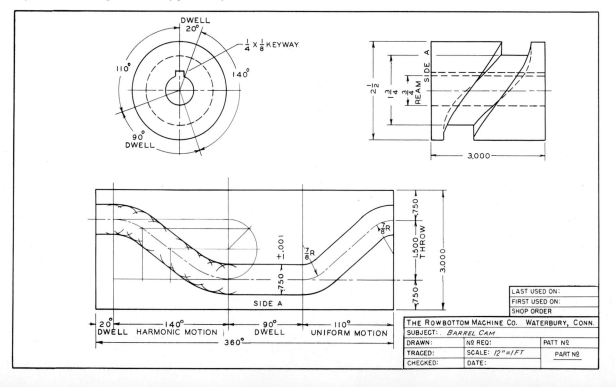

19•6 Cam drawings. A drawing for a face (plate) cam is shown in Fig. 19-6a. Note that the amount of movement is given by the radii for the dwells, 4½″ radius and 7″ radius. Harmonic motion is used, and there are two rollers. A drawing for a barrel (cylindrical) cam is shown in Fig. 19-6b. Note the displacement diagram. There are two dwells and two kinds of motion. For laying out harmonic motion, refer to Art. 19·5, Fig. 19-5.

19•7 Gears are machine elements used to transmit motion or force. There are many kinds of gears, a few of which are illustrated in Fig. 19-7a. The operation of simple spur gears may be explained as follows: If two wheels or circular disks are in contact, as in Fig. 19-7b, both will revolve if one is turned. If the smaller wheel is two-thirds the diameter of the larger wheel, it will make 1½ revolutions for 1 revolution of the larger wheel if no slipping occurs. If the driven wheel is hard to turn, there will be slipping. To prevent this, *teeth* are added to the wheels (Fig. 19-7c) to form *spur gears*. The shape of teeth is such that the same kind of motion is obtained as with rolling wheels that do not slip. A *spur gear* and *pinion* are

Fig. 19-7a. Some gears: 1, 2, and 3 are spur gears; 4 is a bevel gear; 5 is a spur gear (pinion); 6 is a rack (5 and 6 together are called a *rack and pinion*); 7 is an internal gear. *(The Fellows Gear Shaper Company)*

illustrated in Fig. 19-7c. The small gear is the pinion. A cut spur gear is shown in Fig. 19-7d.

Fig. 19-7b. Friction wheels.

Fig. 19-7c. Gear and pinion.

Fig. 19-7d. Cut spur gear. *(The Fellows Gear Shaper Company)*

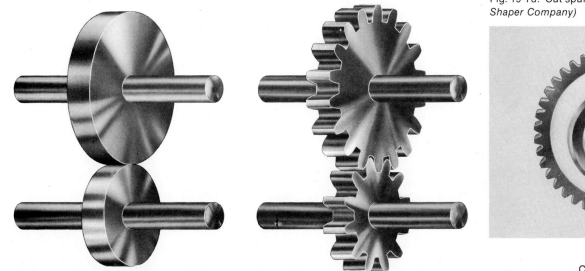

Fig. 19-7e. Rack and pinion.

Fig. 19-7f. Rack and pinion. *(The Fellows Gear Shaper Company)*

A *rack* and a *pinion* are illustrated in Figs. 19-7e and 19-7f. A rack is simply a gear with a straight pitch line instead of a circular pitch line. A *worm* and a *wheel* are shown in Fig. 19-7g. They generally mesh at right angles. The worm is similar to a screw and may have single or multiple threads.

19•8 Gear terms. Names of some parts of gears are illustrated in Fig. 19-8. Note the three diameters: *outside diameter, root diameter,* and *pitch diameter.* The pitch diameter corresponds to the diameter of the rolling wheel that is replaced by the gear. There are two kinds of pitch: *circular pitch* (illustrated) and *diametral pitch.* The circular pitch is the distance from a point on one tooth to the same point on the next tooth measured along the pitch circle; it equals the circumference of the pitch circle divided by the number of teeth. The diametral pitch is a ratio, or number, obtained by dividing the number of teeth by the pitch diameter. The *addendum* is the distance that the gear tooth extends above (outside) the pitch circle. The *dedendum* is the distance that the gear tooth extends below (inside) the pitch circle.

19•9 Gear teeth. Involute and cycloidal curves are used for gear-teeth forms. The information given in this chapter is for the $14\frac{1}{2}°$ involute system ($14\frac{1}{2}°$ or 20° is generally used). The $14\frac{1}{2}°$ or 20° refers to the pressure angle (Fig. 19-9a). The pressure angle and the distance between centers determine the diameters of the base circles. Note that the base circle (from which the involute is derived) is smaller than the pitch circle (Figs. 19-9a and 19-9b).

In Fig. 19-9b, R_A is the radius of the pitch circle of the gear with center at A, and R_B is the radius of the pitch circle of the pinion with center at B. $R_A + R_B$ equals the distance between centers. The line pressure, T_A T_B, through O

Fig. 19-7g. Worm and wheel.

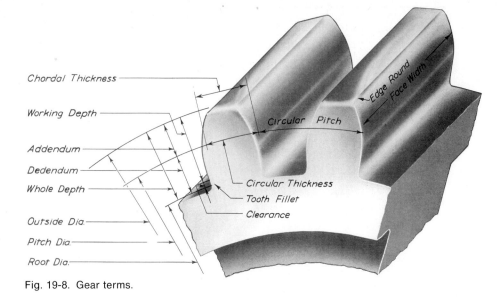

Fig. 19-8. Gear terms.

19·10 Gear formulas. The following information and formulas are for use in finding the required dimensions, and so forth, for standard $14\frac{1}{2}°$ involute gears:

$$N = \text{number of teeth} = DP$$
$$= \frac{\pi D}{P} = D_0 P - 2$$

$$a = \text{addendum} = \frac{1}{P} = \frac{p}{\pi}$$

$$b = \text{dedendum} = \frac{1.157}{P} = \frac{1.157p}{\pi}$$

$$c = \text{clearance} = \frac{0.157}{P} = \frac{0.157p}{\pi}$$

$$h_t = \text{whole depth} = a + b$$
$$= \frac{2.157}{P} = \frac{2.157p}{\pi}$$

$$D = \text{pitch diameter} = \frac{N}{P} = D_0 - 2a$$

$$D_0 = \text{outside diameter} = \frac{N+2}{P}$$
$$= D + 2a = \frac{(N+2)p}{\pi}$$

$$D_R = \text{root diameter} = D - 2b$$
$$= D_0 - 2(a+b)$$

$$P = \text{diametral pitch} = \frac{N}{D} = \frac{\pi}{p}$$

$$p = \text{circular pitch} = \frac{\pi D}{N} = \frac{\pi}{P}$$

(the point of tangency of the pitch circles) makes the pressure angle ϕ (Greek letter phi) with the perpendicular to the line of centers. Angle ϕ is shown extra large for clearness. Then AT_A and BT_B, drawn to the tangent points T_A and T_B, are the radii of the base circles. A point, x, on a cord (line of pressure $T_A\,T_B$) will describe involutes from the base circles as the cord winds and unwinds and represents the outlines of gear teeth outside the base circles. The part of the gear tooth inside the base circle is a radial line.

Fig. 19-9a. The pressure angle.

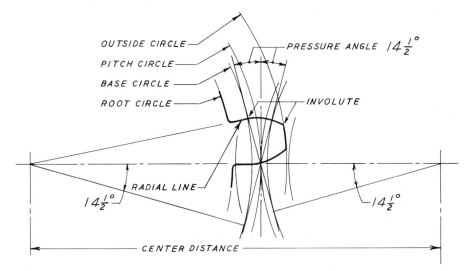

Fig. 19-9b. Gear action, base circle, etc.

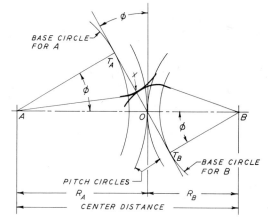

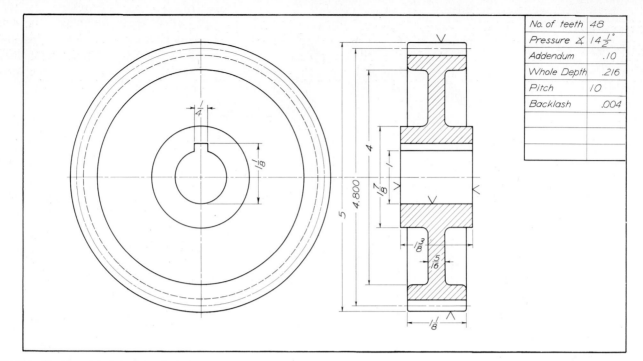

No. of teeth	48
Pressure ∠	14½°
Addendum	.10
Whole Depth	.216
Pitch	10
Backlash	.004

Fig. 19-11a. Working drawing of a cut spur.

19·11 Gear drawings. It is not necessary to show the teeth on drawings of gears. A drawing for a cut spur gear is shown in Fig. 19-11a. The gear *blank* should be drawn with dimensions for making the pattern and for the machin-

Fig. 19-11b. Gears in elevation.

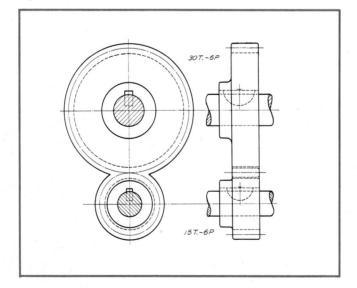

ing operations. Notes should also be included giving the necessary information for cutting the teeth, the accuracy required, the material, and so forth. On assembly drawings the representation shown in Fig. 19-11b may be used with such notes as may be necessary.

A spur gear drawing is shown in Fig. 19-11c. The pressure angle is 20°. Note the complete dimensions and the information which is given.

19·12 Bevel gears. When two gear shafts intersect, bevel gears are used. These gears may be thought of as replacing rolling cones (Fig. 19-12a at A, B, C, and D). If the gears are the same size and the shafts are at right angles, they are called *miter gears*. A single bevel gear is shown in Fig. 19-12b and a pair of bevel gears in Fig. 19-12c. The smaller of two bevel gears is called the *pinion*.

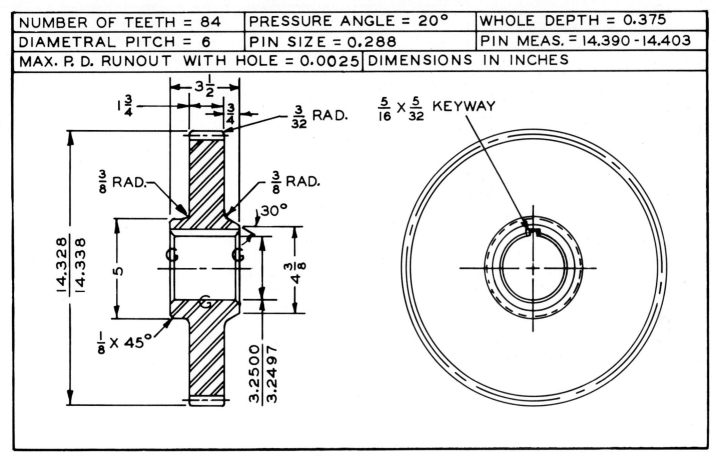

NUMBER OF TEETH = 84	PRESSURE ANGLE = 20°	WHOLE DEPTH = 0.375
DIAMETRAL PITCH = 6	PIN SIZE = 0.288	PIN MEAS. = 14.390 - 14.403
MAX. P. D. RUNOUT WITH HOLE = 0.0025	DIMENSIONS IN INCHES	

Fig. 19-11c. A spur gear drawing. *(The Fellows Gear Shaper Company)*

Fig. 19-12a. Rolling cones.

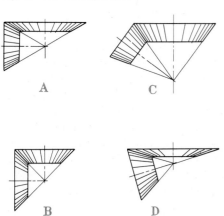

A   C

B   D

Fig. 19-12b. A bevel gear. *(The Fellows Gear Shaper Company)*

Fig. 19-12c. A pair of bevel gears.

19·13 Bevel-gear terms. Some information about bevel gears is given in Fig. 19-13. The Greek letters in the illustration are identified in the following list:

GREEK LETTERS

α = alpha, δ = delta, Γ = gamma

α = addendum angle
δ = dedendum angle
Γ = pitch angle
Γ_R = root angle
Γ_0 = face angle
a = addendum
b = dedendum
a_N = angular addendum
A = cone distance
F = face
D = pitch diameter
D_0 = outside diameter
N = number of teeth
P = diametral pitch
R = pitch radius

19·14 Bevel-gear drawing. Working drawings of bevel gears require the dimensions for machining the blank, together with the necessary gear information. An example of a working drawing for a cut bevel gear is shown in Fig. 19-14.

19·15 Gear information may be obtained from the publications of the American Standards Association and by a study of books on mechanism, machine design, and the subject of gears.

19·16 Problem suggestions. Group 19, page 532. Three lists are presented. List 1 includes basic elementary problems. Selections from Lists 2 and 3 may be made for more advanced students when time permits.

List 1: Cam problems 19·1, 19·3, 19·4, 19·5, 19·7.
Gear problems 19·12, 19·13.
List 2: Cam problems 19·2, 19·6, 19·9.
Gear problems 19·14, 19·15.
List 3: Cam problems 19·8, 19·10.

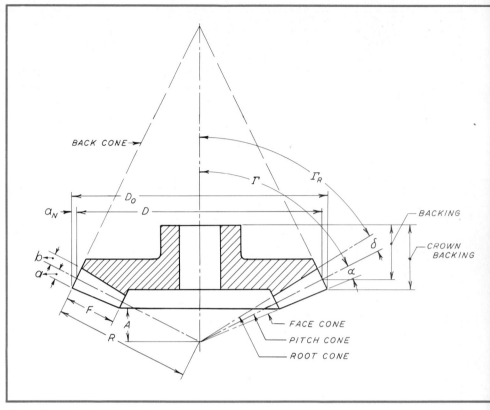

Fig. 19-13. Some bevel-gear terms.

Fig. 19-14. Drawing of a bevel gear.

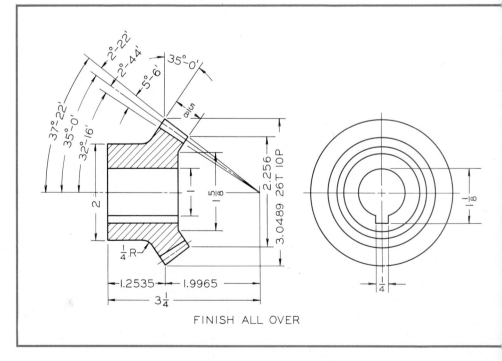

FINISH ALL OVER

20
Surface developments and intersections

Fig. 20-2a. Soft-drink cartons are cut in a flat pattern and then folded. *(Olin Packaging Division, Olin Mathieson Chemical Corporation)*

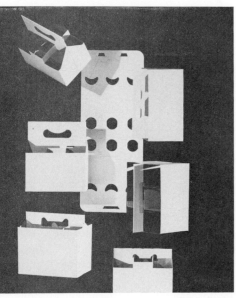

20·1 The drafting of sheet material is an important application of mechanical drawing in a great many industries. Some familiar items made from sheet materials include pipes, ducts for hot- or cold-air systems, parts of buildings, aircraft, automobiles, storage tanks, cabinets, office furniture, boxes and cartons, package containers for frozen foods, manufactured products, and countless other items.

Such uses require drawings made to provide patterns on flat sheets of material which can be folded, rolled, or otherwise formed to provide the required shape. Sheet materials used include paper, various cardboards, plastics and films, metals (steel, tin, copper, brass, aluminum, etc.), wood, fiberboard fabrics, etc.

20·2 Package design has become a great industry based upon engineering and the fine arts. Packages are used for a multitude of products, ranging from foods to furniture. They are designed for sales appeal and for protection in shipment, and they may be intended for temporary or permanent use.

Mass production of packages or containers at a reasonable cost is necessary for most items. The soft-drink carrier is a familiar example (Fig. 20-2a). It is made of strong kraftboard, white surfaced to permit attractive printing and design.

Flat patterns are printed, cut, creased, folded, glued (if necessary), and completed, all on machines designed especially for the purpose (Figs. 20-2b and 20-2c).

Fig. 20-2b. Twenty-up die on cylinder bed, showing makeready on cylinder. Dies are used to cut the sheet material for making packages. *(Olin Packaging Division, Olin Mathieson Chemical Corporation)*

Fig. 20-2c. Phase just prior to glue lap contact. *(Olin Packaging Division, Olin Mathieson Chemical Corporation)*

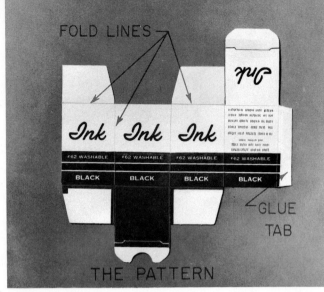

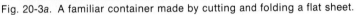

Fig. 20-3a. A familiar container made by cutting and folding a flat sheet.

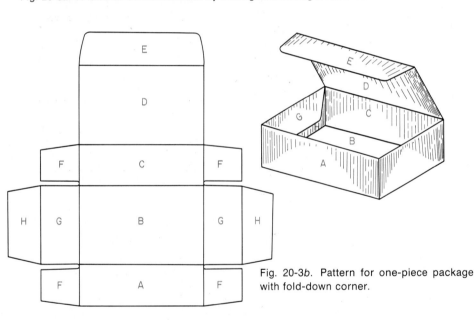

Fig. 20-3b. Pattern for one-piece package with fold-down corner.

Fig. 20-3c. Patterns for a box and cover.

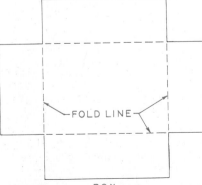

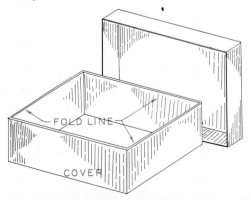

20•3 Pattern layouts for fold-up packages. Packages and cartons are made of many materials and in many thicknesses. Some are made of thin or medium-thickness paper stock (Figs. 20-3a and 20-3b) which can be folded easily into the desired form. Some are designed so that no glue is required, and some may have glue on one or more tabs. The design of the pattern layout for a particular purpose and the lettering, color, and artwork are all a part of an important industry.

Packages made of cardboard, corrugated board, and many other materials require allowances for thickness. Boxes made in two parts, a container and a cover (Fig. 20-3c), and a slide-in box (Fig. 20-3d), are examples. Observe various cartons and packages to see many interesting and challenging problems in the development of surfaces.

20•4 Flat material items of a permanent type require carefully laid-out patterns. Lamp shades (Fig. 20-4a), wastebaskets, card files, pencil boxes, jewelry cases, and many other items are made in whole or in part of cardboard, plastic, hardboard, etc., and require patterns, as do even the clothes we wear.

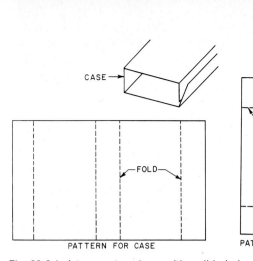

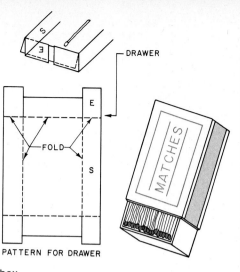

PATTERN FOR CASE

PATTERN FOR DRAWER

Fig. 20-3d. A two-part package with a slide-in box.

Fig. 20-4a. The shade is part of a conical surface.

The birdhouse in Fig. 20-4b is one of many things which can be made from flat material. The illustration shows grooved creases for the folds. A waterproof glue may be used to fasten where required, but short bolts or paper fasteners serve the purpose.

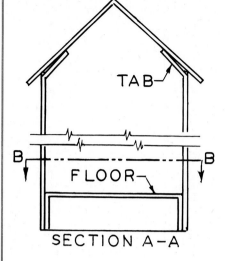

SECTION A–A

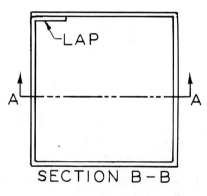

SECTION B–B

Fig. 20-4b. Patterns for birdhouses and boxes are made of rather thick and stiff materials; corrugated board folded, as shown, or separate pieces of wood cut to required sizes.

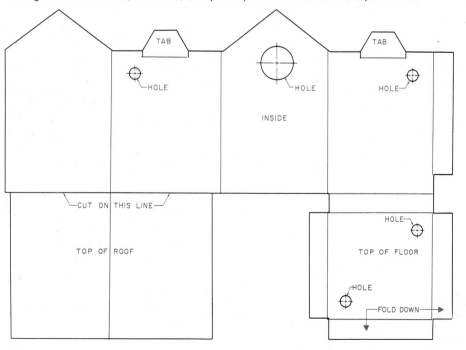

20·5 Sheet-metal drafting. A large class of metalwork is made from sheets of metal which are formed into the required shape by bending or folding up and fastening by rivets, seams, soldering, or welding. Figure 20-5a shows a schematic arrangement of the Kennedy stratified air-swept-tube mill system for raw ore and clinker grinding. For sheet-metal work, the drawings consist of the representation of the finished object and the drawing of the shape of the flat sheet which, when rolled or folded and fastened, will form the object. This second drawing is called the *development,* or *pattern,* of the piece; making it comes under the term *sheet-metal pattern drafting.*

A great many thin-metal objects without seams are formed by die stamping or by pressing a flat sheet into shape under heavy presses. Examples range from brass cartridge cases and household utensils to steel wheelbarrows and parts of automobiles and aircraft. Other kinds of thin-metal objects are made by spinning, for example, some brass and aluminum ware. In stamped and spun work, the metal is stretched out of its original shape.

The operations for the preparation of sheet-metal work are performed on machines. These operations include cutting, folding, wiring, forming, turning, beading, and so forth. Some machines and operations are shown in Fig. 20-5b.

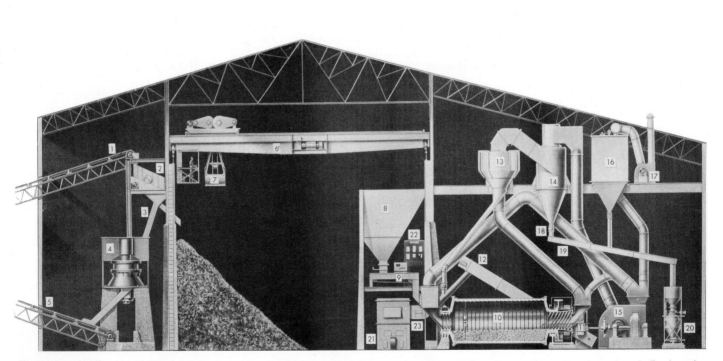

Fig. 20-5a. Schematic arrangement of Kennedy stratified air-swept-tube mill system. *(Kennedy Van Saun Manufacturing & Engineering Corporation)*

1 Belt conveyor—Feed to Crusher	9 Weighing Feeder	17 Dust Filter Exhauster
2 Vibrating Screen	10 Stratified Air-swept Tube Mill	18 Rotary Air Locks
3 Oversize Return Chute	11 Cross Conveyor for Oversize	19 Finished Material Conveyor
4 Gearless Gyratory Crusher	12 Return Conveyor for Oversize	20 Automatic Pneumatic Transport Pump
5 Belt Conveyor—Closing Crusher Circuit	13 Radial Flow Classifier	21 Hot Air Furnace
6 Traveling Crane	14 Cyclone Collector	22 Instrument and Control Cubicle
7 Clamshell Bucket	15 Mill Exhauster	23 Automatically Controlled Tempering Air Damper
8 Mill Feed Hopper	16 Dust Filter	

Fig. 20-5b. Some of the machines used in sheet-metal working. *(The Peck, Stow, and Wilcox Company)*

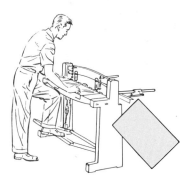

SQUARING SHEARS

Used for trimming and squaring sheet metal.

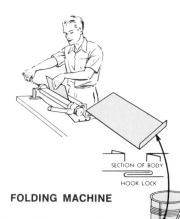

SECTION OF BODY

HOOK LOCK

FOLDING MACHINE

The Folding Machine is used extensively for edging sheet metal or the forming of locks or angles.

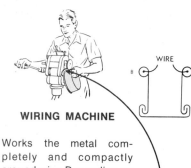

WIRE

WIRING MACHINE

Works the metal completely and compactly around wire. Depending on shape of work, seats to receive wire are prepared on Folder, Brake or Turning Machine.

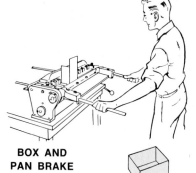

BOX AND PAN BRAKE

A small bench mounted brake for straight bends up to full length of machine or for box and pan work up to 3 inch depth.

AA—Showing edges turned by Pexto Burring Machine. Note right-angle burr on body of can, and a still more pronounced burr on the bottom piece. The edge on bottom is turned smaller than on the body.

BURRING MACHINE

A difficult operation to master but practice will produce uniform flanges on sheet metal bodies. Prepares the burr for bottoms preparatory to setting down and double seaming.

FORMING MACHINES

Used for forming flat sheets into cylinders of various diameters such as stove pipe, the bodies of vessels, cans, etc. Made in a variety of sizes and capacities.

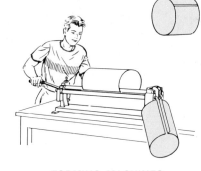

A—This shows how bottom edge of body, and bottom of Can are prepared by Burring Machine for Setting-Down.

B—The Pexto Setting-Down Machine closes the seam as shown here. It works both speedily and accurately.

SETTING DOWN MACHINE

The Setting Down Machine prepares the seams in body of vessels for double seaming.

TURNING MACHINE

Used to prepare a seat in bodies to receive a wire. The operation is completed with use of Wiring Machine.

AA—Seats for Wire—made on the Turning Machine.

DOUBLING SEAMING MACHINE

Offered in various styles and follows the setting down operation.

BEADING MACHINE

For ornamenting and stiffening sheet metal bodies.

Surface developments and intersections 295

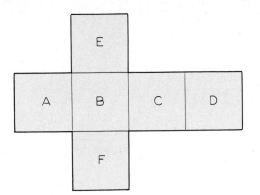

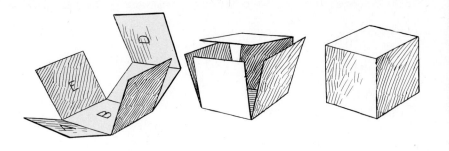

Fig. 20-6a. Pattern for a cube.

20•6 Development. There are two general classes of surfaces: plane and curved. The six faces of a cube are plane surfaces. The bases of a cylinder are plane surfaces, whereas the lateral surface is curved. Curved surfaces which can be rolled in contact with a plane surface, such as cylinders and cones, are called *single curved* and can be exactly developed.

Another kind of curved surface is the *double-curved* surface, such as spheres and spheroids. These surfaces cannot be exactly developed; however, approximate developments can be made.

It is possible to cut a piece of paper so that it can be folded into a cube, as in Fig. 20-6a. The shape cut out is the pattern of the cube. There are five regular solids, and their patterns are

made as shown in Fig. 20-6b. A good understanding of the nature of developments may be gained by laying out the foregoing shapes on rather stiff drawing paper. These shapes can then be cut out and their patterns folded to form the figures. The joints can easily be secured with adhesive tape.

Thus, the pattern for any piece that has plane surfaces may be made by

Fig. 20-6b. The five regular solids.

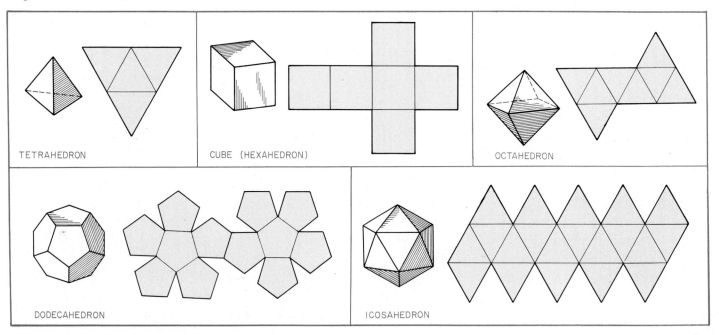

TETRAHEDRON

CUBE (HEXAHEDRON)

OCTAHEDRON

DODECAHEDRON

ICOSAHEDRON

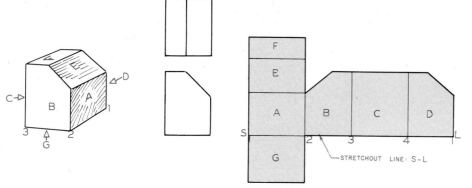

Fig. 20-6c. A pattern for a prism, showing stretchout line and lap.

first deciding where the seam is to be. Usually, for economy of solder or rivets and time, the seam is taken on the shortest line; then, each face is opened in order, so the pattern shows each face in its true size. One example, the development of a prism, is illustrated in Fig. 20-6c. The lines inside the pattern are called *folding,* or *crease,* lines. The dash lines around the development at the right indicate extra material to allow for lap in making joints.

The length of the pattern for a prism is measured on a straight line called the *stretchout line* (Fig. 20-6c). This line measures the shortest distance around the prism. The base must be perpendicular to the edges so that it will form the stretchout line when the faces of the prism are unfolded in contact with a plane surface.

20·7 Development of prisms. To develop the prism in Fig. 20-7a, draw the stretchout line, *SL,* and on it lay off 1–2, 2–3, 3–4, and 4–1, obtained from the top view. This gives the length of the stretchout and the true distances between the vertical edges. At points 1, 2, 3, 4, and 1 on the stretchout, draw vertical crease lines equal in length to the corresponding edges of the prism.

These lengths may be easily projected across from the front view. The true size of the inclined surface is found by the method of auxiliary projection (Chap. 9) and is attached to one of the sides in its proper relationship. The bottom development may be added.

To develop the lateral surface of the triangular prism (Fig. 20-7b), draw the stretchout line, *SL,* and lay off the distances 1–*a,* *a*–2, 2–3, 3–*b,* and *b*–1, taken from the top view. Points *a* and *b* do not locate crease lines but are required to find the line of the cut. Such extra measuring lines are often necessary.

Fig. 20-7a. Development of a pattern for a prism.

Fig. 20-7b. Development of a pattern for a prism.

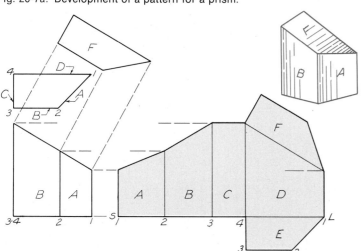

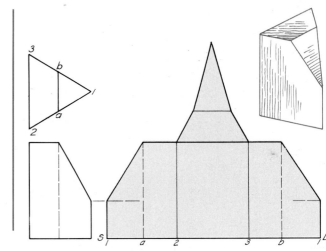

20·8 Oblique prisms are developed by the same method we used for right prisms. The only difference is that the length of the stretchout line is obtained from an auxiliary view of a right section (Fig. 20-8). Pass a plane perpendicular to the edges and draw the auxiliary view, which will show the true distances between the edges. For convenience, draw the stretchout line as an extension of the edge view of the auxiliary plane. On the stretchout line lay off the distances 1–2, 2–3, 3–4, and 4–1. Through 1, 2, 3, 4, and 1 draw lines parallel to the edges as shown, and on them lay off the lengths above and below the stretchout line.

The auxiliary view may be used as a top view if the paper is turned to make the stretchout line horizontal; then, proceed as for a right prism.

Fig. 20-8. Development of a pattern for an oblique prism.

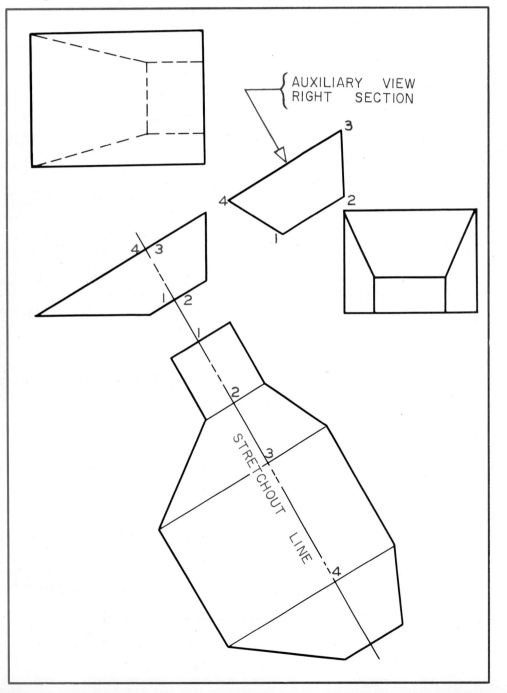

20·9 Cylinders. In geometry we learn that a cylinder may be thought of as a prism with an infinite number of sides. The development of the curved surface of a cylinder, then, might be obtained by placing each face, in order, in contact with a plane surface. The result would be a rectangle with one dimension equal to the length of the cylinder (an element) and the other dimension equal to the distance around the cylinder (the circumference). The developed surface of a cylinder is illustrated in Fig. 20-9, where the cylinder has been rolled out on a plane surface.

For a cylinder the stretchout line is a straight line equal in length to the circumference of the cylinder. If the base of the cylinder is perpendicular to the axis, it will roll out into a straight line and form the stretchout line. If the prism or cylinder does not have a base perpendicular to the axis, a right section must be taken to obtain the stretchout line.

20·10 Development of cylinders. Consider a cylinder as being a many-sided prism. To develop the truncated right cylinder (Fig. 20-10), assume the

Fig. 20-9. Developed surface of a right circular cylinder.

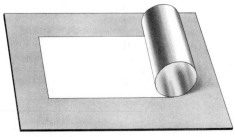

position of any convenient number of edges. On a cylinder these edges, or lines, are called *elements.* For ease of working, these are equally spaced. This makes it possible to obtain the length of the stretchout by stepping off the same number of equal spaces along *SL* as there are on the top view. At each point on the stretchout, draw a vertical measuring line. Project the length of each assumed edge across from the front view to the corresponding line of the development. Draw a smooth curve through the intersection.

Since the surface is curved, the stretchout as obtained is only approximate. The more edges assumed, the closer will be the approximation. It is seldom necessary to have the points less than ¼ in. apart. The accuracy in length of the stretchout may be tested by measuring on it the figured length of the circumference, which equals 3.1416 times the diameter (πD) for a circular cylinder.

20•11 To draw the pattern for a two-piece, or square, elbow (Fig. 20-11). Since this elbow consists of two cylinders cut off at 45°, only one cylinder needs to be developed for a pattern. The explanation of Fig. 20-10 applies to this figure. Lap is allowed as indicated.

20•12 The development of a four-piece elbow is illustrated in Fig. 20-12. To draw the elbow, first draw arcs

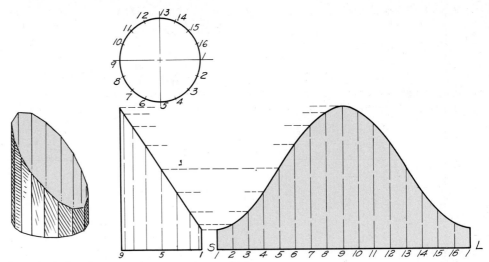

Fig. 20-10. Development of a pattern for a cylinder.

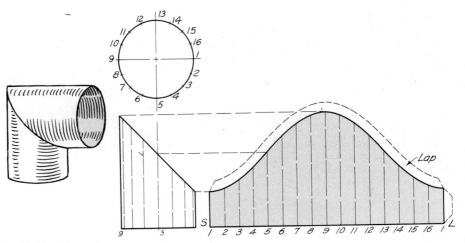

Fig. 20-11. Pattern for a square elbow.

Fig. 20-12. Pattern for a four-piece elbow.

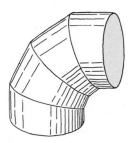
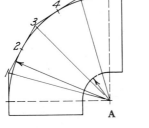
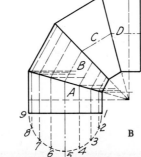
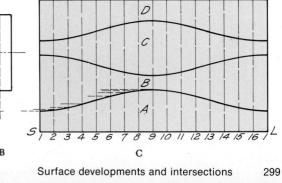

having the desired inner and outer radii, as shown at A. Divide the outer quarter circle into six equal parts. Draw radial lines from points 1, 3, and 5 to locate the joints. Draw tangents to the arcs at points 2 and 4 and complete the figure as shown at B by tangents to the inner quarter circle. With this view completed, we are ready to start development. Draw a circle representing the cross section of the pipe (one-half this view is sufficient). Divide it into a number of equal parts and lay out the stretchout line with the same equal parts. From the circle, project to the elevation to locate the assumed edges. The pattern for the first section is obtained by projecting across from the elevation as shown at C in the same way as in Figs. 20-10 and 20-11.

The patterns for the four pieces may be cut without waste from a rectangular piece if the seams are made alternately on the inside, or throat, line and the outside line. To draw the pattern for the second section, extend the measuring lines of the first section and with the dividers take off the lengths of the assumed edges on the front view, starting with the longest one. The third and fourth sections are made in a similar way. Since the curve is the same for all sections, only one need be plotted and that one can be used as a template (pattern) for the other curves.

20·13 Galvanized-iron, aluminum, and copper moldings and cornices are made up of a combination of cylinder and prism parts. A practical problem in developments is to make the pattern for a mitered piece "return" around a corner as shown in Fig. 20-13. An inspection of the figure shows the method of working to be the same as in Fig. 20-10. Here, however, the section of the molding takes the place of the top view, and its length is laid out on the stretchout line.

20·14 Pyramids and cones. In the case of prisms and cylinders, the stretchout was a straight line with the measuring lines perpendicular to it and parallel to each other. When their edges are all parallel to the front plane, their true lengths always show in the front view. Pyramids and cones, or any objects larger at one end than at the other, will not roll straight; hence, their stretchouts are not straight lines. Since the edges of pyramids and the elements of cones are inclined, they will not show true lengths in the views.

20·15 To find the true length of an edge of a pyramid or an element of a cone. This means to find the true length of a line (see Art. 9·22). If an edge or element is parallel to one of the planes of projection, its true length will show in its projection on that plane. If the line is not parallel, it can then be revolved into a parallel position.

The pyramid at A in Fig. 20-15 is shown by top and front views at B. The edge, OA, does not show in its true length in either view; however, if we draw the pyramid in the position shown at C, the true length of OA is shown in the front view. At C the pyramid has been revolved from the position of B about a vertical axis until the line OA is parallel to the frontal plane. At D the line OA is shown before and after revolving; thus, the construction for finding the true length of a line is as follows: In the top view, with radius OA and center O, revolve the top view of OA until it is horizontal. Project the end of the line down to meet a horizontal line through the front view of A. Join this point of intersection with the front view of O. The true length is shown at OA'.

Fig. 20-13. Pattern for a return miter.

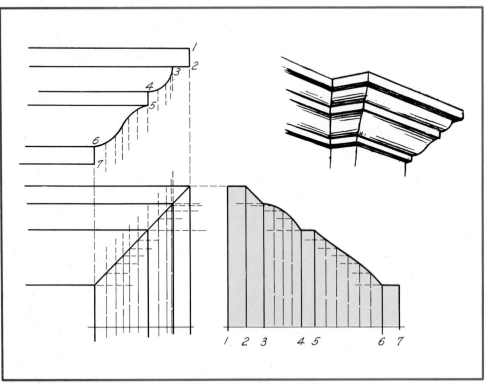

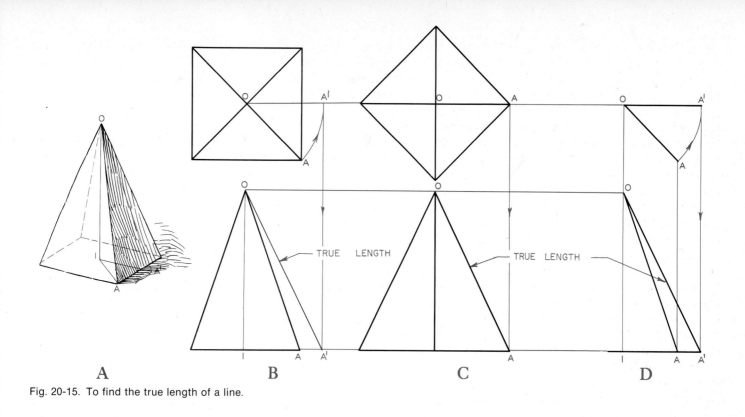

Fig. 20-15. To find the true length of a line.

A   B   C   D

20•16 To draw the pattern for a right rectangular pyramid (Fig. 20-16). Find the true length of one of the edges by swinging it around until it is parallel to the frontal plane, as shown. With this true length as a radius, draw an arc of indefinite length for a measuring arc (curved stretchout). On this, mark off as chords the four edges of the base 1–2, 2–3, 3–4, and 4–1. Connect the points; then draw crease lines by joining each point with the center.

Fig. 20-16. Development of a pattern for a right rectangular pyramid.

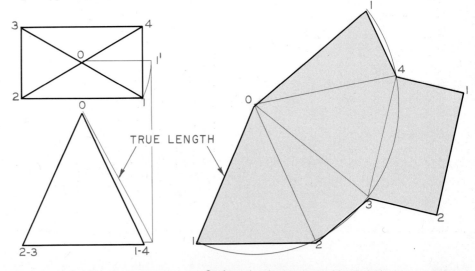

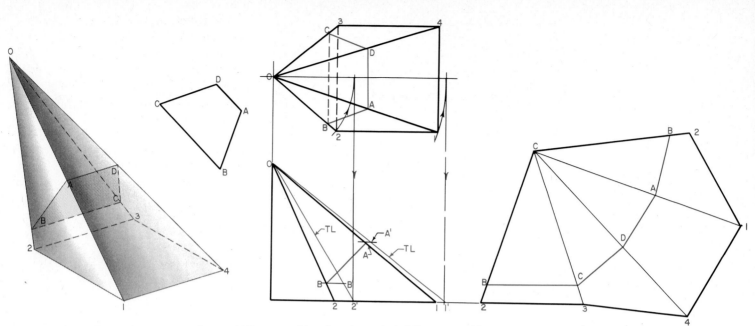

Fig. 20-17. To develop a pattern for an oblique pyramid or for a truncated oblique pyramid.

20·17 To develop the pattern for an oblique pyramid or a truncated oblique pyramid (Fig. 20-17). First find the true lengths (TL) of the lateral edges by revolving them parallel to the frontal plane as shown for edges 0–2 and 0–1. Edge 0–2 is revolved in the top view and projected to 0–2′ in the front view, where it shows the true length of edge 0–2. In like manner find the true length of edge 0–1. Edge 0–2 = edge 0–3. Edge 0–1 = edge 0–4.

Start the development by laying off 2–3. Locate point O by intersecting arcs with centers 2 and 3 and radius true length of 0–2′ from front view. Construct triangles 0–3–4, 0–4–1, and 0–1–2 with the true lengths of the sides to complete the development as shown.

For a truncated pyramid with the inclined surface ABCD, find the true lengths of OA, OB, OC, and OD. For this pyramid OA = OD and OB = OC. The true lengths of OB and OC are shown at OB′ in the front view and of OA and OD at OA′. Lay off these true lengths on the corresponding edges of

the development and join them to find the development of the lateral surface of the frustum. The inclined surface is shown in the auxiliary view and could be attached to the lateral surface as indicated.

20·18 Cones. The curved surface of a cone may be thought of as being made up of an infinite number of triangles. The development of the curved surface might be obtained by placing each triangle, in order, in contact with a plane surface. The result would be a sector of a circle having a radius equal

Fig. 20-18. Developed surface of a cone.

to an element of the cone and an arc equal in length to the circumference of the base of the cone. The developed surface of a cone is illustrated in Fig. 20-18.

20·19 To draw the pattern for a right circular cone. From Fig. 20-19 it will be seen that the stretchout line for a cone is a circle arc with a radius equal to the slant height of the cone. Considering the cone as a many-sided pyramid, draw on the top view the base ends of a convenient number of imaginary edges (elements) with a large number of equal spaces. With the slant height taken from the front view as a radius (OA in Fig. 20-19), draw an arc of indefinite length as a measuring arc. On this, step off as many spaces as were assumed in the top view and at the same distances apart. Connect the end points with the center. The resulting sector is the developed surface. If the cone is cut off straight across as in Fig. 20-19, draw another arc with OC as a radius after developing the lateral surface of the complete cone.

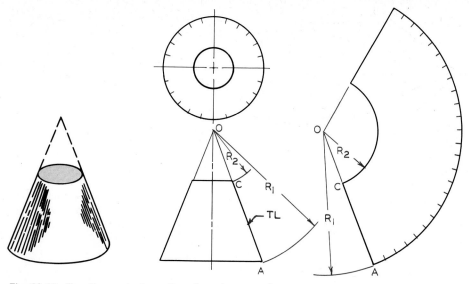

20•20 The pattern for a truncated circular cone. If the cone is cut off at an angle as in Fig. 20-20, first develop the full cone by drawing the developed position of each element and numbering it to avoid mistakes. Then find the true length of each element from the base to the cut surface by revolving it around the axis until it is parallel to the front plane, or, in other words, by projecting it across to the outside line in the front view. Lay off these true lengths on the corresponding lines on the pattern and connect the points. The elements and lines have been stopped at the cut surface to preserve clearness.

Fig. 20-19. Development of a pattern for a frustum of a cone.

Fig. 20-20. Development of a pattern for a truncated right circular cone.

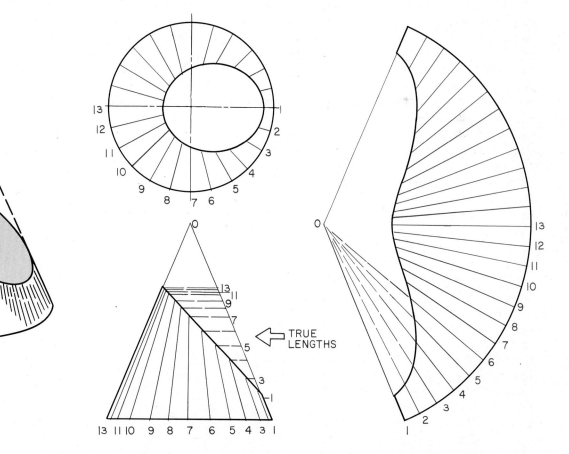

TRUE LENGTHS

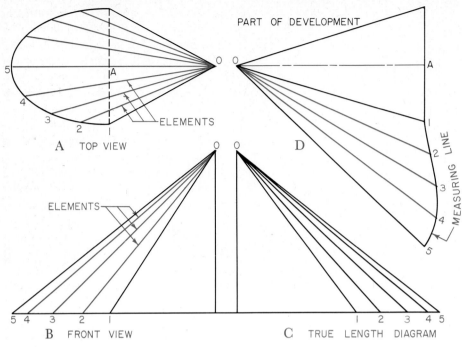

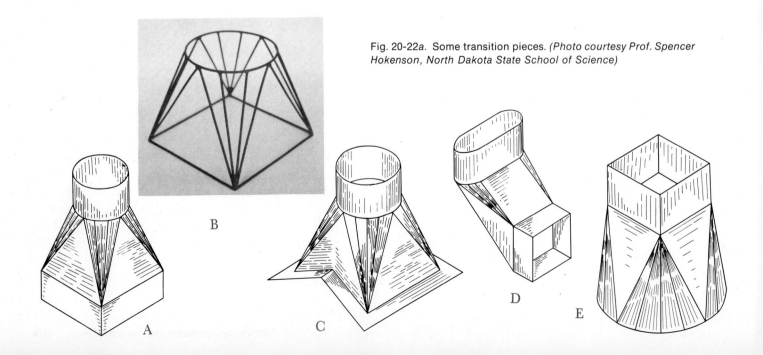

PART OF DEVELOPMENT

A TOP VIEW

ELEMENTS

D

MEASURING LINE

ELEMENTS

B FRONT VIEW

C TRUE LENGTH DIAGRAM

Fig. 20-21. Triangulation used in developing the surface of an oblique cone.

20·21 Triangulation is a convenient method for the approximate development of surfaces which cannot be exactly developed. It consists of dividing the surface into triangles, finding the true lengths of the sides, and then constructing the triangles in regular order on a flat surface. By using triangles with one short side, the plane triangles will approximate the curved surface. Triangulation is sometimes used for single curved surfaces.

The development of part of an oblique conical surface in Fig. 20-21 illustrates the use of triangulation. Divide the surface into triangles. For a closer approximation more triangles should be used than are shown here. Find the true lengths of the elements by revolving them parallel to the frontal plane or construct a true-length diagram as at C. At C, lay off 0–1, 0–2, etc., equal to 0–1, 0–2, etc., taken from the top view at A and draw 0–1, 0–2, etc., at C, which will be the true lengths of the elements. To lay out the pattern at D, construct the triangles in the order in which they occur, taking distances 1–2, 2–3, etc., from the top view and 0–1, 0–2, etc., from the true-length diagram.

20·22 Transition pieces are used to connect pipes or openings of different shapes, sizes, or positions. Transition pieces have a surface made up of parts of surfaces which may be plane, or curved, or both. A few transition pieces are suggested in Fig. 20-22a. A model of the square-to-round transition piece at A is shown at B.

A square-to-round transition piece (Fig. 20-22b) being formed in the plant of Dreis & Krump Manufacturing Company is described as follows: "A square-

Fig. 20-22a. Some transition pieces. *(Photo courtesy Prof. Spencer Hokenson, North Dakota State School of Science)*

A

B

C

D

E

to-round transition is easily made in two pieces. Illustrated is the positioning of one of the pieces for making the last of the 8 partial bends on the second conical corner. This conical bending is done by moving one end of the plate out the proper distance for each partial bend while the point for the square corner remains fixed. When completed, the round end is 12″ in diameter and the opposite end 4′ by 5′ and the height is 6′. The material is ¼″ steel plate. The floor-to-floor time for the complete bending of each section as shown in the machine is approximately 30 minutes.''

20·23 Development of a transition piece. As stated in Art. 20·22, transition pieces are made up of parts of surfaces, and they are developed by triangulation. This consists of dividing a surface into triangles (exact or approximate) and laying them out on the developed pattern in regular order.

The example shown in Fig. 20-23a connects two square ducts, one of which is at 45° with the other. It will be seen that this piece is made up of eight triangles, four of one size and four of another size. To draw the developed

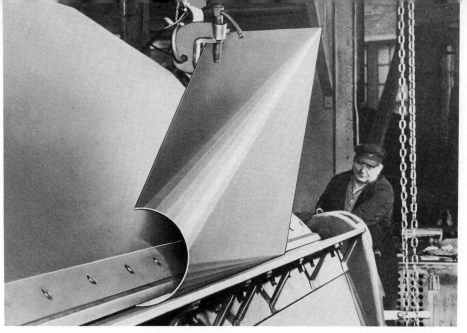

Fig. 20-22b. Forming a square-to-round transition piece. *(Dreis & Krump Manufacturing Company)*

surface, find the true size of each triangle and place them in the proper order. Lines 1–2, 2–3, 3–4, and 4–1 show in their true size, as do lines AB, BC, CD, and DA. Find the true length of one of the other lines as for A4. Revolve it parallel to the frontal plane, and the true length shows at 4A' in the front view. Start the development by drawing line

DA. Then with centers at A and D and radius 4A' taken from the front view (true lengths of A4 = D4 = D3, etc.), draw intersecting arcs to locate point 4 on the development. With D as a center draw an arc with radius 4A' and intersect it with an arc of radius 4–3 and center 4 to locate point 3. Proceed to lay off the remaining triangles until completed.

Fig. 20-23a. Development of a simple transition piece, square to square.

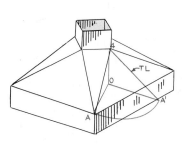

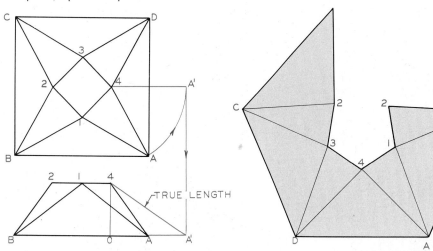

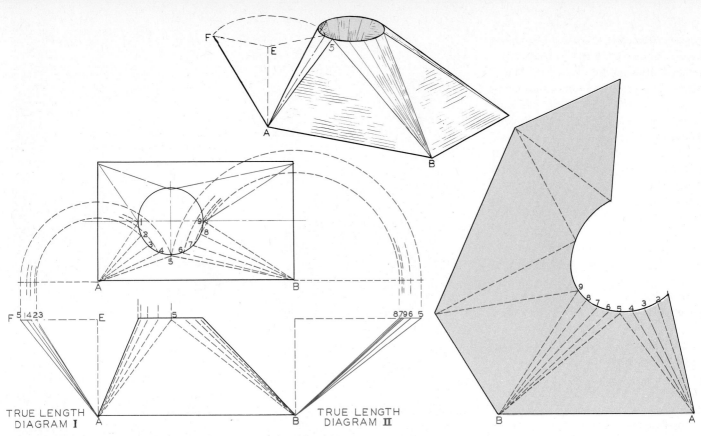

Fig. 20-23b. Development of a rectangular-to-round transition piece.

The example shown in Fig. 20-23b connects a round pipe with a rectangular one. From this picture it is seen that this piece is formed by four triangles. Between these triangles are four conical parts with apexes at the corners of the rectangular opening and bases each one-quarter of the round opening.

Starting with the cone whose apex is at A, divide its base 1–5 into a number of equal parts, as 2, 3, 4, and draw the lines A2, A3, A4 to give triangles approximating the cone. Find the true length of each of these lines. This is done in practical work by constructing a separate diagram, as at I. The construction is based on the fact that the true length of each line is the hypotenuse of a triangle whose altitude is the altitude of the cone and whose base is the length of the top view of the line.

On the front view, draw the vertical line AE as the altitude of the cone. On the base EF lay off the distances A1, A2,

and so forth, taken from the top view. This is done in the figure by swinging each distance about the point A in the top view and dropping perpendiculars to EF. Connect the points thus found with the point A in diagram I to obtain the desired true lengths. Diagram II, constructed in the same way, gives the true lengths of lines B5, B6, and so forth, of the cone whose apex is at B. After the true-length diagrams are constructed, start the development with the seam at A1. Draw a line A1 equal to the true length of A1. With 1 as a center and radius 1–2 taken from the top view, draw an arc. Intersect this arc with an arc from center A and radius equal to the true length of A2, thus locating the point 2 on the development. With 2 as center and radius 2–3, draw an arc and intersect it by an arc with center A and radius of the true length of A3. Proceed similarly with points 4 and 5 and draw a smooth curve through the points 1, 2,

3, 4, and 5 thus found. Then attach the true size of the triangle A5B, locating point B on the development by intersecting arcs from A with radius AB taken from the top view, and from 5 with the radius the true length of B5. Continue until the piece is completed.

20·24 Intersections. When a line pierces a plane, the point where the line passes through the plane is called the *point of intersection* (Fig. 20-24a). When two plane surfaces meet, the line where they come together, or where one passes through the other, is called the *line of intersection* (Fig. 20-24b). When a plane surface meets a curved surface, or where two curved surfaces meet, there is a line of intersection which may be either a straight line or a curved line, depending upon the surfaces and/or their relative positions.

It is necessary for the package designer, the sheet-metal worker, and the machine designer to be able to locate the point at which a line pierces (intersects) a surface and to locate the line of intersection between two surfaces.

20·25 Intersecting prisms. Several examples of intersecting surfaces are illustrated in Figs. 20-25a and 20-25b.

To draw the line of intersection of two prisms, first start the orthographic views. In Fig. 20-25c a square prism passes through a hexagonal prism. Through the front edge of the square prism, pass a plane parallel to the frontal plane. The top view of this plane appears as a line AA. The intersection of the plane AA with one of the faces of the vertical prism shows in the front view as line aa and is crossed by the front edge of the square prism at point 1. Point 1 is a point on both prisms and, therefore, a point in the desired line of intersection. Plane BB is parallel to plane AA and contains an edge of the inclined prism, which meets at point 2 in the front view. Points 1 and 2 are in both planes; therefore, a line joining them will be in both planes and a part of the line of intersection. Plane BB also determines point 3.

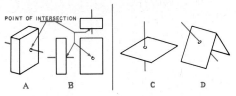

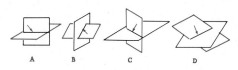

Fig. 20-24a. The intersection of a line and a plane is a point.

Fig. 20-24b. The intersection of two planes is a line. The arrow points to the line of intersection.

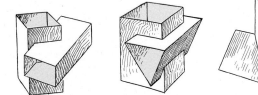

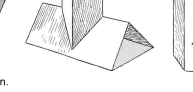

Fig. 20-25a. Some lines of intersection.

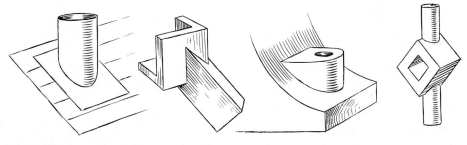

Fig. 20-25b. Some lines of intersection.

Fig. 20-25c. Intersecting prisms.

Fig. 20-25d. Intersecting prisms.

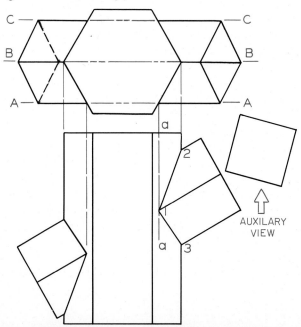

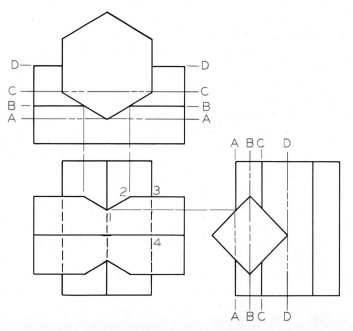

AUXILARY VIEW

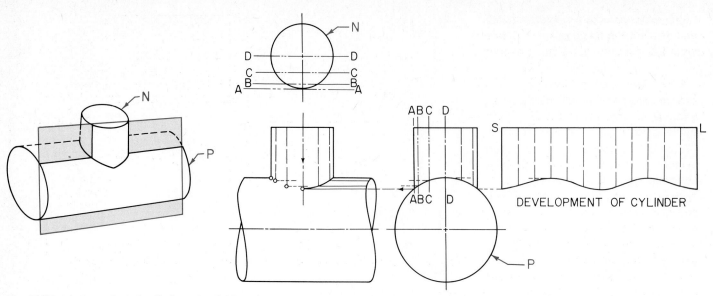

Fig. 20-26a. Intersection of cylinders at a right angle.

These planes are called *cutting planes,* and they may be used for the solution of most problems in intersections. For intersecting prisms, pass planes through all the edges of both prisms within the limits of the line of intersection. Where the lines that are cut from both prisms by the same plane cross, there is a point on the required line of intersection. In Fig. 20-25d four cutting planes are required. The limiting planes are *AA* and *DD,* as a plane in front of *AA* or in back of *DD* would cut only one of the prisms.

20·26 Intersecting cylinders. To draw the line of intersection of two cylinders (Fig. 20-26a). Since there are no edges on the cylinders, it will be necessary to assume positions for the cutting planes. Plane *AA* contains the front line (element) of the vertical cylinder and cuts a line (element) from the horizontal cylinder. Where these two lines intersect in the front view, there is a point on the required curve. Each plane cuts lines from both cylinders which intersect at points common to both cylinders. The development of the verti-

cal cylinder, obtained by the method of Art. 20·10, is shown in the figure.

The solution for an inclined cylinder is given in Fig. 20-26b, where the positions of the cutting planes are located by an auxiliary view. In the development

of the inclined cylinder the auxiliary view is used to get the length of the stretchout. If the cutting planes have been chosen so that the circumference of the auxiliary view is divided into equal parts, the measuring lines will

Fig. 20-26b. Intersection of cylinders at an angle.

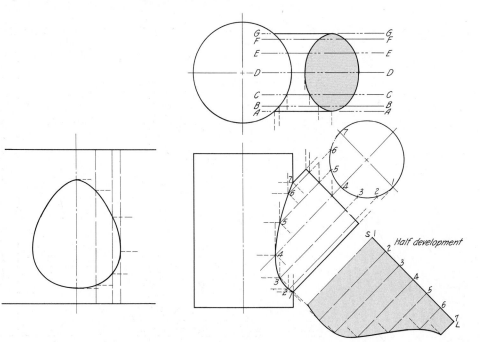

be equally spaced along the stretchout line. Project the lengths from the front view and join ends with a smooth curve.

20·27 Intersecting cylinders and prisms. The intersection of a cylinder and a prism is found by the use of cutting planes, as already described. In Fig. 20-27 a triangular prism intersects a cylinder. The planes *A*, *B*, *C*, and *D* cut lines from the prism and lines from the cylinder which cross in the front view and determine the curve of intersection as shown. The development of the triangular prism is found by taking the length of the stretchout line from the top view and the lengths of the measuring lines from the front view. Note that one plane of the triangular prism (line 1–5 in the top view) is perpendicular to the axis of the cylinder. The curve of intersection on that face is the radius of the cylinder.

20·28 Intersection of cylinders and cones. The intersection of a cylinder and a cone may be found by passing

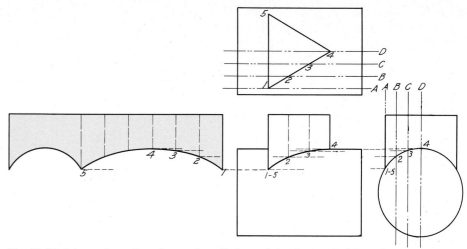

Fig. 20-27. Intersection of a prism and a cylinder and development of the prism.

planes parallel to the horizontal plane, as shown in Fig. 20-28*a*. Each plane will cut a circle from the cone and two straight lines from the cylinder. The straight lines of the cylinder cross the circle of the cone in the top view at points on the curve of intersection. These lines are then projected to the front view, as in Fig. 20-28*b*, where the construction is shown for a single plane. Use as many planes as are necessary to obtain a smooth curve.

Fig. 20-28*a*. Intersection of a cylinder and cone.

Fig. 20-28*b*. A cutting plane.

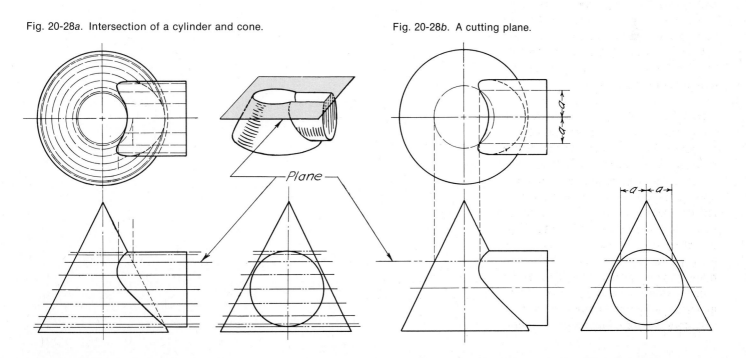

20·29 Intersection of planes and curved surfaces.

The line of intersection of a cone cut by a plane, *MM*, as in Fig. 20-29a, may be found by horizontal cutting planes *A*, *B*, *C*, and *D*. Each plane cuts a circle from the cone and a straight line from the plane *MM*. Thus, points common to both the plane *MM* and the cone are located as shown in the top view. These points, when projected to the front view, give the curve of intersection.

The intersection at the end of a connecting rod is found by passing planes perpendicular to the axis which cut circles as shown in the end view of Fig. 20-29b. The points at which these circles cut the "flat" are projected back as points on the curve.

20·30 Development of a measure.

To draw the development of a measure (Fig. 20-30 at A), draw the view shown in Fig. 20-30 at B with the half circles at top and bottom. Observe that the body is a frustum of a cone. Extend the outline to complete the cone. With *MN* as a radius draw an arc. Step off one-half the circumference of the base on this arc and draw the radial lines *MK* and *ML*. With *M* as a center and *MD* as a radius, draw *PQ*, completing the development of the body. Add the necessary allowance for lap.

To develop the handle, divide it into a number of spaces and step these spaces off on the stretchout *RS*. At *R* lay off one-half the width of the upper end of the handle on each side of the stretchout and at *S* lay off one-half the width of the lower end of the handle on each side. Add allowance for laps and hems. The true development of the lip would require the drawing of lines through each point and finding the length of each line as described for the truncated cone (Fig. 20-20). The usual practical (approximate) method is as follows: On a center line *oa* draw an arc with *OA* as a radius and space one-half

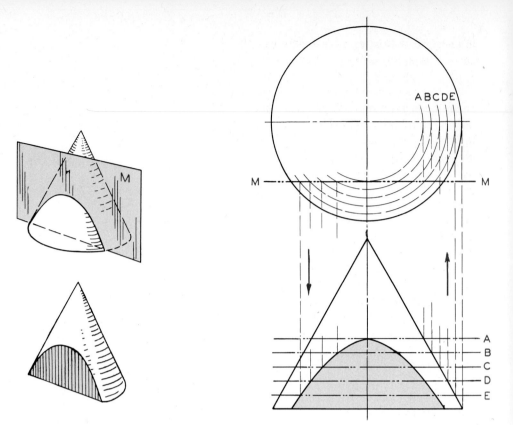

Fig. 20-29a. Intersection of a plane and a curved surface.

the circumference of the top of the body on each side as shown by *dad*. Draw the radii *od*. Increase *OA* by *ac* = *AC* and increase *od* by *de* = *DE*, as obtained from the elevation. Draw *ce* and the perpendicular bisector of *ce* intersecting the center line *g*. With *g* as a center and *gc* as a radius, draw arc *ece*

Fig. 20-29b. Intersection of a plane and a turned surface.

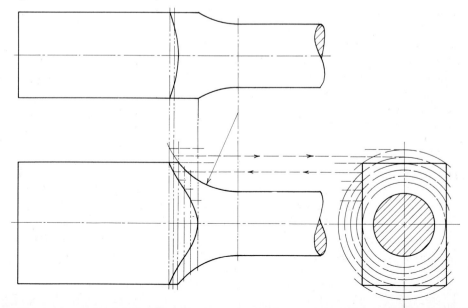

to complete the pattern. Add the necessary material for seams and hems.

20•31 Seams and laps. The basis of sheet-metal pattern drafting is development. For practical work it is necessary to know the processes of wiring, seaming, and hemming and the allowances of material to be made. Open ends of articles are usually reinforced by enclosing a wire in the edge as shown at *A* in Fig. 20-31. The amount added to the pattern may be taken as 2½ times the diameter of the wire. Edges are also stiffened by hemming. Single- and double-hemmed edges are shown at B and C. Edges are fastened by soldering on lap seams (D), folded seams (E), or, the commonest way, grooved seams. The grooved seams are shown in three stages, both inside and outside, at F. The Pittsburgh corner-lock joint is shown at G and the cup joint at H. An important consideration in allowing lap on patterns is the shape of the space left at the corners to prevent thick places in the seam. This is called *notching* and is illustrated on Fig. 20-30 at B at corners *P* and *K*.

20•32 Problem suggestions. Group 20, page 534. Three lists are presented. List 1 includes elementary problems from which a selection can be made for the time available. Selections from List 2 can be made for somewhat more difficult problems to give a more complete course. List 3 may be used according to the ability of the students and the time available, or it may be used in an advanced course. All three lists include a large number of problems to permit a wide selection.

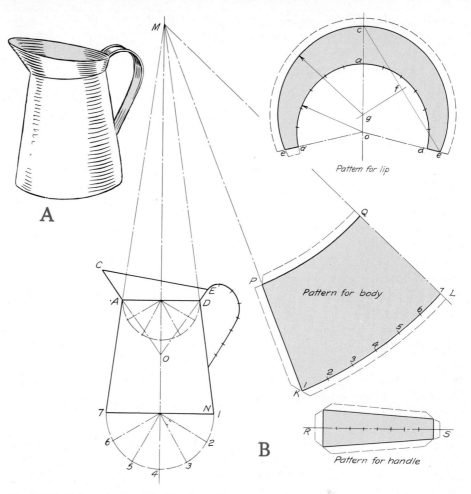

Fig. 20-30. Pattern for a measure.

Fig. 20-31. Wiring, seaming, and hemming.

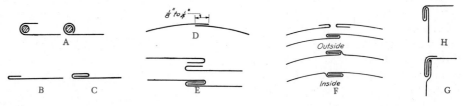

List 1: Development problems 20·1, 20·2, 20·4, 20·5, 20·9, 20·10, 20·14, 20·17, 20·20, 20·22, 20·25, 20·30, 20·33, 20·35.
Intersection problems 20·38, 20·39, 20·42, 20·43, 20·54.

List 2: Development problems 20·3, 20·6, 20·11, 20·13, 20·15, 20·19, 20·23, 20·26, 20·28, 20·34, 20·36.
Intersection problems 20·40, 20·41, 20·44, 20·45, 20·48, 20·51, 20·53, 20·56, 20·58.

List 3: Development problems 20·7, 20·8, 20·12, 20·16, 20·18, 20·24, 20·25, 20·29, 20·31, 20·32, 20·37.
Intersection problems 20·46, 20·47, 20·49, 20·50, 20·52, 20·55, 20·57, 20·59, 20·60.

21
Architectural drafting

21·1 Architectural drawings have to do with the representation and specification of buildings and structures of various kinds. Through the ages the design and appearance of buildings have changed with the materials available. Methods of construction and uses have changed from the classic structures of ancient Greece (Fig. 21-1a) to the modern office building (Fig. 21-1b), and from the log cabin (Fig. 21-1c) to the contemporary residence (Fig. 21-2a). All have involved the use of drawings, whether a marked outline on the ground or the great number of complete drawings for large present-day structures.

21·2 Architectural drawings employ the same general principles as other technical drawings, but there are certain methods of representation, conventional symbols, and practices that are necessary because of the relatively small scale which is usually used for architectural plans.

Fig. 21-1b. An example of a modern office building, the United Engineering Center.

Fig. 21-1a. An example of ancient Greek architecture.

Fig. 21-1c. A log cabin in Bitterroot National Forest, Montana. *(U.S. Forest Service)*

DR. & MRS. HAYMES RESIDENCE
HERBERT BRASHER & ASSOCIATES
ARCHITECTS   - LUBBOCK, TEXAS

Fig. 21-2a. Perspective of a contemporary house. (Herbert Brasher, Architect, Lubbock, Tex.)

In addition to working drawings, pictorial drawings are used to show how the completed structure will look (see wash drawing, Fig. 21-2a). Such pictures, together with preliminary or sketch plans (Fig. 21-2b), present both exterior and interior features and arrangements and provide a basis for starting the working drawings.

However, before starting the working drawings, several preliminary drawings may need to be made for consideration of the general design, exterior appearance, and plan layout. These are gone over until they are satisfactory and meet with the client's approval. Drawings such as Figs. 21-2a and 21-2b may then be made to clarify the whole design.

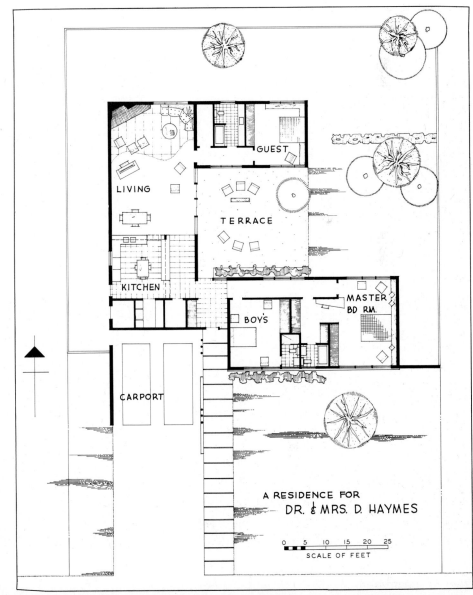

Fig. 21-2b. Plan for house shown in Fig. 21-2a. (Herbert Brasher, Architect, Lubbock, Tex.)

21•3 Lettering and titles. Making architectural drawings, in common with all drawings, requires the ability to letter. The traditional lettering used on architectural drawings is based upon the Old Roman alphabet, as illustrated and explained in Art. 3·15, but variations are used. Plain lettering is in order on architectural working drawings.

Elaborate and important titles may be designed with the Old Roman letters of Fig. 3-15a. The single-stroke letters of Figs. 3-15c and 3-15d serve for titles on working drawings. The titles shown in Figs. 21-3a and 21-3b indicate usual content and treatment of titles on architectural drawings. Some offices use sheets with parts of the title printed, and some use a rubber stamp (Fig. 21-3c) or preprinted adhesive titles which can be applied to the drawing.

In general, lettering should conform with the design. Plain single-stroke letters should be used with the simple design of a contemporary structure. All lettering should be clear and easy to read.

21•4 House styles. The construction, appearance, and plans of houses have developed from the materials available, the climate conditions, and the needs of the occupants. From simple shelters, houses have progressed in convenience with the growth of civilization. Present-day equipment and utilities have removed the restrictions of climate and made it possible to have a comfortable home of any arrangement or design in any part of the country. Electricity provides for conveniences, from lighting and cooking to refrigeration and heating or cooling the house. Gas provides for both heating and refrigeration. The latest information on both electrical and gas conveniences can always be obtained from catalogs and descriptive literature of the manufacturers. There are many kinds of equipment and materials which should be investigated and understood regardless of the style of house that is being considered.

Some traditional types of houses are illustrated in Figs. 21-4a and 21-4b, with brief notes to enable the student to identify them.

The Cape Cod house of Fig. 21-4a at A is a fundamentally American design which has come down from colonial times. It is a conservative type which has retained continuous popularity.

The Dutch colonial house of Fig. 21-4a at B is a modification of early designs. It is identified by the slightly overhanging upper story and contrasting brick or stone lower story.

The Monterey house of Fig. 21-4a at C is of Spanish origin and was developed on the West Coast. It is identified by its graceful lines and by the upper porch, which should face in a southerly direction.

Fig. 21-3a. Title for a public building.

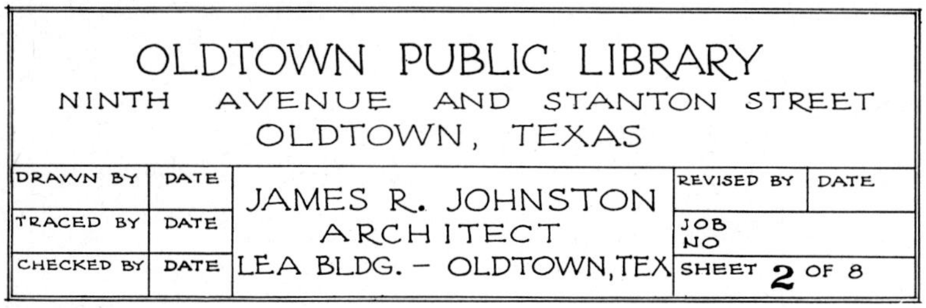

Fig. 21-3b. Title for a residence.

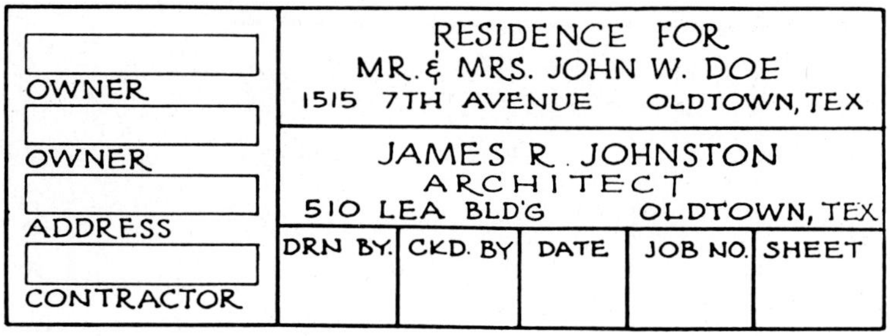

Fig. 21-3c. A printed-form title.

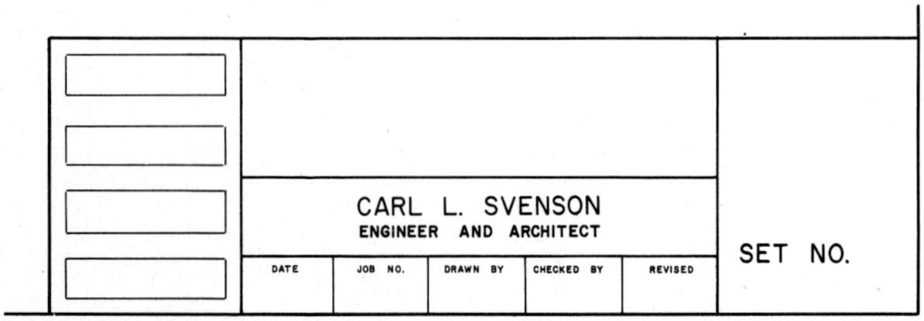

The traditional Tudor house of Fig. 21-4a at D is basically English. It is identified by its half-timbered exterior, separate chimney stacks, arched recessed doorway, and small-paned windows. It presents a certain seventeenth-century feudal air.

The Georgian house of Fig. 21-4b at A is another design from England. It is identified by the simple, bold cornice line and the arched doorway with fanlight above.

The functional house of Fig. 21-4b at B is built without a basement and is different from traditional designs. It is identified by its simplicity, large windows, flat roof, and the preference given to functional capacity rather than architectural style.

The ranch house of Fig. 21-4b at C is one of many modern types of one-story construction. It may be enlarged by additions in almost any direction.

The bungalow of Fig. 21-4b at D is a one-story house which does not present any particular type of architecture. It may be a single-unit design or have wings attached.

Contemporary styles of houses vary greatly and are constantly changing with the development of new materials and methods of construction. A number of designs are illustrated in Arts. 21·2, 21·5 to 21·8, and 21·29 to 21·43.

21•5 Contemporary houses. Contemporary architecture has many forms. For example, there are houses with hip roofs, with gable roofs, or with flat roofs (see Art. 21·15). A multitude of materials are used for walls, from stone to fiber glass; however, most of this chapter will have to do with the use of wood.

Three examples of contemporary architecture are (1) the urban, or city, dwelling, shown in Art. 21·6; (2) the suburban house, shown in Art. 21·7; and (3) the split-level, or hillside, house, shown in Art. 21·8.

Fig. 21-4a. Some styles of houses.

A

B

C

D

Fig. 21-4b. Some styles of houses.

A

B

C

D

21·6 The urban house. The house in Figs. 21-6a and 21-6b is described as a ranch type of slab construction. It is 28 ft 6 in. wide and 69 ft long (or deep). The small width makes this plan suitable for a narrow city lot. There is no basement. A concrete-slab foundation is used. The rectangular shape and simple roof line make the construction less expensive than irregular shapes and "cut-up" roofs with valleys and other joining surfaces.

Fig. 21-6a. An urban (city) or suburban (metropolitan) dwelling. (George Hay, Architect, Media, Pa.; photo courtesy Better Homes & Gardens magazine)

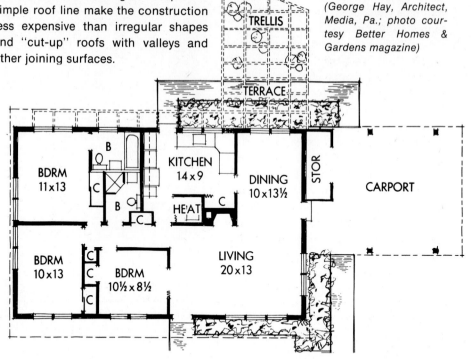

Fig. 21-6b. Plan for the house of Fig. 21-6a. (George Hay, Architect, Media, Pa.; photo courtesy Better Homes & Gardens magazine)

21·7 The western house. The house in Figs. 21-7a to 21-7d is described as a western house for young homemakers. This type of house provides for outdoor living in a suburban location and has picture windows. It is of frame construction with exterior walls of vertical sheathing. There is no basement, but a concrete slab may be used for the foundation.

A study of the plan (Fig. 21-7b) will show that the kitchen is located without outside walls. To make up for this,

Fig. 21-7a. Western house. (Wurster, Bernardi and Emmons, Architects, AIA, San Francisco, Calif.)

Fig. 21-7b. Plan for the house of Fig. 21-7a. (Wurster, Bernardi and Emmons, Architects, AIA, San Francisco, Calif.)

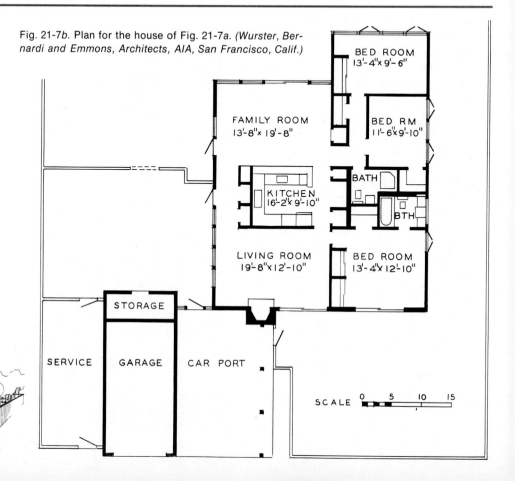

it has a monitor (Fig. 21-7c) to provide window space. The general construction can be understood from the sections (Fig. 21-7d).

21•8 The split-level house. The house in Figs. 21-8a and 21-8b is described as a *split-level* (there are three levels) home with simple lines. Overall dimensions are 44 ft by 32 ft. There is a family room and a garage on the exposed basement level. All three levels meet as they lead from a central entrance. The bedroom wing is slightly higher than the living area. Exterior plywood and battens every 16 in. give the house strong vertical lines. These vertical lines are relieved by horizontal grouping of dark panels, windows, and siding at the gable ends of the house.

Comparison of the traditional houses of Figs. 21-4a and 21-4b with the contemporary designs of Figs. 21-2a and 21-2b and Figs. 21-6a to 21-8a will reveal some of the developments in design which have taken place. Architects have made use of new types of materials, more efficient methods of construction, and modern conveniences now available. As a result, new architectural designs have been developed that have helped to provide the improved living conditions of the present day.

21•9 Parts of a house. The essential parts of a house are illustrated in Fig. 21-9a. All these parts do not appear in every house and different materials may be used for some of the parts.

Wood frame walls are first built up with studs or other structural members and with sheathing, boards or plywood, and sheathing paper. After the sheathing paper has been put on, wood or asbestos siding, shingles, stucco, or veneers of brick or stone are added. A typical wall with wood siding is shown in Fig. 21-9b and with brick veneer in Fig. 21-9c.

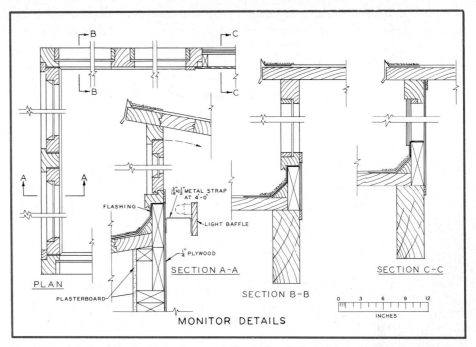

Fig. 21-7c. Monitor details of the house of Fig. 21-7a. *(Adapted from drawings of Wurster, Bernardi and Emmons, Architects)*

Fig. 21-7d. Sections for the house of Fig. 21-7a. *(Adapted from drawings of Wurster, Bernardi and Emmons, Architects)*

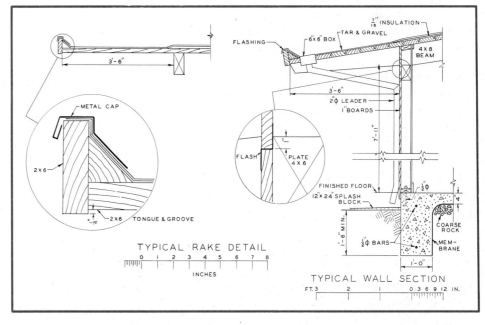

Interior walls may be finished with lath and plaster, gypsum wallboard, interior plywood, fiberboard, asbestos-cement board, wood paneling, wall tile, and so forth. The walls may be papered, painted, or finished in a variety of ways.

21•10 Classes of drawings. There are four general classes of architectural drawings: (1) preliminary sketches, (2) display and competitive drawings, (3) working drawings, and (4) special detail drawings.

21•11 Preliminary sketches. These include freehand studies of the arrangement of rooms, general appearance of elevations, and other matters for study and consideration. A number of small freehand plans (called *thumbnail sketches* because of their small size) are made at first. Although these are made somewhat in proportion, they are not drawn to scale. Schemes that show promise of a satisfactory solution are then worked up in larger sketches using an approximate scale for the larger dimensions. Tracing paper is often used to work out and preserve different arrangements by making one sketch over another. The best layout can then be selected, drawn to scale, and worked up in greater detail.

21•12 Display and competitive drawings. These are more or less elaborate preliminary drawings of a proposed

Fig. 21-8a. A split-level house. *(George Hay, Architect, Media, Pa.; photo courtesy Better Homes & Gardens magazine)*

Fig. 21-8b. Plan for the house of Fig. 21-8a. *(George Hay, Architect, Media, Pa.; photo courtesy Better Homes & Gardens magazine)*

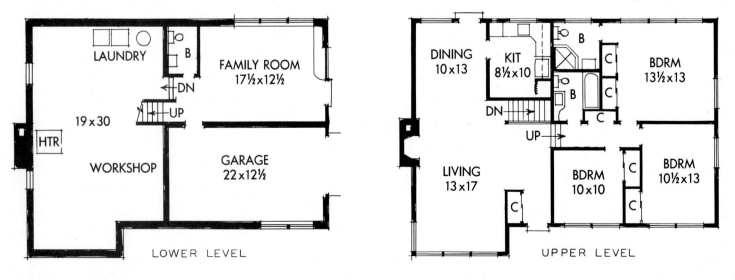

1. Gable end	21. Siding
2. Louver	22. Shutters
3. Interior trim	23. Exterior trim
4. Shingles	24. Waterproofing
5. Chimney cap	25. Foundation wall
6. Flue linings	26. Column
7. Flashing	27. Joists
8. Roofing felt	28. Basement floor
9. Roof sheathing	29. Gravel fill
10. Ridge board	30. Heating plant
11. Rafters	31. Footing
12. Roof valley	32. Drain tile
13. Dormer window	33. Girder
14. Interior wall	34. Stairway
finish	35. Subfloor
15. Studs	36. Hearth
16. Insulation	37. Building paper
17. Diagonal sheathing	38. Finish floor
18. Sheathing paper	39. Fireplace
19. Window frame	40. Downspout
and sash	41. Gutter
20. Corner board	42. Bridging.

Fig. 21-9a. Essential parts of a house. *(From National Bureau of Standards Circular 489)*

Fig. 21-9b. Wall with wood siding. *(From National Bureau of Standards Circular 489)*

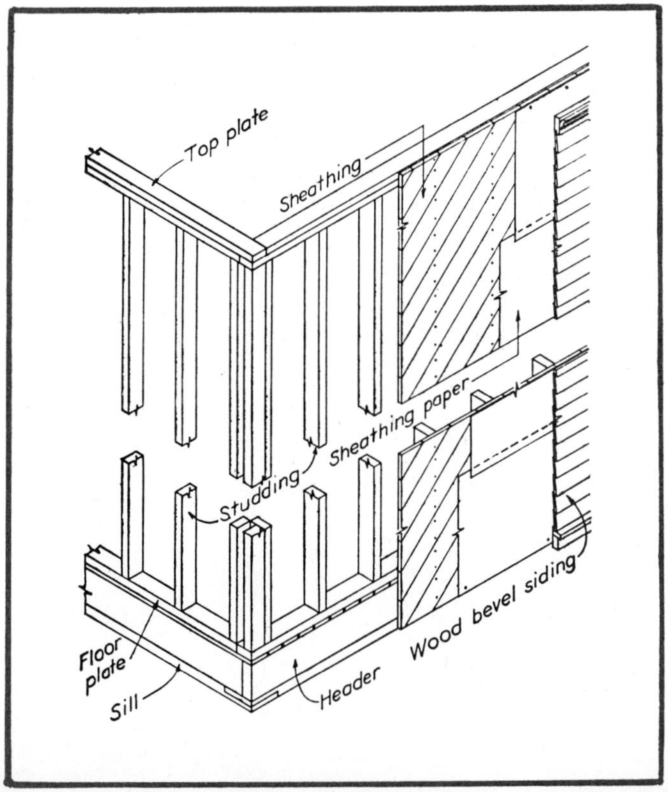

Fig. 21-9c. Wall with brick veneer. *(From National Bureau of Standards Circular 489)*

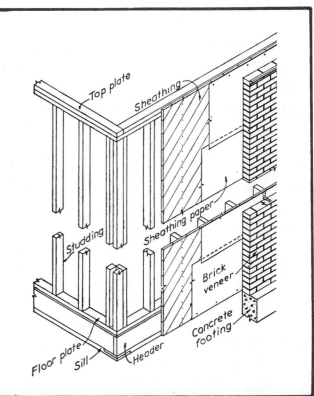

building. Plans and elevations, often including a perspective, are used but without working information. They are rendered in water color, airbrush, pen and ink, pencil, pastels, or crayon to make them legible and attractive. An airbrush-rendered perspective of a contemporary house is shown in Fig. 21-2a, and a pen-and-ink perspective is shown in Fig. 21-29.

21•13 Working drawings. These form the most important class of drawings and include plans, elevations, sections, and detail drawings which, when read with the specifications for details of materials, finish, and so forth, give the working information for the erection of the building. Working drawings for a house are in Figs. 21-29 to 21-35.

21•14 Scales. The architect's scale is described in Art. 2·25. Ordinary house plans and plans for small buildings are drawn to the scale of $\frac{1}{4}'' = 1'$. The usual scale for larger buildings is $\frac{1}{8}'' = 1'$. Plot plans (Art. 21·35) may be drawn at $\frac{1}{16}'' = 1'$ or $\frac{1}{32}'' = 1'$. Larger scales are used for drawings of parts that cannot be shown with sufficient detail on the small-scale drawings. Wall sections may be drawn at $1'' = 1'$ or $1\frac{1}{2}'' = 1'$. Other scales used for details include $\frac{1}{2}'' = 1'$, $\frac{3}{4}'' = 1'$, $3'' = 1'$, $6'' = 1'$, and full size.

Some variations in notation on architectural drawings are indicated in Fig. 21-14. Dimensions may be placed above the dimension line, as at A, or in a space, as at B. Dimension lines may use regular arrowheads to indicate the extent of a dimension, as at A; dots, as at B; or a cross line, as at C. Leaders may terminate as at E, F, or G. Certain other variations will be found on architectural drawings, as many architects have their characteristic practice.

21•15 Roofs. Some basic roof types are illustrated and named in Fig. 21-15. Each one has a use which may be influenced by the shape and interior arrangement, and method of supporting.

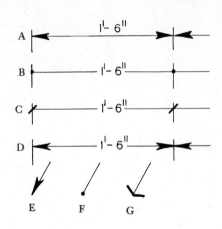

Fig. 21-14. Some variations used on architectural drawings.

21•16 House framing. The framework of a building must be strong and rigid to ensure low maintenance costs over a long period of years. For residences light frame construction is used. This varies somewhat with different builders and in different parts of the country.

Fig. 21-15. Some types of roofs.

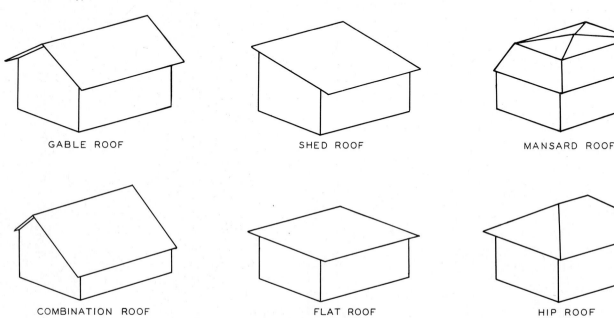

GABLE ROOF

SHED ROOF

MANSARD ROOF

COMBINATION ROOF

FLAT ROOF

HIP ROOF

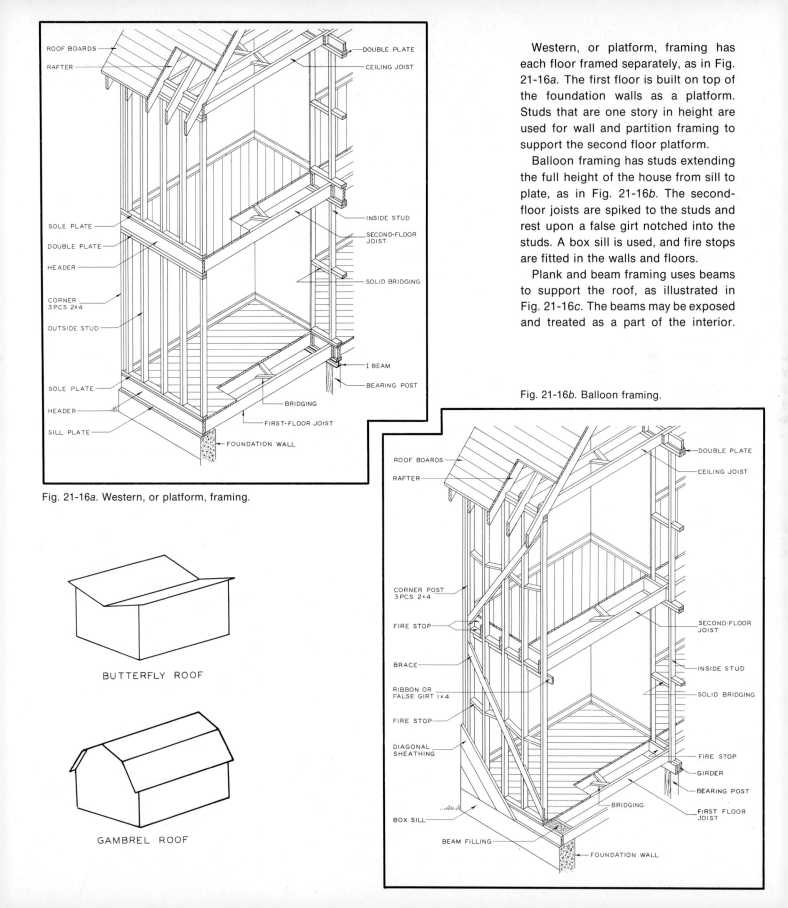

Fig. 21-16a. Western, or platform, framing.

Western, or platform, framing has each floor framed separately, as in Fig. 21-16a. The first floor is built on top of the foundation walls as a platform. Studs that are one story in height are used for wall and partition framing to support the second floor platform.

Balloon framing has studs extending the full height of the house from sill to plate, as in Fig. 21-16b. The second-floor joists are spiked to the studs and rest upon a false girt notched into the studs. A box sill is used, and fire stops are fitted in the walls and floors.

Plank and beam framing uses beams to support the roof, as illustrated in Fig. 21-16c. The beams may be exposed and treated as a part of the interior.

Fig. 21-16b. Balloon framing.

Labels in Fig. 21-16a:
ROOF BOARDS
RAFTER
DOUBLE PLATE
CEILING JOIST
SOLE PLATE
DOUBLE PLATE
HEADER
CORNER 3 PCS 2×4
OUTSIDE STUD
INSIDE STUD
SECOND-FLOOR JOIST
SOLID BRIDGING
SOLE PLATE
HEADER
SILL PLATE
FOUNDATION WALL
I BEAM
BEARING POST
BRIDGING
FIRST-FLOOR JOIST

BUTTERFLY ROOF

GAMBREL ROOF

Labels in Fig. 21-16b:
ROOF BOARDS
RAFTER
DOUBLE PLATE
CEILING JOIST
CORNER POST 3 PCS 2×4
FIRE STOP
BRACE
RIBBON OR FALSE GIRT 1×4
FIRE STOP
DIAGONAL SHEATHING
BOX SILL
BEAM FILLING
SECOND-FLOOR JOIST
INSIDE STUD
SOLID BRIDGING
FIRE STOP
GIRDER
BEARING POST
FIRST FLOOR JOIST
BRIDGING
FOUNDATION WALL

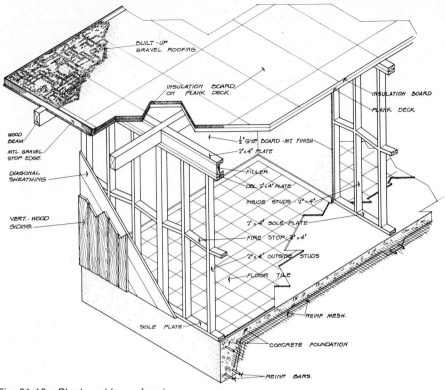

Built-up gravel roofing

Insulation board on plank deck.

Insulation board

Plank deck

Wood beam

Mtl. gravel stop edge.

Diagonal sheathing

Vert.-wood siding.

½" Gyp. board - int. finish

2" x 4" plate

Filler.

Dbl. 2" x 4" plate

Inside studs - 2" x 4"

2" x 4" sole plate

Fire stop - 2" x 4"

2" x 4" outside studs

Floor tile

Sole plate

Reinf. mesh.

Concrete foundation

Reinf. bars.

Fig. 21-16c. Plank and beam framing.

21·17 Sizes of lumber are specified by *nominal* dimensions, which differ from the actual dimensions of the *surfaced* (or smoothed) pieces as, for example, *S4S,* which means surfaced on four sides. Dimensions of some common sizes of lumber and boards are given in the table, Fig. 21-17.

21·18 Sill details. Types of sill and wall construction are shown in Figs. 21-18a to 21-18i. Note the metal shield for protection against termites in Figs. 21-18a, 21-18b, and 21-18h. "Crawl space" is provided under the floor in Figs. 21-18a and 21-18b. Construction for houses without basements often makes use of concrete slabs, as shown in Figs. 21-18c, 21-18d, and others. Regular construction where a basement is used is shown in Fig. 21-18h.

Fig. 21-17. Some sizes of lumber.

Lumber					
Nominal size	2×4	2×6	2×8	2×10	2×12
Dressed size	$1^5/_8 \times 3^5/_8$	$1^5/_8 \times 5^1/_2$	$1^5/_8 \times 7^1/_2$	$1^5/_8 \times 9^1/_2$	$1^5/_8 \times 11^1/_2$
Nominal size	4×6	4×8	4×10	6×6	6×8
Dressed size	$3^5/_8 \times 5^1/_2$	$3^5/_8 \times 7^1/_2$	$3^5/_8 \times 9^1/_2$	$5^1/_2 \times 5^1/_2$	$5^1/_2 \times 7^1/_2$
Nominal size	6×10	8×8	8×10		
Dressed size	$5^1/_2 \times 9^1/_2$	$7^1/_2 \times 7^1/_2$	$7^1/_2 \times 9^1/_2$		
Boards					
Nominal size	1×4	1×6	1×8	1×10	1×12
Actual size, common boards	$^{25}/_{32} \times 3^5/_8$	$^{25}/_{32} \times 5^5/_8$	$^{25}/_{32} \times 7^1/_2$	$^{25}/_{32} \times 9^1/_2$	$^{25}/_{32} \times 11^1/_2$
Actual size, shiplap	$^{25}/_{32} \times 3^1/_8$	$^{25}/_{32} \times 5^1/_8$	$^{25}/_{32} \times 7^1/_8$	$^{25}/_{32} \times 9^1/_8$	$^{25}/_{32} \times 11^1/_8$
Actual size, tongue and groove	$^{25}/_{32} \times 3^1/_4$	$^{25}/_{32} \times 5^1/_4$	$^{25}/_{32} \times 7^1/_4$	$^{25}/_{32} \times 9^1/_4$	$^{25}/_{32} \times 11^1/_4$

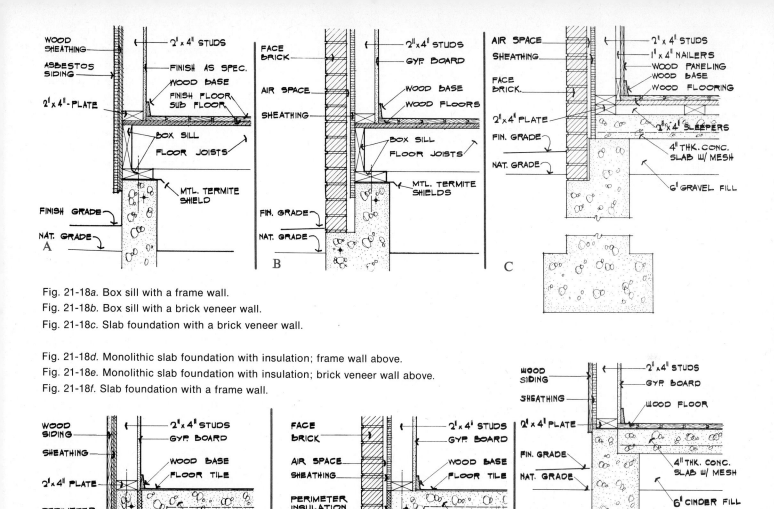

Fig. 21-18a. Box sill with a frame wall.

Fig. 21-18b. Box sill with a brick veneer wall.

Fig. 21-18c. Slab foundation with a brick veneer wall.

Fig. 21-18d. Monolithic slab foundation with insulation; frame wall above.

Fig. 21-18e. Monolithic slab foundation with insulation; brick veneer wall above.

Fig. 21-18f. Slab foundation with a frame wall.

Fig. 21-18g. Slab foundation with insulation; frame wall above.

Fig. 21-18h. Box sill for basement construction.

Fig. 21-18i. Slab foundation with a masonry wall.

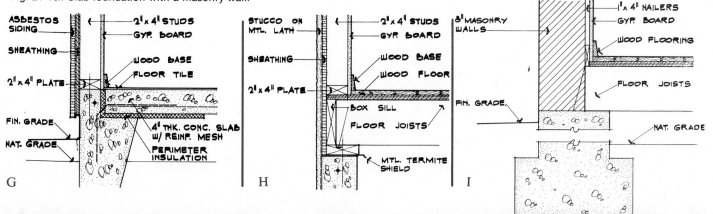

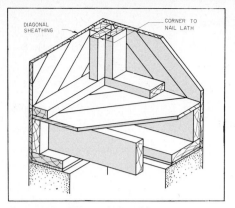
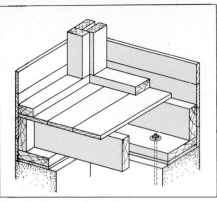

Fig. 21-19a. Diagonal sheathing.

Fig. 21-19b. Horizontal sheathing.

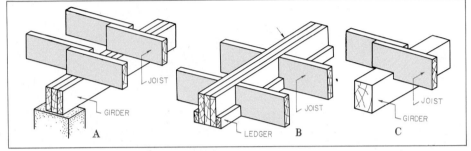

Fig. 21-19c. Girder to support floor joists.

Fig. 21-20a. Roof framing.

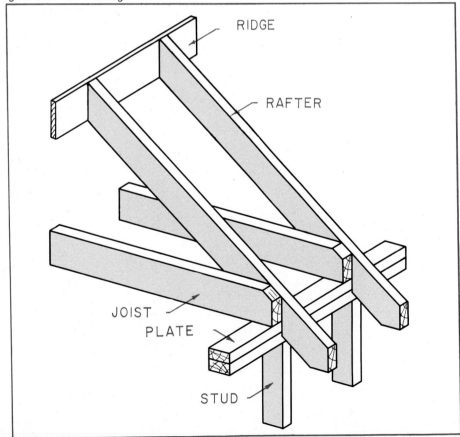

21•19 Corner studs and sheathing.
The arrangement of corner studs shown in Fig. 21-19a is simple and satisfactory. Another arrangement, shown in Fig. 21-19b, requires greater care in making it up. Diagonal sheathing and subflooring are shown in Fig. 21-19a, and horizontal sheathing and subflooring in Fig. 21-19b. Plywood has come into general use for sheathing and subflooring. Anchor bolts, Fig. 21-19b, are used to anchor the building to the foundation. The diameter of these bolts should be from $5/8$ to $3/4$ in. They should be spaced about 8 ft apart and should extend through the sill and about 18 in. into the foundation.

Three constructions for girders supporting the inside ends of floor joists are shown at A, B, and C in Fig. 21-19c.

21•20 Roof framing and cornice details.
The usual roof-framing members are shown and named in Fig. 21-20a. The joints between the walls and the roofs of the houses are finished by cornices. Box cornices, which conceal the rafters, are shown in Figs. 21-20b and 21-20c. An open cornice, which exposes the rafters, is shown in Fig. 21-20d. Closed-in overhanging rafters are shown in Fig. 21-20e with a built-up gravel roof. The note COND @ BRICK indicates the condition if brick were used in place of the wood siding. Plank-and-beam construction is shown in Fig. 21-20f, with exposed beams outside and inside. Note the end view of the beam and that the laminated (built-up) beam uses sectional indication for the number of laminations. The built-in, metal-lined gutter shown in Fig. 21-20g is a somewhat formal style of cornice.

21•21 Stairways.
In drawing an inside stairway (Fig. 21-21), first make a diagram to find the number of steps and the space required. The riser, or height from one step to the next, is generally about $6\frac{1}{2}$ to $7\frac{1}{2}$ in. The width of the

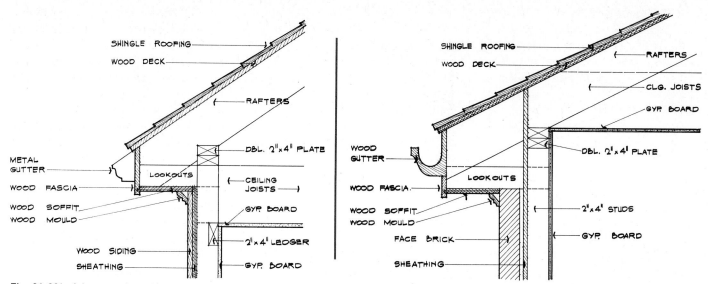

Fig. 21-20b. A box cornice with a metal gutter.

Fig. 21-20c. A box cornice with a wood gutter.

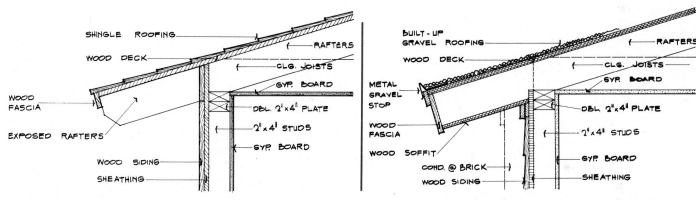

Fig. 21-20d. An open cornice with exposed rafters.

Fig. 21-20e. Boxed rafters with a sloped soffit.

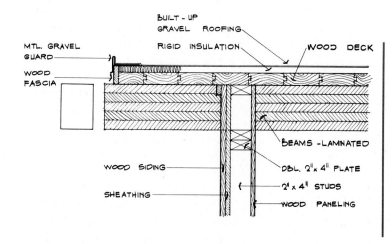

Fig. 21-20f. Exposed-beam and deck construction.

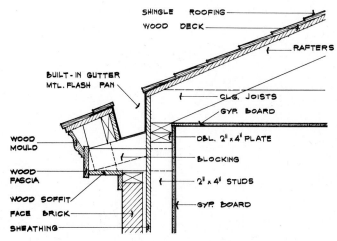

Fig. 21-20g. A cornice with a built-in metal-lined gutter.

tread is such that the sum of riser and tread is about 17½ in. (a 7-in. riser and 11-in. tread is a general standard). On the plan the lines represent the edges of the risers and are drawn as far apart as the width of the tread, as shown in the illustration. Note the use of the scale to divide the floor-to-floor height into the number of risers. On working drawings, the entire flight is not drawn but is broken to show what is on the floor under it. The other end of the flight is shown on the floor above (Fig. 21-21). All risers must be of equal height, as any variation may cause a misstep and accident. Natural light should be used to illuminate stairs rather than enclose them in walls that restrict light.

For outside stairs or steps, as in a garden, and so forth, the risers are made lower and the treads are made wider. A person's gait and stride increase and lengthen unconsciously when he is outdoors.

The plan at A is for a straight-run, or single-run, stairway. Plans for other than straight-run stairways are shown at B, C, and D.

Fig. 21-21. Some stair details and layouts.

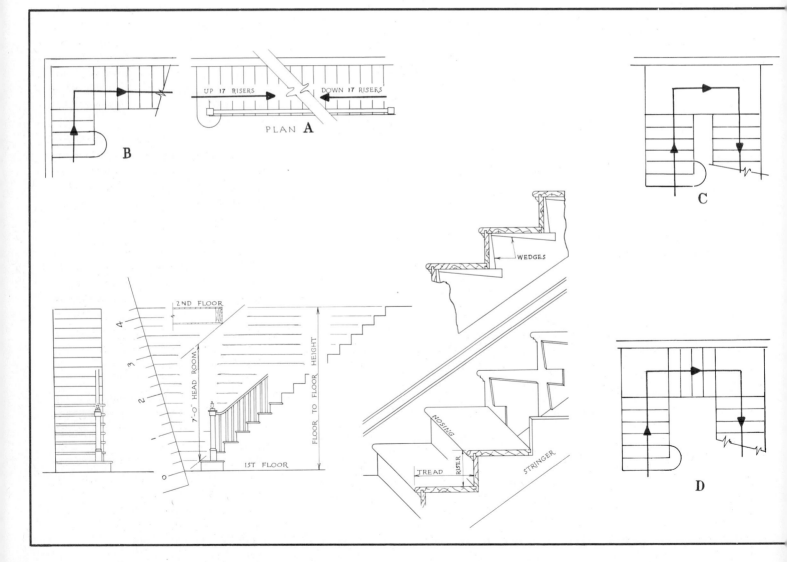

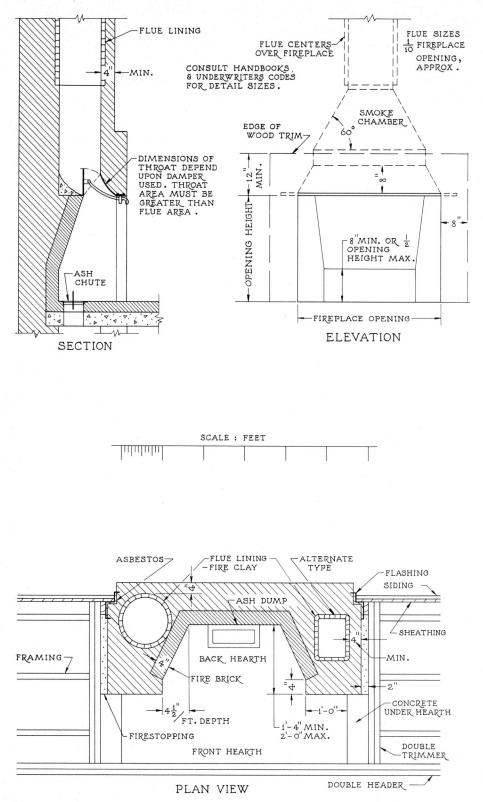

21·22 Fireplaces form an important center of interest in contemporary residences. The placing of the fireplace and the design of the mantle are important factors of decor. Proper design is necessary to avoid smoky or other unsatisfactory operation. The names of some parts and suggested construction of a fireplace are shown in Fig. 21-22.

21·23 Windows. Different types of windows are being used in contemporary house designs, and some are indicated in Fig. 21-23a. Casement windows are hinged at the sides to swing open. Projected windows are hinged at the top or bottom. Slider windows move sidewise instead of up and down, as ordinary double-hung windows do. Fixed and picture windows are coming into greater use with the increased use of air conditioning.

Sizes of windows depend upon the sizes of the glass panes and the number of panes. Lists giving the sizes of sash can be obtained from window companies or suppliers of building materials. A drawing of a wood sash with the names of the parts is shown in Fig. 21-23b. The thickness of the sash is $1\frac{3}{8}$ in., and large ones may be up to $2\frac{1}{4}$ in. thick. Sections of an ordinary double-hung window in a wood-frame wall are shown in Fig. 21-23b. Detail sections for a double-hung window in a brick veneer wall are shown in Fig. 21-23c and in a masonry wall in Fig. 21-23d.

Steel and aluminum window frames and sash are being widely used instead of wood. Photographs of aluminum windows are shown in Fig. 21-23e. Detail sections of an aluminum window in a brick veneer wall are shown in Fig. 21-23f and in a masonry wall in Fig. 21-23g. Some casement window details for brick masonry walls are shown in Fig. 21-23h.

Fig. 21-22. Fireplace details

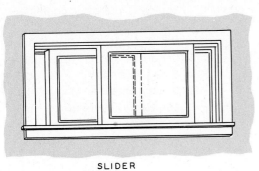

SLIDER PROJECTED CASEMENT

Fig. 21-23a. Types of windows.

Fig. 21-23b. Window sash and sections of frame.

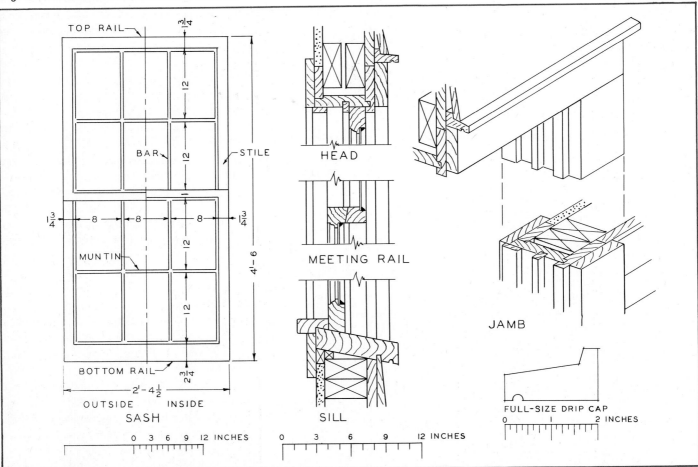

TOP RAIL

$\frac{3}{4}$

12

BAR

12

STILE

$1\frac{3}{4}$ 8 8 8 $1\frac{3}{4}$

12

MUNTIN

12

4'- 6

BOTTOM RAIL

$2\frac{3}{4}$

2'- 4$\frac{1}{2}$

OUTSIDE INSIDE

SASH

HEAD

MEETING RAIL

SILL

JAMB

FULL-SIZE DRIP CAP

0   1   2 INCHES

0 3 6 9 12 INCHES

0 3 6 9 12 INCHES

Fig. 21-23c. Detail sections of a double-hung window in a brick veneer wall.

Fig. 21-23d. Detail sections of a double-hung window in a masonry wall.

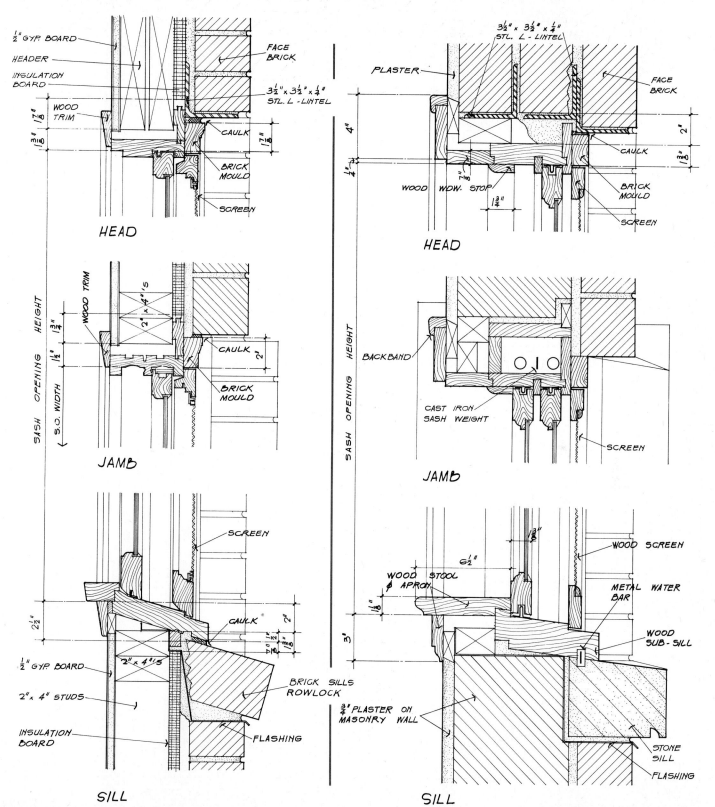

Fig. 21-23c (left column):

HEAD
- ½" GYP. BOARD
- HEADER
- INSULATION BOARD
- WOOD TRIM
- ⅛" / 1⅞"
- ⅜" / 1⅛"
- FACE BRICK
- 3½" x 3½" x ¼" STL. L - LINTEL
- CAULK
- 1⅞"
- BRICK MOULD
- SCREEN

JAMB
- WOOD TRIM
- 2" x 4"'S
- SASH OPENING HEIGHT
- 1⅜"
- 1½"
- S.O. WIDTH
- CAULK
- 2"
- BRICK MOULD

SILL
- 2½"
- ½" GYP. BOARD
- 2" x 4"'S
- 2" x 4" STUDS
- INSULATION BOARD
- SCREEN
- CAULK
- 2"
- 1⅛" / 1⅜"
- BRICK SILLS ROWLOCK
- FLASHING

Fig. 21-23d (right column):

HEAD
- 3½" x 3½" x ¼" STL. L-LINTEL
- PLASTER
- 4"
- ¼"
- WOOD WDW. STOP
- 7/16"
- 1¾"
- FACE BRICK
- CAULK
- 1⅜" / 2"
- BRICK MOULD
- SCREEN

JAMB
- SASH OPENING HEIGHT
- BACKBAND
- CAST IRON SASH WEIGHT
- SCREEN

SILL
- 3"
- 1⅛"
- WOOD STOOL & APRON
- 6½"
- 3/16"
- WOOD SCREEN
- METAL WATER BAR
- WOOD SUB-SILL
- ¾" PLASTER ON MASONRY WALL
- STONE SILL
- FLASHING

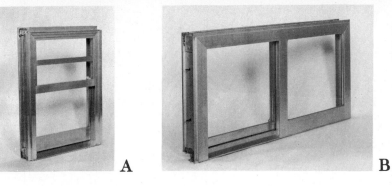

A **B**

Fig. 21-23e. Aluminum double-hung window at A and a sliding window at B. *(American Window & Door Company, Inc.)*

Fig. 21-23f. Details of a double-hung aluminum window in a brick wall.

Fig. 21-23g. Details of a sliding aluminum window in a masonry wall.

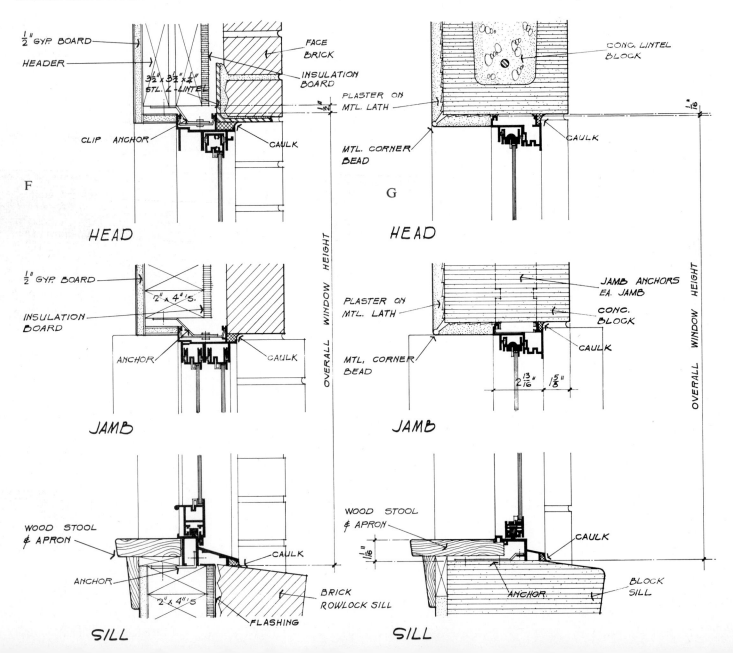

Fig. 21-23h. Casement window details.

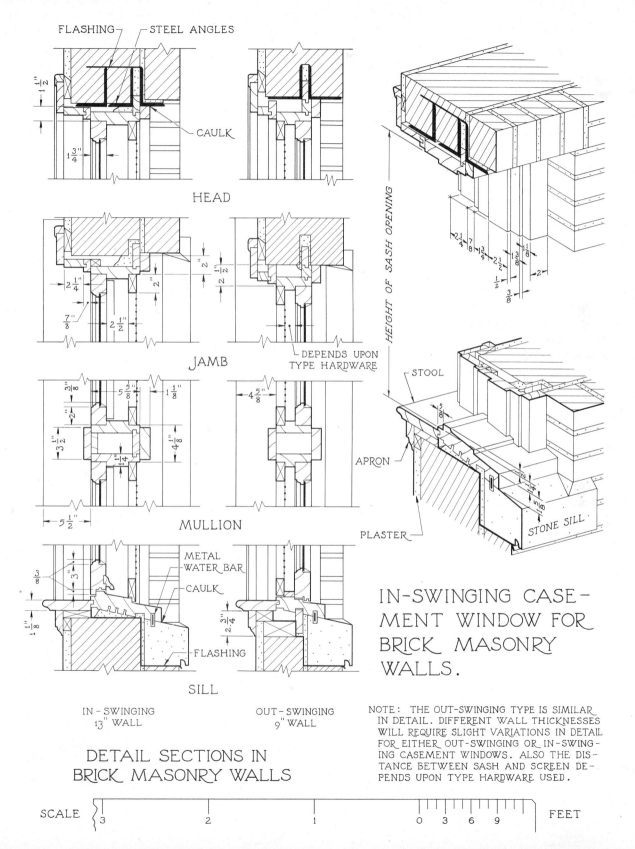

FLASHING — STEEL ANGLES

$1\frac{1}{2}$"

CAULK

$1\frac{3}{4}$"

HEAD

$2\frac{1}{4}$"

$\frac{7}{8}$"

$2\frac{1}{2}$"

2"

$2\frac{1}{2}$"

2"

2"

JAMB

DEPENDS UPON
TYPE HARDWARE

$\frac{3}{8}$"

2"

$3\frac{1}{2}$"

$5\frac{5}{8}$"

$1\frac{1}{8}$"

$1\frac{1}{4}$"

$4\frac{1}{8}$"

$5\frac{1}{2}$"

$4\frac{5}{8}$"

MULLION

METAL
WATER BAR

CAULK

$\frac{3}{8}$"

3"

$1\frac{1}{8}$"

$2\frac{3}{4}$"

FLASHING

SILL

IN-SWINGING
13" WALL

OUT-SWINGING
9" WALL

DETAIL SECTIONS IN
BRICK MASONRY WALLS

HEIGHT OF SASH OPENING

$2\frac{1}{4}$ $\frac{7}{8}$ $\frac{3}{4}$ $2\frac{1}{2}$ $\frac{3}{8}$ $\frac{1}{8}$

$\frac{1}{2}$ $\frac{3}{8}$ 2

STOOL

$\frac{5}{8}$

APRON

$1\frac{1}{4}$

$\frac{5}{8}$

PLASTER

STONE SILL

IN-SWINGING CASE-
MENT WINDOW FOR
BRICK MASONRY
WALLS.

NOTE: THE OUT-SWINGING TYPE IS SIMILAR
IN DETAIL. DIFFERENT WALL THICKNESSES
WILL REQUIRE SLIGHT VARIATIONS IN DETAIL
FOR EITHER OUT-SWINGING OR IN-SWING-
ING CASEMENT WINDOWS. ALSO THE DIS-
TANCE BETWEEN SASH AND SCREEN DE-
PENDS UPON TYPE HARDWARE USED.

SCALE 3   2   1   0 3 6 9   FEET

21•24 Doors. Usual heights of doors are 6 ft 8 in. and 7 ft 0 in. Width may vary for some purposes from 2 ft 0 in. to 3 ft. 0 in., but the usual widths are 2 ft 8 in. and 3 ft 0 in. Thicknesses may be 1⅜ in. or 1¾ in. for interior doors and from 1¾ in. to 2½ in. for exterior doors. Exterior doors are usually made larger to allow access for furniture and traffic.

Doors are made of wood, either solid or built up and veneered. They are also made of metal over wood cores or of hollow metal. An interior door with the names of parts is shown at A in Fig. 21-24a and for an exterior door at B. Other interior doors are shown at C and D. Doors may be flush or have one or more panels. Door framing details for a door in a wood wall are shown in Fig. 21-24b. Details for an entrance are

Fig. 21-24a. A few door patterns.

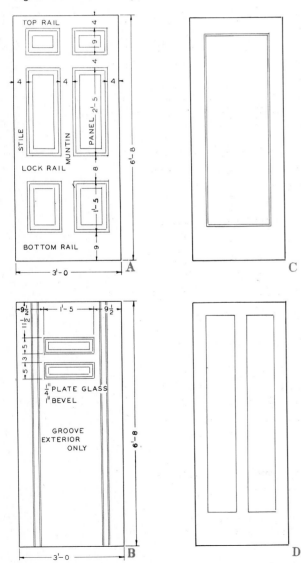

Fig. 21-24b. Door framing details.

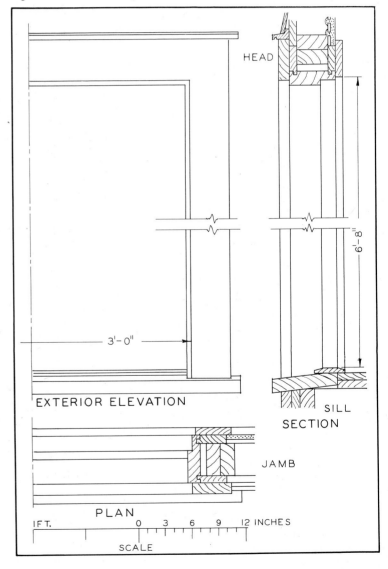

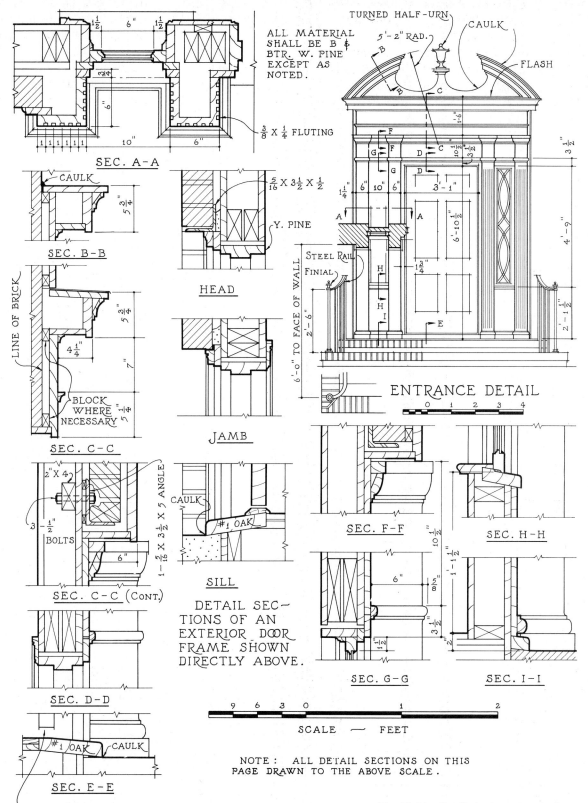

ALL MATERIAL
SHALL BE B &
BTR. W. PINE
EXCEPT AS
NOTED.

$\frac{3}{8}$ X $\frac{1}{4}$ FLUTING

SEC. A-A

CAULK

SEC. B-B

LINE OF BRICK

BLOCK
WHERE
NECESSARY

SEC. C-C

2" X 4

3 - $\frac{1}{2}$"
BOLTS

SEC. C-C (CONT.)

SEC. D-D

#1 OAK   CAULK

SEC. E-E

BRASS THRESHOLD

$\frac{5}{16}$ X 3$\frac{1}{2}$ X $\frac{1}{2}$

Y. PINE

HEAD

JAMB

CAULK

1 - $\frac{5}{16}$ X 3$\frac{1}{2}$ X 5 ANGLE

#1 OAK

SILL

DETAIL SEC-
TIONS OF AN
EXTERIOR DOOR
FRAME SHOWN
DIRECTLY ABOVE.

TURNED HALF-URN   CAULK

5'- 2" RAD.

FLASH

STEEL RAIL
FINIAL

6'-0" TO FACE OF WALL

2'- 6"

ENTRANCE DETAIL

0   1   2   3   4

SEC. F-F

SEC. H-H

SEC. G-G

SEC. I-I

9 6 3 0   1   2

SCALE ⁓ FEET

NOTE: ALL DETAIL SECTIONS ON THIS
PAGE DRAWN TO THE ABOVE SCALE.

Fig. 21-24c. Details for an entrance door.

21·25 Symbols. The small scale (1/8″ = 1′–0″ or 1/4″ = 1′–0″) used on general plans makes it necessary to use symbols, since it would not be possible to show actual details. Such details, where required, are drawn to a larger scale. Details in some cases (such as shown in Fig. 21-24c. Metal framing for doors is preferred to wood because metal is more durable and provides much more structural stability. Aluminum framing for a door in a residence is shown in Fig. 21-24d and for a public building in Fig. 21-24e. those showing sections of trim and moldings) may be full size.

Templates are available for drawing many of the symbols used on architectural drawings and are in regular use in architects' offices to save time drawing symbols.

Fig. 21-24d. Metal frame for a metal door.

Fig. 21-24e. Metal door frame in a public building.

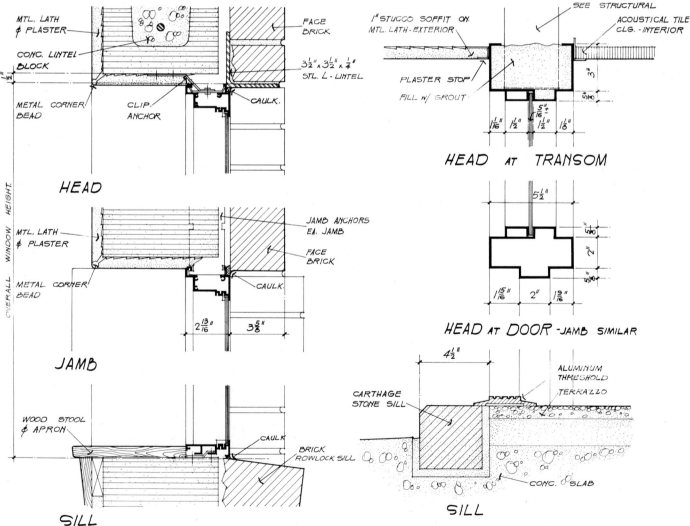

21·26 Wall architectural symbols consist of parallel lines drawn to represent the thickness (Fig. 21-26a). Some symbols for doors are shown in Fig. 21-26b; single lines show the direction of opening or swing. Various windows are represented by the symbols in Fig. 21-26c. Symbols for building materials are shown in Fig. 21-26d.

21·27 Electrical symbols to represent wiring, outlets, switches, and so forth, are shown by the American Standards symbols of Fig. 21-27. These are used on house plans to show the locations of the outlets, fixtures, switches, etc., and the circuit makeup.

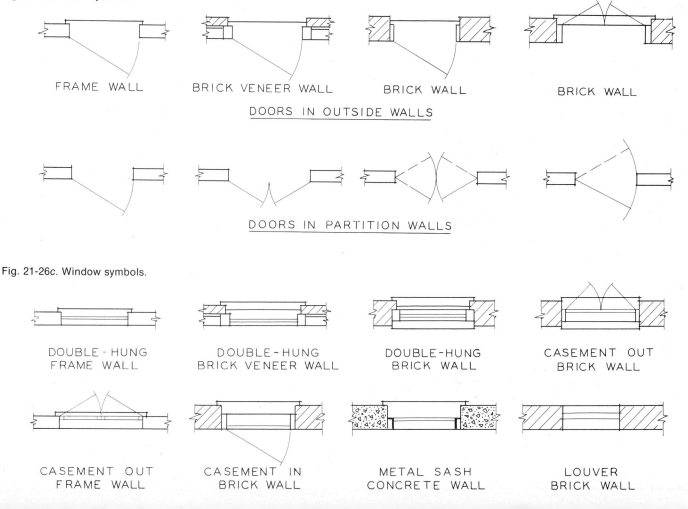

Fig. 21-26a. Wall symbols.

Fig. 21-26b. Door symbols.

Fig. 21-26c. Window symbols.

Fig. 21-26d. Symbols for building materials.

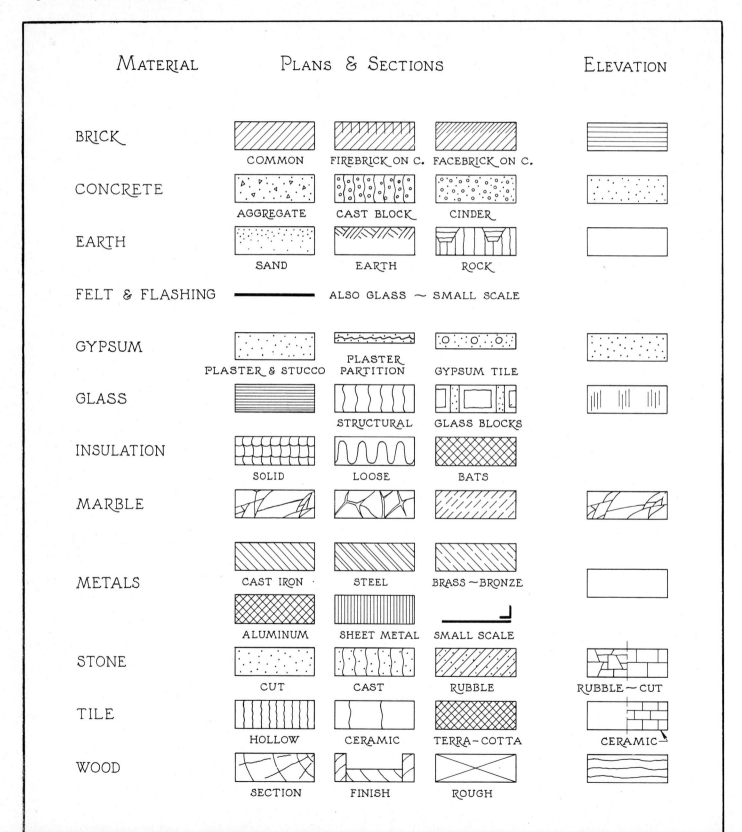

MATERIAL	PLANS & SECTIONS			ELEVATION
BRICK	COMMON	FIREBRICK ON C.	FACEBRICK ON C.	
CONCRETE	AGGREGATE	CAST BLOCK	CINDER	
EARTH	SAND	EARTH	ROCK	
FELT & FLASHING	ALSO GLASS ~ SMALL SCALE			
GYPSUM	PLASTER & STUCCO	PLASTER PARTITION	GYPSUM TILE	
GLASS		STRUCTURAL	GLASS BLOCKS	
INSULATION	SOLID	LOOSE	BATS	
MARBLE				
METALS	CAST IRON	STEEL	BRASS ~ BRONZE	
	ALUMINUM	SHEET METAL	SMALL SCALE	
STONE	CUT	CAST	RUBBLE	RUBBLE ~ CUT
TILE	HOLLOW	CERAMIC	TERRA-COTTA	CERAMIC
WOOD	SECTION	FINISH	ROUGH	

Fig. 21-27. Electrical symbols.

GENERAL OUTLETS

Ceiling	Wall	
○	─○	Outlet
Ⓑ	─Ⓑ	Blanked Outlet
Ⓓ		Drop Cord
Ⓔ	─Ⓔ	Electric Outlet

For use only when circle used alone might be confused with columns, plumbing symbols, etc.

Ⓕ	─Ⓕ	Fan Outlet
Ⓙ	─Ⓙ	Junction Box
Ⓛ	─Ⓛ	Lamp Holder
ⓁPS	─ⓁPS	Lamp Holder with Pull Switch
Ⓢ	─Ⓢ	Pull Switch
Ⓥ	─Ⓥ	Outlet for Vapor Discharge Lamp
Ⓧ	─Ⓧ	Exit-light Outlet
Ⓒ	─Ⓒ	Clock Outlet (Specify Voltage)

CONVENIENCE OUTLETS

Duplex Convenience Outlet

Convenience Outlet other than Duplex
1=Single, 3=Triplex, etc.

WP — Weatherproof Convenience Outlet

R — Range Outlet

S — Switch and Convenience Outlet

R — Radio and Convenience Outlet

▲ — Special Purpose Outlet (Des. in Spec.)

⊙ — Floor Outlet

SWITCH OUTLETS

S	Single-pole Switch
S_2	Double-pole Switch
S_3	Three-way Switch
S_4	Four-way Switch
S_D	Automatic Door Switch
S_E	Electrolier Switch
S_K	Key-operated Switch
S_P	Switch and Pilot Lamp
S_{CB}	Circuit Breaker
S_{WCB}	Weatherproof Circuit Breaker
S_{MC}	Momentary Contact Switch
S_{RC}	Remote-control Switch
S_{WP}	Weatherproof Switch
S_F	Fused Switch
S_{WF}	Weatherproof Fused Switch

SPECIAL OUTLETS

⊖ a,b,c,etc.   S a,b,c,etc.

Any standard symbol as given above with the addition of a lower-case subscript letter may be used to designate some special variation of standard equipment of particular interest in a specific set of architectural plans.

When used they must be listed in the Key of Symbols on each drawing and if necessary further described in the specifications.

AUXILIARY SYSTEMS

▣	Pushbutton
□	Buzzer
□	Bell
◇	Annunciator
◄	Outside Telephone
◁	Interconnecting Telephone
▷	Telephone Switchboard
Ⓣ	Bell-ringing Transformer
Ⓓ	Electric Door Opener
F	Fire-alarm Bell
F	Fire-alarm Station
✕	City Fire-alarm Station
FA	Fire-Alarm Central Station
FS	Automatic Fire-alarm Device
W	Watchman's Station
W	Watchman's Central Station
H	Horn
N	Nurse's Signal Plug
M	Maid's Signal Plug
R	Radio Outlet
SC	Signal Central Station
□	Interconnection Box
⊪⊪⊪	Battery
—·—·—	Auxiliary System Circuits

Note: Any line without further designation indicates a 2-wire system. For a greater number of wires designate with numerals in manner similar to —·— 12-No. 18W-3/4"C., or designate by number corresponding to listing in Schedule.

□ a,b,c   Special Auxiliary Outlets

Subscript letters refer to notes on plans or detailed description in specifications.

S	Single-pole switch
S_P	Single-pole switch and pilot light
S_3	Three-way switch
S_D	Door-operated switch
⊖	Duplex convenience outlet
⊖	Duplex convenience outlet for 2 circuit installation
R	Electric-range outlet
WP	Weatherproof
M	Vent-hood fan motor
TV△	Television-antenna outlet

▬	Lighting panel
▲	Telephone outlet
J▲	Telephone jack
▣	Push button
◁	Door bell
◯	Ceiling or pendent mounted incandescent-lighting fixture
◯─	Wall mounted incandescent-lighting fixture
├──┤	Surface mounted flourescent-lighting fixture
▣	Recessed incandescent-lighting fixture
▭○▭	Recessed flourescent-lighting fixture
────	Conduit run in ceiling and walls
- - - -	Conduit run under floors and in walls

5,6 ┤┤┤→ {
Arrow indicates home run to lighting panel
Hash lines indicate number of wires
Numerals indicate circuit numbers
}

A — Letters indicate type of lighting fixture

(See lighting-fixture schedule)

PANELS, CIRCUITS, AND MISCELLANEOUS

▬	Lighting Panel
▨	Power Panel
─────	Branch Circuit; Concealed in Ceiling or Wall
─·─·─	Branch Circuit; Concealed in Floor
─ ─ ─	Branch Circuit; Exposed
→→	Home Run to Panel Board. Indicate number of circuits by number of arrows.

Note: Any circuit without further designation indicates a two-wire circuit. For a greater number of wires indicate as follows: ─╫╫─ (3 wires) ─╫╫─ (4 wires), etc.

▬▬▬	Feeders. Note: Use heavy lines and designate by number corresponding to listing in Feeder Schedule.
≡□≡	Underfloor Duct and Junction Box— Triple System

Note: For a double or single systems eliminate one or two lines. This symbol is equally adaptable to auxiliary system layouts.

Ⓖ	Generator
Ⓜ	Motor
Ⓘ	Instrument
Ⓣ	Power Transformer (Or draw to scale.)
⊠	Controller
□	Isolating Switch

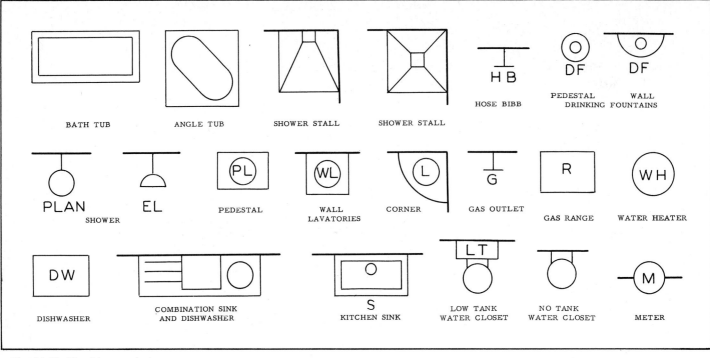

Fig. 21-28. Plumbing symbols.

21·28 Plumbing symbols from American Standards are shown in Fig. 21-28. There are many more, and the latest standard should be consulted for the complete set of these symbols.

21·29 Plans. A plan is a drawing of a horizontal section taken above the floor represented and at such places as will show the walls, doors, windows, and other structural features. It is drawn to include all details relating to the story, such as built-in construction, cabinets, stairways, heating, plumbing, and lighting outlets in walls and ceiling. Ordinary house plans are drawn to the scale of $1/4'' = 1'$.

A set of working drawings for a house is generally called a *set of plans* and includes a basement plan, plot plan, wall section, floor plan, elevations, de-

tails, and so forth. Such a set of plans for the house illustrated in Fig. 21-29 is shown in Arts. 21·30 to 21·35.

21·30 Floor plan. The sketch plan of a house is shown in Fig. 21-30a. The floor plan developed from this sketch is shown in Fig. 21-30b. The following procedure is used: Draw a horizontal line representing the outside face of the front of the house; then draw the interior walls and the interior partitions. Frame walls are drawn 6 in. thick. Locate the doors and windows and draw them with conventional symbols. For sizes of doors and windows refer to the schedules of Fig. 21-35a.

The stairway shown can be laid out as described for Fig. 21-21.

Only one floor plan is required for the house shown. When a second floor

is to be drawn for a two-story house, it is best planned by laying a piece of tracing paper over the first-floor plan. The exterior walls are then traced and the stairway is located. The interior partitions need not be continuous with the first floor. Closets should be provided in the bedrooms and in other rooms of the house as required and as space permits.

21·31 Foundation plan. The foundation layout, or basement plan (Fig. 21-31), must be completely dimensioned because the construction of the house is begun with this plan. It should be checked with the first-floor plan and may be traced from it. Note the foundations for the porch and garage. Windows should be under the first-floor windows.

Fig. 21-29. Pen-and-ink perspective of a house.

Fig. 21-30a. Sketch plan for the house of Fig. 21-29.

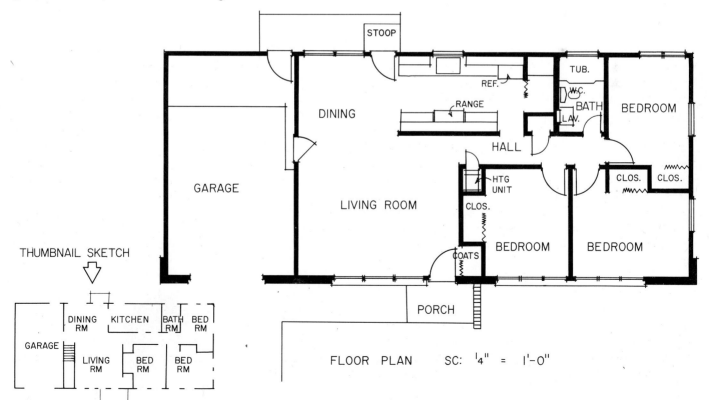

THUMBNAIL SKETCH

DINING RM   KITCHEN   BATH RM   BED RM

GARAGE

LIVING RM   BED RM   BED RM

STOOP

REF.

RANGE

TUB.

W.C.

BATH   BEDROOM

LAV.

HALL

DINING

CLOS.   CLOS.

GARAGE

LIVING ROOM

HTG UNIT

CLOS.

BEDROOM   BEDROOM

COATS

PORCH

FLOOR PLAN   SC: $\frac{1}{4}$" = 1'-0"

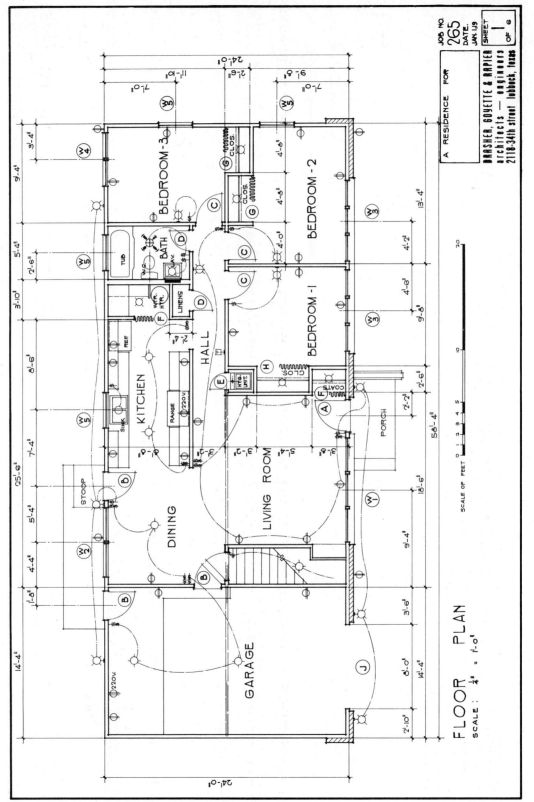

Fig. 21-30b. Floor plan for house of Fig. 21-29.

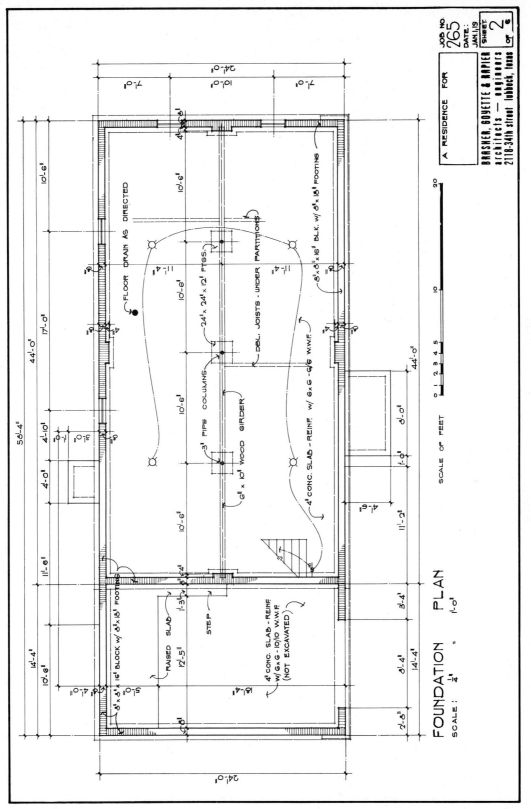

FOUNDATION PLAN

SCALE: 1/4" = 1'-0"

Fig. 21-31. Foundation plan.

21•32 Elevations. A front elevation and a side elevation are shown in Fig. 21-32. Four elevations (front, back, and both sides) are included in a complete set of plans and are required for Federal Housing Administration (FHA) loans. The elevations show the exterior appearance of the house, floor and ceiling heights, openings for windows and doors, roof pitch, and so forth. To draw an elevation, start with the grade line; then, locate the floor levels and the vertical dimensions of other features. Horizontal dimensions can be obtained by projecting a plan view above the elevation drawing, or underneath if tracing paper is used.

21•33 Wall section, door, and window details. A wall section to a larger scale is shown at the left in Fig. 21-33. Other larger-scale drawings are made of the parts that cannot be shown with sufficient detail on the 1/4-in.-scale drawing. Typical door and window details are shown in Fig. 21-33. As the building progresses, the architect furnishes full-size drawings, made with a soft pencil, for millwork, moldings, and any special details.

21•34 Electrical wiring circuits are shown in Fig. 21-34. It shows the location of electric outlets and switches and the location of lights, base plugs, and power outlets for range, dishwasher, washing machine, clothes dryer, etc. A list of symbols is shown to identify the ones shown on the layout. The separate circuits, the 110-volt and the 220-volt lines, are shown. Other needed information is given in specifications.

Fig. 21-32. Elevations.

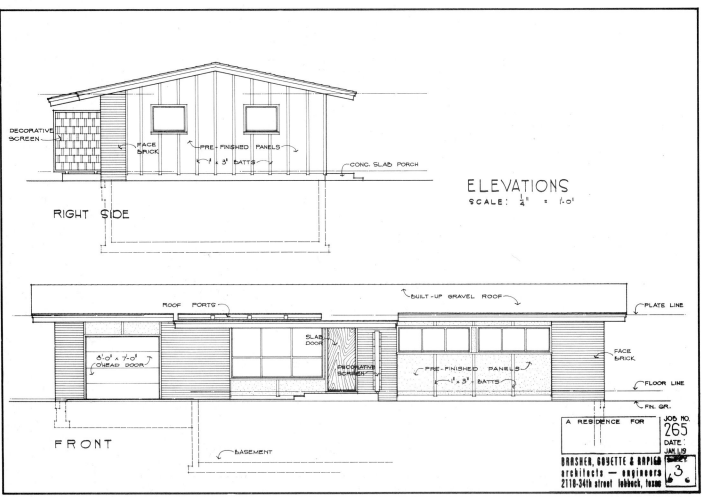

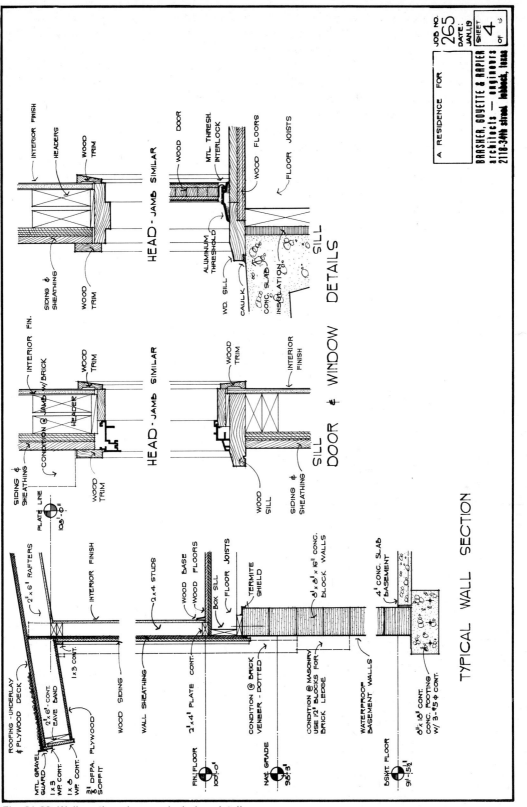

Fig. 21-33. Wall section, door, and window details.

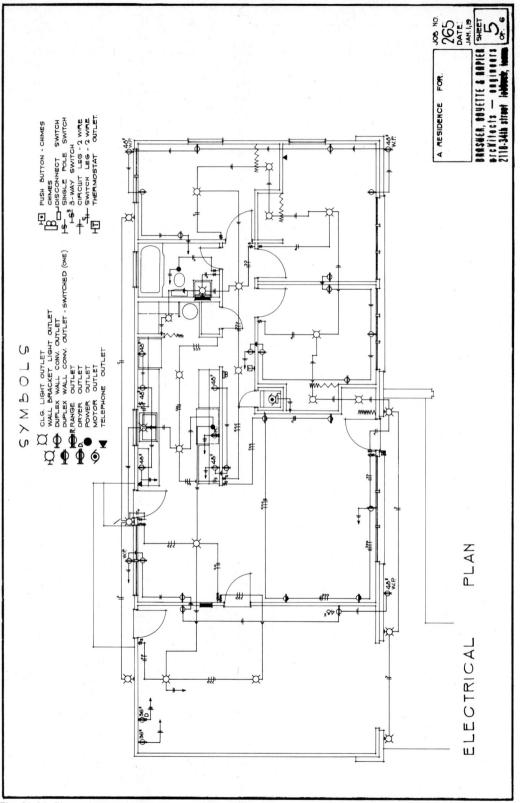

Fig. 21-34. Electrical wiring circuits.

SCHEDULES

WINDOWS					DOORS			
MARK	**SIZE**	**TYPE**	**REMARKS**	**MARK**	**SIZE**		**TYPE**	**REMARKS**
W1	3 - 3'-4" x 5'-2" x 1 3/8"	S.H. ALUM.		A	3'-0" x 6'-8" x 1 3/4"		SLAB - GUM.	W.S.
W2	2 - 3'-4" x 5'-2" x "	S.H. ALUM.		B	2'-8" x 6'-8" x "		SLAB - GUM.	W.S.
W3	3 - 2'-6" x 2'-6" x "	SLIDE - ALUM.		C	2'-8" x 6'-8" x 1 3/8"		SLAB - GUM.	
W4	2 - 2'-6" x 2'-6" x "	SLIDE - ALUM.		D	2'-0" x 6'-8" x "		SLAB - GUM.	
W5	3'-4" x 2'-6" x "	SLIDE - ALUM.		E	1'-8" x 6'-8" x "		SLAB - GUM.	
				F	3'-4" x 6'-8" x "		MODERNFOLD	
				G	4'-4" x 6'-8" x "		MODERNFOLD	
				H	5'-0" x 6'-8" x "		MODERNFOLD	
				J	8'-0" x 6'-8" x "		O'HEAD - TYPE	

Room Finish Schedule

SPACE	FLOORS			WALLS			CEILINGS	WAINSCOT	BASE		REMARKS
	VINYL TILE	CARPET	EXPOSED CONC.	GYP. BRD.-TEXTONE	CER. TILE	ASB. BRD.	GYP. BRD. TEXTONE	CERAMIC TILE 4'-8"	WOOD	CER. TILE COVE	
LIVING ROOM		●		●			●		●		
DINING	●			●			●		●		
KITCHEN	●			●			●		●		
HALL		●		●			●		●		
BATH		●			●		●	●	●		
BED ROOM 1		●		●			●		●		
BED ROOM 2		●		●			●		●		
BED ROOM 3		●		●			●		●		
PANTRY	●			●			●		●		
LINENS & CLOSETS		●		●			●		●		
HTG. UNIT CLOS.	●					●	●		●		
GARAGE			●	●			●				

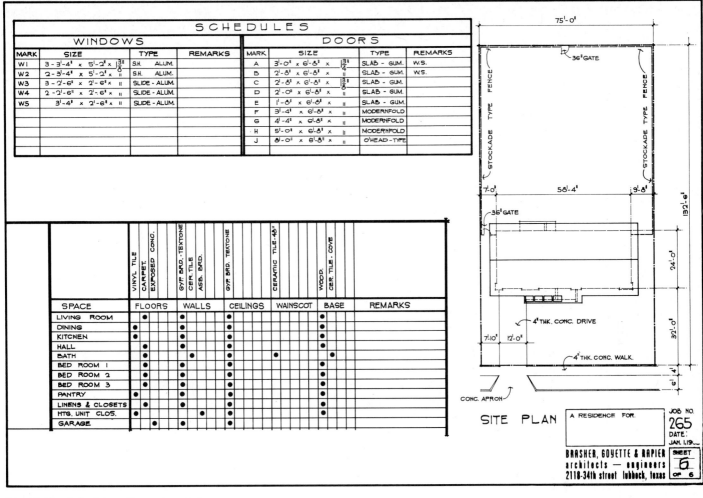

SITE PLAN

A RESIDENCE FOR.

JOB NO. 265
DATE: JAN. 1, 19__
BRASHER, GOYETTE & RAPIER
architects — engineers
2118-34th street lubbock, texas
SHEET 6 OF 6

Fig. 21-35*a*. Schedules, site, and roof plan.

21·35 Site and roof plan. This is a plan of the site showing the location of the house on the lot. It should give complete and accurate dimensions; indicate all driveways and walks; show the location of electric, gas, water, sewer, and telephone lines; and give all other pertinent information required by the city in which it is built. A plot plan is shown as a part of Fig. 21-35*a*. Note the outline of the overhanging roof. Window, door, and room finish schedules are included on this sheet but may be placed where space is available.

Figure 21-35*b* is an alternate plan without a basement.

Fig. 21-35*b*. Alternate floor plan, without a basement, for the house shown in Fig. 21-29.

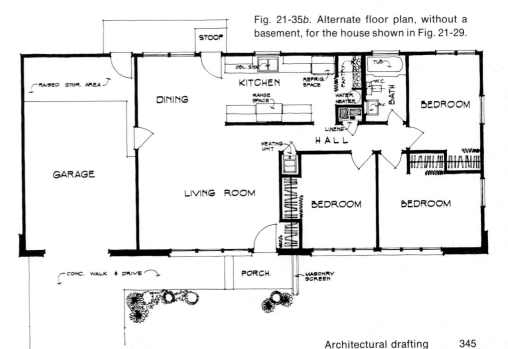

21·36 Contemporary houses for study and comparison. Designs by representative architects are shown in Figs. 21-2a, 21-2b, 21-6a to 21-7b, and 21-37a to 21-44c.

21·37 A split-level house. The house in Figs. 21-37a to 21-37d is described as a split-level house. It is of frame construction with exterior walls of vertical boards for the upper level and brick veneer for the lower level. Foundation walls are of poured concrete. The roof has asphalt shingles and copper flashing. The girders are 6″ I 12 # (I beams, 6″ high, weight 12 lb per ft). Inside walls are 3/8″ gypsum wallboard that are painted or papered except where wainscots or other finishes are desired. Wood-sliding windows are used except in the basement, where top-hinged windows are put in. All floors are oak except those in the bathrooms, recreation room, and kitchen. Both the bathroom floor and walls are of ceramic tile, the recreation room floor is of asphalt tile, and the kitchen floor is of linoleum. There are three levels for the house and a lower level for the garage.

The front elevation in Fig. 21-37c shows the general appearance and gives some dimensions. Complete plans would require elevations from all four directions. The sections in Fig. 21-37d indicate the different floor levels, the walls, and the slope of the roof (7″ vertically for 12″ horizontally).

Fig. 21-37a. A split-level house. *(Herman H. York, Architect, AIA, Jamaica, N.Y.)*

Fig. 21-37b. Plan of house of Fig 21-37a. *(Herman H. York, Architect, AIA, Jamaica, N.Y.)*

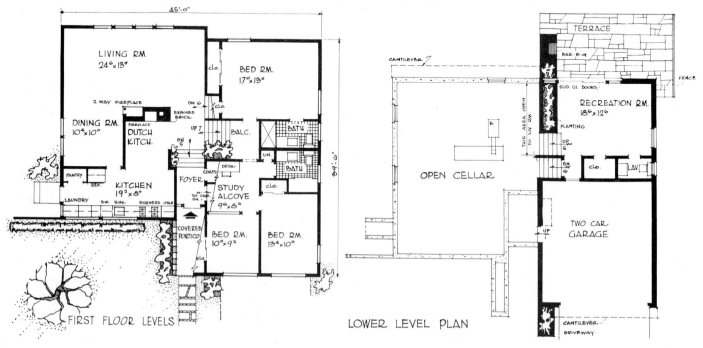

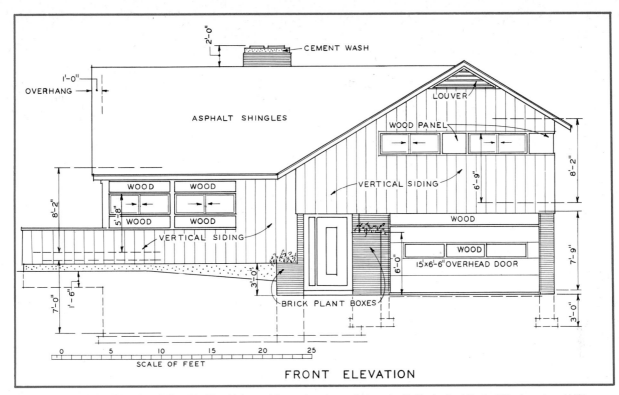

Fig. 21-37c. Front elevation of house of Fig. 21-37a. *(Adapted from drawings of Herman H. York, Architect, AIA, Jamaica, N.Y.)*

Fig. 21-37d. Section of house of Fig. 21-37a. *(Adapted from drawings of Herman H. York, Architect, AIA, Jamaica, N.Y.)*

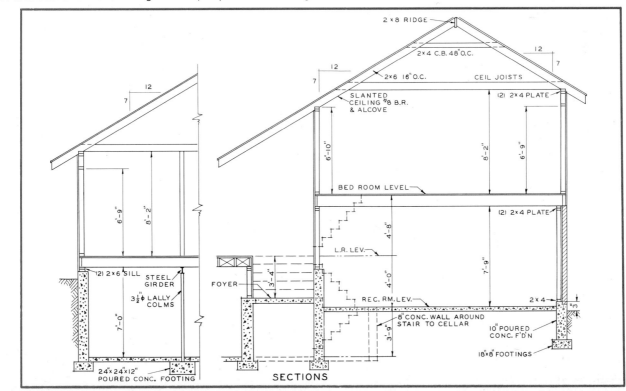

Fig. 21-38a. A house for outdoor living. *(Donald H. Honn, Architect, AIA, Tulsa, Okla.)*

21·38 A house for outdoor living. The house in Figs. 21-38a and 21-38b is described as a distinctly contemporary design, the features of which are evident in the illustrations.

Fig. 21-38b. Plan of house of Fig. 21-38a. *(Donald H. Honn, Architect, AIA, Tulsa, Okla.)*

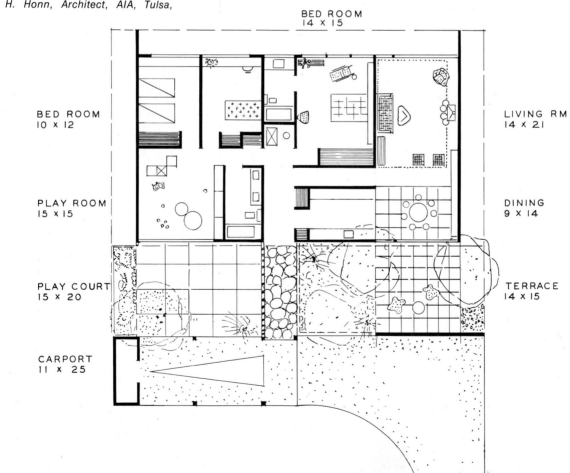

BED ROOM
14 x 15

BED ROOM
10 x 12

LIVING RM
14 x 21

PLAY ROOM
15 x 15

DINING
9 x 14

PLAY COURT
15 x 20

TERRACE
14 x 15

CARPORT
11 x 25

Fig. 21-39a. A one-level house. *(Herman H. York, Architect, AIA, Jamaica, N.Y.)*

21·39 A compact house. The house of Figs. 21-39a and 21-39b is described as a compact house with simple lines and frame construction. Note the use of sliding windows in Fig. 21-39a. On the plan, Fig. 21-39b, see the indication of folding doors (by the use of wavy lines) between the dining room and the family room. The patio and terrace, with sliding doors from the family room and the rear bedroom, provide for outdoor living.

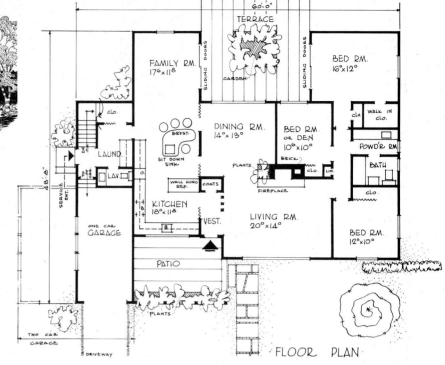

Fig. 21-39b. Plan of house of Fig. 21-39a. *(Herman H. York, Architect, AIA, Jamaica, N.Y.)*

21·40 A house with steel framing. The house in Figs. 21-40a to 21-40c illustrates the use of steel framing for residential construction. The walls are of concrete brick, concrete blocks, and plate glass. Note the overhanging upper level (Fig. 21-40a), and identify it with the partial west elevation shown at A in Fig. 21-40c. The view at A is from the right on the plan in Fig. 21-40b. A typical wall section is shown at B in Fig. 21-40c. Some detail sections are shown at C in Fig. 21-40c and have been numbered to correspond with the numbers on the partial west elevation at A.

Fig. 21-40b. Plan of house of Fig. 21-40a. *(Donald H. Honn, Architect, AIA, Tulsa, Okla.)*

Fig. 21-40a. A house with steel framing. *(Donald H. Honn, Architect, AIA, Tulsa, Okla.)*

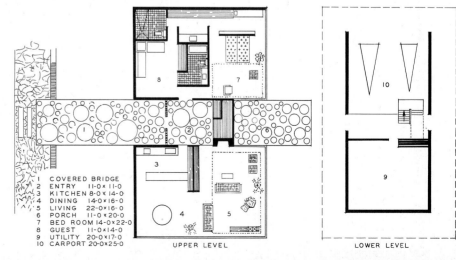

1 COVERED BRIDGE
2 ENTRY 11-0 x 11-0
3 KITCHEN 8-0 x 14-0
4 DINING 14-0 x 16-0
5 LIVING 22-0 x 16-0
6 PORCH 11-0 x 20-0
7 BED ROOM 14-0 x 22-0
8 GUEST 11-0 x 14-0
9 UTILITY 20-0 x 17-0
10 CARPORT 20-0 x 25-0

UPPER LEVEL

LOWER LEVEL

Fig. 21-40c. A partial elevation and some sections of house of Fig. 21-40a. *(Adapted from drawings of Donald H. Honn, Architect, AIA, Tulsa, Okla.)*

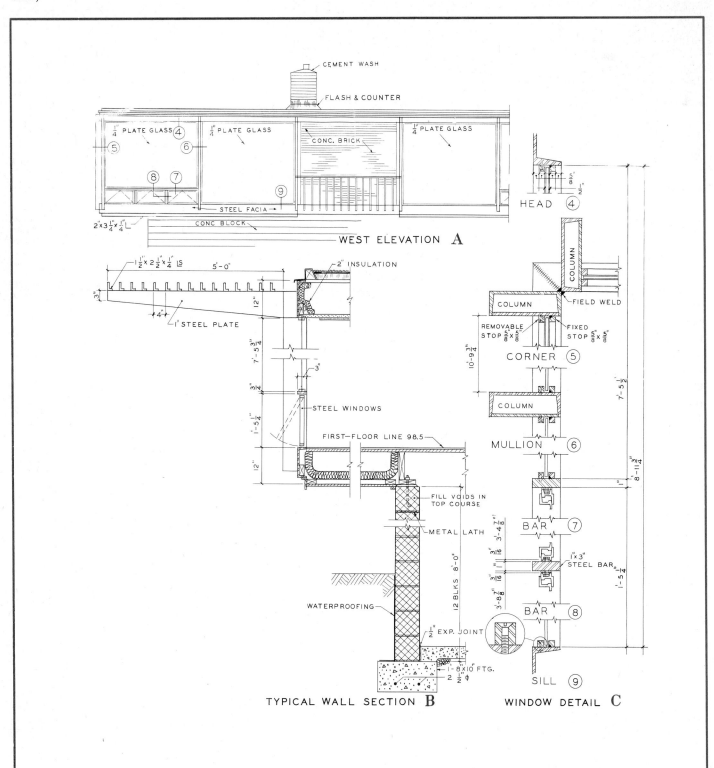

Fig. 21-41a. Northwest house, front. *(Paul Thiry, Architect, FAIA, Seattle, Wash.)*

Fig. 21-41b. Northwest house, rear. *(Paul Thiry, Architect, FAIA, Seattle, Wash.)*

21·41 A house in the Northwest.

The house in Figs. 21-41a to 21-41c is described as in the Northwest mood, that is, simple. This house is constructed entirely of wood. Laminated beams are used over long spans. The exterior is sheathed with vertical-grain redwood left without finish to weather. The roof has white asbestos shingles for fire protection.

21·42 A symmetrical plan.

The house in Figs. 21-42a and 21-42b is described as a symmetrical plan and structure. The architect states: "The fundamental decisions of orientation and lot use permitted a building form based on symmetry about two axes." The structure is of wood with gray cyprus siding, white trim, and orange or brown cement asbestos panels.

Fig. 21-41c. Plan and section of house of Fig. 21-41a. *(Paul Thiry, Architect, FAIA, Seattle, Wash.)*

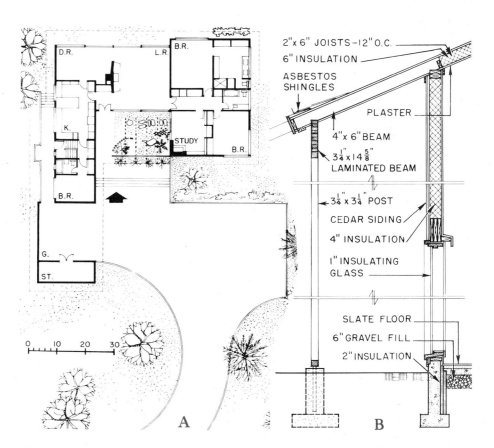

Fig. 21-42a. A house of symmetrical design. *(Cecil D. Elliott, Architect, AIA, and Mervin R. A. Johnson, Associate Architect, Raleigh, N.C.)*

Fig. 21-42b. Plan and section of house of Fig. 21-42a. *(Cecil D. Elliott, Architect, AIA, and Mervin R. A. Johnson, Associate Architect, Raleigh, N.C.)*

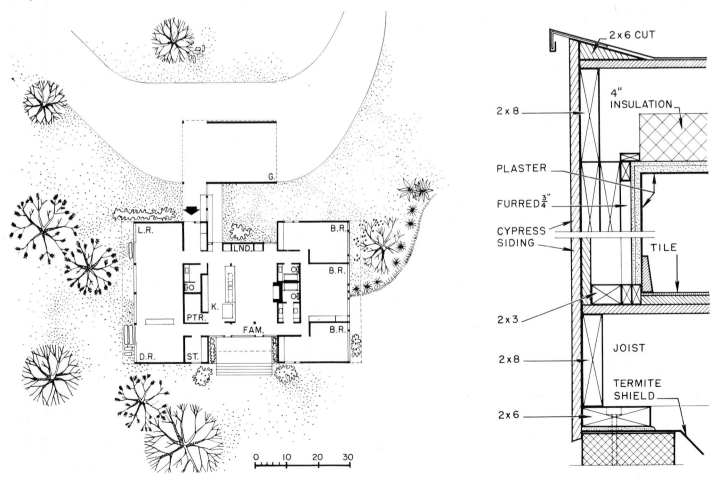

21•43 A small house. The small house in Figs. 21-43a to 21-43d is designed to give the most comfortable living conditions at the lowest cost for those who do not require a lot of room.

The straightforward post-and-beam construction is quick, and the heavy Douglas fir plank ceiling and floor give strength and character to the design of the house. The construction of this house differs from the usual method of framing with studs (Figs. 21-16a and 21-16b). It is framed with posts and beams. After these are in place the floor and roof planks are put on. Then the milled trim, which is used for jamb trim, head, and sill, is put directly on the frame of the windows, doors, and so

Fig. 21-43a. A small house. *(Henry Hill, Architect, AIA, and John W. Kruse, AIA, Associate, San Francisco, Calif.)*

Fig. 21-43b. Plans of house of Fig. 21-43a. *(Adapted from drawings of Henry Hill, Architect, AIA, and John W. Kruse, AIA, Associate, San Francisco, Calif.)*

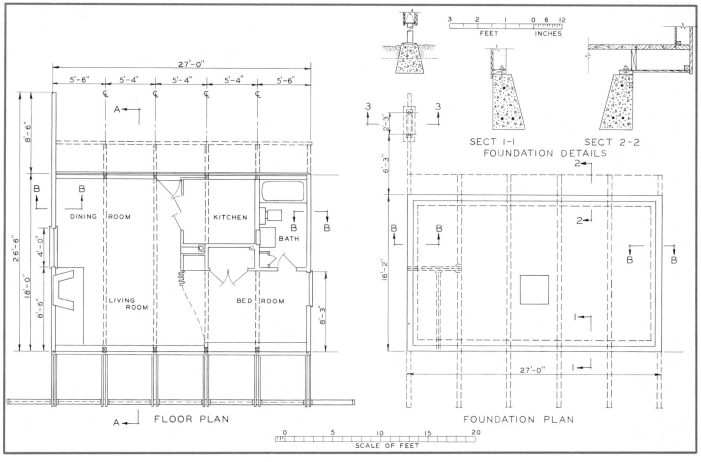

forth. Milled trim is finished to desired form in the mill or factory and is used directly.

The large glass areas are protected by overhang from summer sun and sky glare. Such areas give a feeling of space. The screen panel of Celloglass framing the balcony rail achieves privacy without obstructing the view from the balcony.

Note the curved folding partition between the living and sleeping rooms on the plan (Fig. 21-43b). This figure shows the floor and foundation plans.

Compare the floor plan with the elevations (Fig. 21-43c) and then with the sections (Fig. 21-43d). In order to show the construction more clearly most of the dimensions have been left off the views. The graphic scales will give a comparative idea of the sizes of parts.

Fig. 21-43c. Elevations of house of Fig. 21-43a. *(Adapted from drawings of Henry Hill, Architect, AIA, and John W. Kruse, Architect, AIA, Associate, San Francisco, Calif.)*

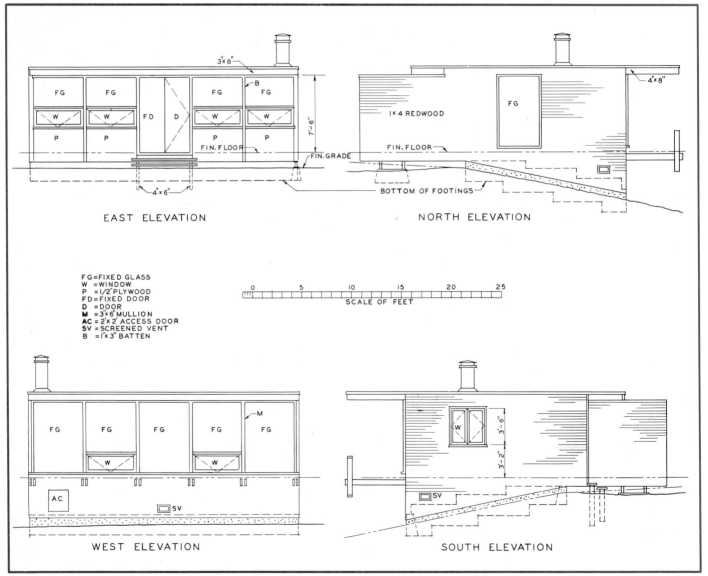

FG = FIXED GLASS
W = WINDOW
P = 1/2" PLYWOOD
FD = FIXED DOOR
D = DOOR
M = 3"x 6" MULLION
AC = 2'x 2' ACCESS DOOR
SV = SCREENED VENT
B = 1"x 3" BATTEN

EAST ELEVATION

NORTH ELEVATION

WEST ELEVATION

SOUTH ELEVATION

Fig. 21-43d. Section of house of Fig. 21-43a. (Adapted from drawings of Henry Hill, Architect, AIA, and John W. Kruse, Architect, AIA, Associate, San Francisco, Calif.)

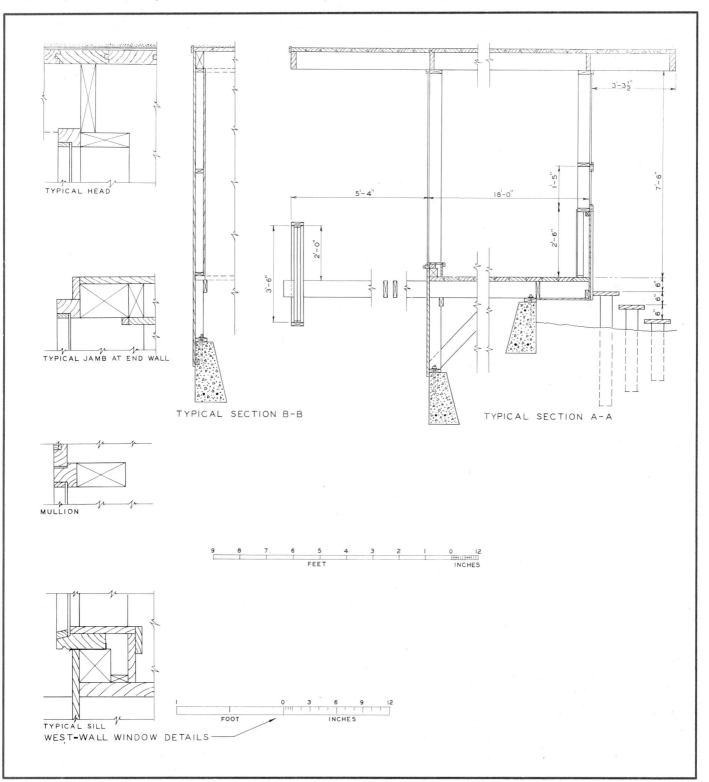

TYPICAL HEAD

TYPICAL JAMB AT END WALL

TYPICAL SECTION B-B

TYPICAL SECTION A-A

MULLION

TYPICAL SILL
WEST-WALL WINDOW DETAILS

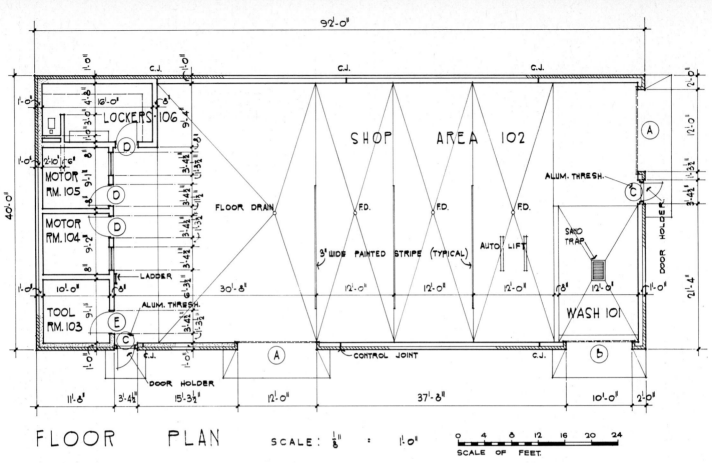

FLOOR PLAN SCALE: $\frac{1}{8}$" = 1'-0"

SCALE OF FEET.

Fig. 21-44a. Floor plan of vocational shop building.

Fig. 21-44b. Elevations of vocational shop building.

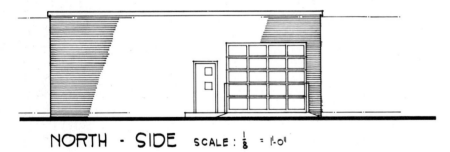

NORTH - SIDE SCALE: $\frac{1}{8}$" = 1'-0"

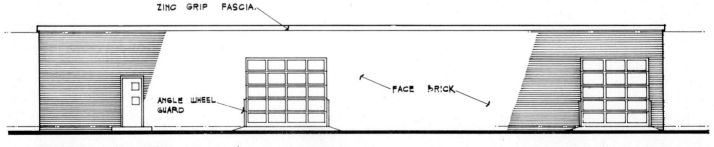

EAST - FRONT SCALE: $\frac{1}{8}$" = 1'-0"

21·44 A vocational shop building.
Some of the drawings for a vocational shop building are shown in Figs. 21-44a to 21-44c. You will notice that the construction of such buildings is different from that of residences. Other types of buildings such as schoolhouses, churches, shops, office buildings, and public buildings differ, and some architects specialize in one or two types of work.

The floor plan (Fig. 21-44a) is arranged for automotive work but could

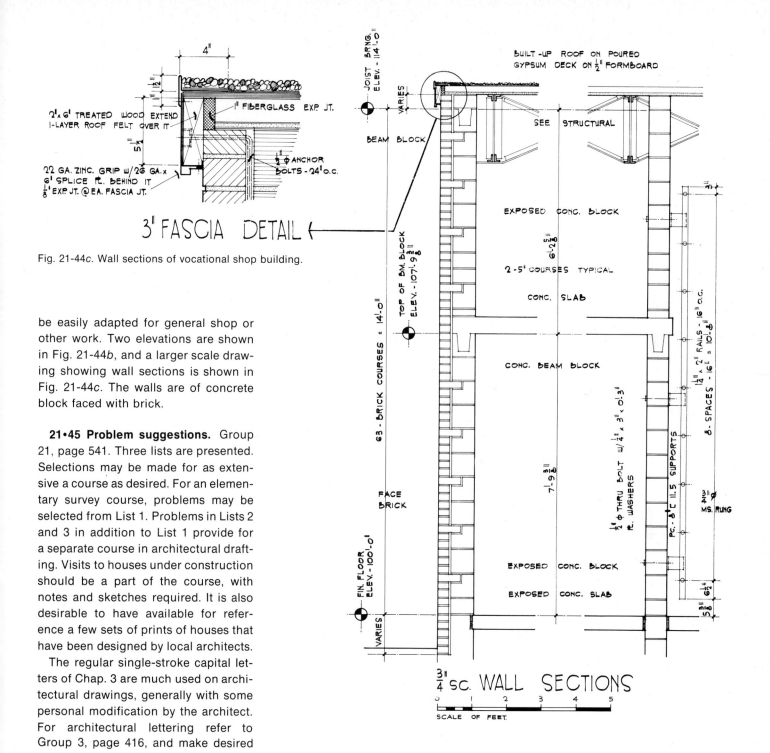

3″ FASCIA DETAIL ←

4″

2″ × 6′ TREATED WOOD EXTEND
1-LAYER ROOF FELT OVER IT

22 GA. ZINC. GRIP w/26 GA. ×
6′ SPLICE P̶. BEHIND IT
1⅛″ EXP. JT. @ EA. FASCIA JT.

1″ FIBERGLASS EXP. JT.

½″ ⌀ ANCHOR
BOLTS - 24″ O.C.

Fig. 21-44c. Wall sections of vocational shop building.

JOIST BRNG.
ELEV. - 114′-0″

VARIES

BEAM BLOCK

TOP OF BM. BLOCK
ELEV. - 107′-9¾″

63 - BRICK COURSES = 14′-0″

FACE
BRICK

FIN. FLOOR
ELEV. - 100′-0″

VARIES

BUILT - UP ROOF ON POURED
GYPSUM DECK ON ½″ FORMBOARD

SEE STRUCTURAL

EXPOSED CONC. BLOCK

2 - 5″ COURSES TYPICAL

CONC. SLAB

CONC. BEAM BLOCK

7′-9⅜″

½″ ⌀ THRU BOLT w/¼″ × 3″ × 0′-3″
P̶. WASHERS

EXPOSED CONC. BLOCK

EXPOSED CONC. SLAB

PC. - 8 ℄ ILS SUPPORTS

5′-2⅝″ 6′-1⅝″

1½″ × 2″ RAILS - 16″ O.C.

8 - SPACES - 16″ = 100′-8″ O.C.

3″ ⌀
M.S. RUNG

6½″ 5″-10⁰

¾″ SC. WALL SECTIONS

0 1 2 3 4 5
SCALE OF FEET.

be easily adapted for general shop or other work. Two elevations are shown in Fig. 21-44b, and a larger scale drawing showing wall sections is shown in Fig. 21-44c. The walls are of concrete block faced with brick.

21·45 Problem suggestions. Group 21, page 541. Three lists are presented. Selections may be made for as extensive a course as desired. For an elementary survey course, problems may be selected from List 1. Problems in Lists 2 and 3 in addition to List 1 provide for a separate course in architectural drafting. Visits to houses under construction should be a part of the course, with notes and sketches required. It is also desirable to have available for reference a few sets of prints of houses that have been designed by local architects.

The regular single-stroke capital letters of Chap. 3 are much used on architectural drawings, generally with some personal modification by the architect. For architectural lettering refer to Group 3, page 416, and make desired selections from Probs. 3·21 to 3·29.

List 1: Problems 21·3, 21·7, 21·9, 21·10, 21·12, 21·15, 21·16, 21·20, 21·22, 21·24, 21·29.

List 2: Problems 21·14, 21·17, 21·18, 21·25, 21·26.

List 3: Problems 21·1, 21·2, 21·19; and selections from 21·30 to 21·45.

22
Structural drafting

Fig. 22-1a. Construction of hanger showing structural-steel arch. U.S. Naval Air Station, Patuxent River, Md. *(Official U.S. Navy Photograph)*

Fig. 22-1b. Steel construction at United States Steel's Lorain works. *(United States Steel Corporation)*

22·1 Structural drafting has to do with the drawings made for the framework and supporting members of structures, such as columns, floor members, roof trusses, bridge trusses, and the great variety of construction work made from structural-steel shapes and plates. An interesting example is illustrated in Fig. 22-1a, where a three-hinged arch is being erected. In Fig. 22-1b the steel frame structure of a storage building at the left is being erected of lighter members than the electric-weld pipe mill at the right. The mill produces standard and line pipe in sizes from $2\frac{3}{8}$ to $5\frac{5}{8}$ in. outside diameter in light wall thicknesses and in long lengths. Rigid frames of steel for the Allen County War Memorial, Fort Wayne, Indiana, are shown in Fig. 22-1c. The *span,* or distance, across the building is 224 ft. A steel truss bridge over the Watauga River on Tennessee State Highway No. 67 is shown in Fig. 22-1d.

The picture of a part of a flat steel truss for a building is presented in Fig. 22-1e. Some structural terms are given in Fig. 22-1f. This truss has been *fabricated,* or made up, in the shop, and, as shown, is ready for shipment to the site of the building. The top horizontal member, or *top chord,* is made of two *angles* (Fig. 22-1f). The *bottom chord* is made of two smaller angles, and the *diagonals* are made of single angles. Notice how the various members are connected by riveting to steel *gusset plates.* The design of structures requires a knowledge of the many subjects included in structural engineering, such as mathematics, stresses, mechanics, properties of materials, meth-

ods of fabricating, and methods of erection. However, the student should know some of the characteristics of drawings made for such purposes and how they differ from other drawings.

Fig. 22-1c. Allen County War Memorial, Fort Wayne, Ind.: 224-ft rigid steel frames. *(Courtesy Engineering News-Record)*

Fig. 22-1d. Watauga River Bridge on Tennessee State Highway No. 67. *(Courtesy Engineering News-Record)*

Fig. 22-1e. Riveted joints in steel construction.

Fig. 22-1f. Some steel construction terms. Compare drawing with photograph of Fig. 22-1e.

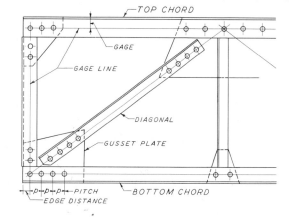

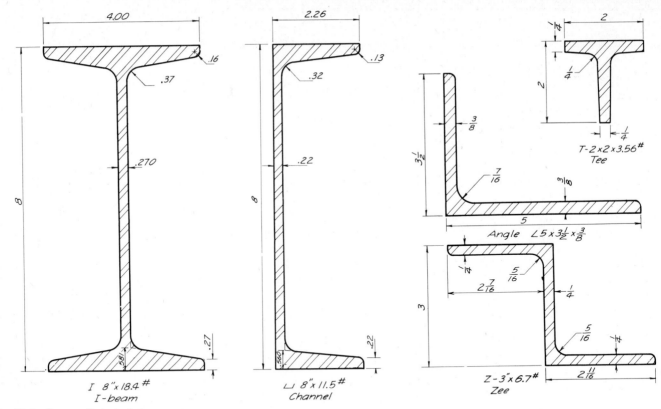

Fig. 22-2a. Some rolled-steel shapes.

22·2 Structural shapes. Structural members are built up of standard rolled shapes, some of which are shown in section in Fig. 22-2a. Such shapes are made in a great variety of sizes and weights, lists of which may be found in the handbook *Steel Construction*[1] or in the handbooks published by the various steel companies. The AISC Handbook contains tables of the properties of the various shapes and of many combinations of shapes; beam and column data; details of standard beam connections; specifications for the design, fabrication, and erection of structural steel for buildings; and a large amount of related information. Dimensions of steel plates are specified by giving the width, thickness, and length thus: Pl. $12 \times \frac{3}{8} \times 24$. Angles are specified by

dimensions giving the length of the legs and thickness of material thus:

$$L \ 5 \times 3\frac{1}{2} \times \frac{3}{8}$$

Other shapes are specified by the main dimension and weight per foot: 18 WF 64 means 18″ wide flange I-beam, 64 lb per ft.

Bar 2 ⊡ means 2″ square bar.

Bar 1 ⊕ means 1″ diameter round bar.

Figure 22-2b shows a number of usual rolled-steel shapes with names, pictures, symbols, and specification.

22·3 Riveting. Structural rivets are shown in Art. 12·33. The Standard symbols for riveting are given in Fig. 22-3a. A button-head structural rivet is shown in Fig. 22-3b.

Many parts made up of rolled shapes and plates can be put together in the structural shop—sometimes a complete roof truss or other assembly. Such rivet-

ing is called *shop riveting* and is shown on drawings by open circles of the diameter of the rivet head (Fig. 22-3c). Parts which cannot be put together in the shop because of size, weight, or other reasons are riveted where the structure is put together (in the field). Such riveting is called *field riveting* and is shown on drawings by blacked-in circles of the diameter of the rivet hole (Fig. 22-3c). The drop-spring bow (Art. 2·34) is convenient for drawing rivets.

Lines on which rivets are spaced are called *gage lines.* The distance between centers along these lines is called the *pitch* (Fig. 22-3c).

22·4 The scales used on structural drawings vary according to the size of the drawing sheet and the size of the structural member or assembly. Usual scales include $\frac{1}{4}″ = 1′-0″$ to $1″ = 1′-0″$. Two scales are often used on the same

[1] *Steel Construction,* or as it is sometimes called, the "AISC Handbook," is published by the American Institute of Steel Construction, New York.

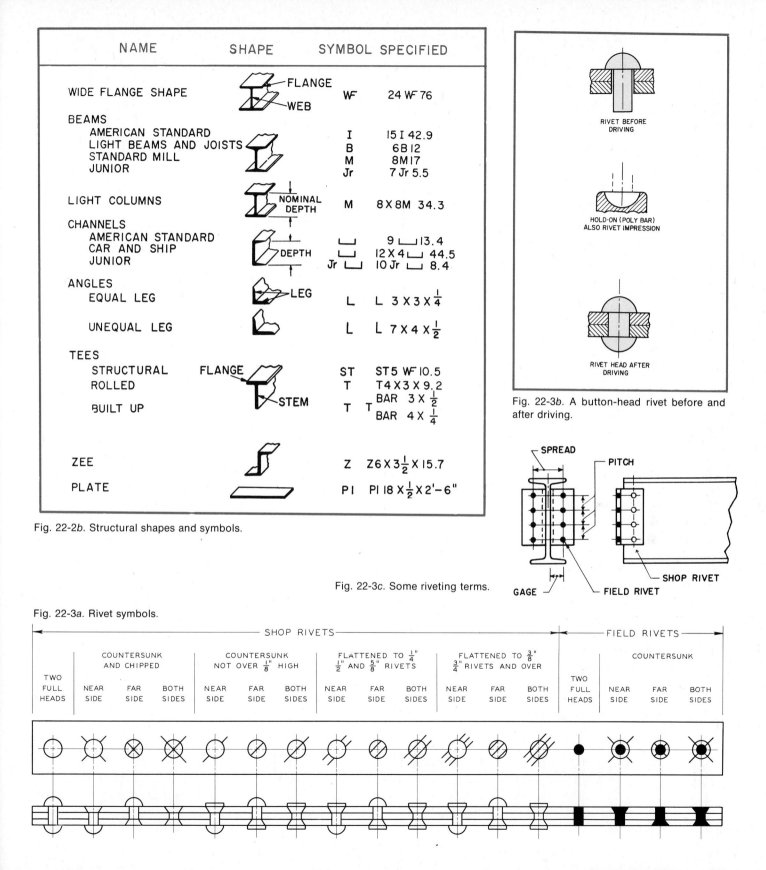

NAME	SHAPE	SYMBOL	SPECIFIED
WIDE FLANGE SHAPE	FLANGE / WEB	WF	24 WF 76
BEAMS			
AMERICAN STANDARD		I	15 I 42.9
LIGHT BEAMS AND JOISTS		B	6 B 12
STANDARD MILL		M	8 M 17
JUNIOR		Jr	7 Jr 5.5
LIGHT COLUMNS	NOMINAL DEPTH	M	8 X 8M 34.3
CHANNELS			
AMERICAN STANDARD	DEPTH	⌐	9 ⌐ 13.4
CAR AND SHIP		⌐	12 X 4 ⌐ 44.5
JUNIOR		Jr ⌐	10 Jr ⌐ 8.4
ANGLES			
EQUAL LEG	LEG	L	L 3 X 3 X $\frac{1}{4}$
UNEQUAL LEG		L	L 7 X 4 X $\frac{1}{2}$
TEES			
STRUCTURAL	FLANGE	ST	ST5 WF 10.5
ROLLED		T	T 4 X 3 X 9.2
BUILT UP	STEM	T	T BAR 3 X $\frac{1}{2}$ / BAR 4 X $\frac{1}{4}$
ZEE		Z	Z 6 X 3$\frac{1}{2}$ X 15.7
PLATE		Pl	Pl 18 X $\frac{1}{2}$ X 2'-6"

Fig. 22-2b. Structural shapes and symbols.

Fig. 22-3b. A button-head rivet before and after driving.

RIVET BEFORE DRIVING

HOLD-ON (POLY BAR) ALSO RIVET IMPRESSION

RIVET HEAD AFTER DRIVING

Fig. 22-3c. Some riveting terms.

SPREAD — PITCH — SHOP RIVET — FIELD RIVET — GAGE

Fig. 22-3a. Rivet symbols.

	SHOP RIVETS												FIELD RIVETS			
	COUNTERSUNK AND CHIPPED			COUNTERSUNK NOT OVER $\frac{1}{8}$" HIGH			FLATTENED TO $\frac{1}{4}$" $\frac{1}{2}$" AND $\frac{5}{8}$" RIVETS			FLATTENED TO $\frac{3}{8}$" $\frac{3}{4}$" RIVETS AND OVER				COUNTERSUNK		
TWO FULL HEADS	NEAR SIDE	FAR SIDE	BOTH SIDES	NEAR SIDE	FAR SIDE	BOTH SIDES	NEAR SIDE	FAR SIDE	BOTH SIDES	NEAR SIDE	FAR SIDE	BOTH SIDES	TWO FULL HEADS	NEAR SIDE	FAR SIDE	BOTH SIDES

view of a drawing, as for the skeleton lines in Fig. 22-7a, where lengths are shown at a smaller scale than the members which make up the truss. A beam or other detail having length is drawn with a small scale, or no scale, for the length dimension and with a larger scale used to show the parts clearly. If two or more beams are the same except for length, one drawing may be used by giving separate length dimensions and identification marks.

22•5 Dimensions. Continuous, unbroken dimension lines are used on structural drawings. The dimensions are placed above dimension lines. Dimensions are given to working points, center lines, and working lines, except lengths. Dimension lines for length and extension lines are drawn in the usual manner. Inch symbols are not used except when needed to avoid a mistake. When dimensions are in feet and inches, the foot symbol is used but not the inch symbol. Some examples follow: 7'–3½; 19'–0; 5'–0¾.

22•6 Structural bolting (Fig. 22-6). High-strength steel bolts may be used in place of rivets for making connections on steel structures. Such bolts are made specially for this purpose. Structural bolts and nuts are of a heavy hexagon type and are made of high-strength steel. Structural bolts are being used for field connections for large and important buildings, bridges, and other structures. Bolts are also being used in some plants for making up assemblies and part assemblies and for work previously done by shop riveting.

22•7 Structural drawings. Assembly or part-assembly working drawings form a large class of structural drawings. These include the "skeleton" or basic and center lines to locate the working points, the structural members, gage lines, location dimensions, notes, and other necessary information. Such a general working drawing is shown in Fig. 22-7a for a small steel roof truss. Since the truss is symmetrical about a vertical center line, it is necessary to

show only one-half of it in the drawing. Notice the lines upon which the design is built and the notes used to designate the various features. The sizes of the gusset plates are given in notes, as are the number and sizes of angles (∟ s). The slope or inclination is indicated by a right triangle, one leg of which is 12 in. A study of the drawing will show that each member is completely dimensioned or described and that dimensions are given to fix the location of each member.

Separate shop drawings are made for complicated or special details and for repeated details.

Diagrams for some roof trusses and bridge trusses are shown and named in Fig. 22-7b. There are many more. The ones shown may have more or fewer panels and may be modified to suit conditions.

Fig. 22-6. A structural bolt and structural bolts in use.

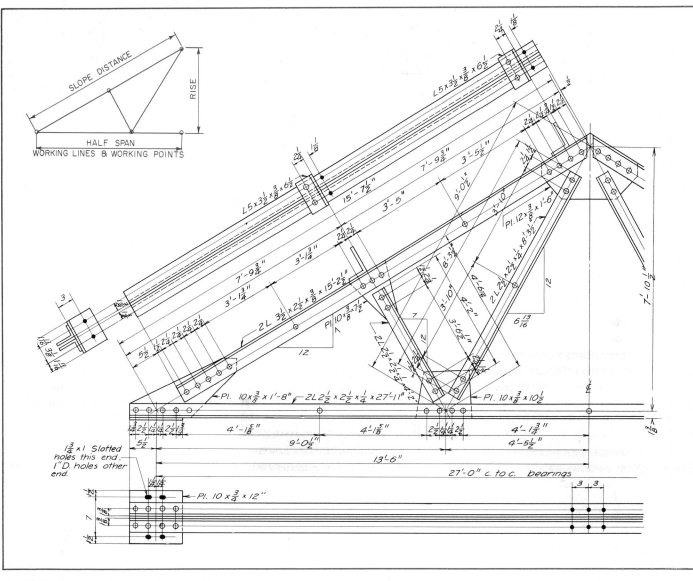

Fig. 22-7a. A structural drawing for a roof truss.

Fig. 22-7b. Roof and bridge truss diagrams.

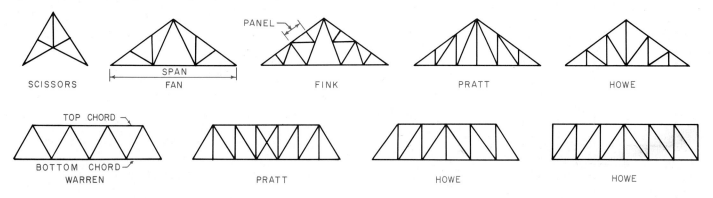

SCISSORS

FAN   SPAN

PANEL

FINK

PRATT

HOWE

TOP CHORD

BOTTOM CHORD

WARREN

PRATT

HOWE

HOWE

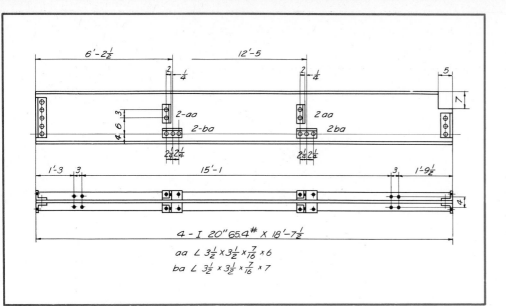

Fig. 22-8. A structural drawing of a beam detail.

22•8 Detail drawings. Shop detail drawings give all the dimensions and information necessary to fabricate (or make) the parts. The location and kind of rivets are shown with everything drawn to scale. The simple beam detail of Fig. 22-8 shows the general characteristics of such drawings. Notice that the dimensions are placed above the dimension lines. The lower view is a section and, on structural drawings, is shown as seen from above.

The connections or angles at the ends of the beam are Standard Beam Connections; it is not necessary to dimension them. At the left end a B5 connection is used and at the right end, a B3 connection. For the sizes of these angles and dimensions, see a steel handbook (the rivets are ¾ in. in diameter).

22•9 Welding (Chap. 17) is increasing in use for putting structural-steel shapes together. Many buildings hav-

ing steel construction are welded throughout. Others are partly welded and partly riveted or bolted. Some details from a drawing for a welded steel truss are shown in Fig. 22-9a. The complete drawing would show all the welded joints, a roof framing plan, bracing, and other details for complete construction.

A steel fabricator's drawing for a standard steel joist is illustrated in Fig. 22-9b. These lightweight joists are very widely used and are fabricated (made) by many steel companies. The companies prepare their own particular details and use the same details for many different jobs.

22•10 Reinforced concrete. Drawings made for reinforced-concrete structures show the dimensions of the concrete members and sections, and they give the sizes and locations of the steel reinforcing material. A part of such a drawing is shown in Fig. 22-10a.

Notice the symbol for the diameter of the steel rods and the representation of the rods by long dashes and blacked-in circles. The rods are drawn as though on different levels on the elevation in order to show how two of them are bent. The section shows them on the same level along the bottom of the beam. The symbol for concrete is shown in Fig. 10-18a. Reinforced-concrete design requires a good knowledge of mathematics, mechanics, and materials and is a specialized field of structural engineering.

The proportions of the materials to be used to give the required strength must be understood—the amounts of cement, sand, gravel or crushed rock, and water—as well as the computation of the size and amount of steel and the placing of the steel.

Many interesting applications of reinforced-concrete construction, such as for dams, retaining walls, bridges, roads, walls, beams, and floors of buildings, can be found in the pages of *Engineering News-Record* and similar magazines.

A method of shortening erection time is the use of precast concrete wall panels, which are cast flat and then tilted up into place. This is illustrated in Fig. 22-10b, which shows a panel being tilted into position with a four-point pickup by a large mobile crane operating from the floor of the building.

22•11 Prestressed concrete drawing. The design drawing for a "prestressed" concrete beam is shown in Fig. 22-11. They are normally made for use on very long spans and precast (poured in removable forms) at a fabricating plant some distance away from the building on which they are to be used. "Prestressed" means that the main longitudinal (lengthwise) steel, which is of a very high stress type, is stressed, or tightened, to a very high degree before the concrete is poured.

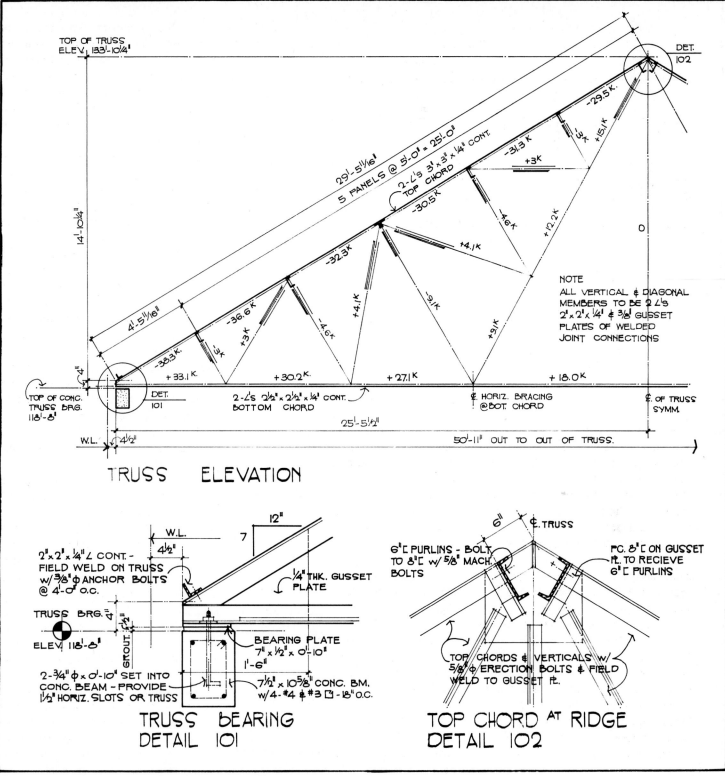

TRUSS ELEVATION

TOP OF TRUSS
ELEV. 133'-10¼"

29'-5¹¹⁄₁₆"
5 PANELS @ 5'-0" = 25'-0"

14'-10¼"

2-∠'s 3"x3"x¼" CONT.
TOP CHORD

-29.5ᴷ
-31.3ᴷ
+3ᴷ
-3ᴷ
+15.1ᴷ
-30.5ᴷ
-4.6ᴷ
+12.2ᴷ
-32.3ᴷ
+4.1ᴷ
-36.6ᴷ
-9.1ᴷ
+3ᴷ
-4.6ᴷ
+9.1ᴷ
-33.3ᴷ.
+4.1ᴷ
-3ᴷ

4'-5¹¹⁄₁₆"

4"

NOTE
ALL VERTICAL & DIAGONAL
MEMBERS TO BE 2 ∠'s
2"x 2"x ¼" & ⅜" GUSSET
PLATES OF WELDED
JOINT CONNECTIONS

0

+ 33.1ᴷ.   + 30.2ᴷ.   + 27.1ᴷ   + 18.0ᴷ

TOP OF CONC.
TRUSS BRG.
118'-8"

DET.
101

2-∠'s 2½"x 2½"x ¼" CONT.
BOTTOM CHORD

₵ HORIZ. BRACING
@ BOT. CHORD

₵ OF TRUSS
SYMM.

25'-5½"

W.L.   4½"

50'-11" OUT TO OUT OF TRUSS.

DET.
102

TRUSS BEARING
DETAIL 101

W.L.
4½"
7   12"

2"x 2"x ¼" ∠ CONT. -
FIELD WELD ON TRUSS
w/ ⅜" φ ANCHOR BOLTS
@ 4'-0" O.C.

¼" THK. GUSSET
PLATE

TRUSS BRG.
¾"
ELEV. 118'-8"

GROUT 1½"

BEARING PLATE
7"x ½"x 0'-10"
1'-6"

2-¾" φ x 0'-10" SET INTO
CONC. BEAM - PROVIDE
1½" HORIZ. SLOTS OR TRUSS

7½"x 10⅝" CONC. BM.
w/ 4-#4 & #3 ☐-18" O.C.

TOP CHORD ᴬᵀ RIDGE
DETAIL 102

6"
₵ TRUSS

6" ⊏ PURLINS - BOLT
TO 8" ⊏ w/ ⅝" MACH.
BOLTS

PC. 8" ⊏ ON GUSSET
PL. TO RECIEVE
6" ⊏ PURLINS

TOP CHORDS & VERTICALS w/
⅝" φ ERECTION BOLTS & FIELD
WELD TO GUSSET PL.

Fig. 22-9a. A structural drawing for welded construction.

After the concrete has set up, or hardened, the prestressing results in all concrete being in compression. Concrete is strong in compression, so the beam will carry larger loads than would otherwise be possible. Stressing the steel after the concrete is set up is a method called *post tensioning*.

Prestressed concrete must be very carefully designed and very accurately detailed. This method of construction is becoming popular.

Fig. 22-9*b*. Fabricator's drawing for a standard steel joist.

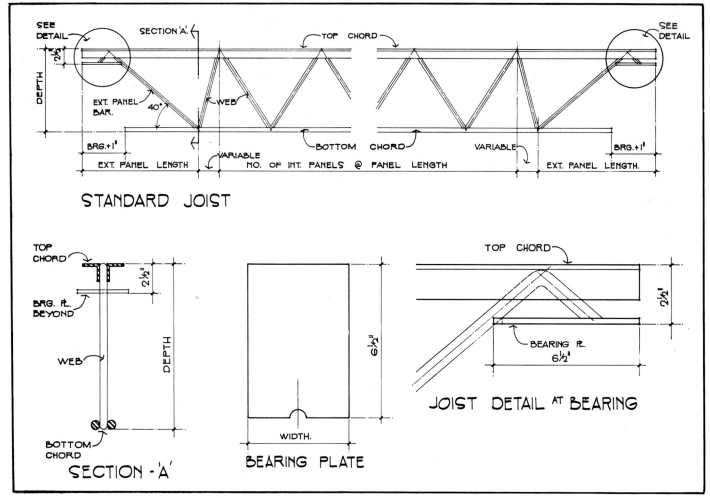

Fig. 22-10*a*. A drawing for reinforced concrete.

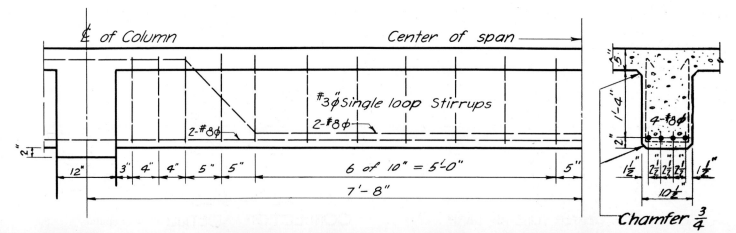

22·12 Problem suggestions. Group 22, page 549. These problems are designed to give an elementary idea of structural drafting and should be accompanied by inspection of buildings under construction, inspection of bridges, and so forth. This chapter gives general information. Structural drafting requires some knowledge of the principles of structural design. Problems 22·1, 22·2, 22·3, 22·4, 22·5.

Fig. 22-10b. Precast concrete wall for NBC television studios, Fairbanks, Calif.

Fig. 22-11. Prestressed-concrete-tee details.

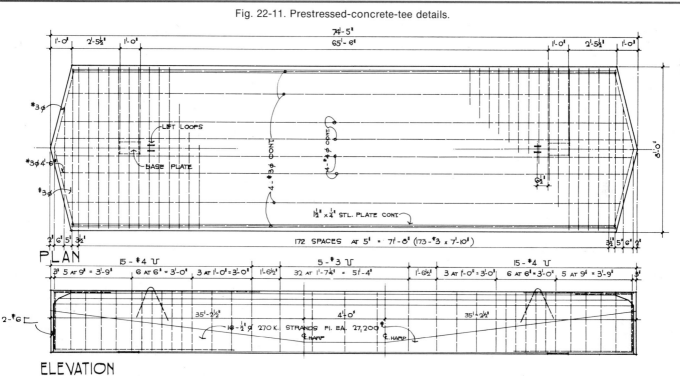

PLAN

ELEVATION

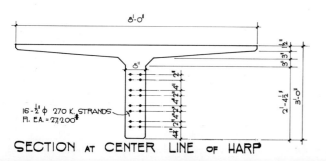

SECTION AT CENTER LINE OF HARP

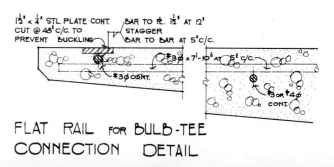

FLAT RAIL FOR BULB-TEE
CONNECTION DETAIL

23
Map drafting:
Engineering and geological

23•1 Maps are essentially one-view drawings of a part of the earth's surface. Early examples were generally artistic representations (Fig. 23-1a; see also Fig. 1-1a) that lacked the exactness found in present-day examples. The

Fig. 23-1a. Benjamin Franklin's map of the Gulf Stream. *(U.S. Coast and Geodetic Survey)*

BENJAMIN FRANKLIN'S MAP OF THE GULF STREAM

uses of maps have multiplied greatly, and maps now appear in a great variety of sizes and forms. Some maps having to do with the ownership of property, such as city plats, must be extremely accurate, particularly as to data noted on the map. The scale is relatively large (50 to 200 feet to the inch). Geographic maps of states or countries which show boundary lines, streams, lakes, coastlines, and relative locations may use a scale of several miles to the inch. As the world has entered the space age, there are maps showing enormous distances in the solar system (Fig. 23-1b).

23·2 Scales used on maps. The civil engineer's scale (Art. 2·26) is used for map drawings. Distances are given in decimals of a foot or meter, such as tenths, hundredths, and so forth. (See the maps in your geography and history books.) Practically all other parts of the world have adopted the metric system, with the kilometer in general use instead of miles.

The scale of a map is generally noted as 1 inch equals 500 feet or 1 part equals 6000 parts, which is noted in the following manner: 1:6000. The scale of 1 inch equals 1 mile can also be shown as 1:63,360. Graphic scales are shown on maps and are always desirable.

Fig. 23-1b. The Solar System. The Sun is a star located in the center of the system with nine planets revolving around it in noncircular orbits. All of the planets move in the same direction around the sun and are located in nearly the same plane. The Earth is ninety million miles (ave. 92.8) from the Sun. The planet Pluto is three and a half billion miles from the Sun. (NASA)

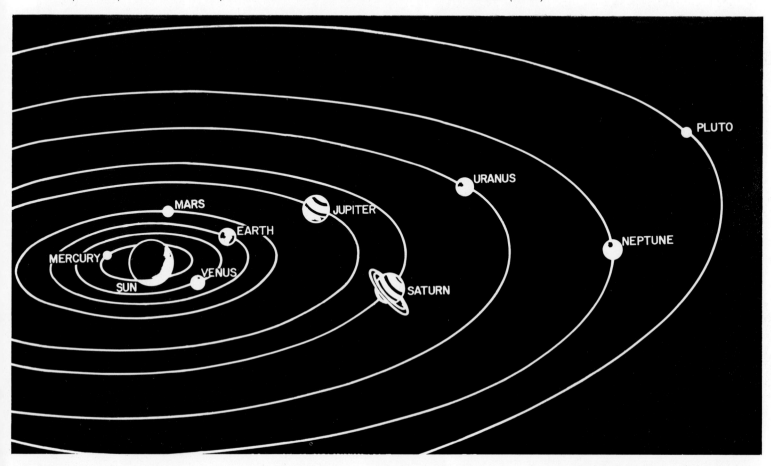

23•3 Plats of a survey. A map to record the boundaries of a tract of land and to identify it is called a *plat*. The amount and kind of information presented will depend upon the purpose for which the map is required. The plat of a plane survey which was made to accompany the legal description of the property is shown in Fig. 23-3. Accuracy of data is all-important and must correspond to the legal description.

23•4 City plat. Maps of cities are made for many purposes, such as to maintain a record of street improvements, to show the location of utilities, and to record sizes and location of property for tax assessments. A part of such a city plat is shown in Fig. 23-4. Notice the numbering of the lots and the location of streets, alleys, sidewalks, and various other details found in a city.

23•5 Operations maps. Engineering and management groups, or government agencies, frequently have projects or programs under discussion which are greatly aided by the use of operations maps. These maps show the relationship of various components to a general plan. Such a map is found in Fig. 23-5. A good presentation will assist greatly in the selling of a program.

Fig. 23-3. Plat of a survey. Note parts which make up the plat: the acreage of each part, the iron pipe locating the corners of the graphics scale, the signature of the surveyor, and the official seal.

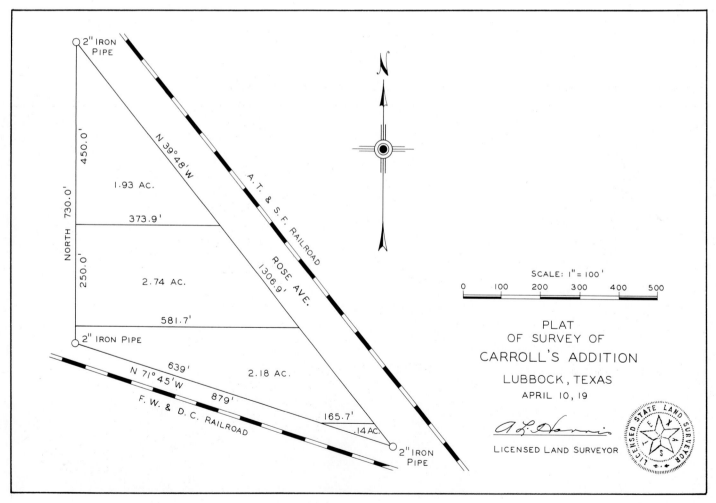

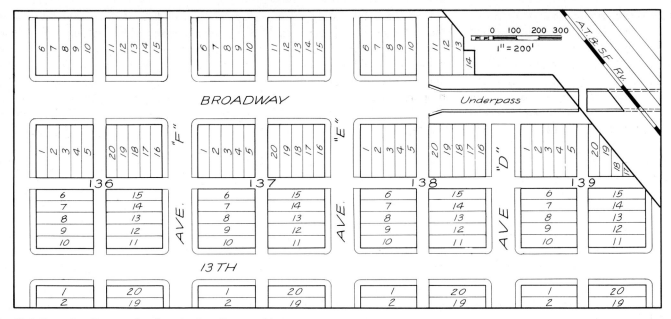

Fig. 23-4. Part of a city map showing streets, alleys, and lots.

Figure 23-5. An oil field operations map. Note scale of kilometers. One kilometer = 0.621 statute mile.

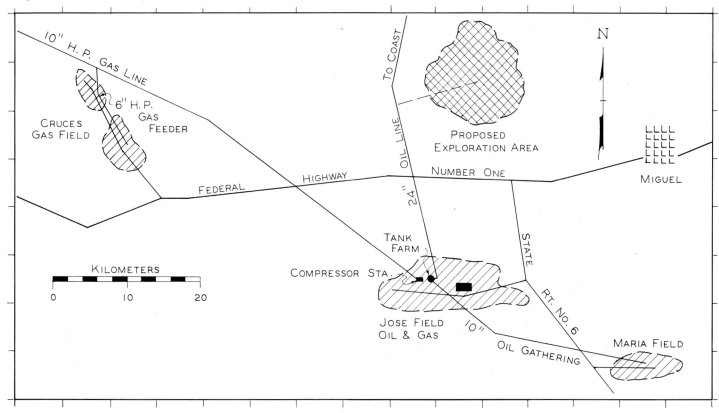

23·6 Contours. Since maps are one-view drawings, vertical distances and variations in ground level do not show. They can, however, be indicated by lines of constant level called *contours*. This is illustrated in Fig. 23-6a, where the contours show the location of lines on the ground that are at stated heights above the ocean (sea level). Contours that are close together indicate a steeper slope than lines that are farther apart. This can be seen by projecting up the intersections of the horizontal level lines with the profile section of Fig. 23-6a, as shown.

It will be observed that the contour map and the profile correspond to the plan and section of an ordinary drawing. Note the horizontal line, *A–A*, or cutting plane, on the contour map which shows the position, or line, on which the profile is taken. Notice how the profile would change if the cutting plane were moved toward the ocean or to some other new position.

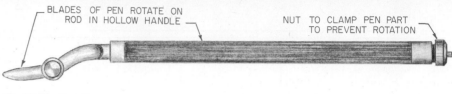

Fig. 23-6b. A contour pen.

Fig. 23-6c. Part of rubber-covered adjustable ruler.

Fig. 23-6d. A metal spline held in place by "ducks."

Spacing of contour intervals will vary according to requirements and the scale of maps. A 10-ft interval may be quite satisfactory, reserving a 5-ft interval for use on larger-scale maps. For close detail work, such as an irrigation project, the contour intervals may be reduced to 0.5 ft, 1 ft, or 2 ft. In case of small-scale maps with a high degree of relief, intervals may be increased from 20 to 200 ft, or even more. As an aid to interpretation, every fifth contour is generally accentuated by drawing a much heavier line (refer to Fig. 23-7a).

One of the fountain tube pens (Fig. 8-4f) will be found most satisfactory for inking contour lines. It is replacing the contour pen (Fig. 23-6b), which has pen blades arranged to turn and follow the contour lines.

Fig. 23-6a. A contour map with a profile.

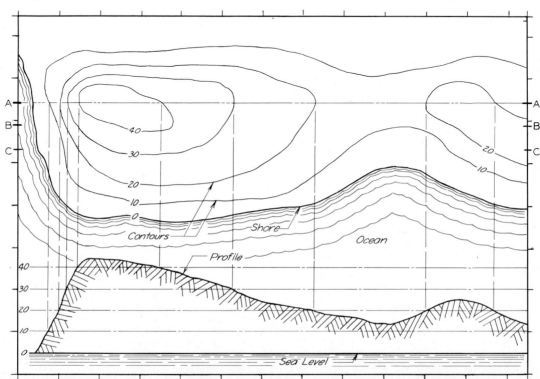

There are many forms of flexible rulers and splines which can be bent to match curves to be drawn. The rubber-covered ruler in Fig. 23-6c has a core composed of a strip of lead and two strips of steel. The spline in Fig. 23-6d is a metal strip which can be bent to fit a desired curve and is held in place by ducks (metal weights), as shown.

23•7 A contour map is shown in Fig. 23-7a; it uses a contour interval of 20 ft (vertical distance between contour lines). The elevation in feet is marked in a break in each contour line. Notice that the drainage is indicated as intermittent streams.

Before a contour map can be drawn, elevations must be obtained in the field for various key points controlling the construction of the contours. Various methods are employed, such as a grid system where all intersection elevations are obtained, plus critical elevations on grid lines; points located by transit and stadia rod with the corresponding elevations calculated by plain table; and by aerial photographic surveys (Fig. 23-7b). All these methods require experience in surveying, an important part of civil engineering.

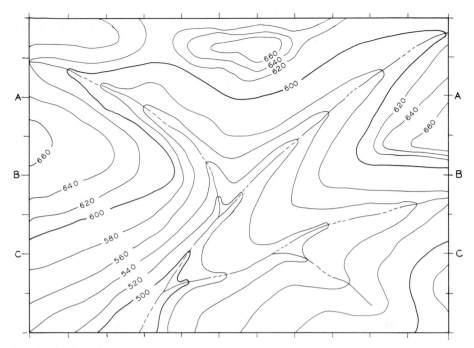

Fig. 23-7a. A contour map.

Fig. 23-7b. Portion of air-photo and topographic map of Concepcion, Chile, compiled by photogrammetric methods. These photos and maps are part of a Chilean-OAS program to speed reconstruction of earthquake-damaged areas and to advance broad planning for national growth. Actual map sheets were done at a scale of 1:2,000 with 1-meter contours. Photos from which maps were prepared are at a scale of 1:10,000. This project is being carried out by a group of companies under the direction of Aero Service Corporation, Philadelphia, a division of Litton Industries.

23·8 Topographic maps are made to give rather complete descriptions of the areas shown. This includes such information as boundaries, natural features, the works of man, vegetation, and relief (elevations and depressions). Symbols are used for many of the features shown on topographic maps, some of which are given in Fig. 23-8a. Maps using topographic symbols can be obtained at nominal cost from the Director, U.S. Geological Survey, Department of the Interior, or the U.S. Coast and Geodetic Survey, Department of Commerce, Washington, D.C. Naval charts (maps) come from the Hydrographic Office in the Bureau of Navigation of the Navy Department. Government map drafting is the finest.

Aeronautical maps make use of special symbols which need to be understood in order to read them. Some symbols from the U.S. Coast and Geodetic Survey are shown in Fig. 23-8b.

Fig. 23-8a. Some conventional symbols used on maps.

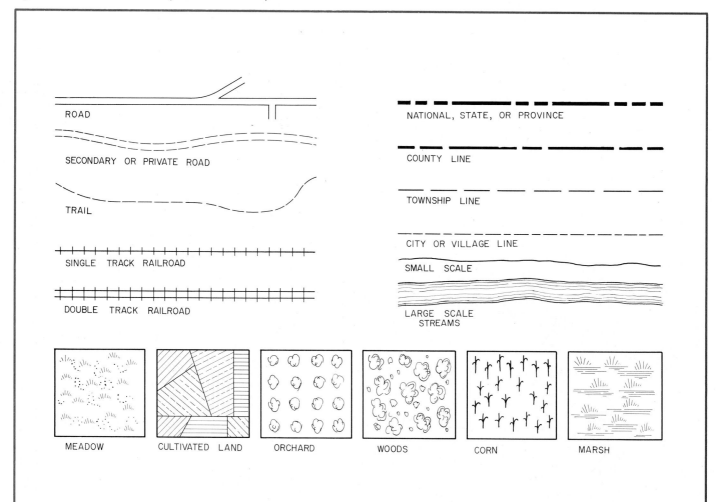

ROAD

SECONDARY OR PRIVATE ROAD

TRAIL

SINGLE TRACK RAILROAD

DOUBLE TRACK RAILROAD

NATIONAL, STATE, OR PROVINCE

COUNTY LINE

TOWNSHIP LINE

CITY OR VILLAGE LINE

SMALL SCALE

LARGE SCALE
STREAMS

MEADOW   CULTIVATED LAND   ORCHARD   WOODS   CORN   MARSH

23•9 Block diagrams. Consideration has been given to mapping in the horizontal plane and the vertical plane by profiles, or sections. To aid in the visual understanding of this three-dimensional problem, use of a *block diagram* is also employed. It is a three-dimensional projection using the isometric view (Fig. 23-9). This block diagram has been developed from Fig. 23-7a. Keep in mind that each contour represents a level plane, similar to a card in a deck of cards. True lengths are measured on the isometric axes.

23•10 Geological mapping. Geology is the science dealing with the makeup and structure of the earth's surface, crusts, and interior depths. As an aid to understanding, the methods of pictorial representation discussed in this book are used in modified form to meet the special needs of this science.

The surface crust of the earth is made up of three groups of rock: igneous (crystalline), sedimentary, and metamorphic. Crystalline rocks, for purposes of this general discussion, are the basic materials making up the earth's crustal ring. This rock was once molten; it has cooled, but it has not been eroded or its makeup changed. Sedimentary rocks, as a rule, are deposited in water in layers of varying thicknesses similar to the layers of an onion. If the onion is cut perpendicular to its axis, a series of concentric rings will be noted. In a slice of the earth's crust made in a sedimentary area, a similar pattern could be seen; a series of layers identifiable by texture, color, and material are visible (refer to pictures of the Grand Canyon). Metamor-

Fig. 23-9. A block diagram shows a block of earth by an isometric view. This picture was made from Fig. 23-7a.

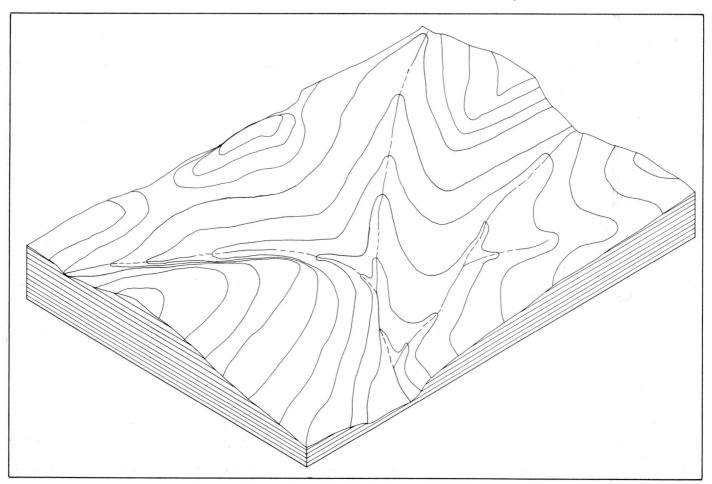

Fig. 23-8b. Some aeronautical chart symbols. *(U.S. Coast and Geodetic Survey)*

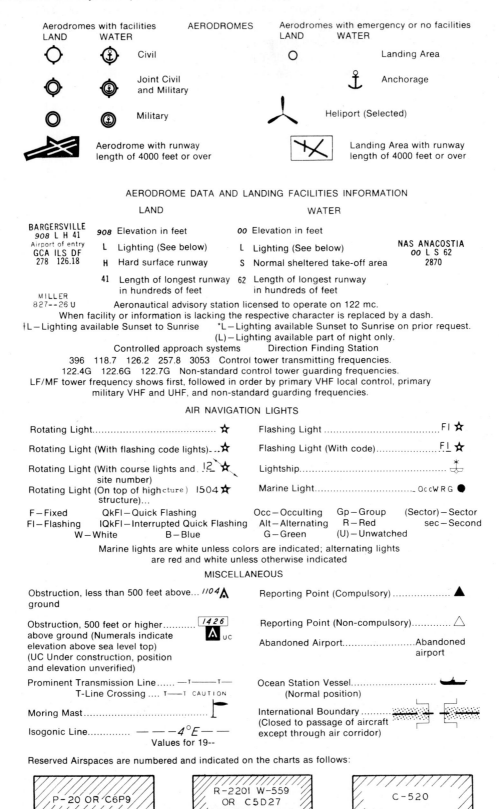

AERODROMES

Aerodromes with facilities
LAND   WATER

○   ⚓   Civil

◎   ⊕   Joint Civil and Military

◎   ◎   Military

Aerodrome with runway length of 4000 feet or over

Aerodromes with emergency or no facilities
LAND   WATER

○   Landing Area

⚓   Anchorage

Heliport (Selected)

Landing Area with runway length of 4000 feet or over

AERODROME DATA AND LANDING FACILITIES INFORMATION

LAND

BARGERSVILLE
908 L H 41
Airport of entry
GCA ILS DF
278 126.18

MILLER
827--26 U

908 Elevation in feet

L Lighting (See below)

H Hard surface runway

41 Length of longest runway in hundreds of feet

WATER

00 Elevation in feet

L Lighting (See below)

S Normal sheltered take-off area

62 Length of longest runway in hundreds of feet

NAS ANACOSTIA
00 L S 62
2870

Aeronautical advisory station licensed to operate on 122 mc.
When facility or information is lacking the respective character is replaced by a dash.
†L—Lighting available Sunset to Sunrise   *L—Lighting available Sunset to Sunrise on prior request.
(L)—Lighting available part of night only.
Controlled approach systems   Direction Finding Station
396 118.7 126.2 257.8 3053 Control tower transmitting frequencies.
122.4G 122.6G 122.7G Non-standard control tower guarding frequencies.
LF/MF tower frequency shows first, followed in order by primary VHF local control, primary
military VHF and UHF, and non-standard guarding frequencies.

AIR NAVIGATION LIGHTS

Rotating Light.. ☆   Flashing Light .... Fl ☆

Rotating Light (With flashing code lights)..☆   Flashing Light (With code).................... Fl ☆

Rotating Light (With course lights and ..!2 ☆   Lightship...
site number)

Rotating Light (On top of high cture) 1504 ☆   Marine Light............................... OccWRG ●
structure)...

F—Fixed   QkFl—Quick Flashing   Occ—Occulting   Gp—Group   (Sector)—Sector
Fl—Flashing   IQkFl—Interrupted Quick Flashing   Alt—Alternating   R—Red   sec—Second
W—White   B—Blue   G—Green   (U)—Unwatched

Marine lights are white unless colors are indicated; alternating lights
are red and white unless otherwise indicated

MISCELLANEOUS

Obstruction, less than 500 feet above... 1104 ▲
ground

Obstruction, 500 feet or higher........... 1426
above ground (Numerals indicate
elevation above sea level top)
(UC Under construction, position
and elevation unverified)

Prominent Transmission Line...... —T——T—
T-Line Crossing .... T——T CAUTION

Moring Mast..

Isogonic Line.............. — — —4°E— —
Values for 19--

Reporting Point (Compulsory) .... ▲

Reporting Point (Non-compulsory)............ △

Abandoned Airport.......................Abandoned
airport

Ocean Station Vessel.............................
(Normal position)

International Boundary..........
(Closed to passage of aircraft
except through air corridor)

Reserved Airspaces are numbered and indicated on the charts as follows:

P-20 OR C6P9	R-2201 W-559 OR C5D27	C-520
Prohibited Area	Restricted, Warning or Danger Area	Caution Area

phic rocks are generally considered to be sedimentary rocks which have been deeply buried, subjected to high temperatures, and so recomposed that they are no longer identifiable as sedimentary rocks.

Nature, being ever-changing, folds, tips, and slices these sedimentary layers in an infinite number of ways. It pierces these layers with intrusions of crystalline rock; it allows sedimentary layers to be formed on top of crystalline rocks and then tips the whole mass, perhaps pushing it for miles, raising it high above sea level or dropping it thousands of feet. The geologist making investigations has the problem of representing what has happened or what a particular area looks like.

Figure 23-10 is a part of a geological surface map. The red lines represent the line of surface exposure of the contact between two formations (the line of the two contacting layers shown in cutting the onion). The geologist locates this in the field and notes his observation point with the "tee" symbol. The direction of this contact (strike) is shown by the top of the tee, and the slope of the contact (dip) is indicated by the figures at the tee, such as 23° on the tee at the right-hand side and below the section line X–X. Since the stem of the tee, in this case, is pointing to the east, or to the right, the dip is 23° to the east; in other words, this formation slopes 23° below the horizontal and to the east. Another tee symbol on the left side shows a 30° dip and to the west. The heavy, broken line near the left edge represents a fault trace (the line along which the layer broke).

Fig. 23-10. Part of a geologic surface map.

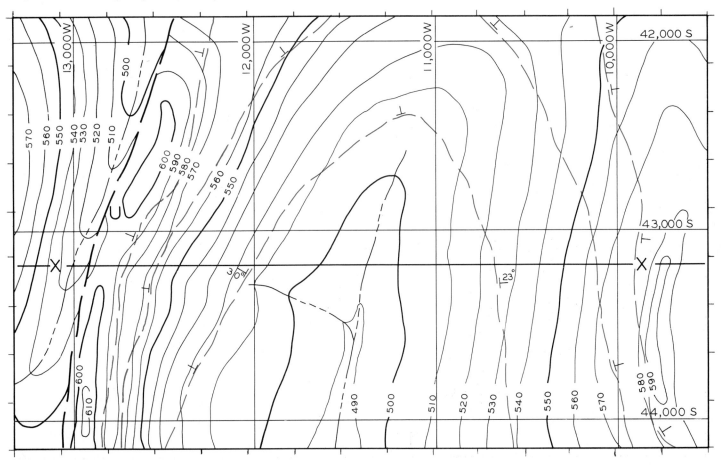

23•11 Geological sections supplement the surface map, and an example (Fig. 23-11) shows in an idealized way what the geologist believes the area below the surface to be like. This is a section along line *X–X* of Fig. 23-10. The dips which the geologist noted are used in developing the curvature of the folds. The geologist determines, too, by means of type section of the region, the various normal thicknesses of each formation, or strata, and applies these values in making this section. The fault, as indicated, shows the area to the right to be upthrown. The relative displacement is apparent by comparing the position of formation *A* on either side of the fault.

23•12 Subsurface mapping is a means of showing details of strata lying below the surface, such as the top or bottom of a given formation or possibly an assumed horizon. Data for constructing such a map is obtained from many sources, such as core holes, electrical logs, seismograph surveys, and so forth. An example is shown in Fig. 23-12, where data were obtained from electrical logs taken in a series of oil wells. The wells are located on a grid pattern, with producing wells indicated by a solid black circle and dry holes by an open circle and outward, extending rays. The top of a producing sand which is cut by a fault on the west is shown. Notice that the contours are numbered with negative values, or subsea depths; the larger the subsea value, the deeper the point below sea level. Section *X–X* shows thickness of sand and the level of the *oil-water contact.*

Fig. 23-11. A geologic section along line X-X of Fig. 23-10.

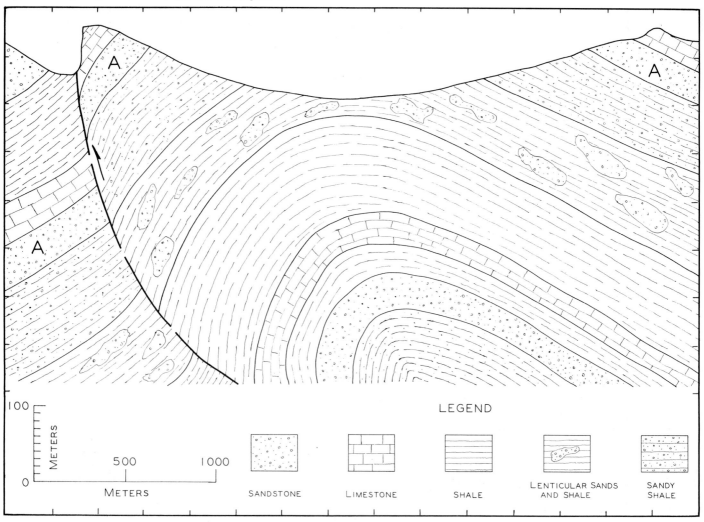

LEGEND

SANDSTONE   LIMESTONE   SHALE   LENTICULAR SANDS AND SHALE   SANDY SHALE

23•13 Geological maps, sections, and so forth, are greatly improved by use of colors. In Fig. 23-10 colors are applied to each of the formations exposed between the red formation contact lines. The same can be done in Fig. 23-11, applying the same colors to the corresponding formations. This device aids in bringing out the three-dimensional relationships of the surface and shape of the structure and helps greatly to understand the geology of the area. Paper prints of the tracing are colored with coloring crayons and rubbed carefully to give smooth, even color texture. Examples of color use may be seen on a U.S. Geological Survey map.

The making of geological maps and drawings is an important part of the extractive minerals industry, particularly for the petroleum part. With the aid of this art it is possible to maintain proper records and information to ensure continued activity in this economic field. Between 40,000 and 50,000 oil wells are drilled each year in the United States, and all this information, obtained and properly recorded, aids in keeping this industry moving forward. Standards for records vary from company to company, but generally they are well covered in the technical literature, such as publications of the A.I.M.E., petroleum branch, the A.A.P.G., U.S. Geological Survey, U.S. Bureau of Mines, and others.

23•14 Notes and definitions. Maps are important in the understanding of the news, in the study of geography and history, in making auto trips, and in

Fig. 23-12. A structural map showing strata details below the surface.

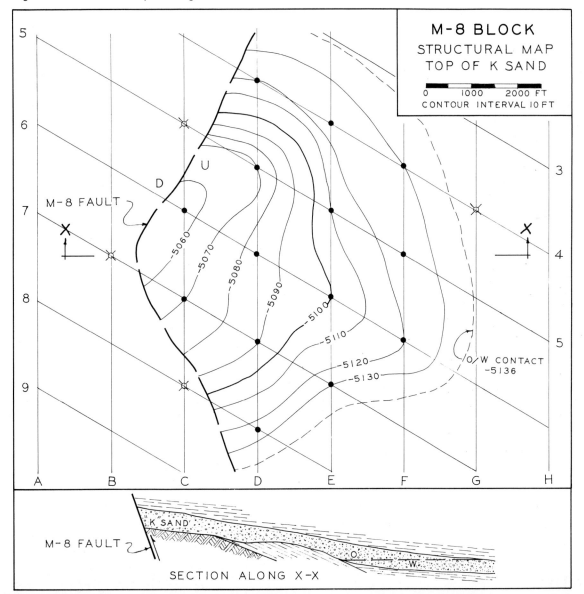

surveying, geology, civil engineering, petroleum engineering, and space exploration.

The earth's surface is in the general form of a sphere. The surface of sphere cannot be exactly developed; however, systems have been devised for making maps of degrees of accuracy to meet the requirements for different purposes. The subject of map projection and the various systems which have been worked out is a rather extensive study and is beyond the scope of this book.

Brief definitions for some of the terms used are listed here. For more complete descriptions refer to books on surveying and geology.

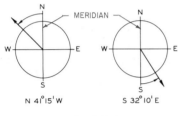

BEARINGS

1. *Bearing:* The direction of a line as shown by its angle with a north-south line (meridian).
2. *Meridian:* North-south line.

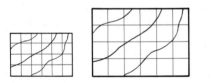

ENLARGING BY GRIDS

3. *Grid:* Generally, a series of uniformly spaced horizontal and perpendicular lines used to locate points by coordinates, or for enlarging or reducing a figure (Art. 4·7).

PROFILE

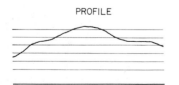

4. *Profile:* A section of the earth on a vertical plane showing the intersection of the surface of the earth and the plane (see Fig. 23-6a).

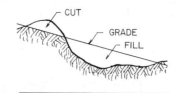

5. *Cut:* Earth to be removed to prepare for construction as for a desired level or slope for a road.
6. *Fill:* Earth to be supplied and put in place to prepare for a construction in order to obtain a desired level or slope.
7. *Grade:* A particular level or slope as a downgrade.

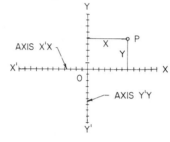

COORDINATE SYSTEM

8. *Coordinate system:* A system for locating points by reference to lines, generally at right angles.

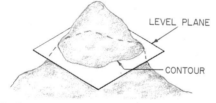

9. *Contour:* A line of constant level showing where a level plane cuts through the surface of the earth (see Fig. 23-6a).
10. *Block diagram:* A pictorial drawing (generally isometric) of a block of earth showing profiles and contours (see Fig. 23-9).

FAULT

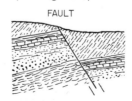

11. *Fault:* A break in the earth's crust with a movement of one side of the break parallel to the line of the break.

STRATA

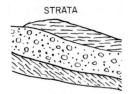

12. *Stratum:* A layer of rock, earth, sand, and the like, horizontal or inclined, arranged in flat form distinct from the matter next to it. (Plural is strata.)

FOLD

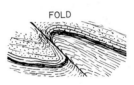

DIP

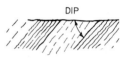

14. *Dip:* The angle that a stratum, or like geological feature, makes with a horizontal plane.
15. *Strike:* The place where a vein crops out, or extension of a stratum in a direction at right angles to a dip.

23·15 Problem suggestions. Group 23, page 549. These problems are designed to give an elementary idea of map drawing. It would add to the value of this study if maps of various kinds could be at hand for inspection.

Problems 23·1 to 23·23 indicate a few of the great variety of maps which are made for many purposes. A selection may be made from these according to the instructor's experience and the local interests of the students.

24
Graphic charts and diagrams

24·1 Graphic charts and diagrams form a very special division of the graphic language for scientists, engineers, statisticians, doctors, and just about everyone else.

The scientist uses charts and diagrams to record and study the results of research. The engineer uses them to record the properties and behavior of materials, operation tests, etc.; the statistician, to study and explain facts and trends of numerical information. Doctors use charts and diagrams to keep records of your temperature, heart action, and body functions when you are sick, and everyone uses them to see about the weather, the stock market, taxes, where the dollar goes, and for a multitude of other purposes. Industrial hazards often make graphic charts of vital importance in providing for health protection. In Fig. 24-1, graphic charts are being made from the records of persons working on atomic submarines and aircraft carriers. Such charts are used to make sure that their doses of radiation remain below permissible limits.

24·2 Definitions. Graphic charts are graphic methods for making information consisting of series of numbers and words visible and for comparing conditions represented by numerical information or mathematical formulas. Graphic charts show trends, such as whether the cost of living, wages, etc., are rising or falling over a period of time and whether one is rising and the other falling.

Graphic charts also provide a quick (approximate) method of obtaining numerical results from mathematical

Fig. 24-1. Drawing a radiation curve from dosimeter readings. The chart is used for a radiation control. *(Newport News Shipbuilding and Drydock Company)*

equations or conditions. The chart in Fig. 24-2a shows the water level in a lake after a heavy rainfall. Note that the normal level is about 30.75 ft; the maximum rise is about 2 ft and occurs about 4 hr after the water starts to rise. A *curve* on a graphic chart is the line shown on the chart (Fig. 24-2b). The "curve" may be a straight line, as at A; a broken line, as at B; a straight line adjusted to plotted points, as at C; a stepped line, as at D; a curve, as at E; or a curve adjusted to plotted points, as at F.

The selection of the proper scales to use is important and often difficult. The vertical and horizontal scales must be such that the curve will give a true picture of the conditions presented. A wrong impression may be given by the angle of slope of the curve (Fig. 24-2c at A and B).

24·3 Printed grid or graph paper (Fig. 24-3) is available in many forms and is both convenient and timesaving. It may be purchased with lines ruled 4, 5, 8, 10, 16, and 20 to the inch and in a great many other forms. Rulings ½ or 1 in. apart, or 5 or 10 spaces apart, may be ruled with a heavier line for convenience in plotting and reading. The rulings may form squares or rectangles.

24·4 Rectangular coordinates. The graph paper mentioned in Art. 24·3 provides a prepared base for plotting curve data of graphic charts on a grid system. The grid system uses two main reference lines called *coordinate axes*.

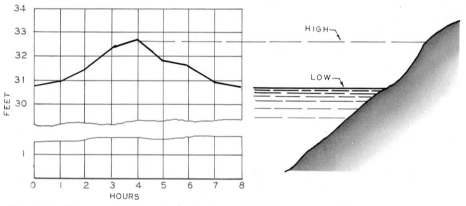

Fig. 24-2a. This graphic chart shows the rise and fall of water on a lake.

Fig. 24-2b. Curves on graphic charts may have different forms.

Fig. 24-2c. A false impression may result if vertical and horizontal scales are not properly selected.

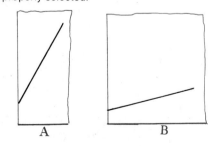

Fig. 24-3. Graph paper is available in a great many forms and printed in different colors.

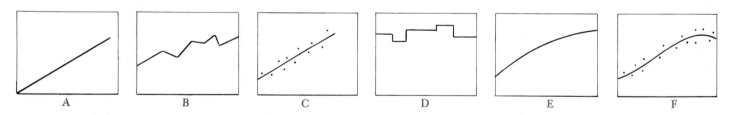

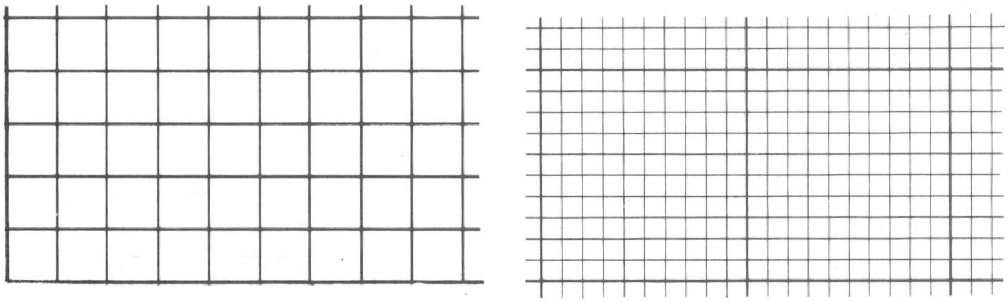

These are two intersecting lines perpendicular to each other at a zero point (Fig. 24-4a). The horizontal axis, X–X', is called the *abscissa,* or X axis, and the vertical axis is called the *ordinate,* or Y axis. These are called *coordinate axes,* and they divide the sheet into four parts, or quadrants. The quadrants are numbered counterclockwise, as shown. Points are plotted by perpendicular measurements from the axes, or zero lines. All four quadrants are used for mathematical charts. Values measured perpendicular to the Y axis and to the right are + (plus), and those to the left are − (minus). Values measured above the X axis are + (plus), and those below are − (minus). Horizontal distances are X coordinates; vertical distances are Y coordinates; thus, for a two-coordinate chart every point has an X and a Y coordinate. The first quadrant, the upper right-hand corner, is removed from Fig. 24-4a in Fig. 24-4b and serves for most rectilinear, or line, charts. The grids may be squares or horizontal or vertical rectangles.

24·5 Rectilinear, or line, charts are made on ruled paper with points plotted from a horizontal axis (X axis) and a vertical axis (Y axis), which means that rectangular coordinates are used. Rectilinear charts are used to show the amount of change during intervals, to show trends, and to show successive values from experiments or recorded information.

A graphic chart may contain one or several curves. A conversion chart with one curve (Fig. 24-5a) is often convenient for changing from one value to another. This one provides for changing from one temperature to another. The time series chart in Fig. 24-5b gives the time in seconds to go a quarter of a mile at different speeds in miles per hour. Graphic charts are often a convenient

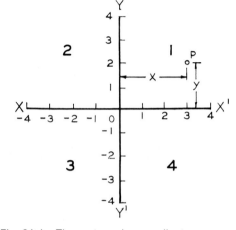

Fig. 24-4a. The rectangular coordinate axes provide the base for plotting many kinds of charts.

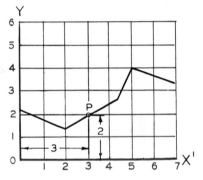

Fig. 24-4b. A graphic chart drawn in the first quadrant is shown here.

Fig. 24-5a. A conversion chart.

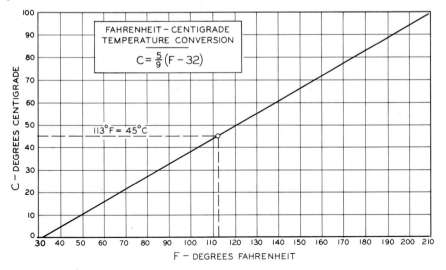

Fig. 24-5b. A time series chart.

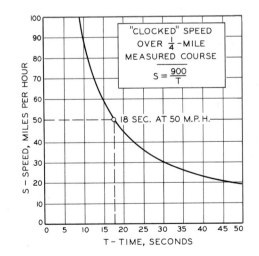

way of visualizing the solutions of a formula. A combination line chart is drawn in Fig. 24-5c. The annual average is given for comparison. There are two curves, one for each region and a third which combines both regions.

24•6 To draw a chart. The following list suggests an order to follow in drawing a chart. (1) Prepare and list, or assemble, the information to be represented. (2) Select the kind of chart best suited to present the information properly. (3) Consider whether to use plain or ready-ruled graphic chart paper. (4) Select a suitable size and proportion to give the desired result. (5) Select the proper scales. (6) If graphic paper is not used, lay off and draw thin horizontal (X axis) and vertical (Y axis) lines. (7) Lay off the scale divisions on the X axis and the Y axis. (8) Letter the scale values at the properly selected divisions on the X axis and the Y axis. (9) Plot the points accurately from the listed information. [The engineer's scale (Art. 2·26) is often convenient for plotting]. (10) Letter a suitable title. If plotted points are indicated, it is generally better to use *open* circles, triangles, squares, etc., rather than crosses or blacked-in circles.

If more than one curve is drawn on a chart, use different lines for each curve (Fig. 24-6). Use a full, continuous line for the most important curve, then a thin line, a long-dash line with a short-dash line, etc., to identify the different curves. In general, the scales and other identifying notes, or captions, are placed beneath the X axis and to the left of the Y axis. For wide charts it is sometimes desirable to show the vertical

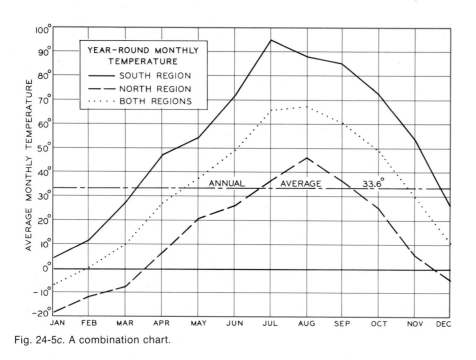

Fig. 24-5c. A combination chart.

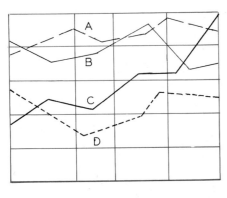

Fig. 24-6. A multiline chart. Use different lines to distinguish different curves.

Fig. 24-7. An engineering test chart.

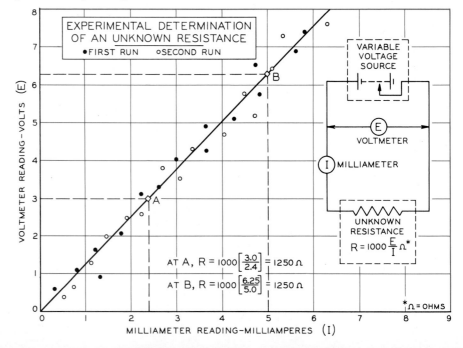

scale at both the right and the left for convenient reading.

24•7 Engineering charts. Experimental data may be plotted from tests and used to obtain an unknown value. In Fig. 24-7 the results of tests have been plotted and show as a straight line curve when drawn in an adjusted position. (Ω is the Greek letter omega.) The curve is a straight line, and values can be taken from two points and inserted in the formula to obtain and check the value of the unknown resistance.

24•8 Nomograms are charts which show the solutions to formulas contain-ing three or more variables. Figure 24-8 is an example of this type of chart. A straight edge from values on the outside scales will cross the inside scale, where the solution to the equation may be read. Nomography is a special divi-sion of chart construction which re-quires more than simple mathematics.

24•9 Bar charts are probably the most familiar and most easily read and understood kind of graphic charts. A bar chart may consist of a single rec-tangle representing 100 percent (Fig. 24-9a). This chart represents the haz-ards of a nuclear explosion by the ver-tical rectangle, or bar. It is divided to show the proportional part, or percent-age, of the total for each part.

To draw a 100 percent bar chart, lay off the long side equal to 100 units (as 10 in. = 100 tenths) with an engineer's scale (Art. 2·26), or 12½ in. = 100 eighths, etc. Select a suitable width. Lay off the percentages of the parts of the total on the vertical side and draw lines parallel to the base. The parts should have distinctive crosshatching, shading, or colors, as shown. This form of chart is preferred to the circular per-centage chart of Fig. 24-10 for engi-neering uses. Lettering must be put in or near the parts and placed so that it can be read easily.

Fig. 24-8. A nomogram provides graphic solutions to an equation when many answers are required and when it would take a great amount of time to work out separate solutions.

Fig. 24-9a. A one-column bar chart used as a 100 percent chart.

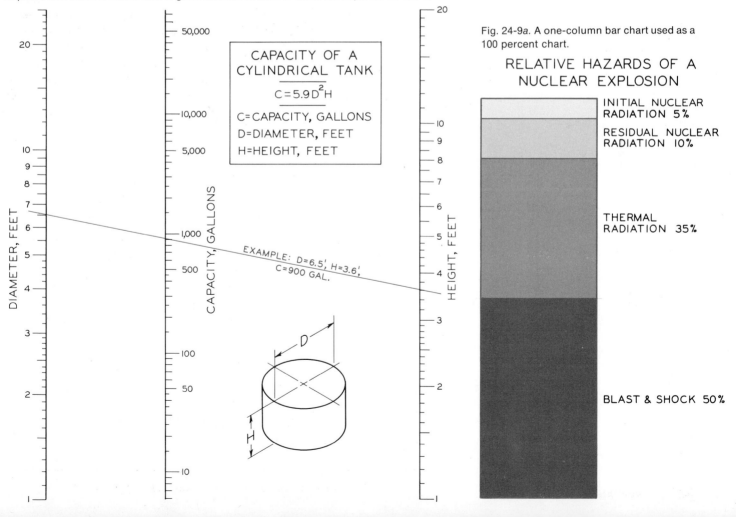

CAPACITY OF A CYLINDRICAL TANK

$$C = 5.9 D^2 H$$

C = CAPACITY, GALLONS
D = DIAMETER, FEET
H = HEIGHT, FEET

EXAMPLE: D = 6.5', H = 3.6', C = 900 GAL.

RELATIVE HAZARDS OF A NUCLEAR EXPLOSION

INITIAL NUCLEAR RADIATION 5%

RESIDUAL NUCLEAR RADIATION 10%

THERMAL RADIATION 35%

BLAST & SHOCK 50%

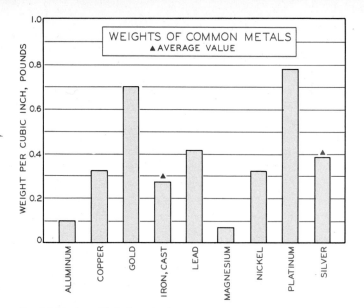

Fig. 24-9*b*. A multiple-bar chart.

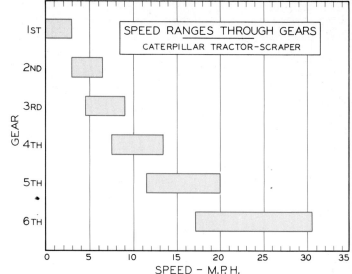

Fig. 24-9*c*. This horizontal-bar chart is a form of progressive chart. (*Caterpillar Tractor Company*)

A multiple-bar chart with vertical bars is shown in Fig. 24-9*b*, where the weights of a number of metals are compared. The heights of the bars are, of course, laid off with the same scale. The widths of the bars are uniform. A bar chart with horizontal bars is shown in Fig. 24-9*c*, which gives speed ranges for a Caterpillar tractor. Note that the

bars do not start at a common line because they show different speed ranges. This is called a *progressive chart*.

A compound-bar chart is shown in Fig. 24-9*d*, where the total length of the bars is made up of two parts. The gray part is the distance traveled at a given speed before starting to apply the brakes. The red part is the distance

traveled in coming to a stop. The gray and the red parts are added together graphically to give the total distance.

The multiple-bar chart shown in Fig. 24-9*e* has minus values, and these are set off below the *X* axis by red bars. The same information is given in Fig. 24-9*f*, where the vertical scale is the same as in Fig. 24-9*e*. The dash line shows the

Fig. 24-9*d*. A compound-bar chart in which the total length of each bar is the sum of two parts.

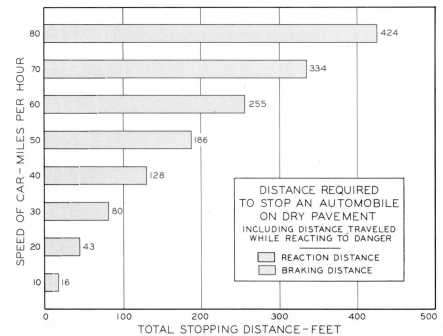

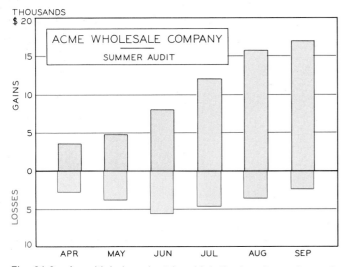

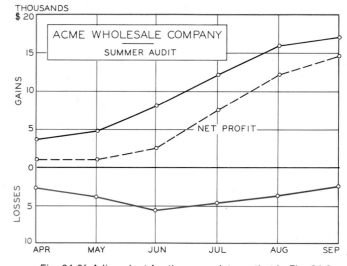

Fig. 24-9e. A multiple-bar chart in which the bars have plus and minus values.

Fig. 24-9f. A line chart for the same data as that in Fig. 24-9e.

net gain and is found by laying off the minus values down from the total-gain values.

24•10 Pie charts, or sector diagrams (Fig. 24-10). This is a form of 100 percent chart in which a circle represents 100 percent and sectors represent parts of the whole.

To draw a pie chart, 3.6° = 1% if a protractor is used, or 7.2 minutes = 1% if the circle represents a clock face. Lay off the percentage for each part on the circle and draw the radial lines; the sectors will represent the parts. The sectors should have distinctive cross-hatching, shading, or coloring. Lettering is very important and should be

placed in the sectors, if possible, or close to them with pointing arrows, as illustrated.

24•11 Tape drafting is a convenient method of preparing graphic charts. Adhesive tape comes in many colors, designs, and widths. It is applied from a roll dispenser (Fig. 24-11) and pressed

Fig. 24-11. Applying adhesive tape to a graphic chart. *(Chart-Pak, Inc.)*

Fig. 24-10. A 100 percent circular chart, or pie chart.

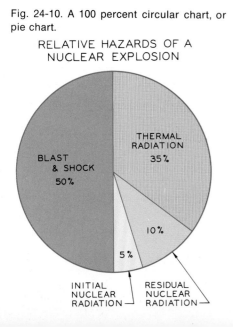

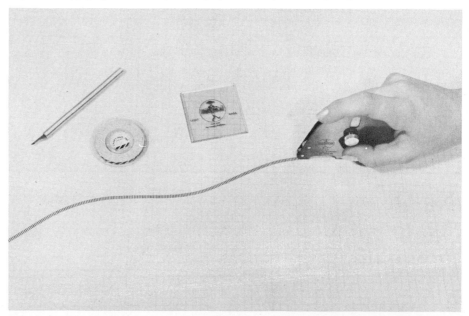

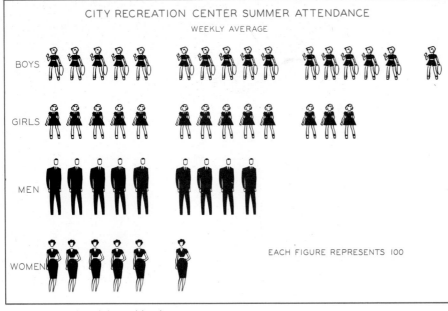

Fig. 24-12*a*. A pictorial graphic chart.

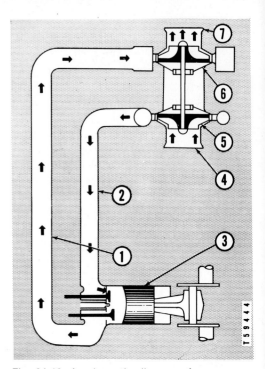

Fig. 24-13. A schematic diagram of an exhaust-gas turbocharging system. *(Caterpillar Tractor Company)*

onto the chart in the desired position. Tapes of selected widths provide a quick and simple way of making bar charts.

24•12 Pictorial charts are, in effect, bar charts which use pictures or symbols in place of bars. Figure 24-12*a* illustrates a pictorial graphic chart. Each figure represents 100 people; it could represent 1000 or any assigned number. The figure is a multiple-bar chart; there are four kinds of individuals represented. Adhesive symbols are available in many forms (Fig. 24-12*b*); they make pictorial charts easy to construct.

24•13 Schematics are diagrams which are more or less pictorial and designed to be easily read. Names of parts and methods of operation can be shown on a schematic. A schematic of an exhaust-gas turbocharging system used on a tractor engine is shown in Fig. 24-13.

24•14 Models have come to occupy an important place in relation to charts and diagrams. The engineer may use a scale model or a full-size mockup, which is sometimes an operative model, to explain or demonstrate to a nontechnical executive.

A *mockup* is a full-size model which may or may not be wholly operative; sometimes it is only partly operative, and sometimes it shows only size and appearance. Such mockups are useful for many purposes, such as checking design, accuracy of details, wiring, interference of parts, faults, and improvements. Mockups are made for a great many products, including automobiles, aircraft, machine tools, reactors, electric motors, space vehicles, and jet engines. Mockups look like the real thing;

Fig. 24-12*b*. A few of the adhesive symbols for use on graphic charts. *(Chart-Pak, Inc.)*

they are made of wood, metal, clay, and other materials, according to the specific purposes for which they are being prepared.

Models are frequently used in the development of aerospace activities. Figure 24-14*a* shows a model of the Advent Communications Satellite. In orbit at 23,000 miles above the equator, it would appear to be more or less stationary over a point on the earth. Three satellites spaced 120° apart around the equator could provide worldwide communication coverage.

The construction of a public utility plant may be preceded by a model made from the drawings to study the layout and appearance (Fig. 24-14*b*). The architect represents important buildings and important projects by perspectives and models for presentation of the appearance, for study and approval, and for promotional purposes.

Fig. 24-14*a*. A model of the Advent Communications Satellite. *(U.S. Army photograph)*

Fig. 24-14*b*. A model of an electric power plant.

24·15 Organization and flow charts.

Organization charts are of many kinds but have the features of a flow chart. Figure 24-15a is an example; it shows the path, or flow, of drawings from the top engineer to the shop. It also shows the organization of the drafting department.

A flow chart may show the path or series of operations in manufacturing a product or in producing a material, such as the flow chart of steelmaking (Fig. 24-15b).

24·16 Charts and elements of charts.

There is an almost endless variety of graphic charts which may be made for visual communication. This chapter has suggested the general character of a few of the great variety of graphic charts and how they are used.

A variety of charts are shown in Figs. 24-16a to 24-16h to indicate some of the elements of chart making and to suggest the ways in which these elements affect the chart.

Every chart should have a suitable title, well lettered and placed within the area of the chart. See the illustrations in Arts. 24·5, 24·7, and 24·9, as well as others.

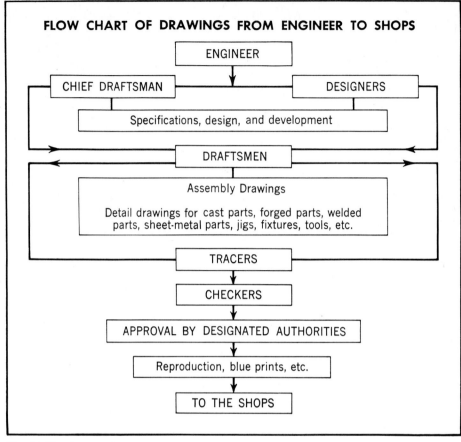

Fig. 24-15a. An organization and flow chart.

Fig. 24-15b. A flow chart of steelmaking. *(American Iron and Steel Institute)*

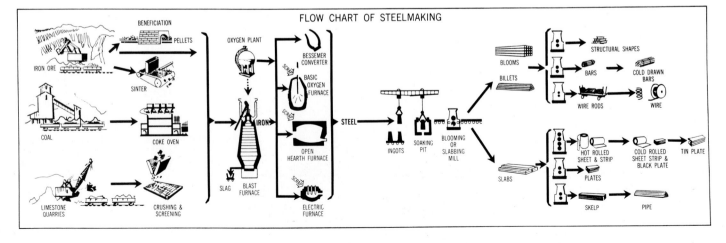

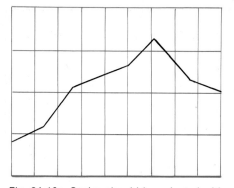

Fig. 24-16a. Scales should be selected with care so that the curve plotted from the data will aid the understanding of the information by its appearance.

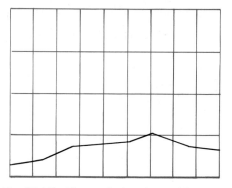

Fig. 24-16b. The vertical scale used here is too small. It gives the effect of very little change in values. The "movement" is slow.

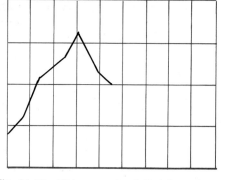

Fig. 24-16c. This curve is plotted from the same data used for Figs. 24-16a and 24-16b. The horizontal scale is too small (if Fig. 24-16a is a correct picture). The "movement" is fast.

Fig. 24-16d. A step chart shows data which remain constant during regular or irregular intervals. This figure might show time periods during which a price remained constant or was raised or lowered.

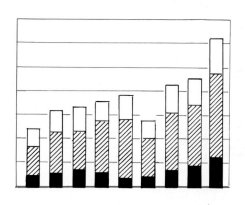

Fig. 24-16e. A shaded-surface, or strata, chart uses shading for contrast. This illustration might show the total amount of each of two materials used each month.

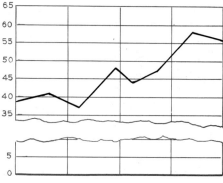

Fig. 24-16f. An omission chart may be used for some purposes, as shown, in order to use a larger vertical scale. There are no values below 35, so a portion of the chart is *broken out*.

Fig. 24-16g. A comparison-bar chart which might be used for two or three values. The illustration might show the amount made (A) and the amount sold (B) of an item by three different companies in one year, or for three years by one company.

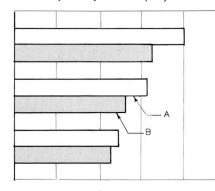

Fig. 24-16h. A multiple-bar chart with divided bars. The bars are divided to show the amount of each of three substances which make up the total.

25
Functional drafting

25·1 Functional drafting is a somewhat new term, but it is not a new practice. Nor is it the companion term of simplified drafting. Drafting is concerned with making a drawing as a means of communication. A drawing has a function to perform, and it should be done in the most effective way. It must be clear, have only one meaning, and be easily read and understood. To be clear, it must have only whatever is necessary of lines, views, notes, and dimensions to give a complete description. It must not leave anything to guess.

25·2 Development of functional drafting. Ancient drawings had pictorial characteristics (Chap. 1), some of which continued with the coming of separate views and projection drawing. With industrial development, progress in functional drafting has continued to take place. Ornamentation decreased to using heavy shade lines, shading cylindrical surfaces, and more or less realistic representation of screw threads and other similar items. Such a drawing is illustrated in Fig. 25-2, where an elevation of a bracket is shown at A; the front elevation of a back plate to which the bracket is attached is shown at B; a side elevation of the box is shown at C; a section lengthwise is shown at D; a plan of the bottom half of the box is shown at E; and a plan of the top is shown at F. Figure 25-2 is from Appletons' *Encyclopedia of Drawing* (1857). The following quotation from the same source indicates interest in functional drawing at that early date.

"Working drawings are complete illustrations of a machine, either as a whole or in detail, sufficient to enable the mechanic to construct it. They should be of a large enough scale, that all the parts may be readily measured, or with dimensions in figures—this last is of importance, even when the scale is measurable. To the mechanic, it saves time and one source of error, but throws more responsibility on the draughtsman. Working drawings should be almost entirely in line, with shading only sufficient to distinguish circular from flat parts."

At the time the above was written and for many years after, shade lines and cylinder shading continued to be used. Then shading and heavy shade lines were discontinued for detail and working drawings but were continued for assembly drawings. They are still used in certain cases for effect, more or less, or as illustration drawings for advertising or in catalogs. Standard lines for

Fig. 25-2. An assembly working drawing with shade lines (about 1857).

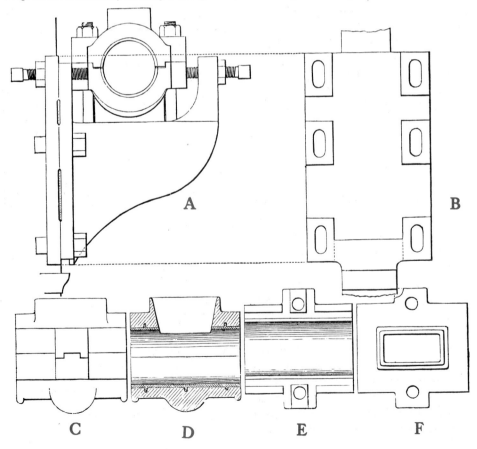

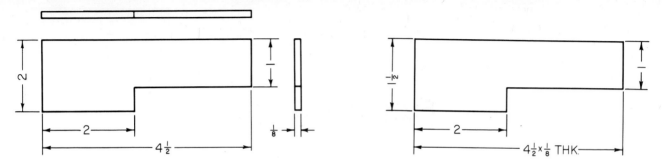

Fig. 25-5a. Conventional and functional drawings. One view is better than two or three views.

inked lines on drawings (Fig. 8-3) came into use as well as symbols for representation of details such as screw threads (Fig. 12-8c) and other standard details. The next big step in the progress of functional drafting was the dropping of the inked drawing, or tracing, and the use of drawings finished with the lead pencil.

25·3 A functional drawing *is a drawing which describes what it is meant to describe, using the fewest views and the fewest lines that will provide the exact information and that can be read and understood by the user without unnecessary difficulty.* It is a clearly stated and exact graphic description in the most direct and easily read form.

Functional means practical, useful and exactly suited to a purpose. A functional drawing must always be made with particular attention to the user. Functional drawing is not a new kind of drawing but is an examination of how the efficiency of graphic description can be improved for some purpose.

25·4 Classes of functional drawing. There are three types of functional drawings.

Class 1: In-company or local working drawings can be simplified in ways peculiar to that company's product, as the employees are familiar with the product. A minimum of detail and information is required. It must be remembered that such drawings, while func-

tional for the company where used, would have little use in another company or for an unrelated product.

Class 2: For a field of industry or engineering of a class such as machine tool, aeronautical, automotive, electrical, etc. In a given industry, drawings can use simplification common to that industry. The various industries have developed simplified drawing practices which serve their own requirements. Some of these practices serve more than one industry and by modification have become general.

Class 3: General functional drawing is a common graphic language which is the basis for all uses of drawings. The *American Drafting Standards Manual* is the accepted authority for the developing of functional drawings in general use and for certain fields of engineering.

25·5 Simplified drafting is one of the factors in functional drafting which has resulted from the increase in the number and complexity of drawings and the increase in understanding of and ability to read orthographic views. It has made it possible to simplify drawings by eliminating some views, parts of views, certain details, lines, and treatments of views. Drawings have been made easier to read by the use of simpler representation and symbols for familiar features and many standard or regular items. (See Chaps. 10 and 12.) The two main reasons for simplification are to make a drawing more functional and to save

time in making the drawing. Some suggestions for simplified drafting are shown in Figs. 25-5a through 25-5h.

One view can often be used to describe a part. A piece of uniform thickness can be shown in one view by using a note to tell the thickness (Figs. 25-5a and 25-5b), where the conventional views are shown at A and the functional view is shown at B. The circular view of

Fig. 25-5b. Conventional and functional drawings.

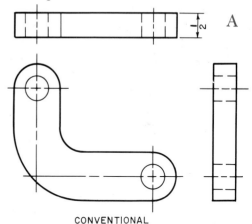

CONVENTIONAL

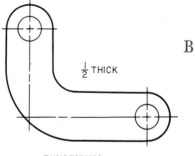

FUNCTIONAL

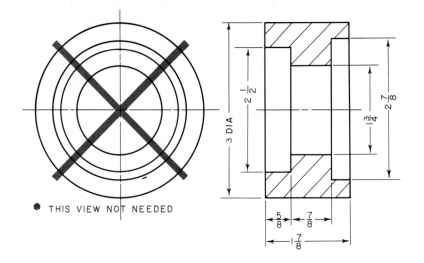

Fig. 25-5c. The left-hand view adds nothing. Omit it.

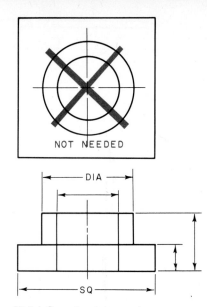

Fig. 25-5d. One view is enough.

many cylindrical parts does not aid in the description, and it is better to omit it in such cases (Figs. 25-5c and 25-5d). When you make drawings, the principle view and a note will often result in a more functional drawing. An unneeded view takes the user's time to find out that it is not needed. The same principle of not drawing unneeded views applies to a greater extent where two views serve better than three views. Care must be taken to select the right two views (see Art. 5·14). When a third view does not tell anything not shown by two views, do not draw it. Note that the top view in Fig. 25-5e does not help.

Holes are negative cylinders; and when holes are to be drilled, reamed, countersunk, etc., notes are used to give the necessary finishing information (see Art. 11·24). Since a note is used, it can be used with a leader, and the location of the hole, or holes, can be shown by center lines (Fig. 25-5f). If it is neces-

Fig. 25-5e. Two views are better than three views.

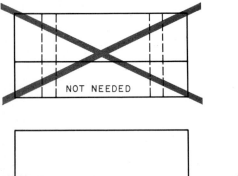

Fig. 25-5f. Holes can sometimes be shown by crossed center lines to locate the centers.

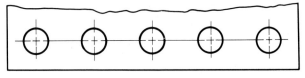

CONVENTIONAL

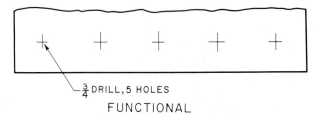

$\frac{3}{4}$ DRILL, 5 HOLES

FUNCTIONAL

5 BOLTS 1×2½

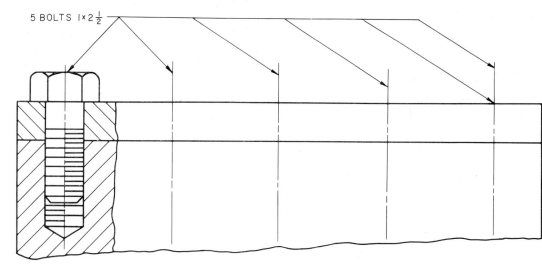

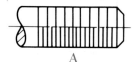

A

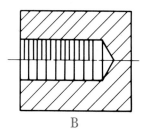

B

Fig. 25-5g. Repeated details do not have to be drawn. Note the simplified screw-thread symbol.

sary to draw a repeating detail, it may be drawn once and indicated by a note in repeated positions (Fig. 25-5g). A simplified screw-thread symbol (not standard) which can be drawn quickly and which keeps an external thread, A, separate from an internal thread, B, is used in Fig. 25-5g.

Other ways of simplifying drawings to make them more functional have become regular practice and have been described in the preceding chapters. Such methods include the use of wide spacing for section lining, or just short lines around the outline, the use of half views or quarter views, broken-out views, symmetrical half views, and simplified screw thread symbols. (See Chaps. 10 and 11.)

Many companies have their own standards for simplified practice. A few examples from Brown & Sharpe Manufacturing Company are shown in Fig. 25-5h. This illustration shows the improvement by comparison. Some of the practices have come into wide use, as they are general in character. When and where and how to use simplified draw-

Fig. 25-5h. Samples of company simplified practice. *(Brown & Sharpe Manufacturing Company)*

CONVENTIONAL
FORMER PRACTICE

SIMPLIFIED
RECOMMENDED PRACTICE

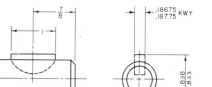

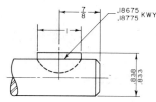

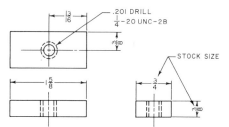

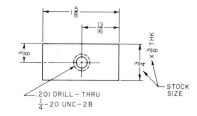

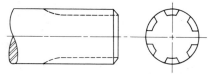

| DRAWING | *INCLINE 75* |

Fig. 25-7*a*. Old-style imitation "hand-printed" letters were anything but functional.

ings are three questions which require experience and thought to be sure of meeting the requirements of functional drawings.

25•6 General rules for functional drafting. These are general rules and are not laws. They are to be considered and used with judgment when they will make a better functional drawing.

1. Legibility is the first rule.
2. If words will describe as well or better, use words.
3. If one view is sufficient, do not use two or three views.
4. If two views are sufficient, do not use three views.
5. Do not draw a repeated detail more than once. Show other positions by center lines or least amount of outline with identification.
6. Use numbers or names to identify standard items. Do not draw them.

7. Do not draw unnecessary hidden lines. If necessary, use long dashes.
8. Do not use sectioning if it is not needed for clarity or if an exterior view will do as well or better.
9. Use freehand or combination work to draw views where suitable.
10. Do not make simple views (or any views) too large. Reduced-size prints are better than large drawings.

25•7 Functional lettering. The first rule is *legibility*. Functional lettering was greatly improved by the work of Charles W. Reinhardt of the Engineering News in the early 1900s by his plain, legible lettering. The development of the American Standards has provided lettering standards for capital and lower-case letters as well as vertical and inclined letters (Fig. 3-1). Capital letters, either vertical or inclined, are in general use.

Early drawings often used regular handwriting for notes and such dimensions as were given. A form of "round writing," made with a wide flat-nib pen which gave shaded characters, was sometimes used. An imitation "printed letter" (Fig. 25-7*a*) was much used until the present simplified single-stroke engineering letters and numbers (Chap. 3) became standard practice.

Legible letters and numbers are a must for functional drawings and most companies prescribe the American Standard, or very similar forms, sometimes with a little variation in a number to make it more functional for their purposes. An example is shown in Fig. 25-7*b*, taken from the Caterpillar Engineering Standards from which the following is quoted: "Lettering must be sharp and dense to assure good reproduction. It may be freehand or with a mechanical guide. The vertical capital letters and numbers illustrated in Fig. 25-7*b* should be used for all purposes. The new style of number is more legible when making reproductions. Characters with cross lines must have the white space divided equally to prevent lines from melting together when reduced prints are made from microfilm. The composition of words and sentences should be arranged in a pleasing and legible form."

Functional lettering is a part of functional drawing and this requires the use of one or more of the methods of lettering according to the means available and the purpose for which the lettering is to be used. Freehand lettering is the most widely used, but templates, guides and scribers, printed and typed adhesives, and special typewriters are used also to help make functional drawings.

Fig. 25-7*b*. A company standard for functional letters and numbers. *(Caterpillar Tractor Company)*

A B C D E F G H I
J K L M N O P Q R
S T U V W X Y Z
1 2 3 4 5 6 7 8 9 0

25•8 Choice of method. Different methods of graphical description, orthographic views, sectional views, pictorial views, technical illustrations, diagrams, etc., have been described in the preceding chapters. Any of these methods, or a combination, may give the best functional drawing, and they should be considered when a question of clearness arises. Sometimes a pictorial view, or part view added to orthographic views, will make a drawing easier to read.

The arrangement of notes, and the arrangement of the views for a number of details on a sheet, can do much to make the drawing functional. Notes should have an orderly arrangement, near enough to where they apply to be seen at first glance. See some illustrations in Chap. 15. Where details of several parts are drawn on a sheet, keep the views of each part together with space to separate them from the views of other parts. Arrange them in order so that the views of any particular part can be easily found. Good placing of notes and views is necessary to make a functional drawing.

25•9 Work savers for making functional drawings consist of methods, tools, materials, and information or references. Some work savers have been mentioned in preceding chapters. They include the use of printed sheets with titles, printed adhesive notes and symbols, typewritten adhesives, standard drawings (Fig. 13-4g), tabular drawings (Fig. 16-9), templates in the great variety available for all symbols, stick lettering, microfilming, camera drafting, graph paper, etc.

The *American Drafting Standards Manual* is a source of general practice and the basis for alteration in making functional drawings. Other American Standards present graphic symbols for almost every kind of industry and field of engineering. These graphic symbols have been accepted and used for great efficiency in making functional drawings.

Half views for views symmetrical about a center line, part views, and enlarged views of small details can all be used to save time and effort and to provide functional drawings. Piping, wiring, and space description can be represented by single lines and symbols on "flat" or isometric drawings, as such drawings are easily read and understood by those who use them. Bolts, screws, washers, pins, and many standard parts can be "called out" in words or listed in a table, without drawing views of them, thus saving time and effort in making functional drawings.

25•10 Dimensions and the functional drawing. Definite dimensioning information, exactly suited to the purpose for which the part is made, is a most important part of functional drawing. Repeated or unnecessary dimensions must not be put on a drawing. From the simplicity of early drawings without dimensions, or with only a few dimensions, functional progress has continued as drawings have become the means of specifying not only the basic size but the accuracy of size, the accuracy of shape or form, the accuracy of relative positions, and the quality or smoothness of surfaces. Dimensioning is no longer simple because the kind and amount of information needed for any part requires a knowledge of how it is to be made, a knowledge of how it is to be used, and plenty of know-how experience.

A functional drawing must have the kind and amount of information necessary, but no more. A simple note will do for a piece of sheet steel $7\frac{1}{4}''$ x $12\frac{1}{2}''$ and $\frac{1}{4}''$ thick, but a vital part in a spacecraft must have the most precise and complete dimensioning information. See Chap. 11 and the latest revision of *American Drafting Standards Manual,* ASA Y14-5, Section 5, Dimensioning and Notes, for accurate and complete standards for dimensions.

26
Problems

26•1 Learning to draw. The important part of any course in mechanical drawing consists of the working of a large number of properly selected and graded problems. The problems that follow are arranged somewhat in the order of difficulty in each of the divisions of the subject, and the methods of presentation are varied to suit the objectives and requirements of the problems. Graphic layouts are given when practicable, as they are definite and save time for both instructor and student. It is not necessary or intended that all the problems be worked; a selection to fit the course should be made by the instructor. A large number of references to text material are given with the problems. These references should be studied by the student before asking for assistance from the instructor. Most drawings are finished in pencil on tracing paper, cloth, or film, so good pencil work should be required from the start. Inking should be left until the ability to make good pencil drawings has been acquired. At some time in the course every student should learn to use ink as there are times when this skill is important.

GROUP 1. LANGUAGE OF DRAWING

26•2 Problems in this group are to consist of brief written reports, after reading in the school or public library. Encyclopedias and other reference books should be consulted. Include such information of interest as may be available. Reports may consist of about 150 words about each man or subject.

Problem 1•1. Gudea.

Problem 1•2. Pont du Gard.

Problem 1•3. Leonardo da Vinci.

Problem 1•4. Thomas Jefferson's drawings.

Problem 1•5. Minot's Ledge lighthouse.

Problem 1•6. San Francisco-Oakland Bay Bridge.

Problem 1•7. Pyramids of Egypt.

Problem 1•8. Arthur Dobbs, M.P.

Problem 1•9. Gaspard Monge.

Problem 1•10. Claude Crozet.

Problem 1•11. Captain John Ericsson.

Problem 1•12. Igor I. Sikorsky.

Problem 1•13. John Fitch.

Problem 1•14. Oliver Evans.

Problem 1•15. Eli Whitney.

Problem 1•16. Robert Fulton.

Problem 1•17. James Watt.

Problem 1•18. James Nasmyth.

Problem 1•19. Matthew Boulton.

Problem 1•20. Henry Ford.

G=
F=
E=
C=
G=
D=
B=
A=

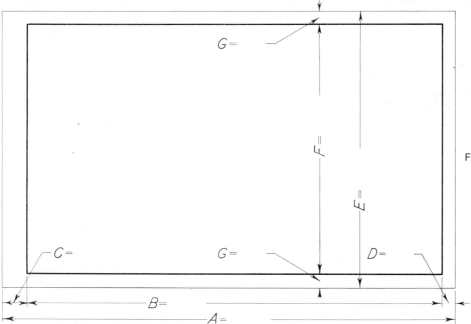

Fig. 26-3*a*. Adjustable layout for any size sheet.

GROUP 2. LEARNING TO DRAW

26•3 General instructions. The trim sizes of sheets recommended by the American Standards Association, as given in Art. 2·5, are in almost universal use in industry and are, therefore, desirable for use in drawing courses. Problems 2·1 to 2·16 are planned for working on 11″ × 17″ sheets. It is possible, of course, to use other sizes and arrangements where necessary or where desired by the instructor. To assist in such cases, Fig. 26-3*a* is given with letters to indicate the dimensions. The desired numerical values can be filled in after the equality signs (=) on the figure. Problems 2·1 to 2·16 and others marked for 11″ × 17″ sheets are designed for the layouts shown on Figs. 26-3*b* and 26-3*c*.

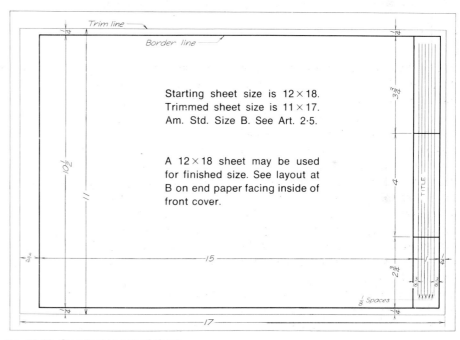

Trim line
Border line
Starting sheet size is 12 × 18.
Trimmed sheet size is 11 × 17.
Am. Std. Size B. See Art. 2·5.
A 12 × 18 sheet may be used
for finished size. See layout at
B on end paper facing inside of
front cover.
10 1/2
11
15
17
3 3/4
4
2 1/4
1/8 Spaces
TITLE

Fig. 26-3*b*. Standard layout of sheet.

Fig. 26-3*c*. Record strip or long block title.

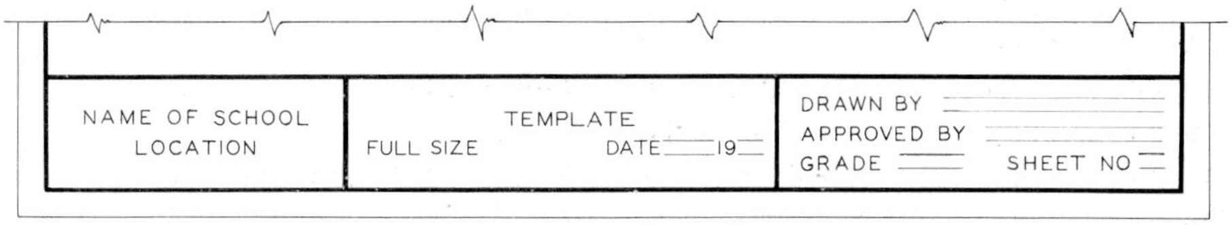

NAME OF SCHOOL
LOCATION
TEMPLATE
FULL SIZE
DATE 19
DRAWN BY
APPROVED BY
GRADE
SHEET NO

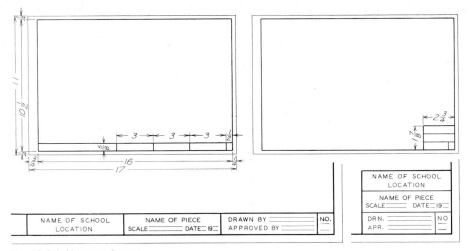

Fig. 26-3d. Alternate layouts.

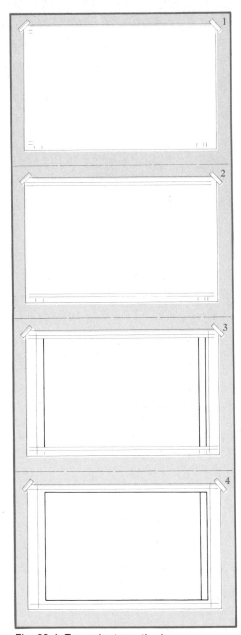

Fig. 26-4. Two-minute method.

Other layouts are suggested on Fig. 26-3d.

On the following figures the numbers enclosed in circles are for locating the starting lines and are always measured full size regardless of the scale of the views of the drawing. When such dimensions are given, the lines that they locate should be drawn first. (These dimensions are not to be put on the completed drawing as they are simply to locate the lines upon which the drawing is built.) Use light, sharp pencil lines and work as accurately as possible. Errors made in starting are not often evident until the drawing is nearly completed. The title for each sheet is given in italics.

If a different size of sheet is used, the figures in the circles should be adjusted to allow more or less space. This is best done by the instructor at first. The student can learn how to locate the views after a little practice. With further experience his judgment will improve.

Since most drawings are now finished in pencil, careful attention should be given to developing the ability to make bright contrasty drawings on either drawing paper or tracing paper. This requires firm, black pencil lines for the view lines and thin, sharp pencil lines for dimension lines, extension lines, and so forth.

A minimum amount of erasing is essential if clean, professional-appearing drawings are to be obtained. A great deal depends upon the care that is given to keeping the pencil point in proper condition at all times. Never sharpen it over the drawing board!

26·4 Layout of the sheet. Read Arts. 2·4 to 2·9. Fasten the sheet to the board as described in Art. 2·7. The outside dimensions to which the finished sheet will be trimmed are 11″ × 17″, with border line and record strip as shown in Fig. 26-3b. The guidelines for lettering in the record strip shown in Fig. 26-3c are not to be put in until the drawing is finished and ready for the title. By following the method illustrated in progressive steps, the layout of a sheet should not take more than two minutes.

Two-minute method (Fig. 26-4). With the scale, measure 17″ near the bottom of the sheet (or on the bottom of the sheet) making short vertical marks, not dots. Measure and mark ¾″ in from the left-hand mark and ¼″ in from the right-hand mark (Fig. 26-4, Space 1). From

this last mark measure 1″ toward the left and mark. Lay the scale vertically near the left of the paper (or on the left edge) and make short horizontal marks 11″ apart. Make short marks ¼″ up from the bottom mark and ¼″ down from the top mark. With the T-square draw horizontal lines through the four marks last

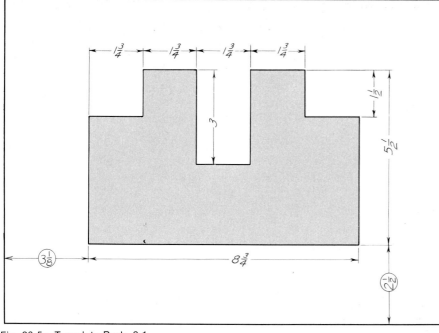

Fig. 26-5a. Template Prob. 2·1.

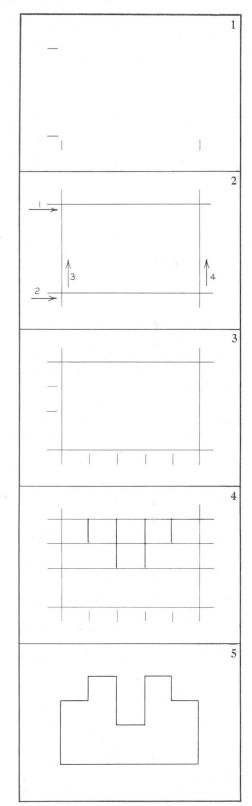

Prob. 2•1. Order of working.

made (Space 2). Next draw vertical lines through the five vertical marks (Space 3). Then brighten up the border lines and the sheet will appear as in Space 4. It is now ready to be used for drawing.

26·5 Problems 2·1 to 2·12 form a set of progressive problems for working on 11″ × 17″ sheets. Problems 2·17 to 2·39 form a set of progressive problems for working on an 8½″ × 11″ sheet. Either set may be used according to the desired size of sheets. Problems 2·13 to 2·16 should be worked early in the course to give practice in using the scales.

Problem 2•1. Make a drawing of the template shown in Fig. 26-5a. In this and several of the one-view drawings, the order of working is shown in progressive steps. These steps should be followed carefully, because they represent the draftsman's procedure in making drawings. Do not simply follow the explanations as being directed for the particular problem, but try to understand the system and the reasons for it. This system, thoroughly mastered at the start, will apply to all drawings and will develop the two requirements in execution: accuracy and speed.

Order of working for drawing the template of Prob. 2·1.

1. Lay out the sheet as described in Art. 26·4.
2. Measure 3⅛″ from left border line, and from this mark measure 8¾″ toward the right.
3. Lay the scale on the paper vertically near (or on) the left edge, make a mark 2½″ up, and from this measure 5½″ more. The sheet will appear as in Space 1.
4. Draw horizontal lines 1 and 2 with the T-square, and vertical lines 3 and 4 with T-square and triangle (Space 2). Be careful to hold the instruments as illustrated in Fig. 2-13. These lines block in the figure.

5. Lay the scale along the bottom line of the figure with the measuring edge on the upper side and make marks 1¾" apart. Then with the scale on line 3, with its measuring edge to the left, measure from the bottom line two successive distances vertically, 2½" and 1½" (Space 3).

6. Through the two marks draw horizontal lines lightly across the figure.

7. Draw the vertical lines with T-square and triangle by setting the pencil on the marks on the bottom line and starting and stopping the lines on the proper horizontal lines (Space 4).

8. Erase the lines not wanted and brighten the lines of the figure to obtain the finished drawing (Space 5).

9. Write your name, sheet number, and date lightly in the record strip. The record strip (or title block) is to be lettered in later.

10. Trim sheet to finished size.

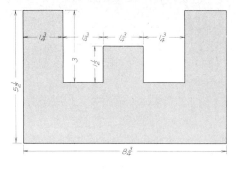

Problem 2·2. Make a drawing for template No. 2. This is an alternate for Prob. 2·1. Use the same layout.

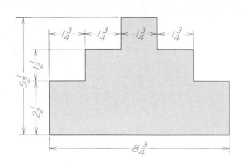

Problem 2·3. Make a drawing of the gage. This is an alternate for Prob. 2·1. Use the same layout and method.

Problem 2·4. Make a drawing of the stencil shown in Fig. 26-5b. This drawing gives practice in accurate measuring with the scale and making neat corners with short lines. The construction shown in the order of working should be drawn very lightly with a well-sharpened 3H or 4H pencil.

Order of working for making a drawing of the stencil of Prob. 2·4.

1. Find the center of the sheet inside the border by laying the T-square blade face down across the opposite corners and drawing short lines where the diagonals intersect (Space 1).

2. Through the center draw a horizontal center line and on it measure and mark off points for the four vertical lines. The drawing will appear as in Space 1.

3. Draw the vertical lines lightly with T-square and triangle. On the first vertical line, at the extreme left, measure and mark off points for all horizontal lines. The drawing will now appear as in Space 2.

4. Draw the horizontal lines as finished lines. Measure points for the stencil border lines on the left side and bottom. The drawing will now appear as in Space 3.

5. Draw the border lines. On the lower and left-hand border lines, measure the points for the ties.

6. Complete the border by drawing the cross lines as finished lines and brightening the other lines (Space 4).

7. Brighten the vertical lines and finish as in Space 5.

8. Write name, sheet number, and date in the record strip. Trim the sheet to finished size.

Fig. 26-5b. Stencil Prob. 2·4.

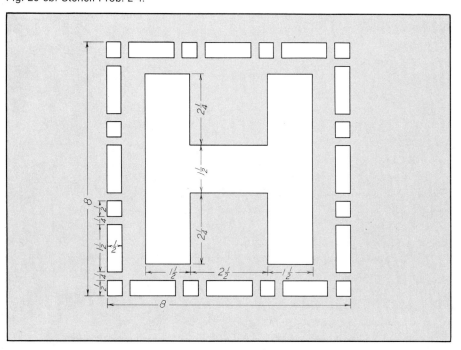

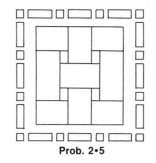

Prob. 2•5

Problem 2•5. Make a drawing of the tile pattern. This is an alternate problem, using the same measurements as in Fig. 26-5b with additional 1 ½″ measurements for the top and bottom strips and for the middle vertical strip.

Problem 2•6. Make a drawing of the shim shown in Fig. 26-5c. This drawing gives practice in the use of the compasses. Read Art. 2·32. When circles and circle arcs occur on a drawing, the first step is to locate the centers accurately; the second is to mark off the radii; the third is to locate the points of tangency and make sure of smooth joints.

Be sure that the lead in the compasses is carefully sharpened and adjusted with the needle point as shown in Fig. 2-32d. Draw intersecting center lines on a separate sheet. Practice handling both the compasses and bow pencil in drawing circles, carefully observing the operations illustrated in Figs. 2-32a and 2-33c. The needle point may be placed at the exact crossing of the two center lines by guiding it with the little finger of the left hand and resting the other fingers of the left hand on the paper.

Tangents occur constantly on all machine drawings and must be drawn neatly and quickly. Accuracy in setting the compasses to a required radius should be practiced. Any error in setting a compass to a required radius is doubled when the diameter is measured.

Note that when two circle arcs are tangent to each other, the point of tangency must lie on a line joining the centers of the arcs as shown at A in Fig. 26-5c.

Fig. 26-5c. Shim Prob. 2·6.

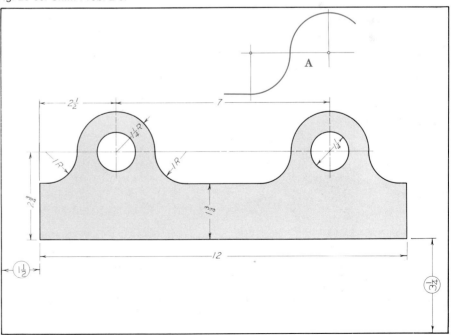

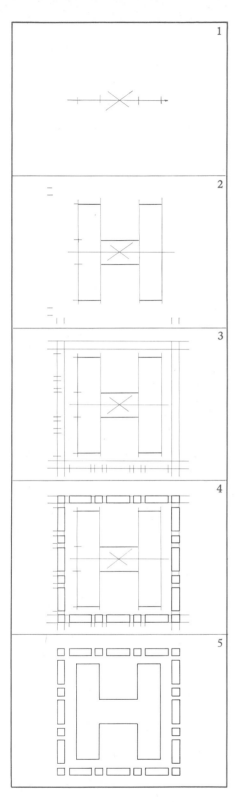

Prob. 2•4. Order of working.

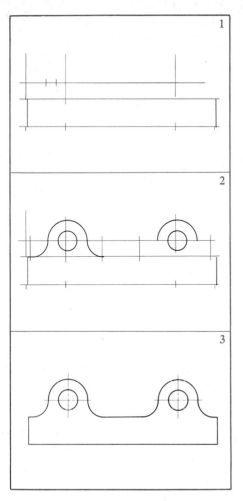

Prob. 2·6. Order of working.

Order of working for making a drawing of the shim of Prob. 2·6.

1. Draw the base line 3¼″ from the bottom. On it measure in 1½″ from the left border, then the distances 2½″, 7″, and 12″ (Space 1).
2. Measure the vertical distances 1¾″ and 2¾″ (Space 1).
3. Draw the horizontal lines, then the vertical lines (Space 1).
4. On the horizontal center line mark points for the radii and draw the two circles, the two semicircles, then the four quarter circles. Be sure to stop at the tangent points (Space 2).
5. Brighten the lines of the figure. Leave the center lines lighter than the outlines, as in Space 3.

6. Write name, sheet number, and date lightly in the record strip, and then trim the sheet.

Problem 2·7. Make a drawing of a brace. Plan a systematic order of working before starting the drawing.

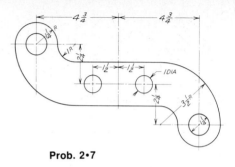

Prob. 2·7

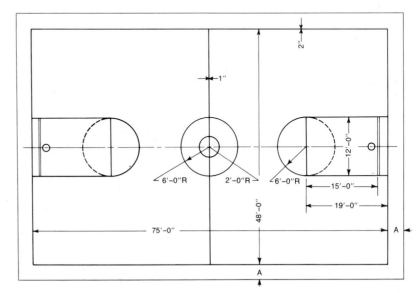

Problem 2·8. Make a drawing to show the layout for a basketball floor. Use a scale of ⅛″ = 1′ (Art. 2·29). Distance A to be at least 3′.

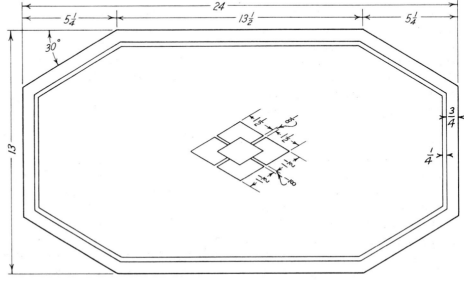

Problem 2·9. Make a drawing of an inlaid tabletop. Draw the horizontal and vertical center lines. Plan a systematic order of working. The central inlay may be varied, using one of the suggestions of Fig. 26-5d or an original design.

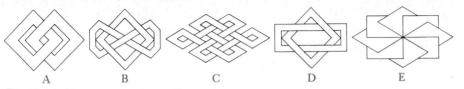

A   B   C   D   E

Fig. 26-5d. Alternate inlay design Prob. 2·9.

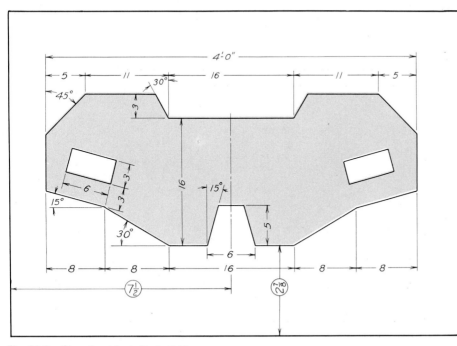

Fig. 26-5e. Shearing blank Prob. 2·10.

Problem 2•10. Make a drawing of the shearing blank shown in Fig. 26-5e. When a view has inclined lines, it should first be blocked in with square corners. Angles of 15°, 30°, 45°, 60°, and 75° are drawn with the triangles after locating one end of the line. See Fig. 2-16b.

Order of working for drawing the shearing blank of Prob. 2·10.

1. Locate vertical center line and measure 2′ on each side (Space 1). Note that this drawing must be made to the scale of 3″ = 1′ (Art. 2·29).
2. Locate vertical distances for top and bottom lines.
3. Draw main blocking-in lines as in Space 2.
4. Make measurements for starting points of inclined lines (Space 3).

5. Draw inclined lines with T-square and triangles (Space 4).
6. Finish as in Space 5.
7. Write name, sheet number, and date in record strip, and trim to size.

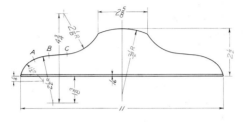

Problem 2•11. Make a drawing of a T-square head. Plan a systematic order of working before starting the drawing. Note tangent points *A, B,* and *C,* and that *BC* is a straight line.

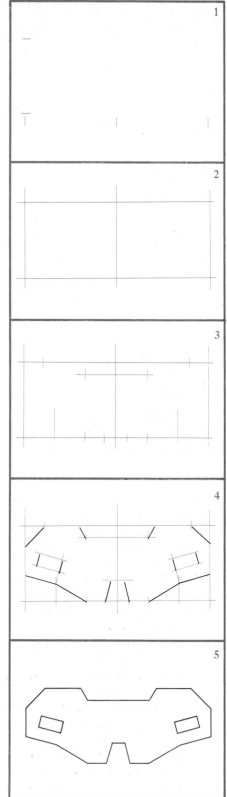

Prob. 2•10. Order of working.

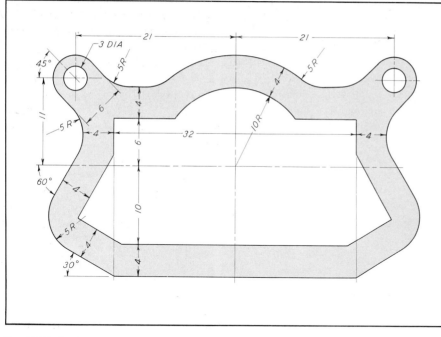

Fig. 26-5f. Cushioning base Prob. 2·12.

Problem 2•12. Make a drawing of the cushioning base (Fig. 26-5f). The drawing is for practice with triangles, compasses, and scale. Centers of arcs and tangent points must be carefully located.

Order of working for drawing the cushioning base of Prob. 2·12.

1. Through the center of the working space, draw horizontal and vertical center lines. Measure horizontal and vertical distances. This drawing must be made to the scale of 3″ = 1′. Then draw horizontal and vertical lines (Space 1).

2. Draw inclined lines with 45° and 30°–60° triangles. Then draw large arcs and two semicircles with tangents at 45° (Space 2).

3. Locate centers and tangent points for the 5″ radius tangent arcs. To do this, measure 5″ perpendicularly from each tangent line and draw lines parallel to the tangent lines.

The intersection of these lines will be the required centers. To find the points of tangency, draw lines from the centers perpendicular to the tangent lines. To find the centers for the 5″ arcs tangent to the middle arc, proceed as follows: Increase the radius of the larger arc by 5″ and draw two short arcs cutting lines parallel to and 5″ above the top horizontal tangent line. These points will be the centers. Lines joining these centers with the center of the large arc will locate the points of tangency of the arcs (Space 3).

Draw all the 5″ tangent arcs above the horizontal center line. Locate points of tangency and draw the two 60° tangent lines. Locate centers and draw the 5″ tangent arcs below the center line.

4. Complete the view by drawing the lines for the opening. Brighten the lines and finish the drawing as shown in Problem 2·12 (Space 4).

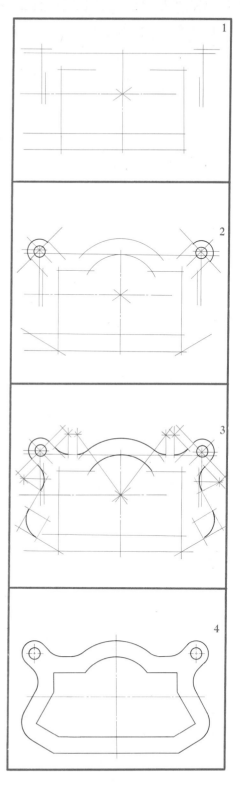

Prob. 2•12. Order of working.

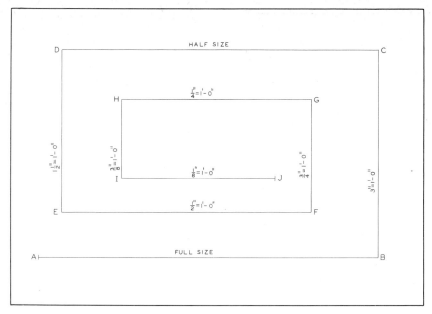

Probs. 2•13 and 2•14

Probs. 2•15 and 2•16

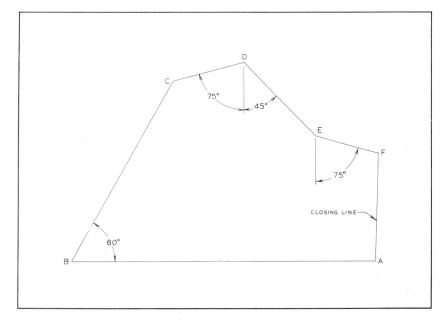

Problem 2•13. Measure the lengths of the lines on the figure in the book at the scales indicated. Record the values in order as:

$$AB = \underline{\quad} \qquad BC = \underline{\quad} \qquad CD = \underline{\quad}$$

Problem 2•14. Draw a figure similar to Prob. 2·13, in a space $5\frac{1}{4}'' \times 7\frac{1}{2}''$. Draw lines at the lengths and to the scales as follows:

$$AB = 11\frac{3}{8}'' \text{ at } 6'' = 1'-0''$$
$$BC = 9'-7'' \text{ at } \frac{3}{8}'' = 1'-0''$$
$$CD = 21'-10'' \text{ at } \frac{1}{4}'' = 1'-0''$$
$$DE = 22'-6'' \text{ at } \frac{1}{8}'' = 1'-0''$$
$$EF = 3'-2\frac{1}{2}'' \text{ at } 1\frac{1}{2}'' = 1'-0''$$
$$FG = 2'-8\frac{1}{2}'' \text{ at } \frac{3}{4}'' = 1'-0''$$
$$GH = 8'-3'' \text{ at } \frac{1}{2}'' = 1'-0''$$
$$HI = 5\frac{3}{4}' \text{ at } 3'' = 1'-0''$$
$$IJ = 3\frac{11}{16}'' \text{ full size}$$

Problem 2•15. Measure the lengths of the lines on the figure in the book at scale assigned by the instructor.

For scale of $1'' = 60'-0''$
For scale of $1'' = 40'-0''$
For scale of $1'' = 30'-0''$
For scale of $1'' = 100'-0''$

Record the values in order as:

$$AB = \underline{\quad} \qquad BC = \underline{\quad} \qquad CD = \underline{\quad}$$

Problem 2•16. Draw a figure similar to Prob. 2·15 in a space $5\frac{1}{4}'' \times 7\frac{1}{2}''$. Use a civil engineer's scale. Draw lines at the angles shown at the lengths as follows for a scale of $1'' = 30'$. Measure closing line to nearest tenth of a foot and note it on your drawing. $AB = 172'$; $BC = 113'$; $CD = 54'$; $DE = 29'$; $EF = 37'$.

26•6 The order of work is given in Figs. 26-6a and 26-6b for a standard sheet $8\frac{1}{2}'' \times 11''$ (trimmed size). The method is the same for other sizes except for the dimensions. If sheets measuring $8\frac{1}{2}'' \times 11''$ trimmed size are used, the method is the same except that measurements are made from the edges of the sheet.

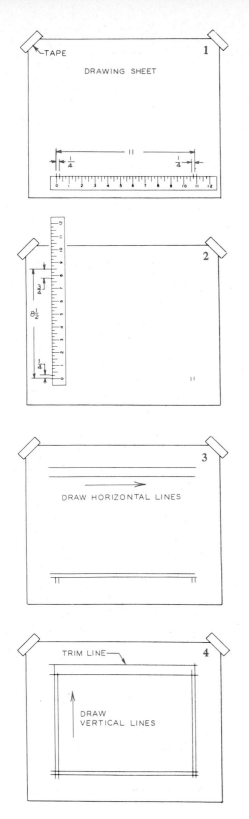

Figure 26-6a at 1. Lay the scale horizontally near the bottom of the sheet and make short vertical marks (not dots) 11″ apart. Hold the scale in position and make short vertical marks ¼″ from the left-hand and right-hand marks.

Figure 26-6a at 2. Lay the scale vertically near the left-hand edge of the sheet and make short horizontal marks (not dots) 8½″ apart. Hold the scale in position and make short marks (not dots) ¾″ down from the top mark and ¼″ up from the bottom mark.

Figure 26-6a at 3. Place the T-square in position and draw light horizontal lines through the four horizontal marks.

Fig. 26-6*b*. Three arrangements of sheets.

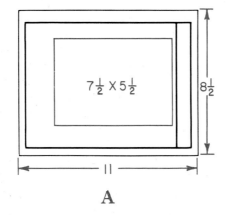

A

Figure 26-6a at 4. Place the T-square and triangle in position and draw light vertical lines through the four vertical marks. Go over the border lines to make them clear and black. Use an F or HB pencil. The sheet is now ready to be used for making a drawing.

Figure 26-6b at A, B, and C. The sheet may be used with the long measurement horizontal, as at A, or vertical, as at B. A title strip may be used, as suggested. The height of the title strip may be ⅝″, or more, to suit the information required by the instructor. Four problems may be worked on an 11″ × 17″ sheet, as at C.

26·7 The problems which follow are one-view drawings for practice in learning to draw. Use light, sharp pencil lines for layout and construction lines. Work carefully and accurately from the very first in order to make neat and clean drawings. Since most drawings are finished in pencil, it is necessary to develop the ability to make drawings which are bright and have contrast. This requires firm, black pencil lines for the view lines on the finished drawings. A drawing of a template is shown in

Fig. 26-6*a*. Layout for 8½″ × 11″ sheet.

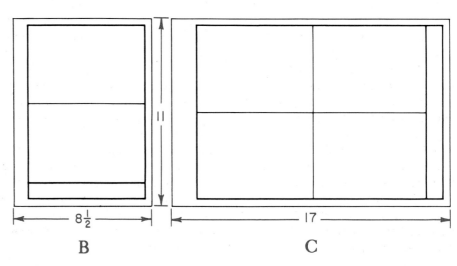

B C

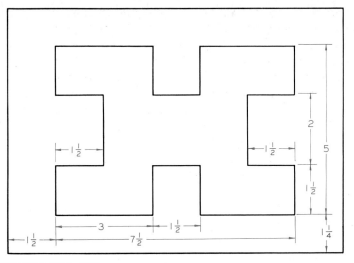

Fig. 26-7. Template Prob. 2·17.

Fig. 26-7. A template is used as a guide for laying out a shape. It may be a form for marking around the outside; it may be an opening of the required shape; or it may be a combination. Irregular curves (Art. 2·36) are forms of outside-inside templates. Complete specifications would include the thickness and kind of material. This template might be made of wood, metal, cardboard, or sheet plastic.

Problems 2·17 to 2·39 are to be worked one problem on an 8½″ × 11″ sheet.

Problem 2•17. Make a drawing of the template shown in Fig. 26-7. Scale: full size. The order of making this drawing is shown in progressive stages. These represent the draftsman's procedure, and the student should try to understand the reason for each one. This system applies to all drawings and will develop accuracy and speed.

Order of working for drawing the template of Prob. 2·17. Space 1. Lay out the sheet as described in Art. 26·6. With the scale horizontally near the bottom of the working space, measure 1½″ from the left border line and make a mark (short dash) as shown. From this mark measure 7½″ to the right and

make another mark. Next, place the scale vertically near the left border line and make a mark 1¼″ up from the lower border line and from this measure up 5″. The sheet will appear as in Space 1.

Space 2. Draw horizontal lines 1 and 2 (use the T-square). Draw vertical lines 3 and 4 (use the 30° triangle and T-square). Be careful to hold the T-square and triangles as in Arts. 2·12 and 2·13. These four lines block in the template.

Space 3. Place the scale just below the bottom line (line 2) and make marks 1½″ apart (hold the scale in the position shown). Next, place the scale vertically to the left of line 3 and measure up from line 2 distances of 1½″ and 2″ and draw horizontal lines (use the T-square).

Space 4. Set the pencil point by the vertical marks and draw vertical lines. Start and stop at the proper horizontal lines as shown. These vertical lines can be the final sharp, black pencil lines, as we know just how long to draw them.

Space 5. Brighten the necessary parts of the horizontal lines to show the template by sharp, black lines. If the construction lines are made very light, they need not be erased. This is usual office practice for most drawings; however, erasures may be made if necessary for clearness.

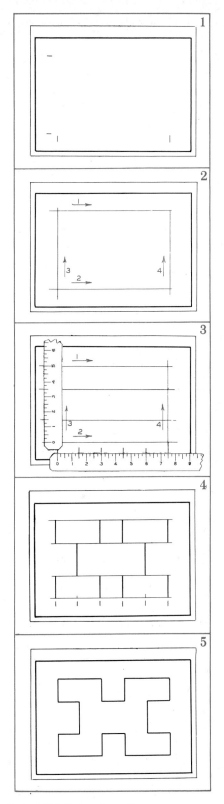

Prob. 2•17. Order of working.

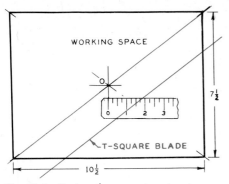

Fig. 26-8a. To locate a one-view drawing.

26·8 To locate a one-view drawing. Given the working space of $10\frac{1}{2}'' \times 7\frac{1}{2}''$.

Sometimes the view is located from the center of the working space (Fig. 26-8a). To find the center O, lay the T-square blade (or a triangle) across the opposite corners of the space and draw short lines where the diagonals cross. Through O draw horizontal and vertical lines from which to lay off measurements.

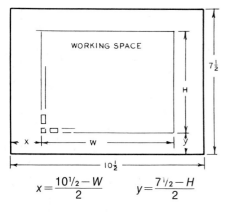

$$x = \frac{10\frac{1}{2} - W}{2} \qquad y = \frac{7\frac{1}{2} - H}{2}$$

Fig. 26-8b. To locate a one-view drawing.

Sometimes the view is located from the border lines (Fig. 26-8b). For the working space of $10\frac{1}{2}'' \times 7\frac{1}{2}''$, let $W =$ width of the view, then $x = \frac{1}{2}(10\frac{1}{2}'' - W)$. Let $H =$ height of the view, then $y = \frac{1}{2}(7\frac{1}{2}'' - H)$. Thus, for Prob. 2·18, the width $W = 7\frac{1}{4}''$, so $10\frac{1}{2}'' - 7\frac{1}{4}'' = 3\frac{1}{4}''$, and one-half of $3\frac{1}{4}'' = 1\frac{5}{8}'' = x =$ distance in from the left border line. The height $H = 5\frac{1}{4}''$, so $7\frac{1}{2}'' - 5\frac{1}{4}'' = 2\frac{1}{4}''$

and one-half of $2\frac{1}{4}'' = 1\frac{1}{8}'' = y =$ distance up from the bottom border line.

The distances x and y may be more or less than one-half the free space to allow for dimensions and notes. The distance below the view is often made more than the distance above to give a better balance.

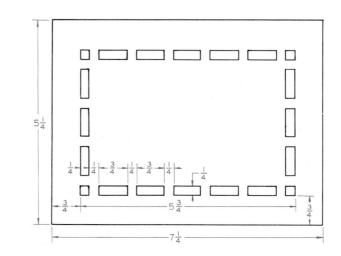

Problem 2·18. Make a drawing of the border stencil. Scale: full size. For T-square, triangle, and scale. See Art. 26·8 for the method of locating the view and locate it in the center of the working space. Work up the view following the system explained for Prob. 2·17. When complete, brighten lines necessary to show the view of the border stencil.

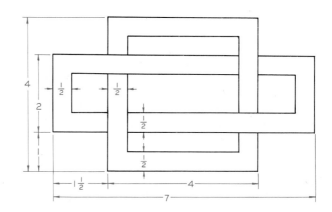

Problem 2·19. Make a drawing of the inlay pattern. Scale: full size. For T-square, triangle, scale, and bow dividers. Draw a $4'' \times 7''$ rectangle in the center of the working space. Locate and draw the $2'' \times 7''$ rectangle and the $4''$ square as shown. With the bow dividers, lay off $\frac{1}{2}''$ inside the rectangle and the square. Draw the parallel lines. Brighten lines necessary.

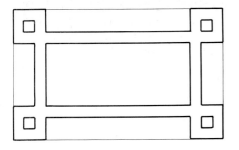

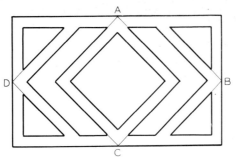

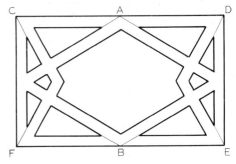

Problem 2·20. Make a drawing of the frame. Scale: 6″ = 1′–0″. For T-square, scale, and bow dividers. Draw a 9″ × 15″ rectangle in the center of the working space. With the dividers lay off three ³/₄″ spaces in both directions from each corner. Draw horizontal and vertical lines. Brighten lines necessary to complete the view.

Problem 2·21. Make a drawing of the grille plate. Scale: 6″ = 1′–0″. For T-square, triangle, scale, and dividers. Draw 9″ × 15″ and 7¹/₂″ × 13¹/₂″ rectangles in the center of the working space. With the dividers locate points A, B, C, and D, the centers of the sides of the large rectangle. From A, B, C, and D draw 45° lines. Measure ³/₄″ inside these lines and draw parallel lines. Brighten lines necessary to show the view.

Problem 2·22. Make a drawing of the inlay pattern. Scale: full size. For T-square, 30°–60° triangle, scale, and dividers. Draw 4¹/₂″ × 7¹/₂″ and 3³/₄″ × 6³/₄″ rectangles. With the dividers locate points A and B, the centers of the long sides of the large rectangle. From A and B draw lines at 30° with the horizontal. From C, D, E, and F draw lines at 60° with the horizontal. Measure ³/₈″ inside these lines and draw parallel lines as shown. Brighten lines necessary to complete the view.

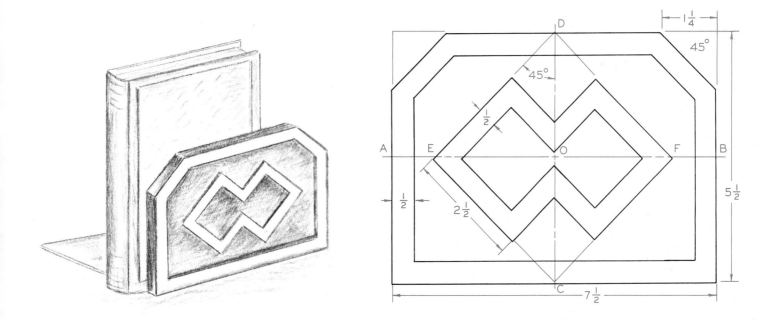

Problem 2·23. A bookend is shown in the picture. Make a drawing for the end view of the bookend. Scale: full size.

First locate a 7¹/₂″ × 5¹/₂″ rectangle in the center of the working space. Draw lines AB and CD through the center O.

Draw 45° lines from C and D to locate points E and F. Draw lines as shown to complete the view.

Problems   411

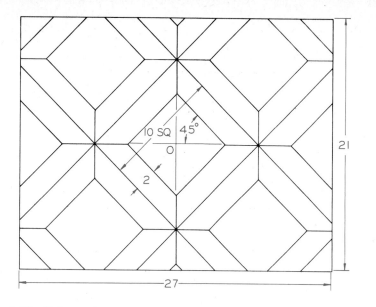

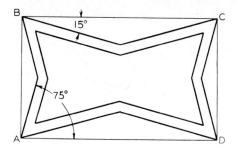

Problem 2•24. Make a drawing of the parquet pattern used in Thomas Jefferson's home, Monticello (Figs. 1-4c and 1-4d). Scale: 3″ = 1′-0″. Lay out a rectangle 32″ × 28″ in the center of the working space. Draw center lines through the center O. Lay out a 10″ square at 45° surrounded by 2″ strips. Complete the drawing as shown. Brighten lines necessary to show the view.

Problem 2•25. Make a drawing of the inlay pattern. Scale: full size. For T-square, both triangles, and scale. Draw a 5″ × 7″ rectangle. From the corners draw lines as shown. Measure ½″ inside these lines and draw parallel lines. Brighten lines necessary to show the view.

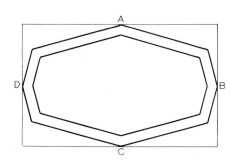

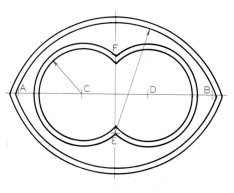

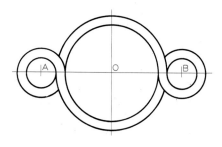

Problem 2•26. Make a drawing of the plate border. Scale: full size. For T-square, both triangles, and scale. Draw a 4½″ × 7½″ rectangle. Locate the points A, B, C, and D, the centers of the sides, with the scale. From points A, B, C, and D draw lines at 15° with the sides of the rectangle using combinations of the two triangles. Measure ⅜″ inside these lines and draw parallel lines. Brighten lines necessary to complete the view.

Problem 2•27. Make a drawing of the double dial plate. Scale: full size. For T-square, triangle, scale, dividers, and compasses. Draw line AB = 7″ and divide it into three equal parts with the dividers. With centers at C and D, draw arcs with radii of 1½″ and 1¾″. With centers at E and F, draw arcs with radii of 3¾″ and 4″ to complete the view.

Problem 2•28. Make a drawing of the ornament. Scale: full size. For T-square, scale, compasses, and bow pencil. Draw line AB = 5⅝″. Locate O, the midpoint of AB. With center at O, draw circles with diameters of 3¾″ and 4½″. With centers at A and B, draw circles with diameters of 1⅛″ and 1⅞″. Brighten lines necessary to show the view.

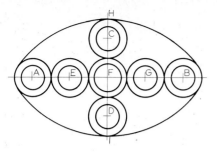

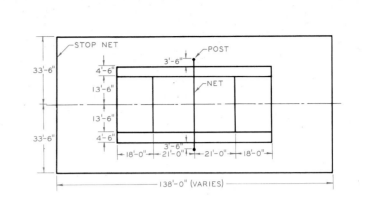

Problem 2·29. Make a drawing of the multiple dial plate. Scale: $3'' = 1'-0''$. For T-square, triangle, scale, compasses, and bow pencil. Draw center lines at right angles. Lay off $FC = FD = FG = FE = EA = GB = 6''$. With centers at $A, B, C, D, E, F,$ and G, draw circles with a diameter of $6''$. With center at F, draw a circle with a diameter of $4\frac{1}{2}''$. With centers at $A, B, C, D, E,$ and G, draw circles with a diameter of $4''$. With centers at H and I, draw tangent arcs with a radius of $18''$. Brighten lines necessary to show the view.

Problem 2·31. Make a plan drawing of a tennis court to be used for either singles or doubles. The scale may be $1'' = 20'-0''$ (for engineer's scale) or $1'' = 16'-0''$ (for architect's scale). The court lines are drawn as single lines with a note to tell the width. Brighten lines to show the plan clearly.

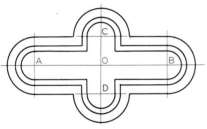

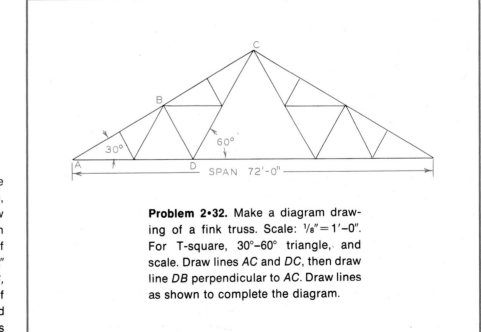

Problem 2·30. Make a drawing of the frame. Scale: $6'' = 1'-0''$. For T-square, triangle, scale, and bow pencil. Draw intersecting lines at right angles through the center of the working space. Lay off $AO = OB = 5\frac{1}{4}''$ and $OC = OD = 2\frac{1}{4}''$ with the scale. With centers at $A, B, C,$ and D draw semicircles with radii of $1\frac{1}{8}'', 1\frac{1}{2}'',$ and $2\frac{1}{4}''$. Draw horizontal and vertical tangent lines. Brighten lines necessary to show the view.

Problem 2·32. Make a diagram drawing of a fink truss. Scale: $\frac{1}{8}'' = 1'-0''$. For T-square, 30°–60° triangle, and scale. Draw lines AC and DC, then draw line DB perpendicular to AC. Draw lines as shown to complete the diagram.

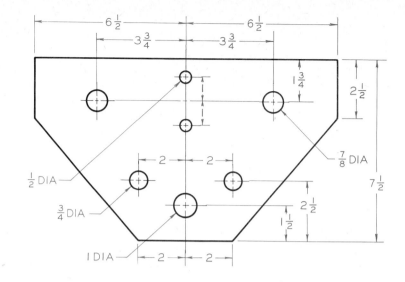

Problem 2•33. A picture of a 1-ton trolley is shown. Make a drawing for laying out the side plate of a 1-ton trolley. Scale: 6″ = 1′–0″. Locate the view in the center of the working space. Brighten lines to show the view.

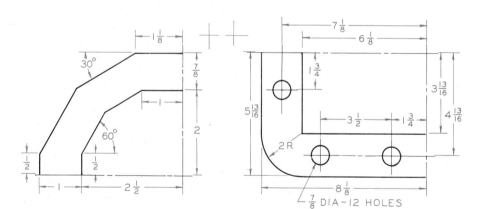

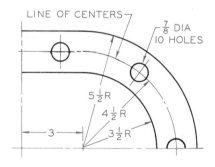

Problem 2•34. One-quarter of a sheet brass stamping is shown. Make a drawing of the complete stamping. Scale: full size. Locate the view in the center of the working space. Brighten lines to show the view.

Problem 2•35. Make a drawing of the gasket for a steam chest cover. Scale: 6″ = 1′–0″. Locate the view in the center of the working space. Only one-quarter of the gasket is shown, but a complete view is required.

Problem 2•36. Make a drawing of the gasket for the service plate. Scale: 6″ = 1′–0″. Locate the view in the center of the working space. Only one-quarter of the gasket is shown, but a complete view is required. Note that 10 holes, equally spaced, are required. Use the dividers to locate the holes on the line of centers.

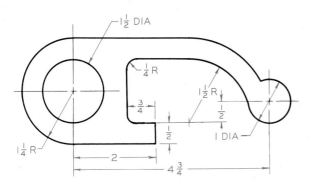

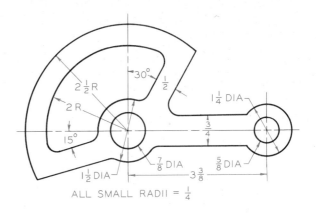

Problem 2•37. Make a drawing of the release lever. Scale: full size. Use compasses and bow pencil. Make neat tangent joints.

Problem 2•38. Make a drawing of the adjustable sector. Scale: full size. Make neat tangent joints. Use compasses and bow pencil.

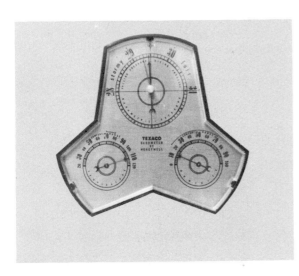

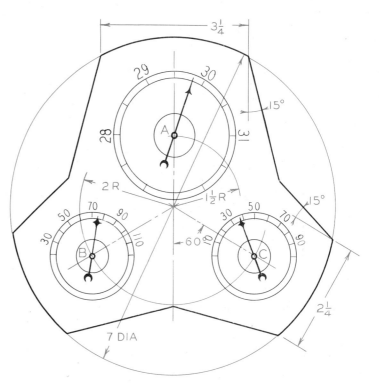

Problem 2•39. A picture of a weather instrument is shown. Draw the front view of the weather instrument. Scale: full size. The barometer dial at A shows barometer pressure; the thermometer dial at B shows temperature; and the hygrometer dial at C shows humidity. First, draw the outside diameter (7") and locate the centers of the three dials. At center A draw circles with diameters of 7/8", 2 3/8" and 2 5/8". At B and C draw circles with diameters of 5/8", 1 5/8", and 1 7/8". For dial A, 12 principal divisions are shown (to be laid off with the 30°–60° triangles). Each of these may be divided into 5 parts to measure tenths of an inch (not shown on the drawing). Dials B and C have the upper half divided into 10 principal divisions (use bow dividers). Each of these may be divided into 5 parts to measure 2 degrees on dial B and 2 percent on dial C (not shown on the drawing). Brighten lines to show the view.

Fig. 26-9. Layouts for one, two, or four problems.

A　　　　　　B　　　　　　C

GROUP 3.   LETTERING

26·9 Lettering is best learned in short, unhurried periods. The problems are planned for a working space of 7½″ wide and 5¼″ high (minimum space 7″ × 5″). One problem may be worked on an 8½″ × 11″ sheet with the layout of Fig. 26-9 at A, or two problems with the layout of Fig. 26-9 at B, or four problems on an 11″ × 17″ sheet as at C. Use an F or HB pencil with a long conical point (Fig. 3-4). The lettering should be black as most drawings are now made on tracing paper, tracing cloth, or film. They must be black in order to reproduce clearly by blueprinting or other

methods. Use a 2H pencil to rule very light guidelines for the heights of the letters. Place the sheet far enough up from the bottom of the drawing board so that your elbow can rest on the board. Rotate the pencil in the fingers after each few strokes to keep the point in shape and sharpen as often as necessary to keep a proper point.

Before starting a sheet, read over the text which applies to the assigned problem and make a few practice letters. Vertical and inclined lettering problems are given and both, or either one, may be assigned. If time permits, a problem should be assigned from Probs. 3·17 to 3·20 to be used as a cover sheet for

the drawings made in the course.

The problems, or a selection from them, may be used for lettering practice with pen and ink (Figs. 3-5a and 3-5b). Inking should not be attempted until the student is proficient with the pencil. For ink letters use a penholder with a cork grip and set the pen well into the holder. Always use drawing ink for lettering. To get cleancut letters, it is necessary to wipe the pen frequently with a cloth penwiper. Tube-point pens (Fig. 3-17a) give excellent results for lettering and for arrowheads and are coming into general use. They maintain a uniform width of line for the point selected.

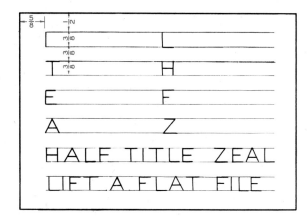

Problem 3·1. ⅜″ vertical capitals in pencil. Complete each line. Draw a few very light vertical guidelines (Art. 3·3).

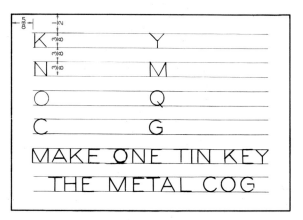

Problem 3·2. ⅜″ vertical capitals in pencil. Complete each line. Draw a few light vertical guidelines.

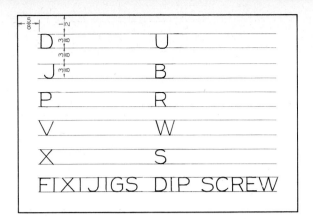

Problem 3·3. ³/₈″ vertical capitals in pencil. Complete each line.

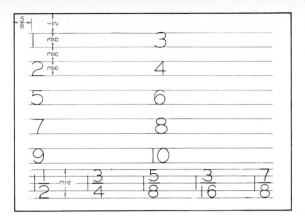

Problem 3·4. ³/₈″ vertical numerals in pencil. Make total height of fractions two times height of numerals.

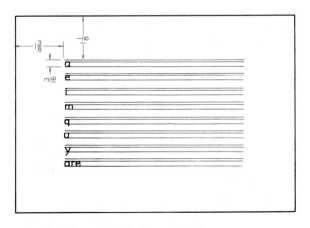

Problem 3·5. ³/₁₆″ vertical capitals in pencil. Complete each line. If used for ink, use Gillott's 404 pen or thinnest-line tube-point pen.

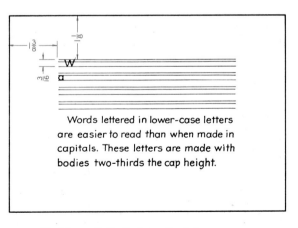

Problem 3·6. ³/₁₆″ vertical lower-case letters in pencil. Rule for eight lines of letters with No. 6 lettering guidelines (Art. 3·3) or for ³/₁₆″ letters.

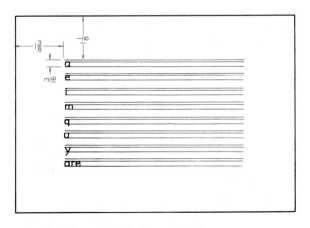

Problem 3·7. ³/₁₆″ vertical lower-case letters (same as Prob. 3·6 but in ink). Rule for guidelines and lettering as for Prob. 3·6. Use a tube-point pen.

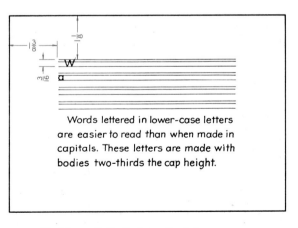

Problem 3·8. ³/₁₆″ vertical lower-case letters in pencil. Rule guidelines as for Prob. 3·7. If used for ink, do sentence once in pencil and once in ink.

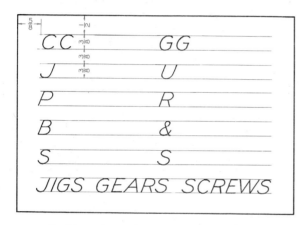

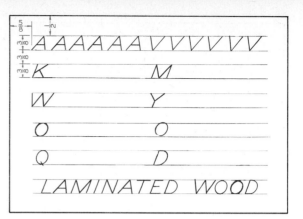

Problem 3·9. ⅜″ inclined capitals in pencil. Complete each line. Draw a few very light inclined guidelines (Art. 3·11).

Problem 3·10. ⅜″ inclined capitals in pencil. Complete each line.

Problem 3·11. ⅜″ inclined capitals in pencil. Complete each line.

Problem 3·12. ⅜″ inclined numerals in pencil. Make total height of fractions two times height of numerals.

Problem 3·13. ³⁄₁₆″ inclined capitals in pencil. Complete each line. If used for ink, use Gillott's 404 pen or thinnest-line tube-point pen.

Problem 3·14. ³⁄₁₆″ inclined lower-case letters in pencil. Rule for eight lines of letters with No. 6 lettering guidelines or for ³⁄₁₆″ letters. Complete each line.

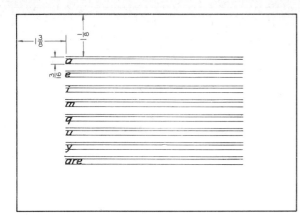

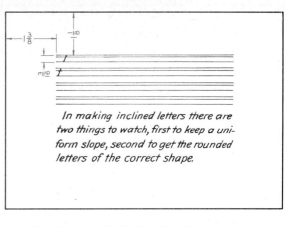

Problem 3•15. ³/₁₆″ inclined lower-case letters (same as Prob. 3·14 but in ink). Rule for guidelines and lettering as for Prob. 3·14. Use Esterbrook 854, Hunt 512, or equivalent tube-point pen.

Problem 3•16. ³/₁₆″ inclined lower-case letters in pencil. Rule guidelines as for Prob. 3·15. If used for ink, do sentence once in pencil and once in ink.

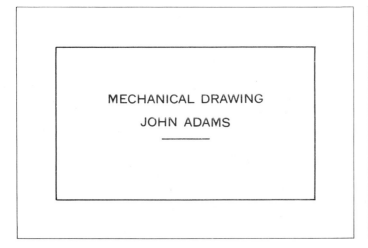

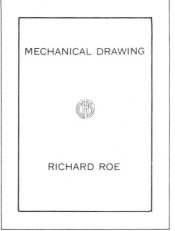

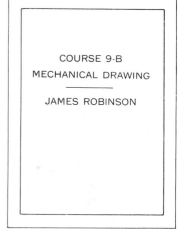

Problem 3•17. Suggested design for cover for drawings. Choose proper-size letters.

Problem 3•18. Suggested design for cover for drawings. Choose proper-size letters.

Problem 3•19. Suggested design for cover for drawings. Choose proper-size letters.

Problem 3•20. Suggested design for cover for drawings. Choose proper-size letters.

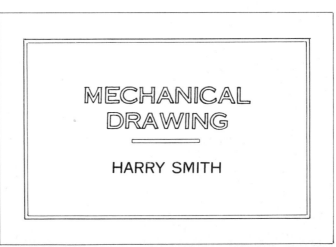

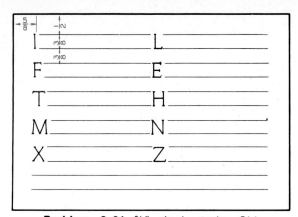

Problem 3·21. ⅜″ single-stroke Old Roman letters in pencil. Rule a few very light vertical guidelines (Art. 3·3). Use an F or HB pencil and letter as indicated. Complete each line by repeating the letters. On the last line, letter: FIX LINTEL "HZ."

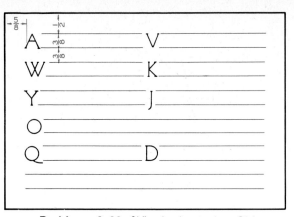

Problem 3·22. ⅜″ single-stroke Old Roman letters in pencil. Rule as indicated. Complete each line by repeating the letters. On the last line letter the words: LAMINATED WOOD.

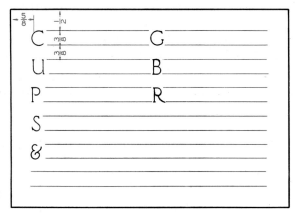

Problem 3·23. ⅜″ single-stroke Old Roman letters in pencil. Rule as indicated. Complete each line by repeating the letters. On the last line letter the words: BRIDGE SPACE RULE.

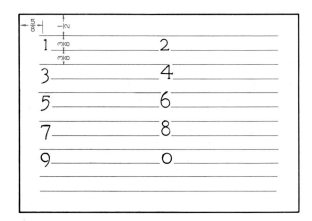

Problem 3·24. ⅜″ vertical numerals in pencil. Rule as indicated. Complete each line by repeating the numerals. On the last line letter the date: month, day, and year.

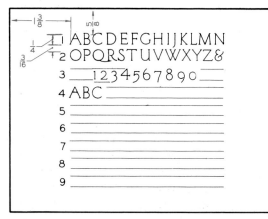

Problem 3·25. ¼″ single-stroke capitals in pencil. Rule guidelines for nine lines of letters. Make the first three lines very carefully. Repeat the same copy twice on the next six lines. If used for ink lettering, do the first three lines in pencil. Do the next three lines, first very lightly in pencil and over them in ink. Do the last three lines directly in ink. Use a Hunt 512, Esterbrook 802, or equivalent tube-point pen.

Problem 3•26. ¼″ single-stroke lower-case letters in pencil. The bodies of the letters are ⅛″ high (one-half the height of the capital letter). Rule guidelines as indicated. Letter the alphabet on lines 1, 2, 3, and 4. On lines 5 and 6 letter: The traditional lettering used on architectural drawings is based on the Old Roman alphabet. On lines 7 and 8 letter your name and the month, day, and year.

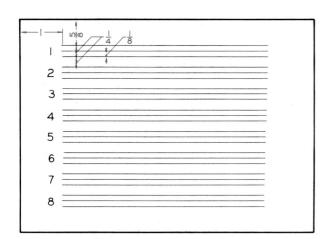

Problem 3•27. Rule guidelines as directed for Prob. 3·26. Letter the following: (on line 1) Words lettered in lower-case letters (on line 2) are easier to read than when made in (on line 3) capitals. These letters are made with (on line 4) bodies one-half the height of the capital letter. (Repeat on lines 5, 6, 7, and 8.)

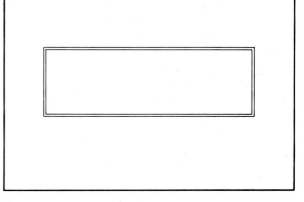

Problem 3•28. In the center of a space lay out a rectangle 5″ wide and 1½″ high. Letter a title similar to the one shown. Do not copy it.

Problem 3•29. Using the Roman alphabet shown in Fig. 3-15a, design a title page or cover sheet containing the words ARCHITECTURAL DRAWING and your name.

GROUP 4.
DRAFTING CONSTRUCTIONS

26•10 The working of a number of geometrical exercises is valuable both for the practice of accuracy in the use of instruments and for becoming familiar with the constructions that occur most frequently in drafting. Understanding and practice of geometrical constructions enables the draftsman to use them when needed. Such understanding also provides the basis for speed and accuracy in all drawing.

1. The problems must be worked accurately.
2. Use a sharp 2H or 3H pencil.
3. Make all construction lines thin and light.
4. Leave all construction lines as drawn. Do not erase them and do not go over them.
5. Locate points by two short intersecting lines.
6. Show the length of a line by two short dashes crossing the line.
7. Make the result lines thin and bright.
8. Be accurate.

There are three sets of problems. Problems 4·1 to 4·24 provide a group from which to select fundamental constructions. Problems 4·25 to 4·33 provide a group of one-view drawings for practice in the use of constructions. Problems 4·34 to 4·67 provide extra problems from which a selection of fundamental constructions may be made.

26•11 Problems 4·1 to 4·24 are designed for working in a space 5¼" wide by 3¾" high. Two problems may be worked on an 8½" × 11" sheet, laid out as in Fig. 26-11.

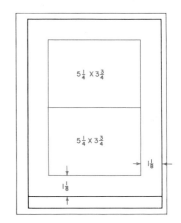

Fig. 26-11. Layouts for Probs. 4·1 to 4·24.

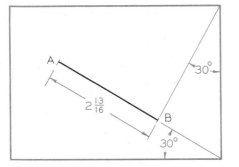

Problem 4•1. Bisect line *AB*.

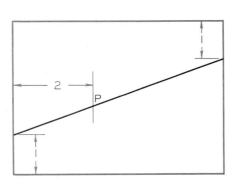

Problem 4•2. Erect a perpendicular at point *P*.

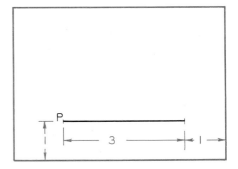

Problem 4•3. Erect a perpendicular at point *P*.

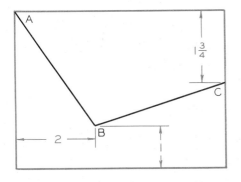

Problem 4•4. Bisect the angle *ABC*.

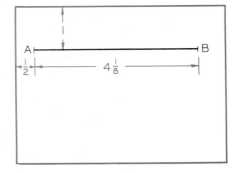

Problem 4•5. Divide the line *AB* into seven equal parts.

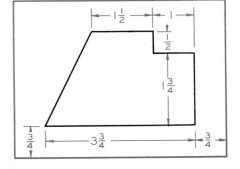

Problem 4•6. Reduce the figure to two-thirds size by triangulation.

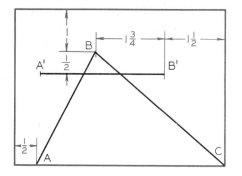

Problem 4•7. Copy the angle *ABC* with side *AB* located at *A'B'*.

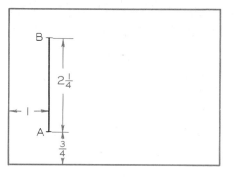

Problem 4•8. On *AB* as one side, construct a triangle. Other sides are 3″ and 4″ long.

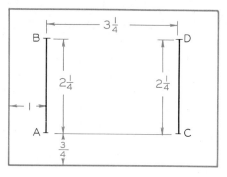

Problem 4•9. On *AB* and *CD* construct equilateral triangles. On *AB* and *CD* as bases, construct isosceles triangles with sides 3¼″ long with all triangles pointing in.

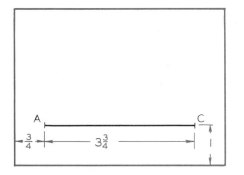

Problem 4•10. Construct a right triangle by the 3-4-5 method. One side is *AB*, and the other is 2⅛″ long.

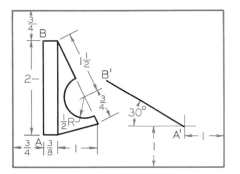

Problem 4•11. Copy the guide plate with line *AB* at *A'B'*.

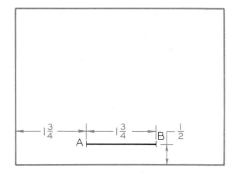

Problem 4•12. Construct a regular pentagon on *AB* as a side.

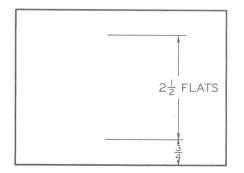

Problem 4•13. Draw a regular hexagon in center of space. Flats are 2½″.

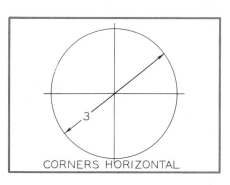

CORNERS HORIZONTAL

Problem 4•14. Draw a regular hexagon inscribed in the circle, in the center of the space.

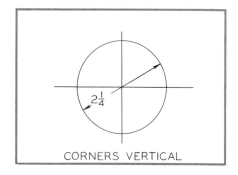

CORNERS VERTICAL

Problem 4•15. Draw a regular hexagon about the circle in the center of the space. Place the distance across the corners vertically.

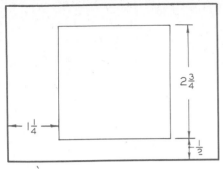

Problem 4•16. Draw a regular octagon in the square.

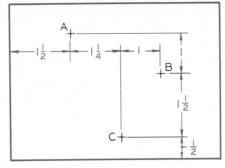

Problem 4•17. Draw a circle through points *ABC*. Measure and record the diameter to nearest ¹/₃₂″.

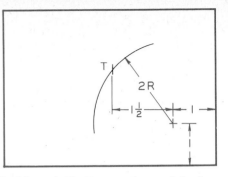

Problem 4•18. Draw a tangent to the arc at point *T*.

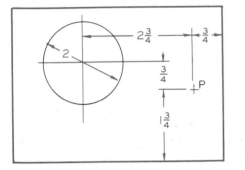

Problem 4•19. Draw a tangent to the circle from point *P*.

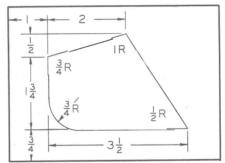

Problem 4•20. Draw tangent arcs at each corner of the plate with the radii indicated. Mark centers and tangent points.

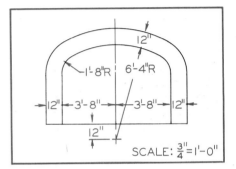

Problem 4•21. Draw the arch. Scale: ³/₈″ = 1′–0″. Mark centers and tangent points.

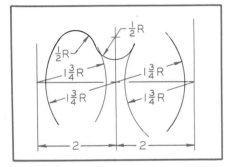

Problem 4•22. Draw tangent arcs to complete the figure. Mark tangent points.

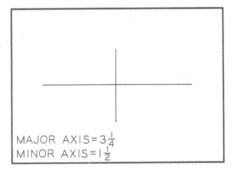

MAJOR AXIS = 3¼
MINOR AXIS = 1½

Problem 4•24. Draw an approximate ellipse. Use method assigned by instructors.

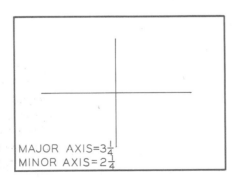

MAJOR AXIS = 3¼
MINOR AXIS = 2¼

Problem 4•23. Draw an ellipse. Use method assigned by instructors.

26•12 Problems 4·25 to 4·33 are single views selected from drawings of various details. A few of these problems should be drawn up to give practice in accuracy by using geometrical methods. Since only one view is shown, the dimensions may be omitted unless required by the instructor.

Use an 8½″ × 11″ sheet for each of these problems. Draw the view shown carefully and accurately. Tangent points and centers of arcs are to be found and marked. The approximate width and height of each view, without dimensions, in full-size inches are given as an aid in locating the views.

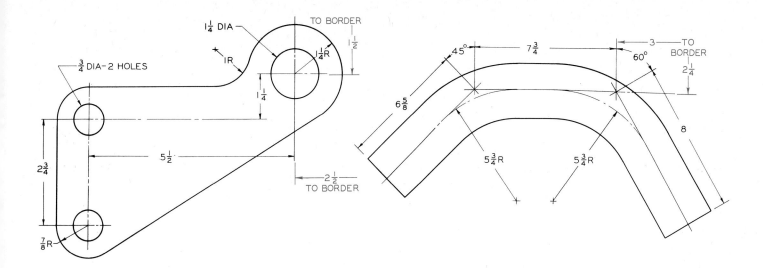

Problem 4·25. Draw the view of the line-up guide. Scale: full size. Use light, thin lines to show construction for finding centers of arcs. Mark tangent points.

Problem 4·26. Draw the view of the special pipe bend of 2½″ steel pipe. Scale: 6″ = 1′-0″. 2½″ standard pipe is 2⅞″ outside diameter; inside diameter is 2.469″. Use light, thin lines to show construction for finding centers of arcs. Mark tangent points. Do not show hidden lines for inside diameter unless required by the instructor.

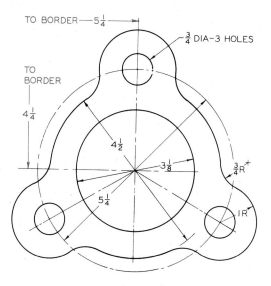

Problem 4·27. Draw the view of the gasket. Scale: full size. Show construction with light, thin lines.

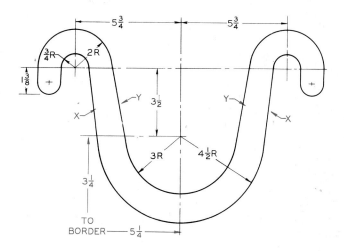

Problem 4·28. Draw the view of the hanging support. Scale: 6″ = 1′-0″. The tangent straight lines *X* and *Y* may be drawn by the method of Art. 4·25 or 4·29, or it may be drawn by trial (by eye). Ask your instructor which method to use. Mark tangent points *T*.

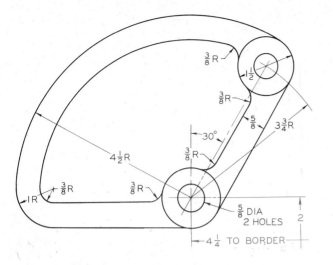

Problem 4•29. Draw the view of the sector. Scale: full size. Show construction by light, thin lines. Locate centers of arcs and mark tangent points.

4½

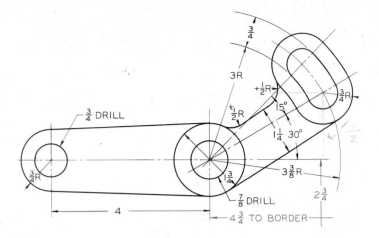

Problem 4•30. Draw the view of the adjustable link. Scale: full size. Show construction by light, thin lines.

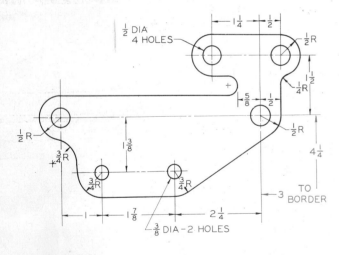

Problem 4•31. Draw the view of the holding bracket. Scale: full size. Show construction by light, thin lines. Material: Sheet brass. Thickness: No. 9 Brown & Sharpe gage (0.1144").

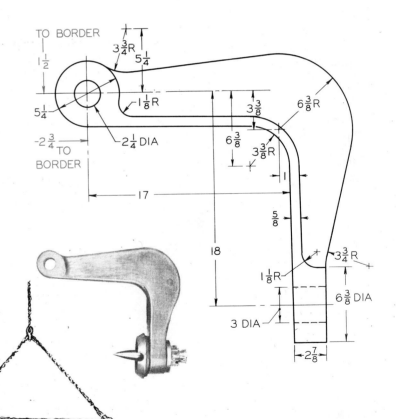

Problem 4•32. Draw the view of the end-loading hook. Scale: 3" = 1'-0". Show construction by light, thin lines.

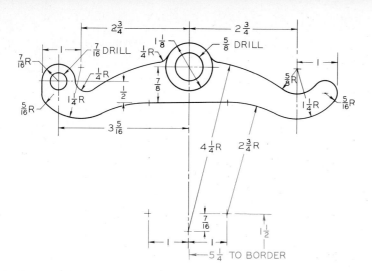

Prob. 4•33. Draw the view of the valve rocker for the steam cylinder of a pump. Scale: full size. This view has many tangent arcs. (Refer to Arts. 4·28 and 4·29.) Show construction by light, thin lines. Mark tangent points.

26•13 Problems 4·34 to 4·67. Two problems may be worked on an 8½″ × 11″ sheet, laid out as in Fig. 26-13, or four may be worked on an 11″ × 17″ sheet divided into four parts. These problems are to be laid out from the printed directions. Work with light, thin construction lines and do not erase them. Brighten result lines.

Fig. 26-13. Layout for two problems on an 8½″ × 11″ sheet.

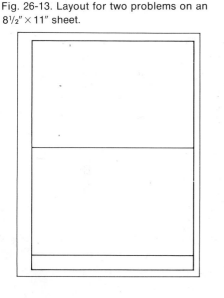

Problem 4•34. Near the center of the space draw a line 3¹¹⁄₁₆″ long and bisect it. Art. 4·2.

Problem 4•35. Near the center of the space draw a line 3⁷⁄₁₆″ long and bisect it. Art. 4·2.

Problem 4•36. Draw a horizontal line 5½″ long and 1½″ above bottom of the space. Erect a perpendicular to the line at a point 1″ to the left of the right-hand end of the line. Art. 4·3.

Problem 4•37. Draw a vertical line near the center of the space. Locate a point O, 2″ down from the top of the space and 1″ in from the left side. Erect a perpendicular to the line from point O. Art. 4·4.

Problem 4•38. Above the center of the space draw a horizontal line 5¹³⁄₁₆″ long. Divide it into seven equal parts geometrically. Art. 4·6.

Problem 4•39. To the left of the center draw a vertical line 3⁷⁄₁₆″ long and divide it into five equal parts geometrically. Art. 4·6.

Problem 4•40. Locate a point ¾″ above lower line of space and 1″ from left side. Draw lines joining the middle points of the upper and right-hand sides of the space. Bisect the angle between these lines. Art. 4·2.

Problem 4•41. Locate a point ¾″ below the middle of the upper line of the space. Draw lines joining this point with the lower right-hand corner and with the middle of left side of space. Bisect the angle. Art. 4·2.

Problem 4•42. Draw a vertical line ¾″ from left edge of space. From a point on this line ¾″ below top of space draw another line making any angle. Copy this angle so that one side is ¾″ from right side of space and vertex is ¾″ from bottom of space. Art. 4·8.

Problem 4•43. From the middle of left side of space draw lines to upper and lower right-hand corners. Copy this angle so that one side is horizontal and ½″ above bottom of space. Art. 4·8.

Problem 4•44. Draw a horizontal line 4¾″ long and 1″ above bottom of space. On it as a base construct a triangle having sides of 4⅛″ and 3¼″. Art. 4·9.

Problem 4•45. Draw a vertical line 2⅞″ long and 1½″ from left side of space. On it construct a triangle having sides of 5⅛″ and 4¾″. Art. 4·9.

Problem 4•46. Draw a horizontal line 4½″ long and 1″ above bottom of space. Using this as the longer of two sides, construct a right triangle by the 6-8-10 method. Art. 4·13.

Problem 4•47. Draw a regular hexagon 3¾″ across corners. Art. 4·20.

Problem 4•48. Draw a regular hexagon 4⅛″ across flats. Art. 4·19.

Problem 4•49. Draw a regular pentagon in a circle with a diameter of 3¾". Art. 4·17.

Problem 4•50. Draw a regular octagon in a 3½" square. Art. 4·21.

Problem 4•51. Locate three points as follows: Point *A*, 3¾" from left edge of space, 4¼" from bottom of space; *B*, 5¼" from left edge, 2⅝" from bottom; *C*, 2" from left edge, 1¾" from bottom. Draw a circle through *A*, *B*, and *C*. Art 4·23.

Problem 4•52. Locate a point ½" from bottom of space and ½" from left edge. Draw lines from this point to middle of top of space and to lower right-hand corner. Draw an arc tangent to these two lines with a radius of 1½". Art. 4·26.

Problem 4•53. Draw an arc having a radius of 3½", with its center ¾" from top of space and 1¾" from left edge. Find the length of an arc of 60°. Art. 4·32.

Problem 4•54. From the left edge of the space draw a horizontal line 1½" long and 1¼" below top of space. From right edge draw a horizontal line 1½" long and 1¼" above bottom of space. Join these two lines by an ogee curve. Point *E* to be one-third the distance from *B* and *C*. Art. 4·27.

Problem 4•55. Draw an equilateral triangle in the center of the space, sides ¾" long. Draw one turn of an involute of the triangle. Art. 4·35.

Problem 4•56. Locate a point 2¾" below top of space and 2" from left side

of space. With this point as a center draw a circle having a diameter of 3". Draw an involute of the right half of the circle. Art. 4·37.

Problem 4•57. Draw horizontal and vertical lines through the center of the space. Draw one turn of a spiral of Archimedes in a 4" diameter circle. Art. 4·38.

Problem 4•58. Draw an ellipse having a major axis of 4" and a minor axis of 2½". Use concentric-circle method. Art. 4·42.

Problem 4•59. Draw an ellipse having a major axis of 4" and a minor axis of 1". Use trammel method. Art. 4·41.

Problem 4•60. Draw an approximate ellipse having a major axis of 4½" and a minor axis of 3¼". Art. 4·43.

Problem 4•61. Divide a 4" circle into five equal parts and draw a five-pointed star by connecting opposite points.

Problem 4•62. In a 4" circle draw interlaced equilateral triangles. The bands are ¼" wide.

Problem 4•63. With a 30°–60° and 45° triangles together, draw the six-pointed star.

Problem 4•64. In a 4" circle draw interlaced squares making the bands ¼" wide.

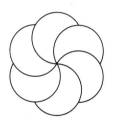

Problem 4•65. Draw a 4" circle. With six equally spaced radii as diameters, draw circle arcs.

Problem 4•66. Variation of Prob. 4·65 using 5, 8, or 12 radii.

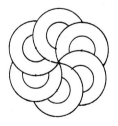

Problem 4•67. Variation of Prob. 4·65 or 4·66 adding a concentric-circle arc one-half the radius of first arc.

GROUP 5. SHAPE DESCRIPTION

26·14 The problems in this group are for practice in representing objects by views in order to gain a thorough understanding of the theory of shape description. Chapter 5 should be studied carefully first. Views and pictures are given for some of the problems to assist the student in visualizing the object. In others, two views are given, from which the student is to work out the third view. In still others, pictures are given from which the student is required to determine what views are necessary, to plan and arrange the views in

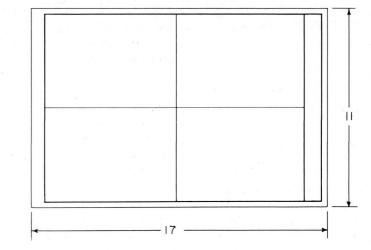

Fig. 26-14c. Layout for four problems on an 11″ × 17″ sheet.

the working space, and then to work out the views. It is necessary to read Arts. 5·16 to 5·18 for an explanation of a systematic method of placing the views on a drawing.

Most problems in this group can be worked on an 8½″ × 11″ sheet laid out as in Fig. 26-14a or 26-14b. Four prob-

lems may be worked on an 11″ × 17″ sheet laid out as in Fig. 26-14c. The solution for one problem on an 8½″ × 11″ sheet is shown in Fig. 26-14d and for two problems in Fig. 26-14e. Some problems are planned for working on an 11″ × 17″ sheet (Fig. 26-14c) without the division lines.

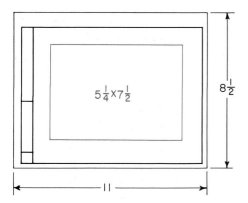

Fig. 26-14a. Layout for one problem on an 8½″ × 11″ sheet.

Fig. 26-14b. Layout for two problems on an 8½″ × 11″ sheet.

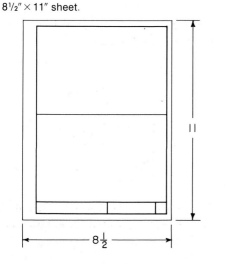

Fig. 26-14d. Solution for one problem on a sheet for Prob. 5·1.

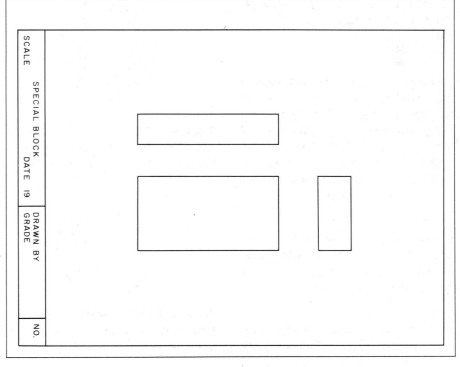

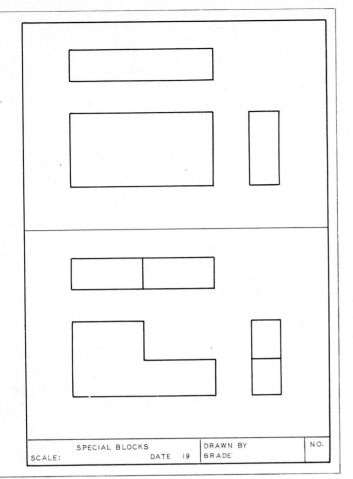

SPECIAL BLOCKS

SCALE: DATE 19   DRAWN BY
                           GRADE   NO.

Fig. 26-14e. Solution for two problems on a sheet for Probs. 5·1 and 5·2.

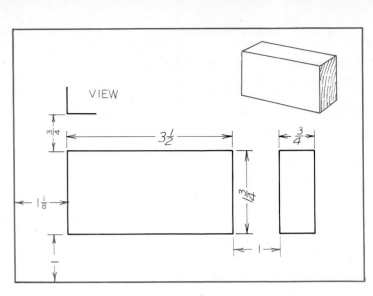

VIEW

Problem 5•1. Lay out an 8½″ × 11″ sheet as in Fig. 26-14a. Draw a 5¼″ × 7½″ rectangle in the center of the working space, as shown in red. Use a light pencil line. A picture and two views of a special block are given. Draw three complete views. Scale: full size. Do not copy the picture. When completed, the sheet will appear as in Fig. 26-14d.

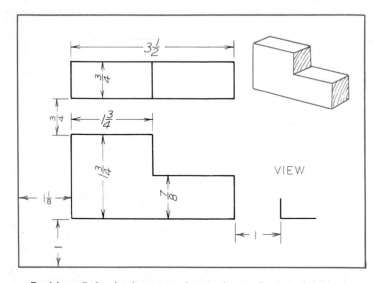

VIEW

Problem 5•2. A picture and two views of a special block are given. Draw three complete views. Scale: full size.

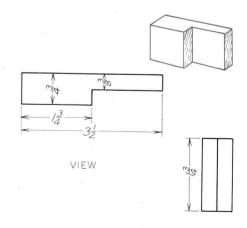

VIEW

Problem 5•3. Draw three complete views of the half lap.

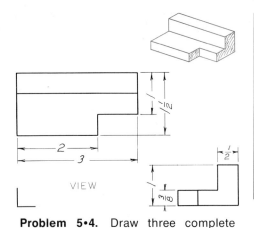

Problem 5•4. Draw three complete views of the corner stop.

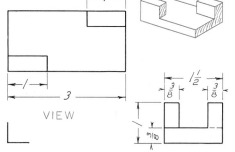

Problem 5•5. Draw three complete views of the spacer.

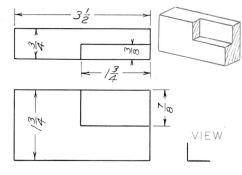

Problem 5•6. Draw three complete views of the adjusting piece.

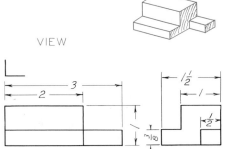

Problem 5•7. Draw three complete views of the plug-in end piece.

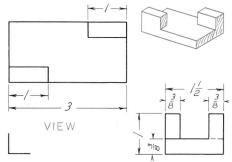

Problem 5•8. Draw three complete views of the check plate.

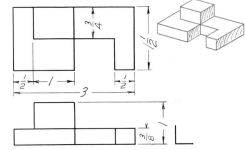

Problem 5•9. Draw three complete views of the line-up gage.

Problem 5•10. Draw three views of the end stop.

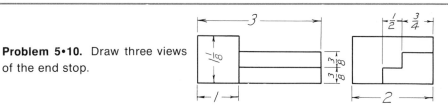

Problem 5•11. Draw three views of the intermediate stop.

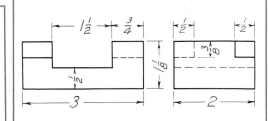

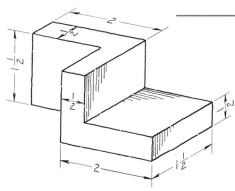

Problem 5•12. Draw three views of the angle spacer.

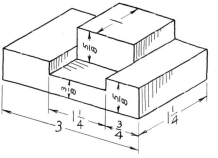

Problem 5•13. Draw three views of the rear base.

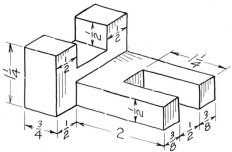

Problem 5•14. Draw three views of the double lock.

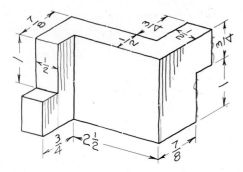

Problem 5•15. Draw three views of the offset spacer.

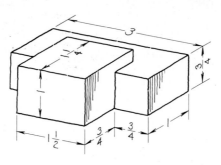

Problem 5•16. Draw three views of the front base.

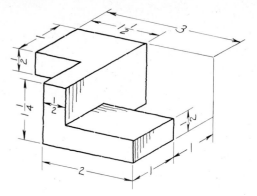

Problem 5•17. Draw three views of the angle stop.

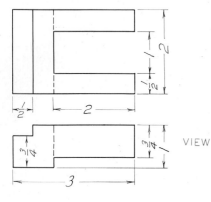

VIEW

Problem 5•18. Draw three views of the guide fork.

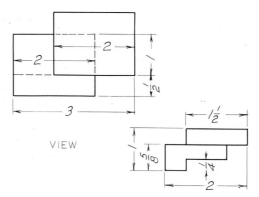

VIEW

VIEW

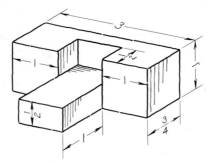

Problem 5•19. Draw three views of the locating slide.

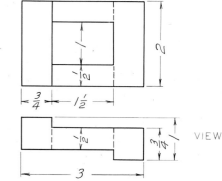

VIEW

Problem 5•20. Draw three views of the guide center.

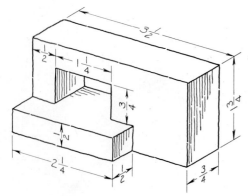

Problem 5•21. Draw three views of the offset guide.

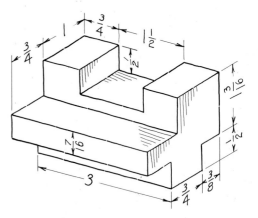

Problem 5•22. Draw three views of the end anchor.

Problem 5•23. Draw three views of the cross slide.

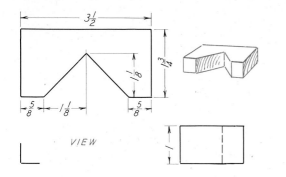

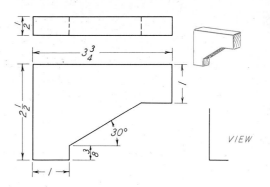

Problem 5•24. Draw three views of the V-block.

Problem 5•25. Draw three views of the plate bracket.

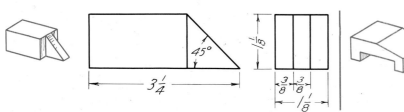

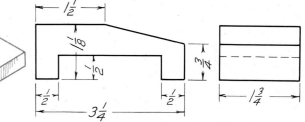

Problem 5•26. Draw three views of the stop.

Problem 5•27. Draw three views of the crossover.

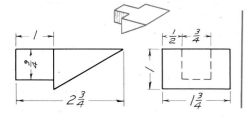

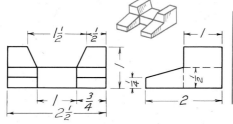

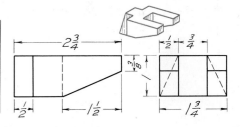

Problem 5•28. Draw three views of the plug stop.

Problem 5•29. Draw three views of the placer.

Problem 5•30. Draw three views of the adjustable slide.

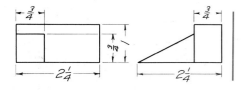

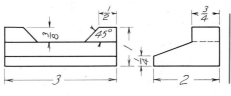

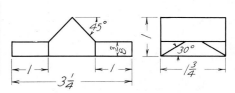

Problem 5•31. Draw three views of the adjusting block.

Problem 5•32. Draw three views of the groove support.

Problem 5•33. Draw three views of the V-support.

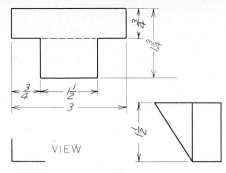

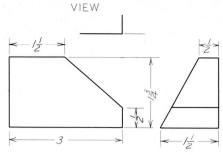

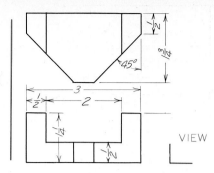

Problem 5•34. Draw three views of the angle stop.

Problem 5•35. Draw three views of the former.

Problem 5•36. Draw three views of the fitting.

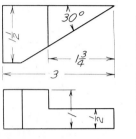

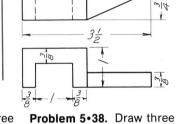

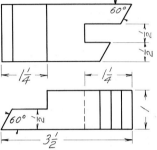

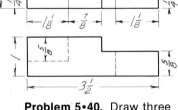

Problem 5•37. Draw three views of the wedge.

Problem 5•38. Draw three views of the holder.

Problem 5•39. Draw three views of the lock stop.

Problem 5•40. Draw three views of the middle stop.

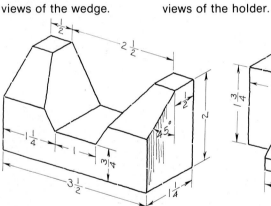

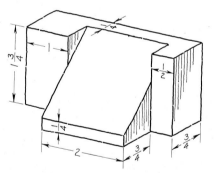

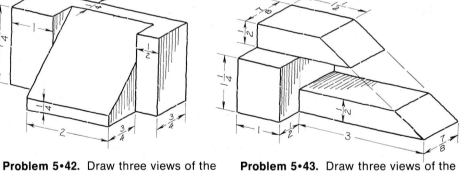

Problem 5•41. Draw three views of the Y-guide.

Problem 5•42. Draw three views of the end stop.

Problem 5•43. Draw three views of the latch.

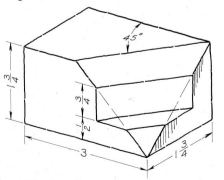

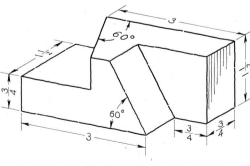

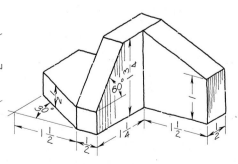

Problem 5•44. Draw three views of the corner lock.

Problem 5•45. Draw three views of the wedge spacer.

Problem 5•46. Draw three views of the double angle.

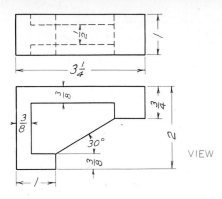

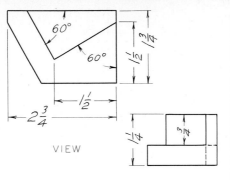

Problem 5·47. Draw three views of the bracket.

Problem 5·48. Draw three views of the locator.

Problem 5·49. Draw three views of the V-slide.

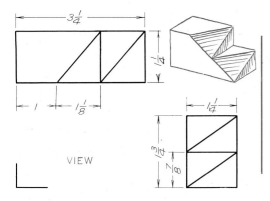

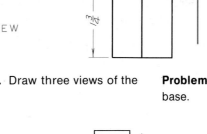

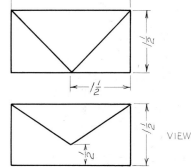

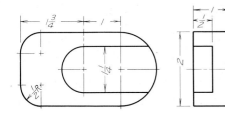

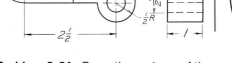

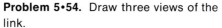

Problem 5·50. Draw three views of the locator.

Problem 5·51. Draw three views of the filler.

Problem 5·52. Draw three views of the base.

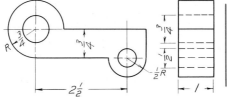

Problem 5·53. Draw three views of the plate.

Problem 5·54. Draw three views of the link.

Problem 5·55. Draw three views of the bearing.

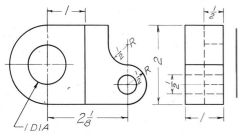

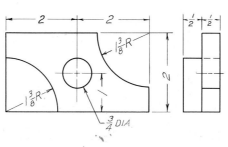

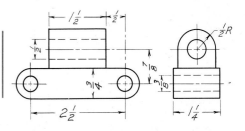

Problem 5·56. Draw three views of the link.

Problem 5·57. Draw three views of the locating plate.

Problem 5·58. Draw three views of the sliding guide.

Problem 5•59. A line is missing from one of the views of each of the objects shown at A to X. Make a freehand sketch (enlarged) of the views and supply the missing line. Dimensions may be taken from the graphic scales with the dividers to draw the views with the instruments, if desired. Measure carefully.

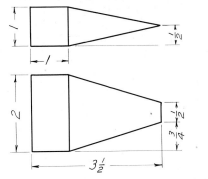

Problem 5·60. Draw three views of the wedge.

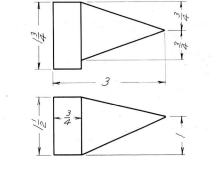

Problem 5·61. Draw three views of the positioner.

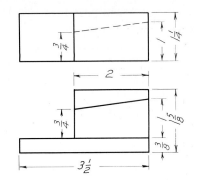

Problem 5·62. Draw three views of the holder.

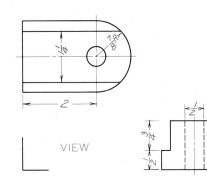

VIEW

Problem 5·63. Draw three views of the slide.

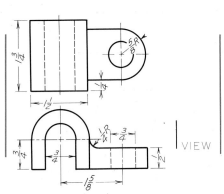

VIEW

Problem 5·64. Draw three views of the holder.

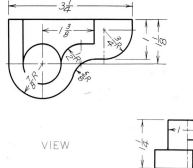

VIEW

Problem 5·65. Draw three views of the pivot.

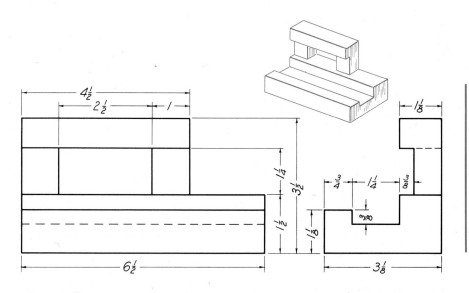

Problem 5·66. Draw three views of the support guide. Scale: full size. Use 11″ × 17″ sheet.

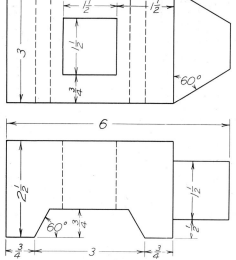

Problem 5·67. Draw three views of the locating support. Use 11″ × 17″ sheet.

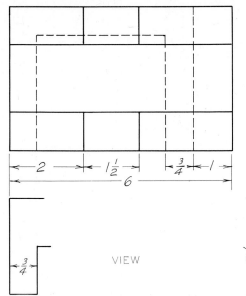

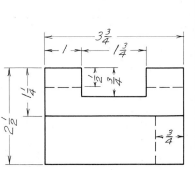

Problem 5·68. Draw three views of the slotted bracket. Draw full size or half size according to size of sheet used.

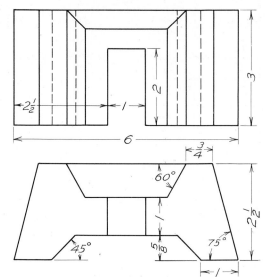

Problem 5·69. Draw three views of the base. Use 11″ × 17″ sheet.

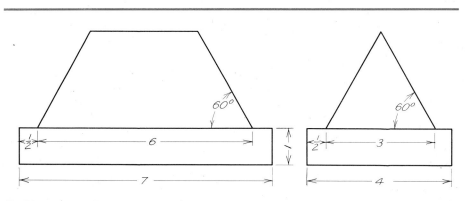

Problem 5·70. Draw three complete views of the fulcrum. Find height from the right-hand view. Use 11″ × 17″ sheet.

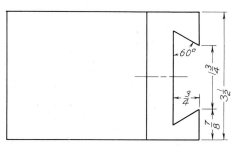

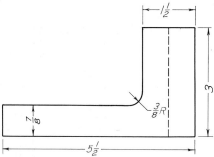

Problem 5·71. Draw three views of the cast-iron dovetail. Lay off one-half of 1¾″ on each side of the center line in the top view and draw 60° lines to intersect the ¾″ depth line. Use 11″ × 17″ sheet.

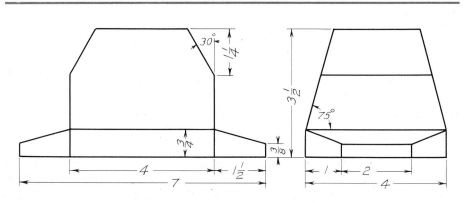

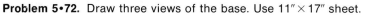

Problem 5·72. Draw three views of the base. Use 11″ × 17″ sheet.

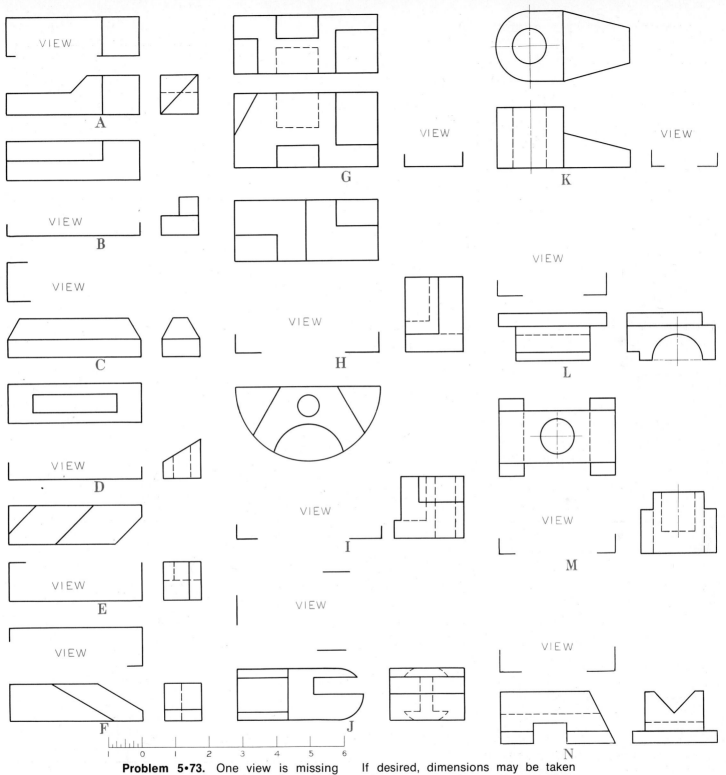

Problem 5·73. One view is missing from each of the objects A to N. Make a freehand sketch (enlarged) showing three complete views of each object. If desired, dimensions may be taken from the graphic scale with the dividers to draw the views with the instruments. Measure carefully.

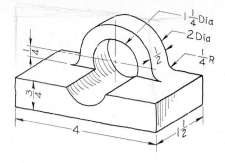

Problem 5•74. Draw three views of the base guide. Use 11″ × 17″ sheet.

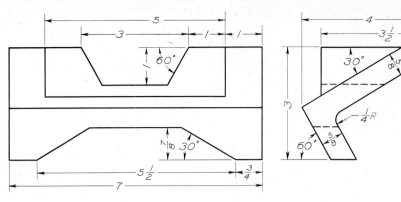

Problem 5•75. Draw three views of the separator. Use 11″ × 17″ sheet.

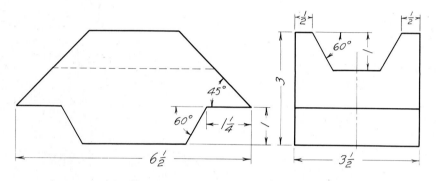

Problem 5•76. Draw three views of the cross slide. Use 11″ × 17″ sheet.

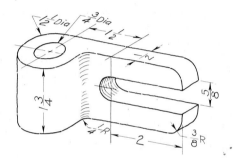

Problem 5•77. Draw two views of the vertical stop. Use 8½″ × 11″ sheet.

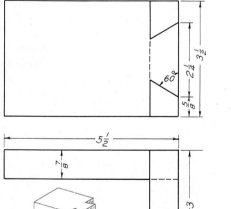

Problem 5•78. Draw three views of the dovetail joint. Use 11″ × 17″ sheet.

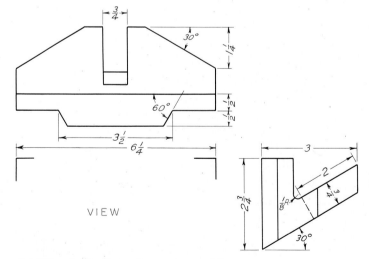

VIEW

Problem 5•79. Draw three views of the secondary guide lug. Use 11″ × 17″ sheet.

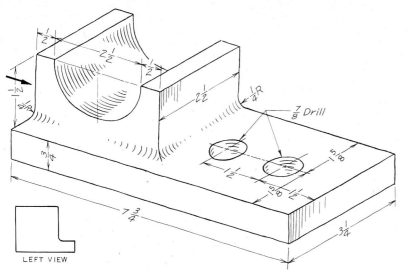

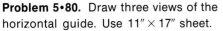

LEFT VIEW

Problem 5•80. Draw three views of the horizontal guide. Use 11″ × 17″ sheet.

Problem 5•81. Draw three views of the vertical guide. Use 11″ × 17″ sheet.

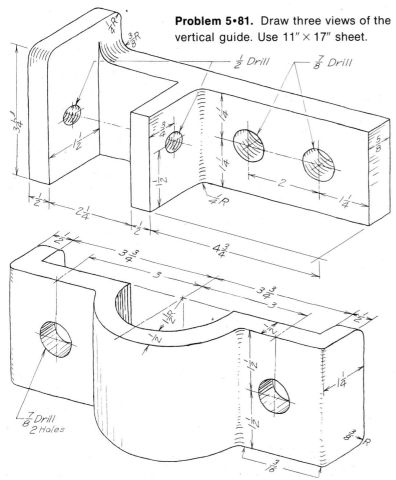

Problem 5•82. Draw three views of the side cap. Use 11″ × 17″ sheet.

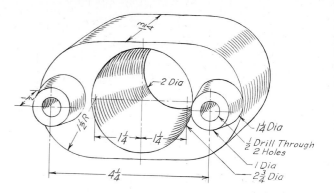

Problem 5•83. Draw three complete views of the rocker block. The ½″ holes extend through the piece. Use 11″ × 17″ sheet.

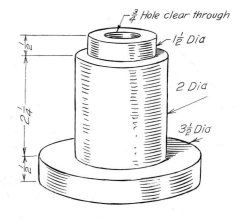

Problem 5•84. Draw two complete views of the cast-iron collar. Use 8½″ × 11″ sheet with the long side vertical.

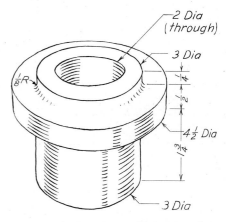

Problem 5•85. Draw two complete views of the stud bushing. Use 8½″ × 11″ sheet with the long side vertical.

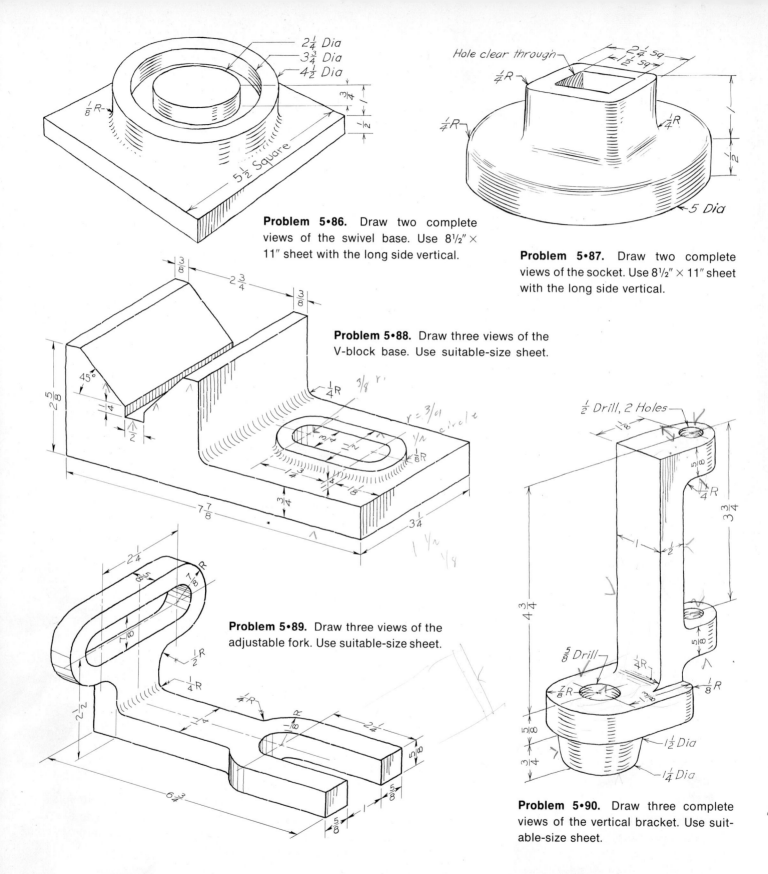

Problem 5·86. Draw two complete views of the swivel base. Use 8½″ × 11″ sheet with the long side vertical.

Problem 5·87. Draw two complete views of the socket. Use 8½″ × 11″ sheet with the long side vertical.

Problem 5·88. Draw three views of the V-block base. Use suitable-size sheet.

Problem 5·89. Draw three views of the adjustable fork. Use suitable-size sheet.

Problem 5·90. Draw three complete views of the vertical bracket. Use suitable-size sheet.

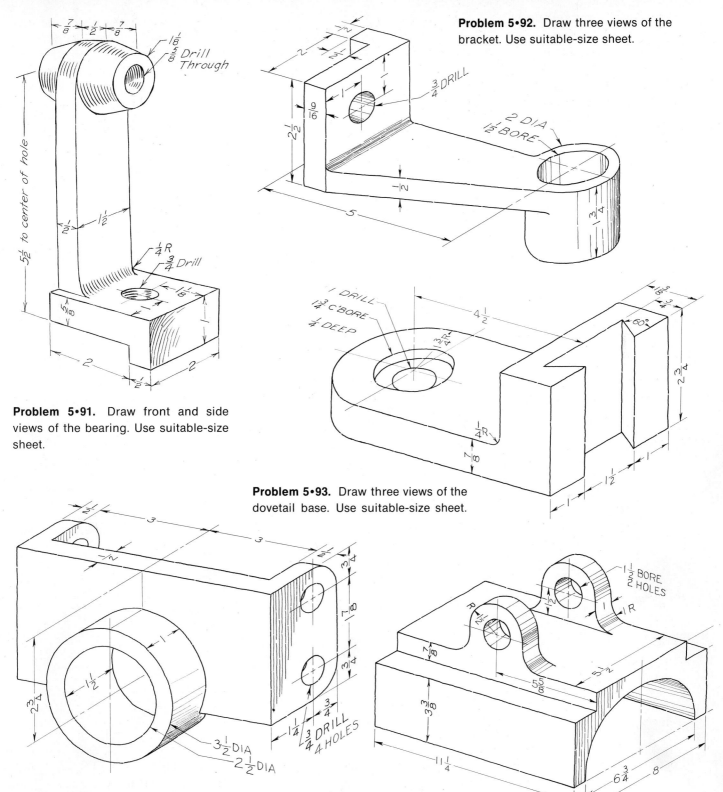

Problem 5·92. Draw three views of the bracket. Use suitable-size sheet.

Problem 5·91. Draw front and side views of the bearing. Use suitable-size sheet.

Problem 5·93. Draw three views of the dovetail base. Use suitable-size sheet.

Problem 5·94. Draw three views of the post bearing. Use suitable-size sheet.

Problem 5·95. Draw three views of the keeper. Use suitable-size sheet.

GROUP 6. SKETCHING

26•15 General instructions. Use 8½″ × 11″ paper with or without the border lines. For two problems the layout of Fig. 26-15a may be drawn or sketched in. Bond, ledger, or drawing paper may be used, either plain or graph (ruled in squares for orthographic views or isometric ruling for pictorial views). All

distances and angles are to be estimated by "eye." One or two problems may be worked on a sheet. For one problem, place the sheet with the long side horizontal and omit the division line. Any of the problems shown by pictures in Groups 5 and 13 may be used for sketching problems.

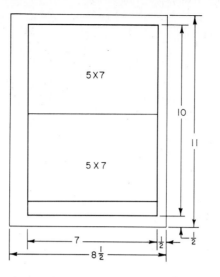

Fig. 26-15a. Layout for two sketches on an 8½″ × 11″ sheet.

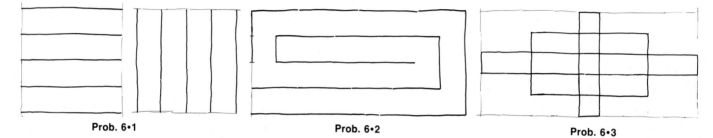

Prob. 6•1   **Prob. 6•2**   **Prob. 6•3**

Problems 6•1, 6•2, 6•3. Line exercises. Sketch a rectangle about 3″ × 6½″ with light lines. Sketch the exercise shown.

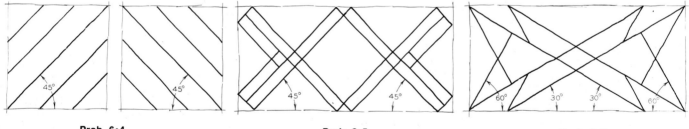

Prob. 6•4   **Prob. 6•5**   **Prob. 6•6**

Problems 6•4, 6•5, 6•6. Line exercises. Sketch a rectangle about 3″ × 6½″ with light lines. Sketch the exercise shown.

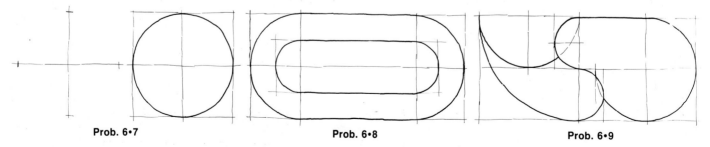

Prob. 6•7   **Prob. 6•8**   **Prob. 6•9**

Problems 6•7, 6•8, 6•9. Circle and arc exercises. Sketch a rectangle about 3″ × 6½″ with light lines. Sketch the exercise shown.

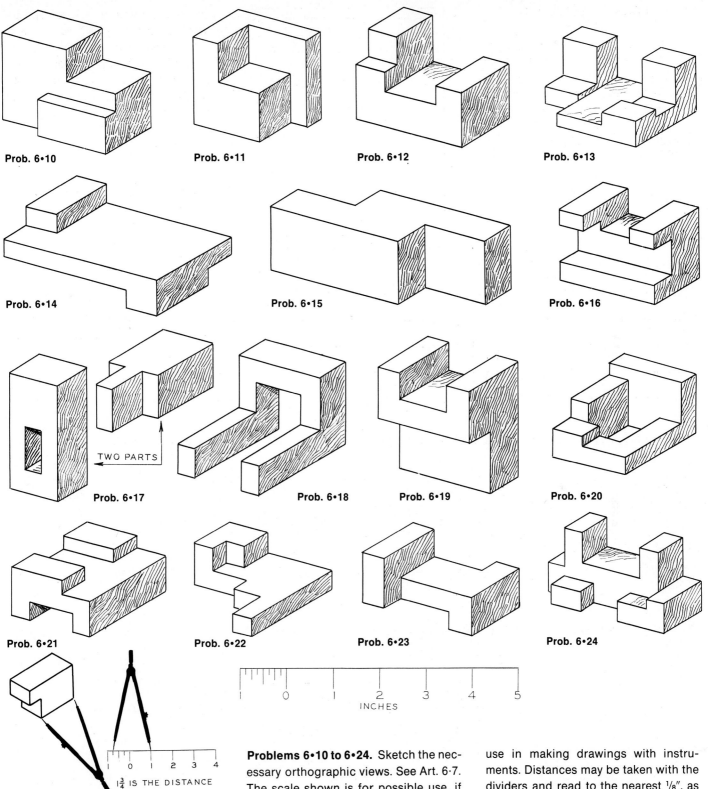

Prob. 6·10

Prob. 6·11

Prob. 6·12

Prob. 6·13

Prob. 6·14

Prob. 6·15

Prob. 6·16

Prob. 6·17

TWO PARTS

Prob. 6·18

Prob. 6·19

Prob. 6·20

Prob. 6·21

Prob. 6·22

Prob. 6·23

Prob. 6·24

$1\frac{3}{4}$ IS THE DISTANCE

Fig. 26-15b. Use of scale.

0 1 2 3 4 5
INCHES

Problems 6·10 to 6·24. Sketch the necessary orthographic views. See Art. 6·7. The scale shown is for possible use, if desired, for checking proportions or for use in making drawings with instruments. Distances may be taken with the dividers and read to the nearest $\frac{1}{8}$", as shown in Fig. 26-15b.

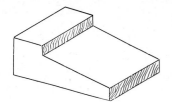

Prob. 6·25

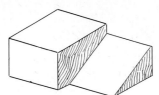

Prob. 6·26

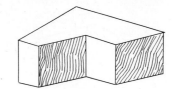

Prob. 6·27

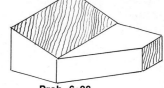

Prob. 6·28

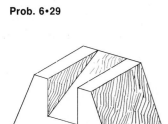

Prob. 6·29

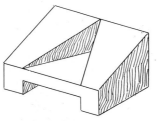

Prob. 6·30

Prob. 6·31

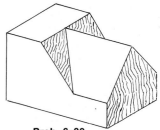

Prob. 6·32

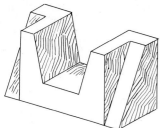

Prob. 6·33

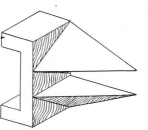

Prob. 6·34

Prob. 6·35

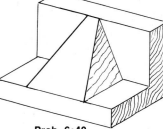

Prob. 6·36

Prob. 6·37

Prob. 6·38

Prob. 6·39

Prob. 6·40

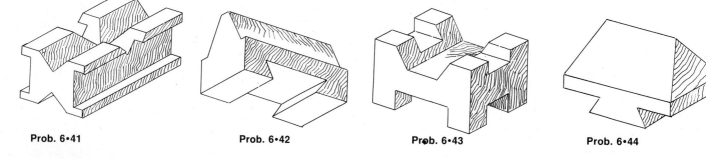

Prob. 6·41

Prob. 6·42

Prob. 6·43

Prob. 6·44

Problems 6·25 to 6·44. Sketch the necessary ortho-graphic views. See Art. 6·7. See Fig. 26-15*b* for use of the scale.

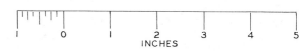

INCHES

446   CHAPTER 26

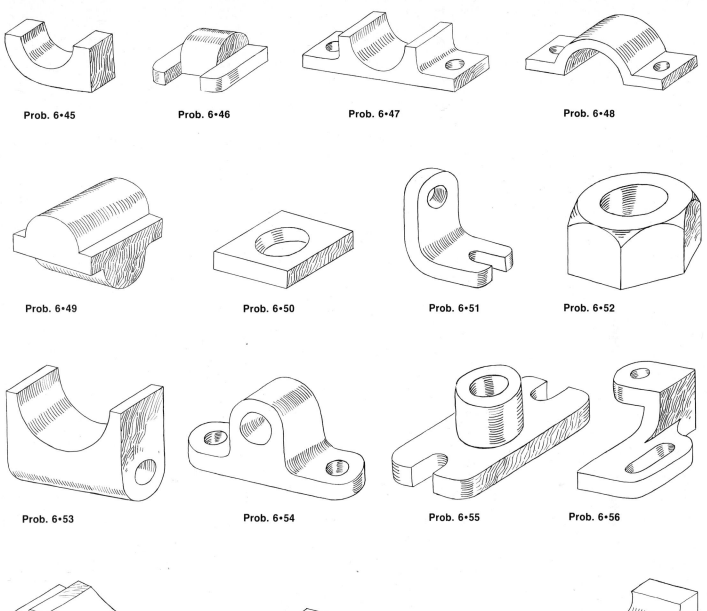

Prob. 6•45

Prob. 6•46

Prob. 6•47

Prob. 6•48

Prob. 6•49

Prob. 6•50

Prob. 6•51

Prob. 6•52

Prob. 6•53

Prob. 6•54

Prob. 6•55

Prob. 6•56

Prob. 6•57

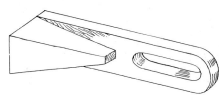

Prob. 6•58

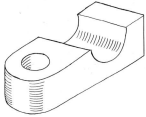

Prob. 6•59

Problems 6•45 to 6•59. Sketch the necessary ortho-graphic views. See Art. 6·7. See Fig. 26-15*b* for use of the scale.

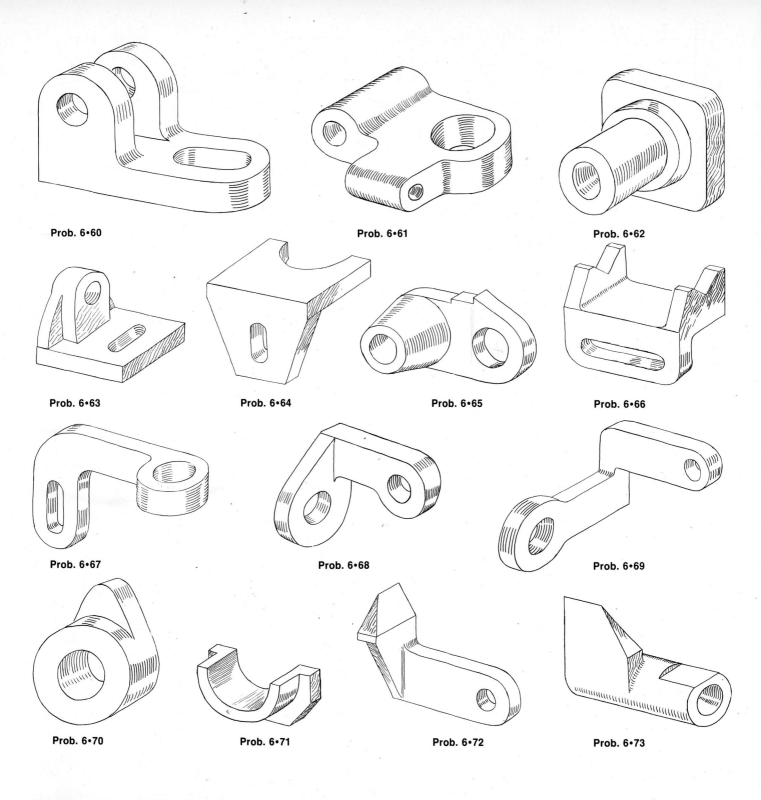

Prob. 6·60

Prob. 6·61

Prob. 6·62

Prob. 6·63

Prob. 6·64

Prob. 6·65

Prob. 6·66

Prob. 6·67

Prob. 6·68

Prob. 6·69

Prob. 6·70

Prob. 6·71

Prob. 6·72

Prob. 6·73

Problems 6·60 to 6·73. Sketch the necessary orthographic views. See Art. 6·7. See Fig. 26-15b for use of the scale.

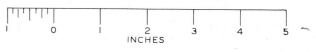

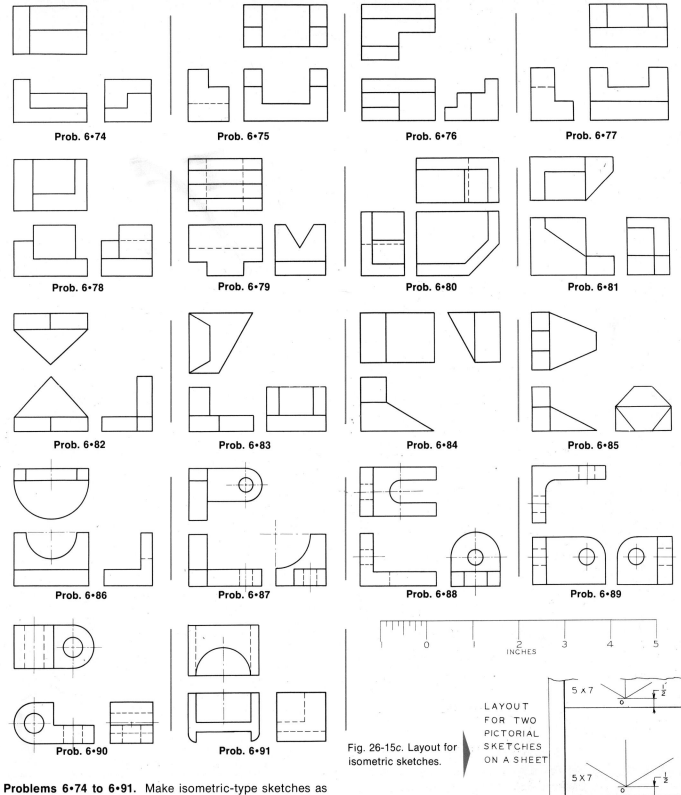

Prob. 6·74 **Prob. 6·75** **Prob. 6·76** **Prob. 6·77**

Prob. 6·78 **Prob. 6·79** **Prob. 6·80** **Prob. 6·81**

Prob. 6·82 **Prob. 6·83** **Prob. 6·84** **Prob. 6·85**

Prob. 6·86 **Prob. 6·87** **Prob. 6·88** **Prob. 6·89**

Prob. 6·90 **Prob. 6·91**

Fig. 26-15c. Layout for isometric sketches.

INCHES

LAYOUT FOR TWO PICTORIAL SKETCHES ON A SHEET

5 X 7

5 X 7

Problems 6·74 to 6·91. Make isometric-type sketches as assigned by the instructor. See Art. 6·9 and Fig. 26-15c.

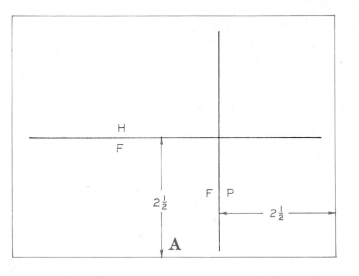
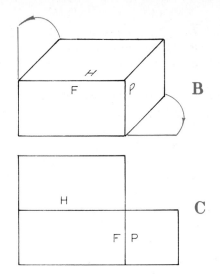

Fig. 26-16a. Representation of planes for showing projections of points and lines.

GROUP 7. READING GRAPHICS

26·16 Study Chaps. 5 and 7 before starting these problems. Space for one problem is approximately 5″ high by 7″ wide, laid out as at A in Fig. 26-16a. This represents the three planes H, F, and P, opened up as at B and C. The planes are located by the intersections and identified by the letters H, F, and P. Points are represented by small letters, a, b, c, etc., and lines by letters at each end as line ab, cd, etc. Use short crossed lines to locate a point. Top views use the superscript H, as a^H; front views use F, as a^F; and side views use a^P. In the problems which follow, points are in back of F, below H, and to the left of P.

Problem 7·1. Draw three views of point a, 1¾″ from F, ½″ from H, and 1¼″ from P. The solution of Prob. 7·1 is shown in Fig. 26-16b. The projection lines shown in red, if drawn, should be light, thin lines.

Problem 7·2. Draw three views of point b, 3″ from P, 1″ from F, and 1¼″ from H. Letter the projections correctly. Do not draw projection lines.

Problem 7·3. Draw three views of points a and b. Point a: ¾″ from F, 3″ from P, and 1½″ from H. Point b: 1″ from P, 1¾″ from F, and 1¼″ from H. Letter the projections of the letters correctly. Join the points to show three projections of the line ab.

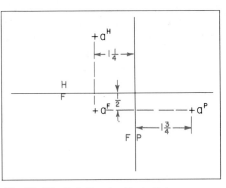

Fig. 26-16b. Solution for Prob. 7·1.

Problem 7·4. Draw three views of points a, b, and c. Point a: 1¾″ from P, ½″ from F, and ¾″ from H. Point b: 1″ from F, 1¾″ from H, and 3½″ from P. Point c: 1″ from H, ¾″ from P, and 1¼″ from F. Letter the projections and join points a, b, and c to show the three views of the triangle abc.

Problem 7·5. Draw three views of each of the points a, b, c, and d. Point a: ¾″ from F, 3″ from H, and ¾″ from P. Point b: ¼″ from F, 3″ from H, and 2¼″ from P. Point c: 2″ from F, 3″ from H, and 2¾″ from P. Point d: ¾″ from F, ½″ from H, and ½″ from P. Join points a and b, b and c, c and d; then, join points a, b, and c to point d to show three views of a triangular pyramid.

Problem 7·6. Draw three views of a line ab parallel to H and inclined backward from left to right.

Problem 7·7. Draw three views of a line ab sloping downward and forward from left to right.

Problem 7•8. Draw three views of a line *ab* sloping forward and upward from left to right.

Problem 7•9. Draw three views of two lines, *ab* and *cd*, which intersect at point *e*: ½″ from *F*, 1″ from *H*, and 1½″ from *P*. Line *ab* slopes forward and upward from the left. Line *cd* slopes backward and upward from the left.

Problem 7•10. Draw three views of two parallel lines, *ab* and *cd*. Both lines slope backward and upward.

Problem 7•11. Draw three views of a triangular card, *abc,* inclined backward and upward at an angle of 60° with *H* and perpendicular to *P.*

Problem 7•14. Draw three views of the V-slide of Prob. 5·49. Locate and letter a point on one of the inclined surfaces and show its three projections.

Problem 7•15. Draw three views of the corner lock of Prob. 5·44. Locate and letter a point on the surface inclined to *H*, *F*, and *P*. Show the three projections properly identified.

Problem 7•16. Draw three views of a semicircular card, perpendicular to *H* and inclined backward from left to right at an angle of 30° with *F*. The diameter is 2″, ½″ from *H* and parallel to *H*. The center of the diameter is 1″ from *F* and 1¾″ from *P*. The card extends downward.

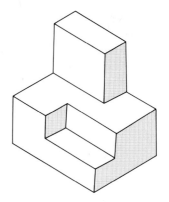

Problem 7•18. Copy the isometric view about twice the size shown. Draw three orthographic views and identify the surfaces with letters as was done for Fig. 7-12. Work freehand or with instruments as directed by the instructor.

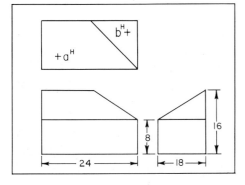

Problem 7•12. Draw three views of the shed. Scale: 1″ = 16′–0″. Spot two points, a^H and b^H, on the roof, about as indicated. Find the front and profile projections and letter them correctly.

Problem 7•13. Draw three views of the end stop of Prob. 5·42 and spot a point *a* on the inclined surface. Locate and letter the three views of the point.

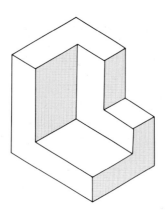

Problem 7•17. Copy the isometric view about twice the size shown. Draw three orthographic views and identify the surfaces with letters as was done for Fig. 7-12. Work freehand or with instruments as directed by the instructor.

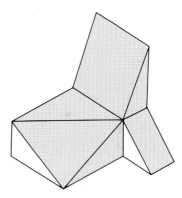

Problem 7•19. Copy the isometric view about twice the size shown. Draw three orthographic views and identify the surfaces with letters as was done for Fig. 7-12. Work freehand or with instruments as directed by the instructor.

GROUP 8. INKING

26•17 Inking or tracing of drawings used to be regular practice. Since pencil work has become regular practice, inking is not often required; but, when it is, the inking must be very well done.

When the ability to do good pencil work has been developed, it does not take very much practice to use a pen instead of a pencil. The regular drawing pen with adjustable nibs may be used, or the set of tube pens. The tube pens give uniform widths of lines without adjustment. They are also very convenient for freehand lettering. Read and refer to Chap. 8 when inking or tracing.

Any of the pencil drawings made in Groups 2, 4, or 5 may be used for inking problems. The following problems are also suggested to provide the student with varied experiences in inking.

Problem 8•1. Make a tracing of the drawing made for Prob. 2·1.

Problem 8•2. Make a tracing of the drawing made for Prob. 2·4.

Problem 8•3. Make a tracing of the drawing made for Prob. 2·7.

Problem 8•4. Make a tracing of the drawing made for Prob. 2·17.

Problem 8•5. Make a tracing of the drawing made for Prob. 2·22.

Problem 8•6. Make a tracing of the drawing made for Prob. 5·69.

Problem 8•7. Make a tracing of the drawing made for Prob. 5·78.

Problem 8•8. Make a tracing of the drawing made for Prob. 5·34.

Problem 8•9. Make a tracing of the drawing made for Prob. 5·79.

Problem 8•10. Make a tracing of the drawing made for Prob. 5·88.

GROUP 9.
AUXILIARIES AND REVOLUTIONS

26•18 Auxiliary views. Study Chap. 9 on auxiliary views before starting the problems. In the layouts of the problems the location is given for the center line or reference line, parallel to the slanting surface, on which the auxiliary view is to be constructed. In the case of symmetrical figures, the center line corresponds to the horizontal center line of the top view. For unsymmetrical figures, the reference line is usually taken at the back on the top view, as in Prob. 9·1. The projection lines from the front view of the object to the auxiliary view are shown in the layouts to aid in starting the problems. If drawn by the student, they should be extremely light so as not to confuse the result. The title for sheets is AUXILIARY VIEWS.

A layout for 8½″ × 11″ sheets is given in Fig. 26-18a, and a layout for 11″ × 17″ sheets is given in Fig. 26-18b. The size of sheet is indicated for the problems. Where 8½″ × 11″ size is given, one problem may be worked in the layout of Fig. 26-18a or two in the layout of Fig. 26-18b. Where 11″ × 17″ size is indicated, one problem is to be worked in the layout of Fig. 26-18b (with the division line left out). Some of the problems may be changed by using a different angle or cutting off part by a plane 3⅜″ above and parallel to the base.

Fig. 26-18a. One problem on an 8½″ × 11″ sheet.

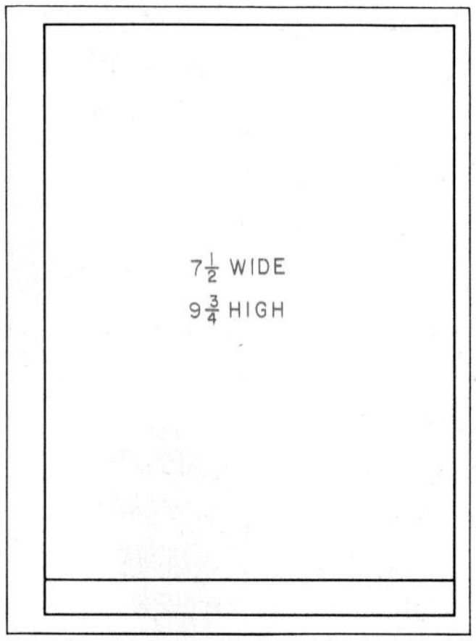

Fig. 26-18b. Two problems on an 11″ × 17″ sheet.

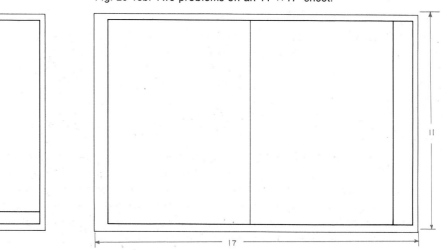

7½ WIDE
9¾ HIGH

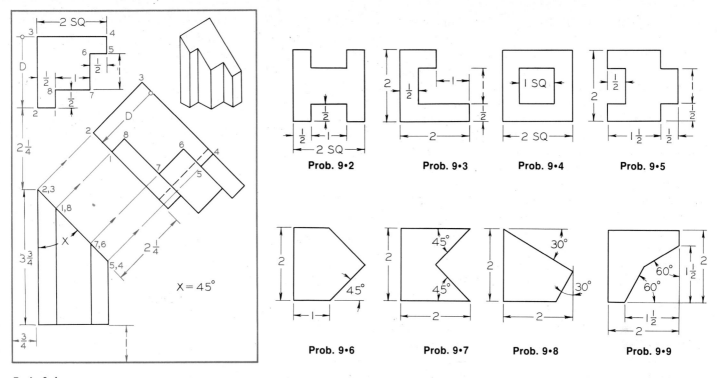

Prob. 9•1

Prob. 9•2   **Prob. 9•3**   **Prob. 9•4**   **Prob. 9•5**

Prob. 9•6   **Prob. 9•7**   **Prob. 9•8**   **Prob. 9•9**

Prob. 9•10   **Prob. 9•11**   **Prob. 9•12**   **Prob. 9•13**

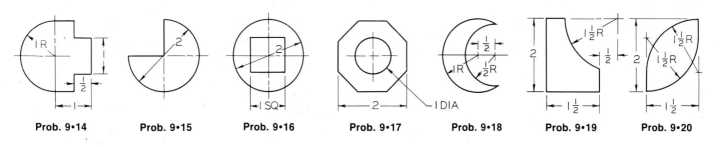

Prob. 9•14   **Prob. 9•15**   **Prob. 9•16**   **Prob. 9•17**   **Prob. 9•18**   **Prob. 9•19**   **Prob. 9•20**

Problems 9•1 to 9•20 are to be worked on 8½″ × 11″ sheets laid out as in Fig. 26-18a. Prob. 9·1 is worked as an example. Only the top views are given for Probs. 9·2 to 9·20. For each problem draw the top and front views and either the complete auxiliary view or the cut face only as directed by the instructor. The angle X may be 45° or 60° as assigned. The total height of the front view is 3¾″ for all problems 9·1 through 9·20.

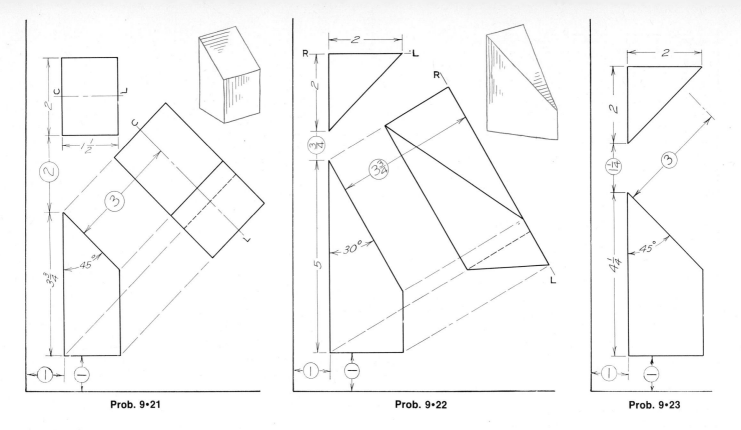

Prob. 9·21

Prob. 9·22

Prob. 9·23

Problems 9·21, 9·22, 9·23 (8½″ × 11″ sheet). Draw the front, top, and complete auxiliary views. The solutions are given for Probs. 9·21 and 9·22. Do not copy but cover the solution; work the problem and compare your solution.

Problems 9·24 to 9·27 (8½″ × 11″ sheet). Draw the front, top, and complete auxiliary views.

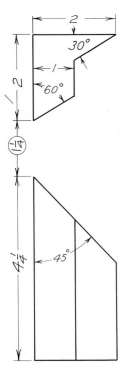

Prob. 9·24

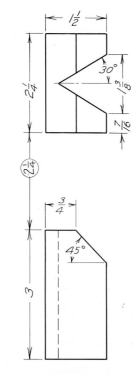

Prob. 9·25

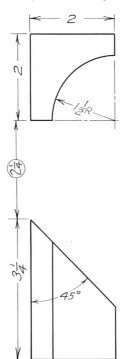

Prob. 9·26

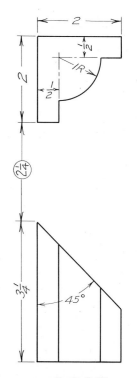

Prob. 9·27

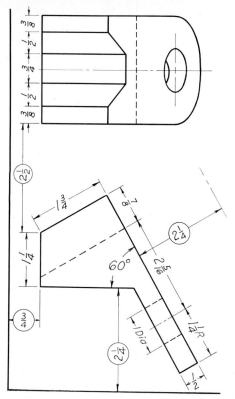

Problem 9•28 (8½″ × 11″ sheet). Make a drawing of the anchor lug including a complete auxiliary view. The hole and rounded end need not be shown in the top view.

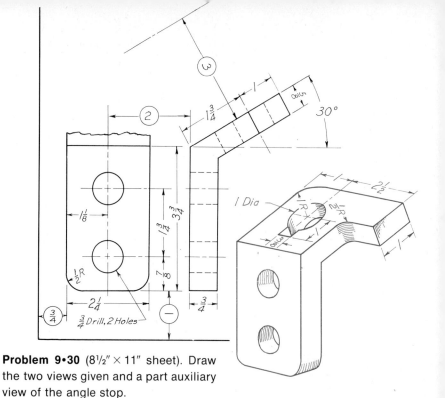

Problem 9•30 (8½″ × 11″ sheet). Draw the two views given and a part auxiliary view of the angle stop.

Problem 9•31 (11″ × 17″ sheet). Scale: full size. (8½″ × 11″ sheet) Scale: 6″ = 1′–0″. A picture and a layout for a piece of hollow molding are shown in the figure. Consider the left-hand view to be the front view. Draw the front and side views as shown. Draw a complete auxiliary view on a plane parallel to the cut face. Refer to Art. 9·5. Note that this will be a right-auxiliary view made on a plane perpendicular to the vertical plane. See Fig. 9-5b and compare with your solution of this problem. Do not copy the picture.

Problem 9•29 (8½″ × 11″ sheet). Make a drawing of the inclined bearing showing an auxiliary view of the inclined face. Will the top view be needed?

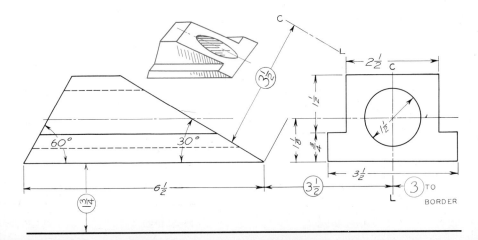

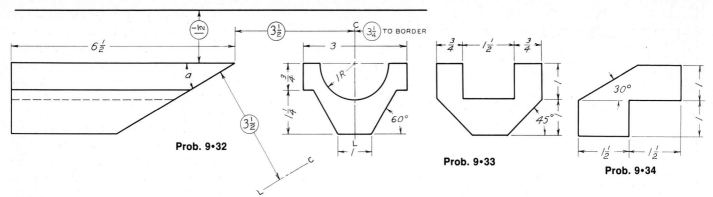

Prob. 9·32

Prob. 9·33

Prob. 9·34

Problem 9·32 (11″ × 17″ sheet). The views of the piece of molding are located from the top of the space. Con-sider the left-hand view to be the front view. Draw the views as shown and complete auxiliary view. Make angle *a* equal to 30° or 45° as directed by the instructor. The problem may be worked on an 8½″ × 11″ sheet. Scale: 6″ = 1′–0″.

Problems 9·33 and 9·34. Alternatives for Prob. 9·32.

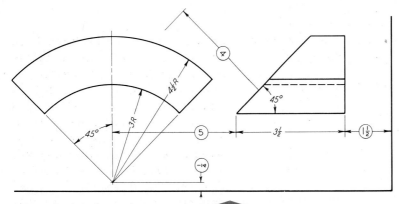

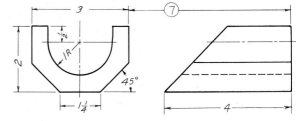

Problem 9·36. Alternative for Prob. 9·35.

Problem 9·35 (11″ × 17″ sheet). Draw the given views and a complete auxil-iary view of the saddle. The problem may be worked on an 8½″ × 11″ sheet with a scale of 6″ = 1′–0″.

Problem 9·37 (11″ × 17″ sheet). Using a layout similar to Prob. 9·31, draw the two views given. From these, draw the complete auxiliary view of the sloping dovetail. Scale: 6″ = 1′–0″ for 8½″ × 11″ sheet.

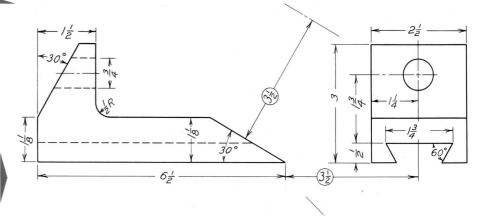

Problem 9·38 (11″ × 17″ sheet). Draw the views given and complete the auxil-iary view of the shaft holder. Use layout similar to Prob. 9·31.

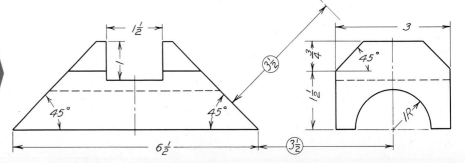

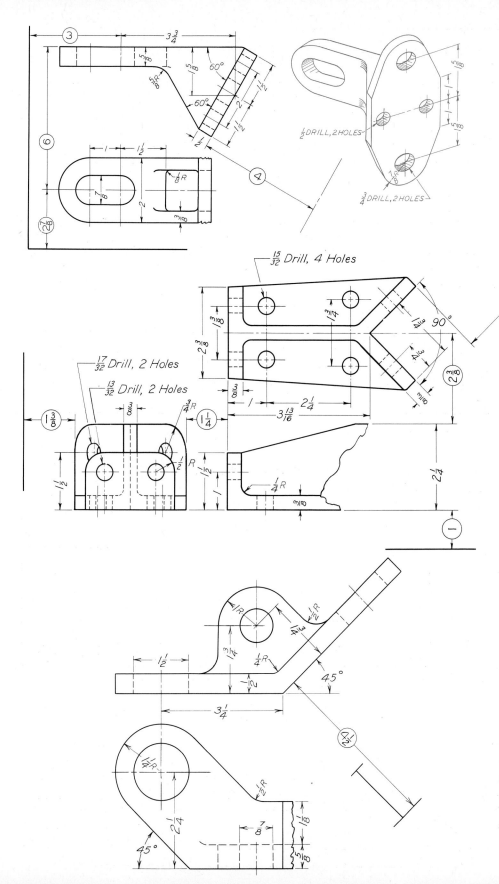

Problem 9·39 (11″ × 17″ sheet). A picture and a layout for an angle plate are shown in the figure. Draw the top view and the part front view as shown. Draw a part auxiliary view where indicated on the layout. Note that this is an auxiliary elevation as it is made on a plane perpendicular to the horizontal plane. See Fig. 9-8a and compare with the solution of your problem. Do not copy the picture. Dimension if required by the instructor.

Problem 9·40 (11″ × 17″ sheet). A top view, a left-side view, and an incomplete front view of an angle spacer are shown on the layout in the figure. Draw the top view, finish the incomplete front view, and draw the side view. The hidden parts of the holes that show as ellipses in the front and side views need not be drawn. Draw a part auxiliary view where indicated in the upper right-hand part of the space (Art. 9·8). Note that this will be an auxiliary elevation as it is made on a plane perpendicular to the horizontal.

Problem 9·41 (11″ × 17″ sheet). A top view and part front view of an angle rail support are shown in the layout in the figure. Draw the top view and the part front view as shown. Draw a part auxiliary view where indicated on the layout. Refer to Art. 9·5. Note that this will be an auxiliary elevation as it is made on a plane perpendicular to the horizontal plane. See Fig. 9-5a and compare with the solution of your problem. Dimension if required by the instructor.

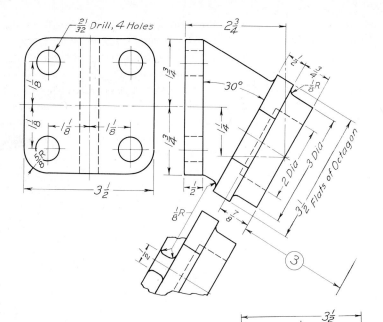

Problem 9•42 (11″ × 17″ sheet). A part front view, a right-side view, and a part auxiliary view of an angle cap are shown on the layout in the figure. Draw the views given and another part auxiliary view where indicated on the layout. Refer to Art. 9·5. Note that this last auxiliary view is a rear auxiliary view and that the one shown on the layout is a front auxiliary view. See Fig. 9-5c and compare with the solution of your problem. Dimension if required by the instructor.

Problem 9•43 (11″ × 17″ sheet). A picture and a layout for an inclined stop are shown. The complete view in the middle of the space is the right-side view. Draw this side view. Draw the part front view shown in the upper left-hand part of the space. Draw a part rear view on both sides of the vertical center line in the lower right-hand part of the space. Draw an auxiliary view of the inclined part. Refer to Art. 9·5. Note that this will be a front auxiliary view.

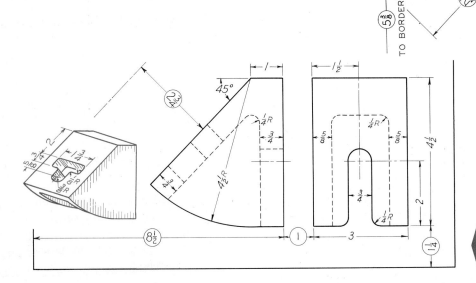

Problem 9•44 (11″ × 17″ sheet). Draw the two views given and an auxiliary view of the inclined face of the angle support.

26•19 Revolutions. Study Arts. 9·12 to 9·18 and learn the rule of revolution before beginning these problems. Revolutions provide an excellent means of understanding the relationship of views. Revolved views are of practical value to show true views of parts at an angle; to find true lengths of lines and true sizes of surfaces (Arts. 9·20 to 9·22); and to draw pictorial views (Chap. 14).

Problem 9•45 (11″ × 17″ sheet). The figure shows the completed problem. It is given for comparison and is not to be copied. Divide the standard sheet into four equal parts. In Space 1 is a three-view drawing of a block in its simplest position. In Space 2 (upper right-hand) the block is shown after being revolved from the position in Space 1, through 45°, about an axis perpendicular to the frontal plane. The front view was drawn first, copying the front view of Space 1, and the top view obtained by projecting up from the front view and across from the top view of Space 1.

In Space 3 (lower left-hand) the block has been revolved from position 1 through 30° about an axis perpendicular to the horizontal plane. The top view was drawn first, copied from the top view of Space 1. In Space 4, the block has been tilted forward from position 2 about an axis perpendicular to the side plane. The side view was drawn first, copied from the side view of Space 2, and the widths of front and top view projected from the front view of Space 2.

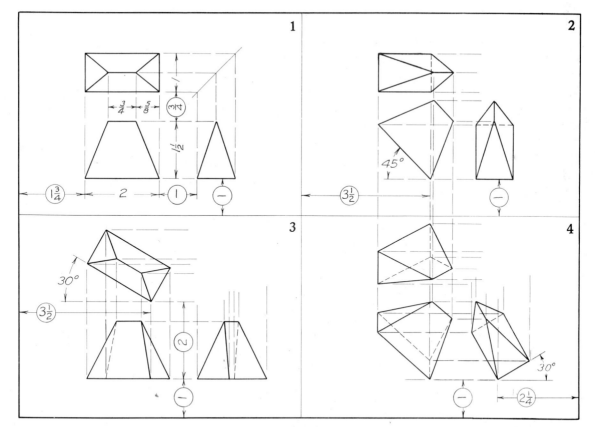

Prob. 9•45. Revolutions.

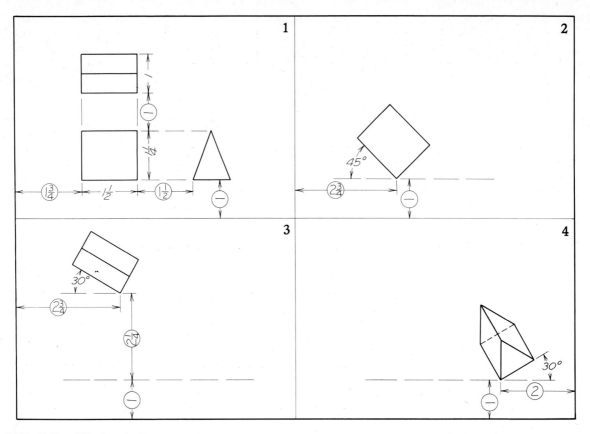

Problem 9·46 (11″ × 17″ sheet). Draw the revolved views of the wedge shown in Space 1. In Space 2, revolve 45° clockwise about an axis perpendicular to the frontal plane and draw three views. In Space 3, revolve 30° forward from position of Space 2. In Space 4, revolve from the position of Space 1 30° counterclockwise about an axis perpendicular to the horizontal plane.

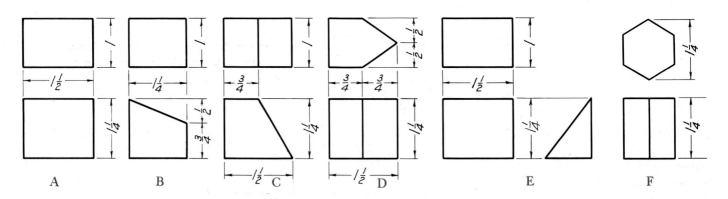

Problem 9·47 (11″ × 17″ sheet). Follow the directions for Prob. 9·46 for the object assigned.

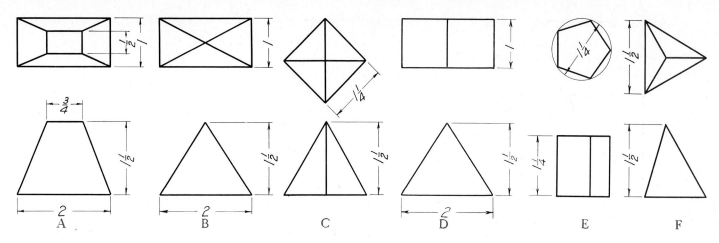

Problem 9•48 (11″ × 17″ sheet). Follow the directions for Prob. 9·46 for the object assigned.

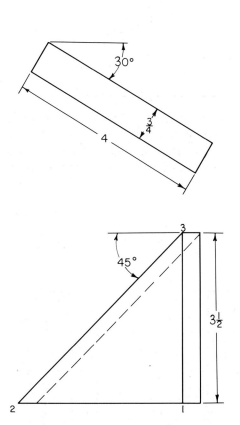

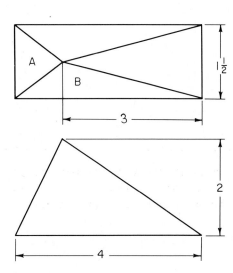

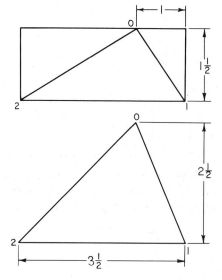

Problem 9•50 (8½″ × 11″ sheet). Draw the views shown. Find the true size of the surfaces *A* and *B* by revolution.

Problem 9•51 (8½″ × 11″ sheet). Draw the views shown. Find the true lengths of lines 0-2 and 0-1 by revolution.

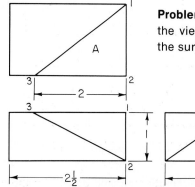

Problem 9•52 (8½″ × 11″ sheet). Draw the views shown. Find the true size of the surface *A* by revolution.

Problem 9•49 (8½″ × 11″ sheet). Draw the views shown. Find the true length of line 2-3 and true size of surface 1-2-3 by revolution.

GROUP 10. SECTIONS

26·20 Sectional views. Study Chap. 10 before starting these problems. The cut surface is to be sectioned with thin lines drawn at 45° and uniformly spaced about 1/16″ or more apart. Wider spacing is coming into favor as regular practice. Some preliminary studies are shown in Figs. 26-20a, 26-20b, and 26-20c. Compare the sectional views with the exterior views.

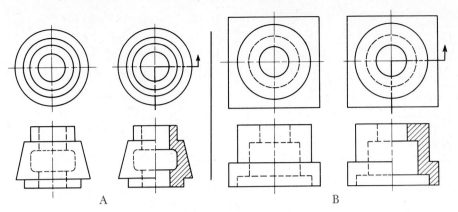

Fig. 26-20c. Sections for study.

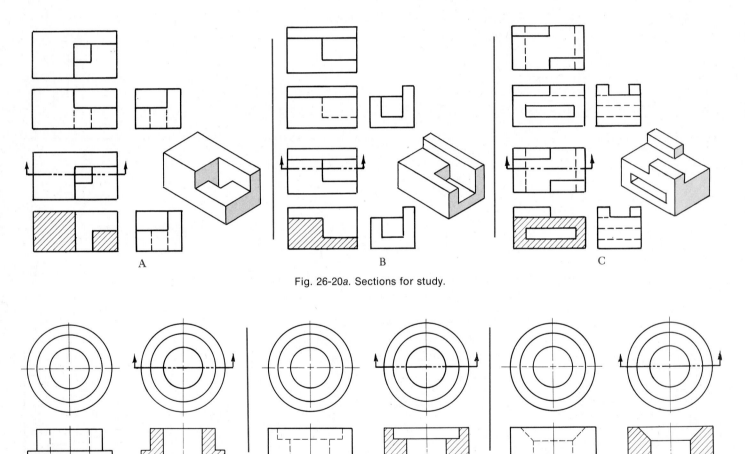

Fig. 26-20a. Sections for study.

Fig. 26-20b. Sections for study.

26·21 Problems 10·1 to 10·33 (8½″ × 11″ sheet) are to be redrawn with the proper view changed to a section. They may be drawn freehand or with instruments as directed by the instructor. The graphic scale of inches may be used to obtain dimensions with the dividers and can then be laid off with a full-size scale.

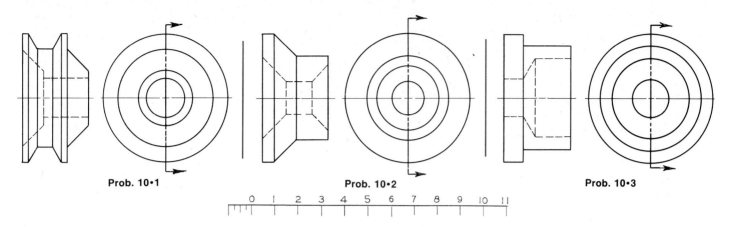

Prob. 10·1

Prob. 10·2

Prob. 10·3

Problems 10·1, 10·2, 10·3. Redraw, freehand or with instruments, as directed by the instructor. Change one view to a section.

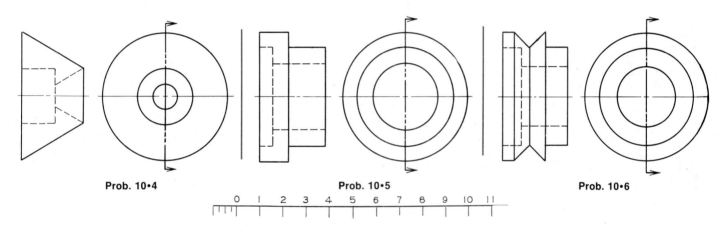

Prob. 10·4

Prob. 10·5

Prob. 10·6

Problems 10·4, 10·5, 10·6. Redraw, freehand or with instruments, as directed by the instructor. Change one view to a section.

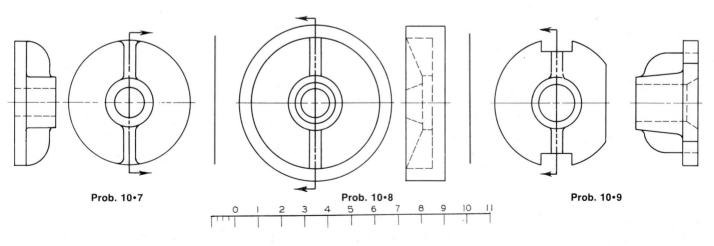

Prob. 10·7

Prob. 10·8

Prob. 10·9

Problems 10·7, 10·8, 10·9. Redraw, freehand or with instruments, as directed by the instructor. Change one view to a section.

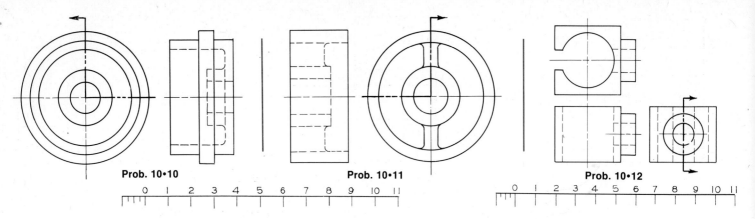

Prob. 10·10   **Prob. 10·11**   **Prob. 10·12**

Problems 10·10, 10·11, 10·12. Redraw, freehand or with instruments, as directed by the instructor. Change one view to a section.

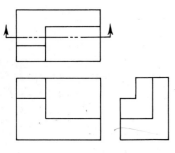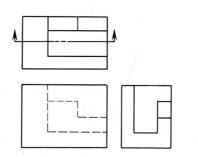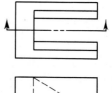

Prob. 10·13   **Prob. 10·14**   **Prob. 10·15**

Problems 10·13, 10·14, 10·15. Redraw, freehand or with instruments, as directed by the instructor. Change one view to a section.

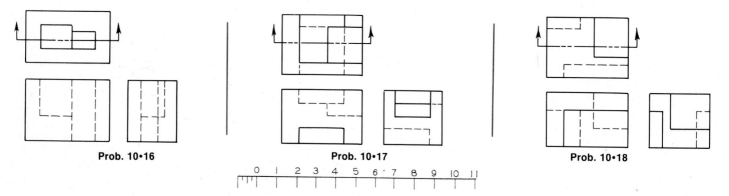

Prob. 10·16   **Prob. 10·17**   **Prob. 10·18**

Problems 10·16, 10·17, 10·18. Redraw, freehand or with instruments, as directed by the instructor. Change one view to a section.

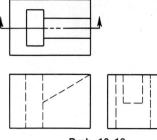

Prob. 10·19

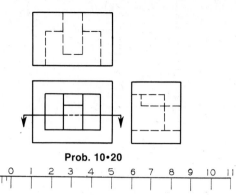

Prob. 10·20

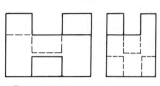

Prob. 10·21

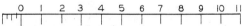

Problems 10·19, 10·20, 10·21. Redraw, freehand or with instruments, as directed by the instructor. Change one view to a section.

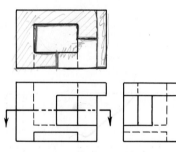

Prob. 10·22

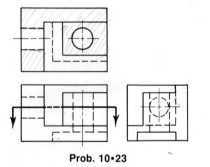

Prob. 10·23

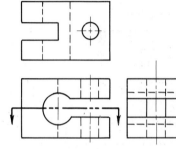

Prob. 10·24

Problems 10·22, 10·23, 10·24. Redraw, freehand or with instruments, as directed by the instructor. Change one view to a section.

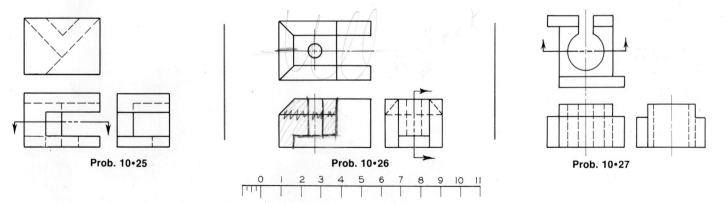

Prob. 10·25

Prob. 10·26

Prob. 10·27

Problems 10·25, 10·26, 10·27. Redraw, freehand or with instruments, as directed by the instructor. Change one view to a section.

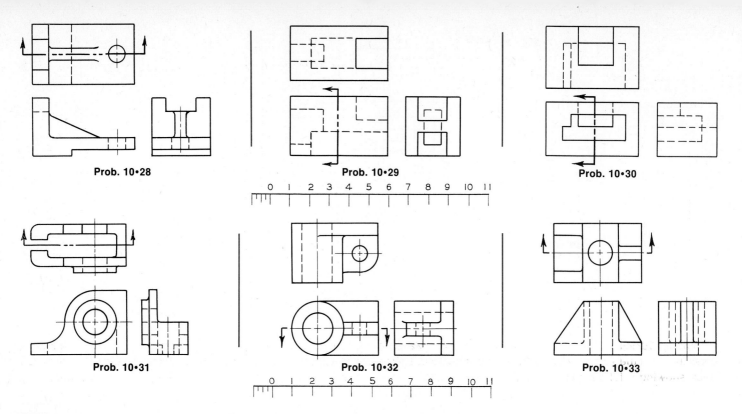

Prob. 10·28

Prob. 10·29

Prob. 10·30

0 1 2 3 4 5 6 7 8 9 10 11

Prob. 10·31

Prob. 10·32

Prob. 10·33

0 1 2 3 4 5 6 7 8 9 10 11

Problems 10·28 to 10·33. Redraw, freehand or with instruments, as directed by the instructor. Change one view to a section.

26·22 Problems 10·34 to 10·55. An examination of the problem will indicate the space required. Some may be worked full size or half size on an 8½″ × 11″ sheet. Most will work full size on an 11″ × 17″ sheet.

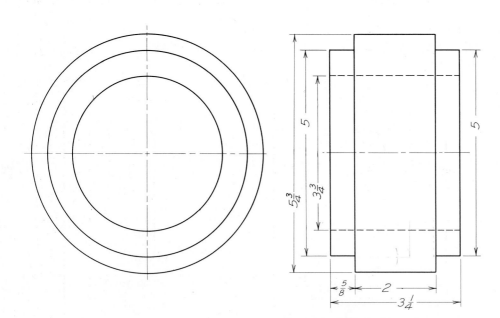

Problem 10·34. Make a drawing of the cylindrical spacer showing a full section.

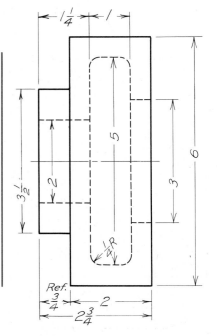

Problem 10·35. Make a drawing of the reducing spacer showing a full section.

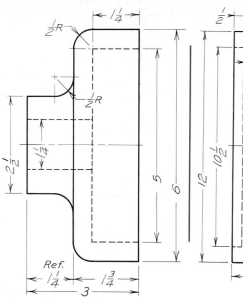

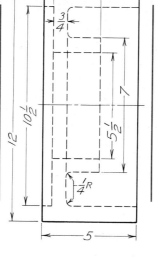

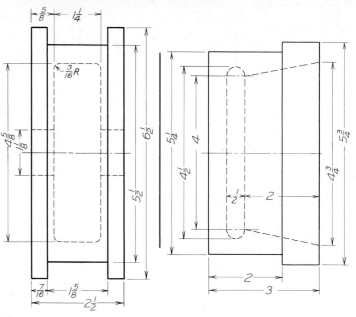

Problem 10·36. Make a drawing of the clamping disk showing a full section.

Problem 10·37. Make a drawing of the collar showing a full section.

Problem 10·38. Make a drawing of the steam piston showing a full section.

Problem 10·39. Make a drawing of the shaft cap showing a full section.

Problem 10·40. Make a two-view drawing of the protected bearing showing the right-hand view as a half section.

Problem 10·41. Make a drawing of the water-piston body showing a full section.

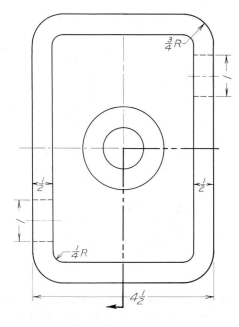

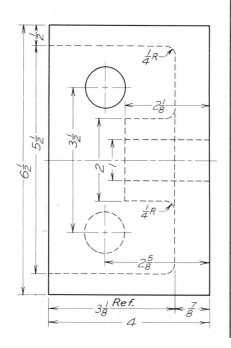

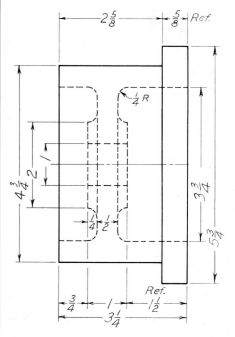

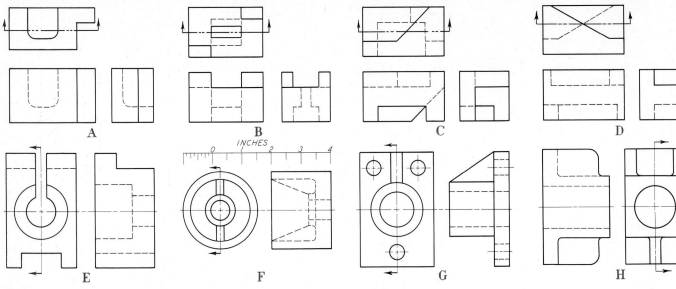

Problem 10•42. Copy the views (enlarged). Show a view in section on the plane indicated. Use the scale to estimate the dimensions for sketching, or for taking off, with the dividers if the views are drawn with the instruments.

A B C D E F G H

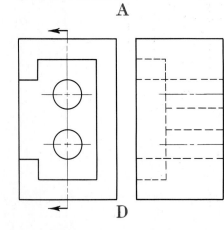
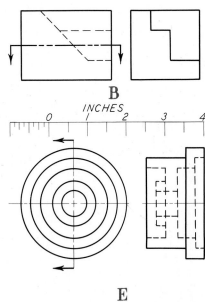
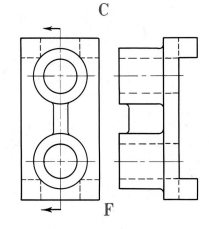

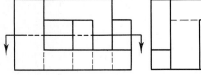
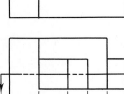
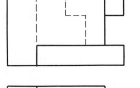
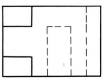
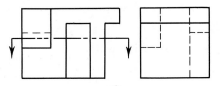
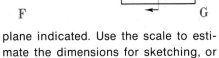

A B C D E F

Problem 10•43. Copy the views freehand (enlarged). Show a view in section on the plane indicated. Use the scale to estimate dimensions for sketching. Work the problem assigned by the instructor.

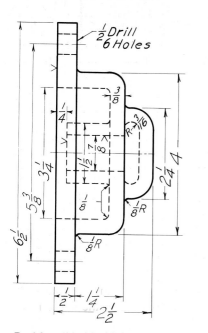

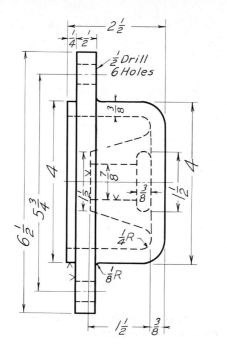

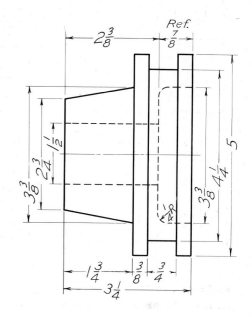

Problem 10•44. Make a two-view drawing of the cylinder head. Show a half section in one of the views.

Problem 10•45. Make a two-view drawing of the cylinder head. Show a half section in one of the views.

Problem 10•46. Make a drawing of the cone spacer showing a full section.

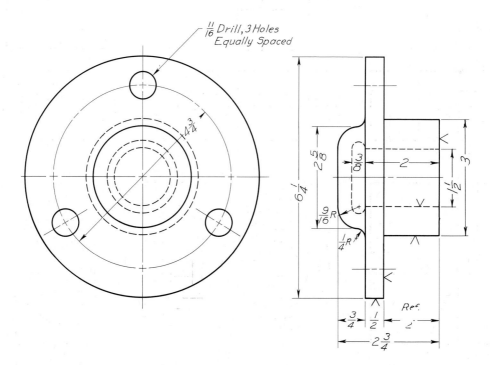

Problem 10•47. Make a two-view drawing of the end cap showing the right-hand view in section.

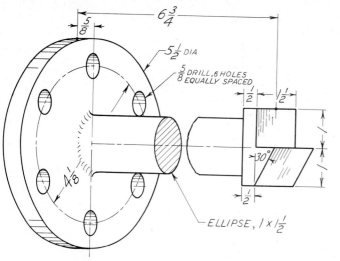

Problem 10·48. Draw the necessary views of the flanged latch. Show a revolved section.

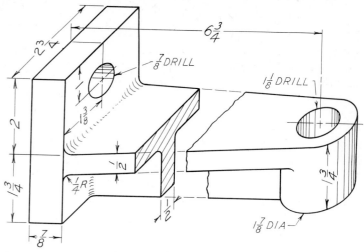

Problem 10·49. Draw the necessary views of the bracket. Show a revolved section.

Problem 10·50. Make a two-view drawing of the hood bearing. Show the right-hand view in section.

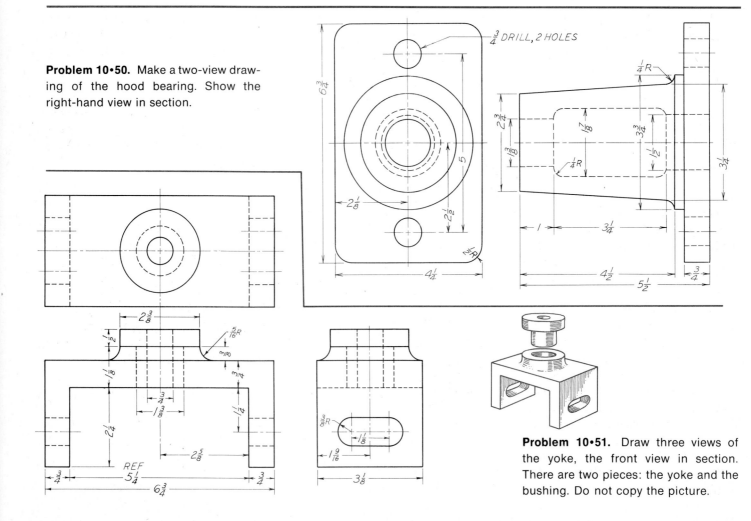

Problem 10·51. Draw three views of the yoke, the front view in section. There are two pieces: the yoke and the bushing. Do not copy the picture.

Problem 10·52. Draw three views of the swivel base, the front view to be in section.

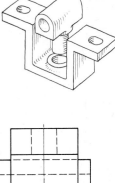

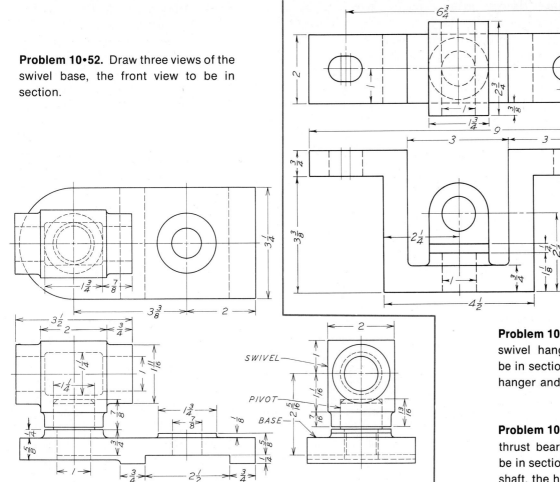

SWIVEL
PIVOT
BASE

Problem 10·53. Draw three views of the swivel hanger, the right-side view to be in section. There are two pieces: the hanger and the bearing.

Problem 10·54. Draw three views of the thrust bearing, the right-hand view to be in section. There are three parts: the shaft, the hub, and the base.

Problem 10·55. All the preceding problems have been sectioned lined as if made of cast iron. Occasionally it is desirable, as an aid in reading assembly drawing, to use one or more of the symbols for other materials as stated in Art. 10·18. This exercise is given for practice with symbolic section lining. Use an 8½″ × 11″ sheet, long way horizontal. Lay off nine rectangles, 1½″ × 2½″, equally spaced, three across and three up and down. In these rectangles draw nine of the symbols shown in Fig. 10-18a as specified by the instructor. Make cast-iron section lines about ³/₃₂″ apart and others in proportion. Letter names of materials under rectangles.

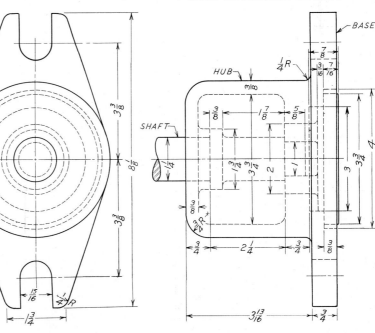

BASE
HUB
SHAFT

GROUP 11. SIZE DESCRIPTION

26·23 Size description, or dimensioning, is a very important part of mechanical drawing. Study Chap. 11 carefully and apply the principles described in it to the solutions of the following problems.

When complete dimensioning is required, work in the following order. Draw the complete views. Select and indicate the finished surfaces if not shown on the views. Put on all extension and dimension lines for size and location dimensions. Add the arrowheads. When you are certain that all dimensions are indicated, fill in the dimensions and add necessary notes.

When only size dimensions are required, put on the necessary extension and dimension lines for that purpose. When only location dimensions are required, put on the necessary extension and dimension lines for that purpose.

One or two of Probs. 11·1 to 11·24 may be worked on an 8½″ × 11″ sheet or four problems may be worked on an 11″ × 17″ sheet. The printed scale was full size before the drawing was reduced. Use the dividers to take off the distances from the scale and draw the views full size.

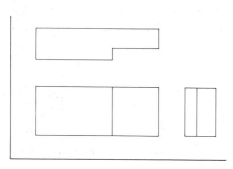

Problem 11·1. Take dimensions from the printed scale with the dividers. Draw the views of the half lap, using a full-size scale. Put on the size dimensions.

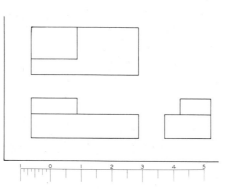

Problem 11·2. Take dimensions from the printed scale with the dividers. Draw the views of the riser, using a full-size scale. Put on the size dimensions.

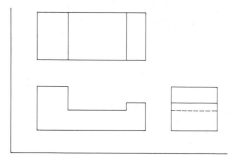

Problem 11·3. Take dimensions from the printed scale with the dividers. Draw the views of the guide, using a full-size scale. Put on the size dimensions.

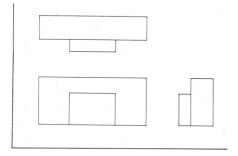

Problem 11·4. Take dimensions from the printed scale with the dividers. Draw the views of the end guide, using a full-size scale. Put on the size dimensions.

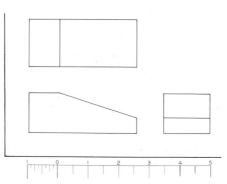

Problem 11·5. Take dimensions from the printed scale with the dividers. Draw the views of the wedge, using a full-size scale. Put on the size dimensions.

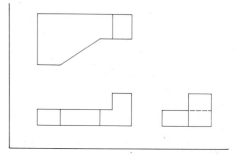

Problem 11·6. Take dimensions from the printed scale with the dividers. Draw the views of the check block, using a full-size scale. Put on the size dimensions.

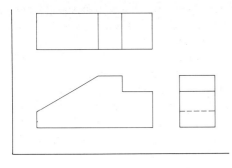

Problem 11·7. Take dimensions from the printed scale with the dividers. Draw the views of the anchor, using a full-size scale. Put on the size dimensions.

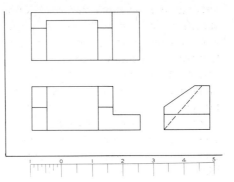

Problem 11·8. Take dimensions from the printed scale with the dividers. Draw the views of the stand, using a full-size scale. Put on the size dimensions.

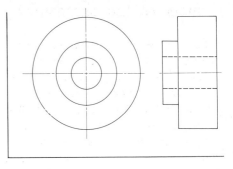

Problem 11·9. Take dimensions from the printed scale with the dividers. Draw the views of the filler, using a full-size scale. Put on the size dimensions.

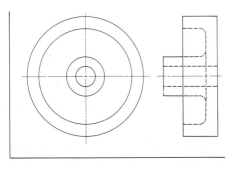

Problem 11·10. Take dimensions from the printed scale with the dividers. Draw the views of the primary roll, using a full-size scale. Put on the size dimensions.

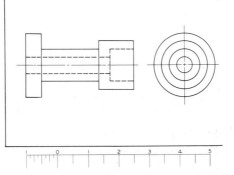

Problem 11·11. Take dimensions from the printed scale with the dividers. Draw the views of the sleeve, using a full-size scale. Put on the size dimensions.

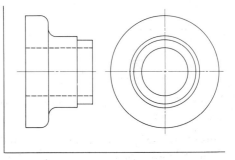

Problem 11·12. Take dimensions from the printed scale with the dividers. Draw the views of the end center, using a full-size scale. Put on the size dimensions.

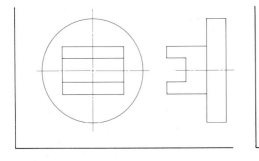

Problem 11·13. Take dimensions from the printed scale with the dividers. Draw the views of the key disk, using a full-size scale. Put on the size dimensions.

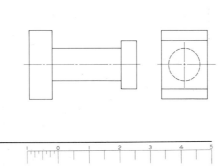

Problem 11·14. Take dimensions from the printed scale with the dividers. Draw the views of the lock, using a full-size scale. Put on the size dimensions.

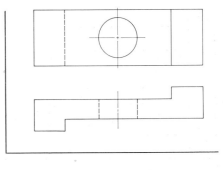

Problem 11·15. Take dimensions from the printed scale with the dividers. Draw the views of the placement hook, using a full-size scale. Put on the size dimensions.

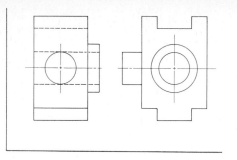

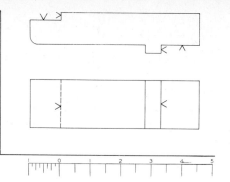

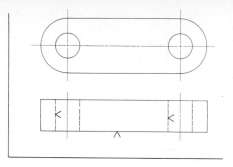

Problem 11·16. Take dimensions from the printed scale with the dividers. Draw the views of the right-angle guide, using a full-size scale. Put on the size dimensions.

Problem 11·17. Take dimensions from the printed scale with the dividers. Draw the views of the gage, using a full-size scale. Put on the location dimensions.

Problem 11·18. Take dimensions from the printed scale with the dividers. Draw the views of the link, using a full-size scale. Put on the location dimensions.

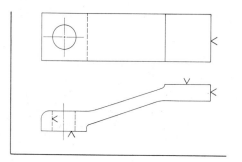

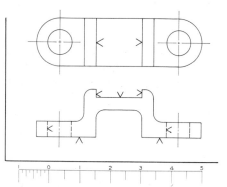

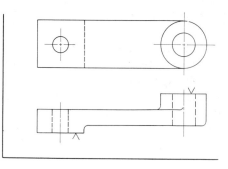

Problem 11·19. Take dimensions from the printed scale with the dividers. Draw the views of the overhang stop, using a full-size scale. Put on the location dimensions.

Problem 11·20. Take dimensions from the printed scale with the dividers. Draw the views of the slide bearing, using a full-size scale. Put on the location dimensions.

Problem 11·21. Take dimensions from the printed scale with the dividers. Draw the views of the vertical guide, using a full-size scale. Put on the location dimensions.

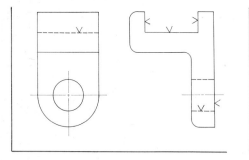

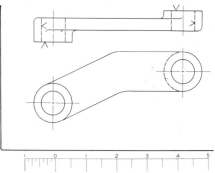

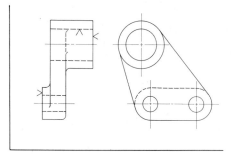

Problem 11·22. Take dimensions from the printed scale with the dividers. Draw the views of the bracket, using a full-size scale. Put on the location dimensions.

Problem 11·23. Take dimensions from the printed scale with the dividers. Draw the views of the rod guide, using a full-size scale. Put on the location dimensions.

Problem 11·24. Take dimensions from the printed scale with the dividers. Draw the views of the bearing, using a full-size scale. Put on the location dimensions.

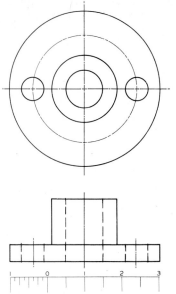

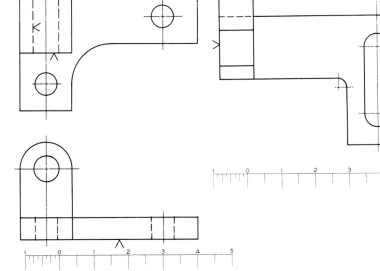

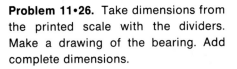

Problem 11·25. Take dimensions from the printed scale with the dividers. Make a drawing of the gland. Add complete dimensions.

Problem 11·26. Take dimensions from the printed scale with the dividers. Make a drawing of the bearing. Add complete dimensions.

Problem 11·27. Take dimensions from the printed scale with the dividers. Make a three-view drawing of the adjustable center. Put on all dimensions using a full-size scale. Locate the views to allow for the dimensions. Use an 11″ × 17″ sheet.

Problem 11·29. Copy the views of the rod guide. Make them two times the size shown in the book. Add complete dimensions.

Problem 11·28. Copy the views of the link guide. Make them two times the size shown in the book. Add complete dimensions.

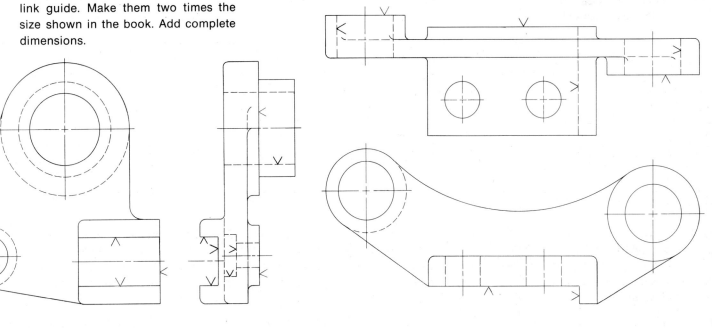

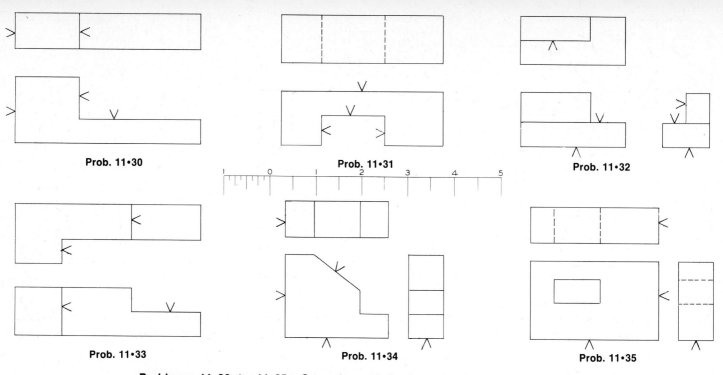

Prob. 11·30

Prob. 11·31

Prob. 11·32

Prob. 11·33

Prob. 11·34

Prob. 11·35

Problems 11·30 to 11·35. Copy the views freehand, enlarged. Add dimensions, using S for size dimensions and L for location dimensions. If desired, the views may be drawn with instruments using the printed scale.

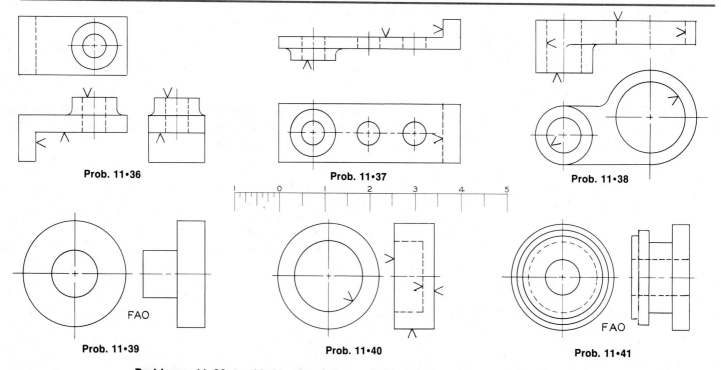

Prob. 11·36

Prob. 11·37

Prob. 11·38

Prob. 11·39

Prob. 11·40

Prob. 11·41

Problems 11·36 to 11·41. Copy the views freehand, enlarged. Add dimensions, using S for size dimensions and L for location dimensions. If desired, the views may be drawn with instruments using the printed scale.

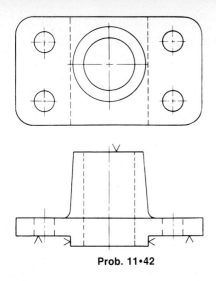

Prob. 11·42

Prob. 11·43

Prob. 11·44

Problems 11·42, 11·43, 11·44. Copy the views freehand, enlarged. Add dimensions, using S for size dimensions and L for location dimensions. If desired, the views may be drawn with instruments using the printed scale. Actual dimensions can then be used.

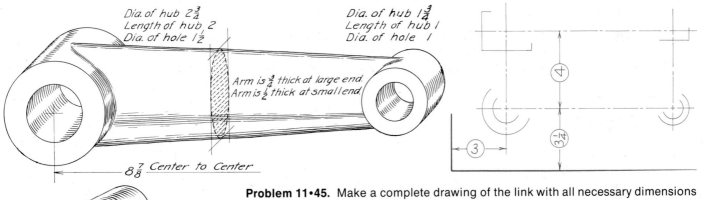

Dia. of hub $2\frac{3}{4}$
Length of hub 2
Dia. of hole $1\frac{1}{2}$

Arm is $\frac{3}{4}$ thick at large end.
Arm is $\frac{1}{2}$ thick at small end.

$8\frac{7}{8}$ Center to Center

Dia. of hub $1\frac{3}{4}$
Length of hub 1
Dia. of hole 1

Problem 11·45. Make a complete drawing of the link with all necessary dimensions and notes. Do not copy the notes and dimensions as given on the picture. The illustration includes the layout for the problem.

Problem 11·46. Make a complete drawing for the bell crank. In the layout, note that a complete front view is suggested with a view at the left to show the vertical arm and a partial top view of the horizontal arm.

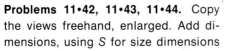

Diam. of hub $1\frac{1}{4}$
" " hole $\frac{3}{4}$
Length of hub $\frac{7}{8}$

$\frac{1}{4}$

$5\frac{1}{4}$ c to c

$\frac{3}{8}$

$\frac{3}{4}$ Rad.

$\frac{3}{4}$

Length of hub $1\frac{3}{8}$

Diam. of hub $2\frac{1}{4}$
" " hole $1\frac{3}{8}$
7 c to c

Diam. of hub $1\frac{1}{2}$
" " hole $\frac{7}{8}$
Length of hub $\frac{7}{8}$

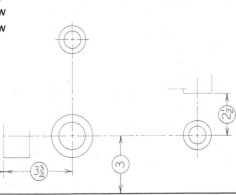

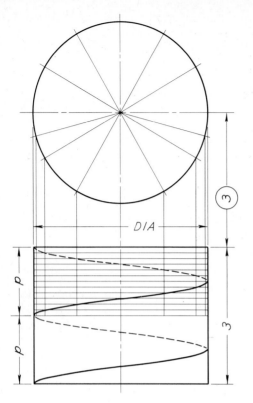

Prob. 12·1

GROUP 12. SCREWS AND BOLTS

26·24 Screws, bolts, and other fastenings are important elements of machines and constructions of all kinds. It is necessary for a draftsman to know the forms of screw threads and the conventional methods of drawing bolts and screws. Read Chap. 12 carefully before starting the problems in this group. Threads are always understood to be single and right-hand unless otherwise specified. A right-hand thread enters when turned clockwise. A left-hand thread enters when turned counterclockwise and is always marked LH on a drawing. When the American Standard form and number of threads per inch are used, it is not necessary to specify except by a note. See the Appendix for complete screw-thread information.

Most of the problems in this group can be worked on an 8½″ × 11″ sheet. Place long side horizontal for one problem. Place long side vertical for two problems. Four problems may be worked on an 11″ × 17″ sheet, long side horizontal, except where otherwise noted.

Problem 12·1 (8½″ × 11″ sheet with the long side vertical). Draw two complete turns of a right-hand helix. Diameter = 4″. Pitch = 1½″. Refer to Art. 12·5.

Problem 12·2 (8½″ × 11″ sheet with the long side vertical). Draw two complete turns of a left-hand helix. Diameter = 4″. Pitch = 1½″.

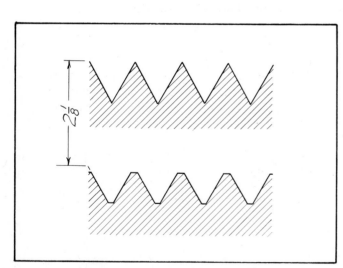

Problem 12·3. Draw the profiles of the V-thread and the American Standard thread. Letter the name of each under it. Pitch = 1″.

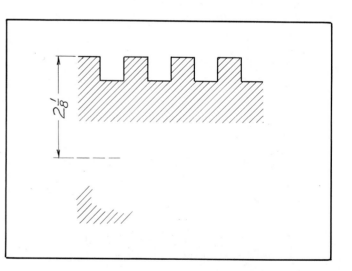

Problem 12·4. Draw the profile of the square thread and one other thread selected from Fig. 12-4c. Pitch = 1″.

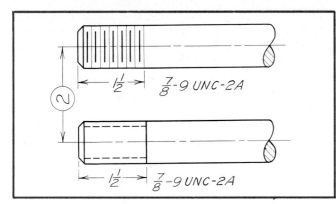

Problem 12·5. Draw the conventional thread representations as specified.

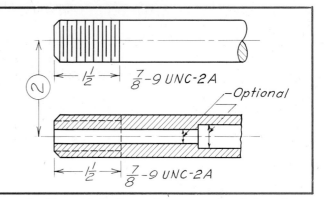

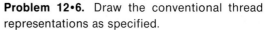

Problem 12·6. Draw the conventional thread representations as specified.

Problem 12·7 (8½″ × 11″ sheet with long side vertical). Draw the views given with thread specifications and dimensions.

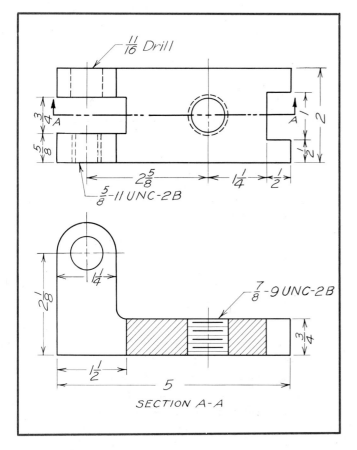

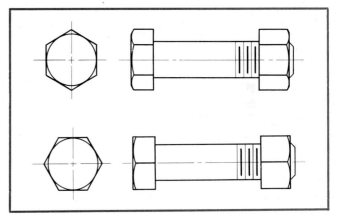

Problem 12·8. Draw the views shown for an American Standard hexagonal bolt and nut. Diameter = ¾″. Length = 3″. Length of thread = 2¼″ × D.

Problem 12·9. Draw the views shown for an American Standard square bolt and nut. Diameter = ¾″. Length = 3″. Length of thread = 2¼″ × D.

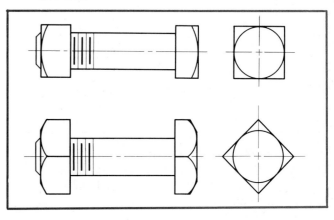

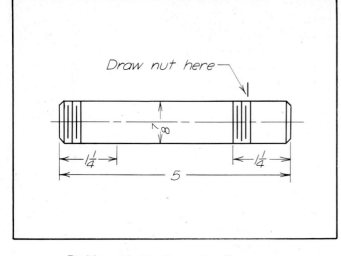

Problem 12·10. Draw the view of the ⁷⁄₈″ stud bolt shown, but with a nut on the right end. Special thread length = 1¼″.

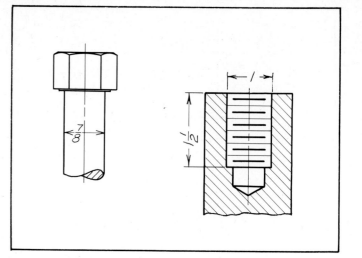

Problem 12·11. Draw a ⁷⁄₈-in. by 3-in. washer-face hexhead cap screw and a 1-in. tapped hole.

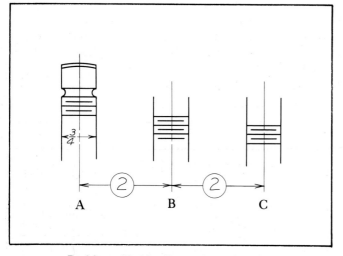

Problem 12·12. Draw three forms of cap screws at A, B and C. Diameter = ⁹⁄₁₆″. Length = 1½″.

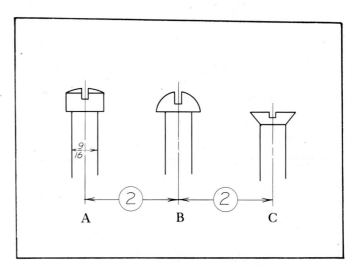

Problem 12·13. Draw three setscrews: one American Standard square head and two headless setscrews. Select a different point for each one.

Problems 12·14 to 12·23. On the center line shown, draw an American Standard bolt and nut for the flange and head plate. Place bolthead at the left and show head across flats. Show nut across corners. Take dimensions from the table.

(See page 481 for problems.)

Problems 12·24 to 12·27. On the center line shown draw a stud with hexagonal or square nut, across flats or corners, as directed by the instructor. Take dimensions from the table.

Problem 12·28. Same as Prob. 12·24 for a tap bolt.
(See page 481 for problems.)

Problem 12·29. Same as Prob. 12·25 for a tap bolt.

Problem 12·30. Same as Prob. 12·26 for a tap bolt.

Problem 12·31. Same as Prob. 12·27 for a tap bolt.
(See page 481 for problems.)

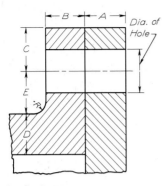

Prob. 12·14 to 12·23.

Prob-lem	Diam. bolt	Diam. hole	Bolt-head	Nut	A	B	C	D	E	R
12·14	5/8	11/16	Hex.	Hex.	5/8	11/16	3/4	5/8	3/4	1/8
12·15	3/4	13/16	Sq.	Hex.	3/4	13/16	7/8	3/4	7/8	3/16
12·16	7/8	15/16	Hex.	Hex.	7/8	1	1	7/8	1	1/4
12·17	1	1 1/8	Sq.	Hex.	1	1 1/8	1 1/8	1	1 1/8	1/4
12·18	1 1/8	1 1/4	Hex.	Hex.	1 1/8	1 1/4	1 1/4	1 1/8	1 1/4	5/16
12·19	5/8	11/16	Sq.	Sq.	11/16	3/4	7/8	11/16	3/4	1/8
12·20	3/4	13/16	Hex.	Sq.	13/16	7/8	1	13/16	7/8	3/16
12·21	7/8	15/16	Sq.	Sq.	15/16	1	1 1/8	15/16	1	1/4
12·22	1	1 1/8	Hex.	Sq.	1 1/16	1 1/8	1 3/8	1 1/16	1 1/8	1/4
12·23	1 1/8	1 1/4	Sq.	Sq.	1 3/16	1 1/4	1 1/4	1 3/16	1 1/4	5/16

See problem directions at bottom of page 480.

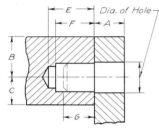

Prob. 12·24 to 12·27.

Prob-lem	Diam. stud	Diam. hole	Nut	A	B	C	E	F	G
12·24	3/4	13/16	Hex.	13/16	7/8	3/4	1 3/4	1 3/8	1
12·25	7/8	15/16	Sq.	15/16	1 1/4	7/8	2	1 9/16	1 1/8
12·26	1	1 1/8	Hex.	1 1/8	1 1/8	1	2 1/4	1 3/4	1 1/4
12·27	1 1/8	1 1/4	Sq.	1 1/4	1 1/2	1 1/8	2 3/4	2 1/8	1 1/2

See problem directions at bottom of page 480.

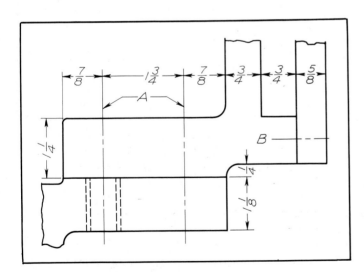

Problem 12·32. Draw the views given. On center line at A, draw 3/4-in. fillister-head cap screws. On center line at B, draw a 3/8-in. flat-head cap screw.

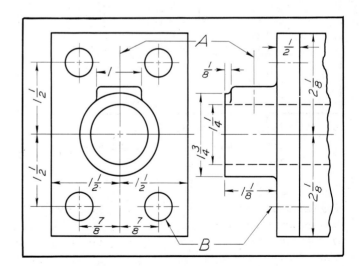

Problem 12·33. Draw the views given. At A, draw a 1/2-in. setscrew (square head or other as directed by the instructor). At B, draw a 9/16-in. hexagon-head cap screw.

GROUP 13. WORKING DRAWINGS

26·25 Study Chaps. 9 and 10 very carefully before starting these problems. Use a definite system. Visualize the shape clearly and locate the views carefully to allow proper placing of dimensions. Use your judgment in selecting a proper scale for the drawing. Complete the views before putting on the dimension lines. Then put in all dimension lines and fill in the dimensions. Add any necessary notes and finally check your drawing.

Some problems in Groups 5, 9, and 10 may be used as working drawings.

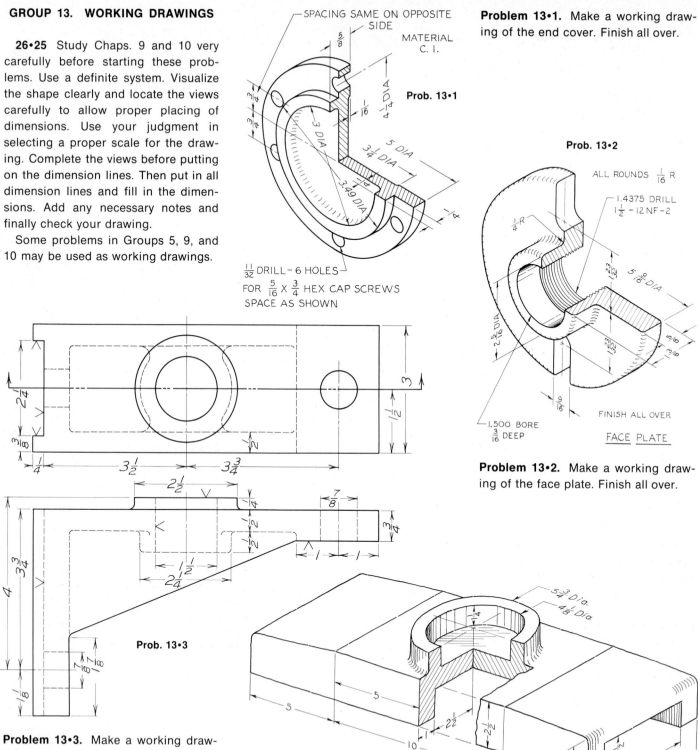

Prob. 13·1

Problem 13·1. Make a working drawing of the end cover. Finish all over.

Prob. 13·2

Problem 13·2. Make a working drawing of the face plate. Finish all over.

Prob. 13·3

Problem 13·3. Make a working drawing of the bracket. Show three views, one in section.

Problem 13·4. Make a working drawing of the cast-iron crosshead shoe.

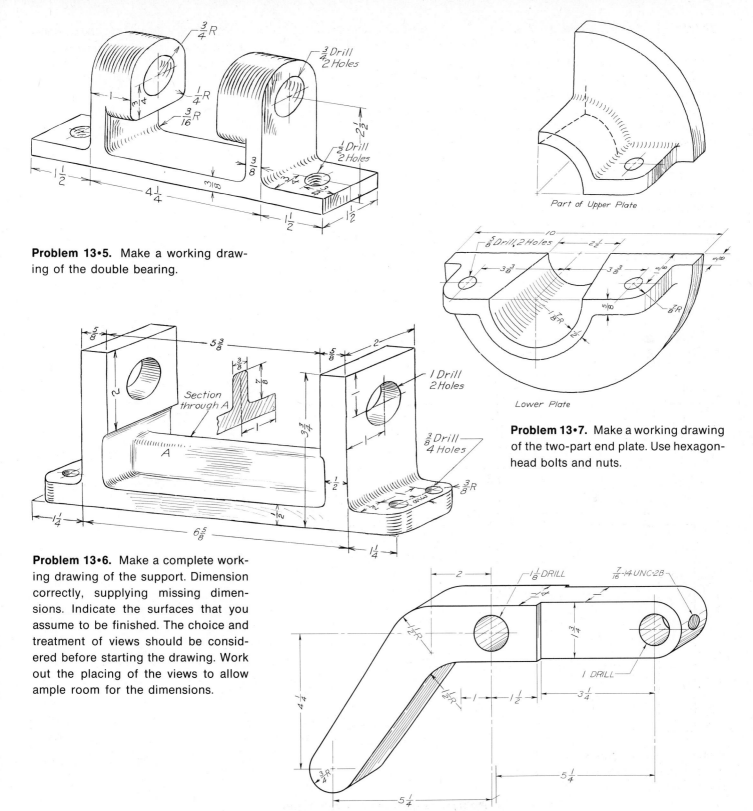

Problem 13·5. Make a working drawing of the double bearing.

Problem 13·6. Make a complete working drawing of the support. Dimension correctly, supplying missing dimensions. Indicate the surfaces that you assume to be finished. The choice and treatment of views should be considered before starting the drawing. Work out the placing of the views to allow ample room for the dimensions.

Part of Upper Plate

Lower Plate

Problem 13·7. Make a working drawing of the two-part end plate. Use hexagon-head bolts and nuts.

Problem 13·8. Make a working drawing of the tripper.

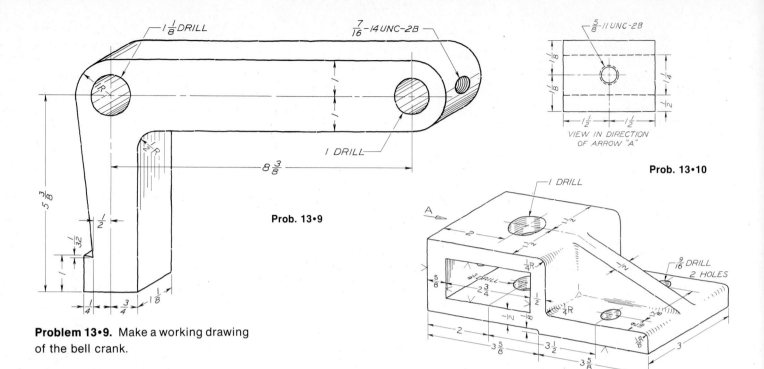

Prob. 13·9

Prob. 13·10

VIEW IN DIRECTION
OF ARROW "A"

Problem 13·9. Make a working drawing
of the bell crank.

Problem 13·10. Make a working drawing of the cast-iron adjustable holder.

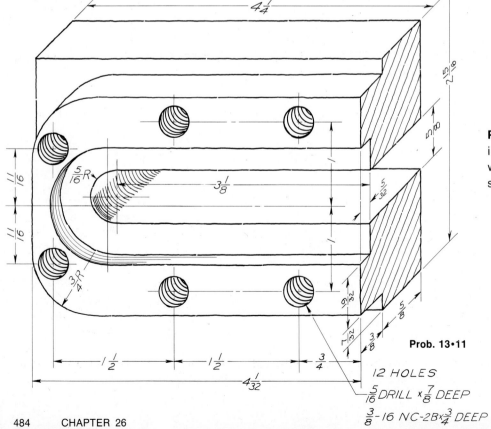

Prob. 13·11

Problem 13·11. Make a working drawing of the fuel-gage block, one-half of
which is shown. Material is machine
steel. Finish all over.

12 HOLES
$\frac{5}{16}$ DRILL x $\frac{7}{8}$ DEEP
$\frac{3}{8}$-16 NC-2B x $\frac{3}{4}$ DEEP

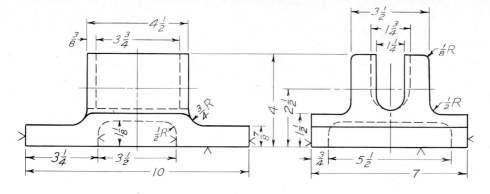

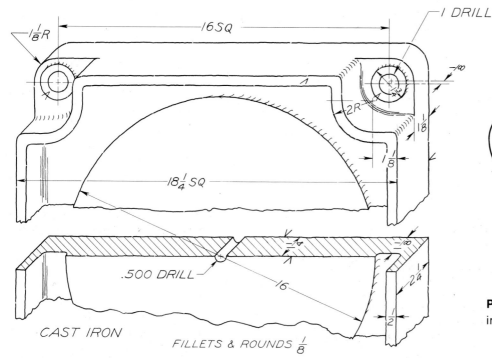

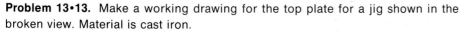

Problem 13·12. Make a three-view working drawing of the slide valve, showing the view at the left as a section. Completely dimension the drawing. Material is cast iron. Add notes where necessary and a suitable title.

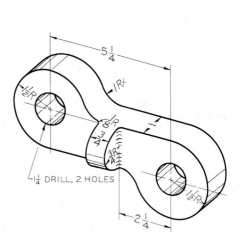

Problem 13·15. Make a working drawing of the link.

Problem 13·13. Make a working drawing for the top plate for a jig shown in the broken view. Material is cast iron.

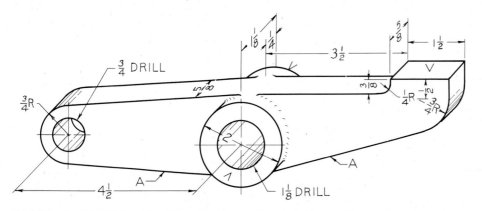

Problem 13·14. Make a working drawing of the pedal lever. The surfaces indicated by the letter *A* are tangent to the under surface of the hub.

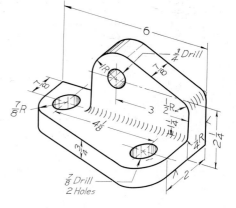

Problem 13·16. Make a working drawing of the base anchor.

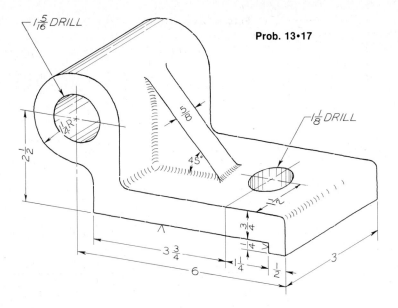

Prob. 13·17

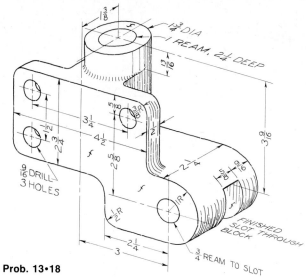

Prob. 13·18

Problem 13·17. Make a working drawing of the cast-iron rod bearing.

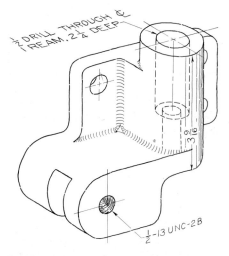

Problem 13·18. Make a working drawing of the slide-arm bracket. Semi-steel casting.

Prob. 13·19

Problem 13·19. Make a complete working drawing of one of the sizes of flange coupling. Choose a suitable scale. Show the bolts and key in position. The missing dimensions are to be supplied by the student.

A	B	C	D	E	F	G	H	I	J	K	L
$1\frac{3}{16}$	$2\frac{1}{2}$	$4\frac{5}{8}$	6	$1\frac{1}{4}$	$2\frac{1}{8}$	$3\frac{1}{4}$	4	$\frac{3}{16}$	$5\frac{1}{4}$	$\frac{7}{16}$	$\frac{1}{4}$
$1\frac{7}{16}$	$2\frac{7}{8}$	$5\frac{5}{8}$	$6\frac{3}{4}$	$1\frac{3}{8}$	$2\frac{1}{4}$	$3\frac{7}{8}$	$4\frac{5}{8}$	$\frac{3}{16}$	$5\frac{3}{4}$	$\frac{1}{2}$	$\frac{5}{16}$
$3\frac{11}{16}$	$6\frac{1}{2}$	10	12	$2\frac{3}{8}$	$4\frac{1}{2}$	$7\frac{1}{4}$	$8\frac{7}{8}$	$\frac{5}{16}$	$10\frac{3}{4}$	1	$\frac{1}{2}$
$3\frac{15}{16}$	7	$10\frac{5}{8}$	$12\frac{1}{2}$	$2\frac{3}{8}$	$4\frac{1}{2}$	$7\frac{1}{2}$	$9\frac{3}{8}$	$\frac{3}{8}$	$11\frac{1}{4}$	1	$\frac{9}{16}$

Prob. 13·20

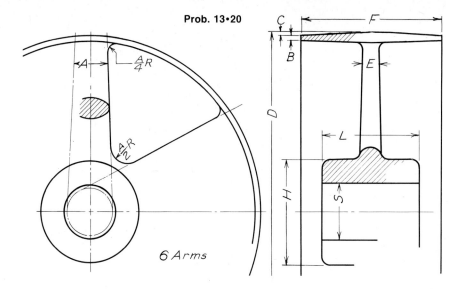

6 Arms

Size	D	F	S	H	L	B	C	A	E
x	8	$3\frac{1}{4}$	$1\frac{1}{4}$	$2\frac{3}{8}$	$2\frac{1}{2}$	$\frac{1}{8}$	$\frac{1}{32}$	$\frac{3}{4}$	$\frac{7}{16}$
y	16	$6\frac{1}{2}$	2	$3\frac{1}{4}$	4	$\frac{3}{16}$	$\frac{1}{16}$	$1\frac{1}{8}$	$\frac{9}{16}$
z	30	$8\frac{1}{2}$	$2\frac{3}{4}$	$4\frac{1}{2}$	$5\frac{1}{2}$	$\frac{1}{4}$	$\frac{3}{32}$	$1\frac{1}{2}$	$\frac{13}{16}$

Problem 13·20. Make a complete working drawing of a cast-iron pulley, with one view in section. Taper of arms about $\frac{1}{2}$″ per foot. For dimensions see accompanying table.

Prob. 13·21

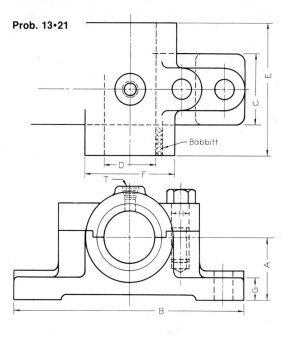

Babbitt

Size	D	A	B	C	E	F	G	H	T
w	1	$1\frac{1}{4}$	$4\frac{3}{4}$	$1\frac{3}{8}$	$2\frac{1}{2}$	$1\frac{3}{4}$	$\frac{1}{2}$	$\frac{3}{8}$	$\frac{1}{8}$ pipe
x	$1\frac{1}{2}$	$1\frac{3}{4}$	$6\frac{3}{4}$	2	$3\frac{3}{4}$	$2\frac{3}{8}$	$\frac{5}{8}$	$\frac{1}{2}$	$\frac{1}{8}$ pipe
y	2	$2\frac{1}{4}$	$8\frac{3}{4}$	$2\frac{1}{2}$	5	$3\frac{1}{2}$	$\frac{3}{4}$	$\frac{1}{2}$	$\frac{1}{4}$ pipe
z	$2\frac{1}{2}$	$2\frac{3}{4}$	$10\frac{3}{4}$	$3\frac{1}{8}$	$6\frac{1}{4}$	$4\frac{3}{8}$	$\frac{7}{8}$	$\frac{7}{8}$	$\frac{1}{4}$ pipe

Problem 13·21. Make a complete working drawing of a babbitted bearing, with front and side views as half sections. Missing dimensions to be supplied by the student. For dimensions see accompanying table.

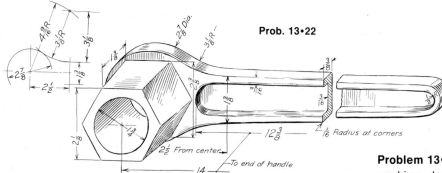

Prob. 13·22

Radius at corners

Problem 13·22. Make a completely dimensioned two-view working drawing of the plug wrench. Show a revolved section through the handle. Consider the choice of views, scale, and placing of views before starting the drawing.

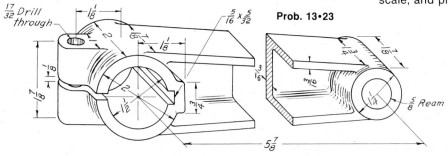

Prob. 13·23

Problem 13·23. Make a two-view working drawing of the lever with all necessary dimensions. Use your judgment regarding finished surfaces.

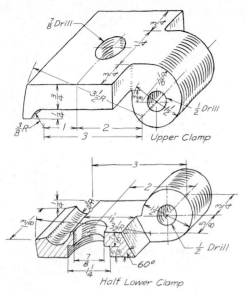

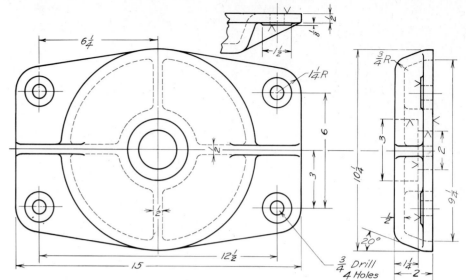

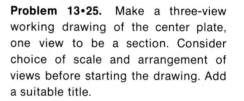

Problem 13•24. Make a working drawing showing the proper views of the upper and lower clamps. One-half of the lower clamp is shown in the figure. Draw the whole clamp. Consider the choice of views, scale, and placing of views before starting the drawing.

Problem 13•25. Make a three-view working drawing of the center plate, one view to be a section. Consider choice of scale and arrangement of views before starting the drawing. Add a suitable title.

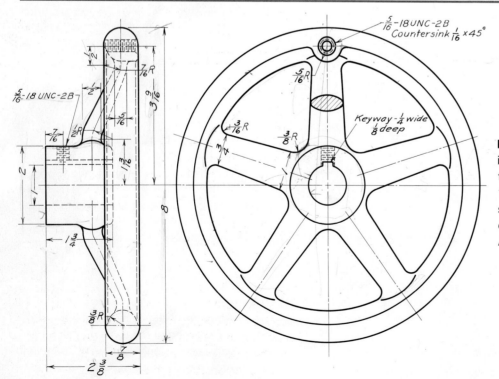

Problem 13•26. Make a two-view working drawing of the handwheel, showing the left view as a section. Read Art. 10·20 regarding arms in section. Consider choice of scale and arrangement of views before starting the drawing. Add a suitable title.

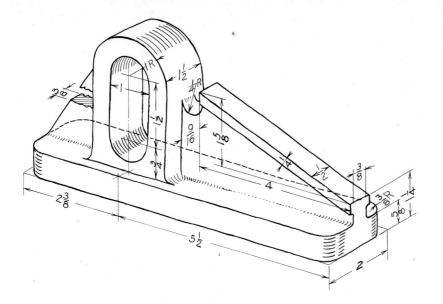

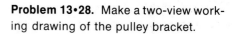

Problem 13·27. Make a working drawing of the adjusting slide. Consider the choice of views and the scale. Work out the spacing of the views to allow ample room for dimensions and notes. Indicate the surfaces that you assume to be finished. Add a suitable title.

Problem 13·28. Make a two-view working drawing of the pulley bracket.

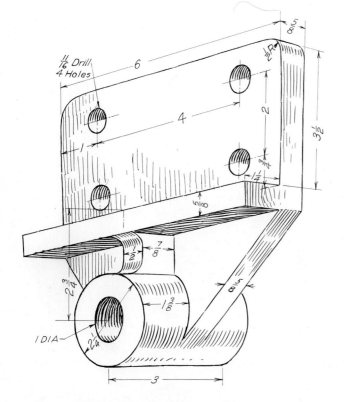

Problem 13·29. Make a working drawing of the bracket bearing.

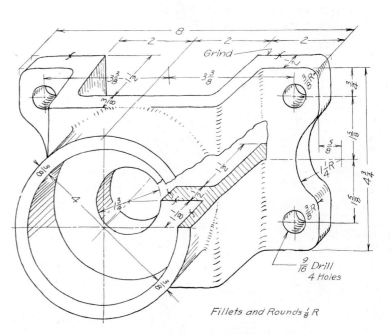

Problem 13·30. Make a three-view working drawing, completely dimensioned, of the bearing holder. Consider the choice of views, scale, and placing of views before starting the drawing.

Problem 13·31. Make a working drawing of the lift-screw bracket.

Problem 13·32. Make a working drawing of the angle bearing. This object is symmetrical, but in the picture a part is broken away to show the interior. Consider choice of views, treatment of views, and scale. Work out the spacing of the views to allow ample room for dimensions and notes. Indicate the surfaces you assume to be finished. Add a suitable title.

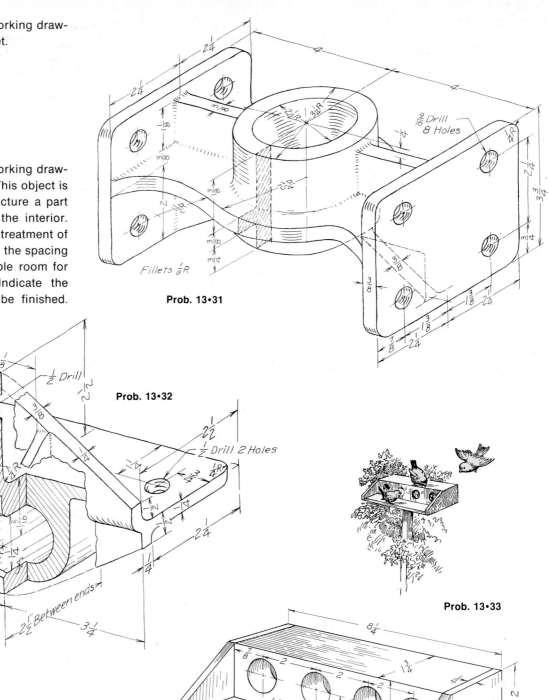

Prob. 13·31

Prob. 13·32

Prob. 13·33

26·26 Problems 13·33 to 13·54. Wood constructions and furniture drawings can generally be drawn assembled with part details, if needed. Select a suitable scale and size of sheet to show the project clearly. Add necessary dimensions and notes.

Problem 13·33. Make a working drawing of the bird feeding stick.

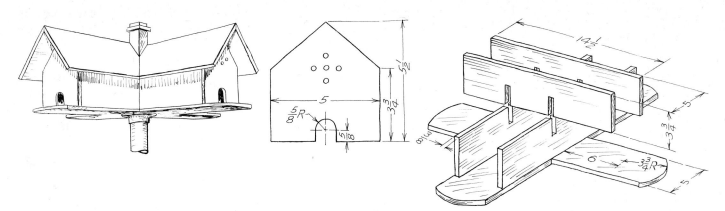

Problem 13·34. Make a working drawing of the martin house. Consider the choice and treatment of views and choice of scale. Material is ⅜″ white pine. Supply details and dimensions not shown in the pictures.

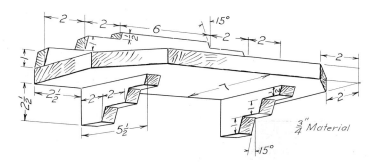

Problem 13·35. Make a working drawing of the radio shelf. Select views and scale.

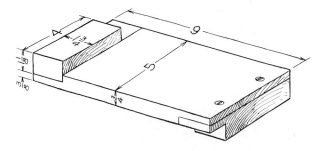

Problem 13·36. Make a working drawing of the bench hook.

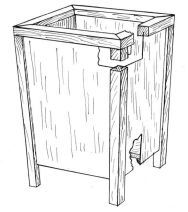

Problem 13·37. Make a working drawing of the waste basket. It is 12″ square at the top, 10″ square at the bottom, and 16″ high. Sides are of hardboard or similar material.

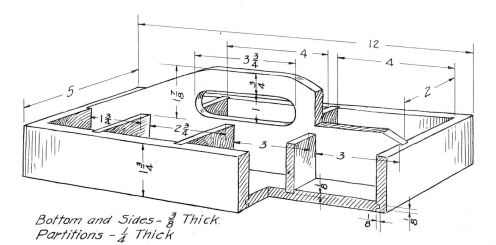

Bottom and Sides - ⅜ Thick.
Partitions - ¼ Thick

Problem 13·38. Make a working drawing of the nail box.

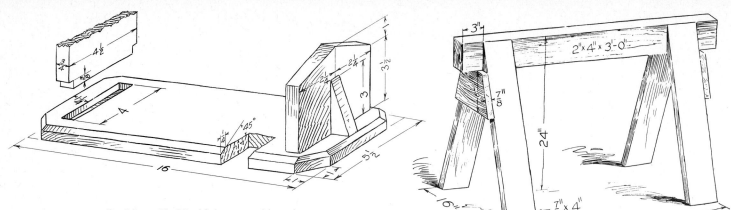

Problem 13•39. Make a working drawing of the bookrack. Select the views and scale.

Problem 13•40. Make a working drawing of the sawhorse. Select views and scale.

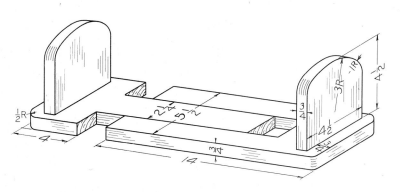

Problem 13•41. Make a working drawing of the adjustable bookrack. Select views and scale.

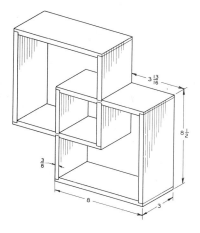

Problem 13•43. Make a working drawing of the shadow box. Construction to be as shown.

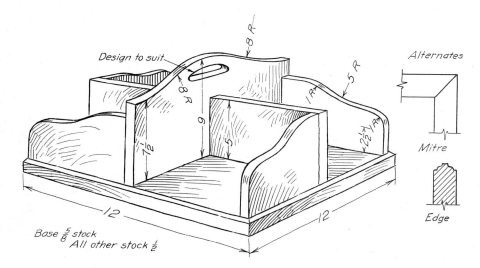

Problem 13•42. Make a working drawing of the four-compartment bookrack. Select views and scale.

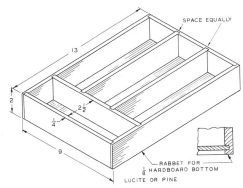

Problem 13•44. Make a working drawing of the silverware box. Construction as shown.

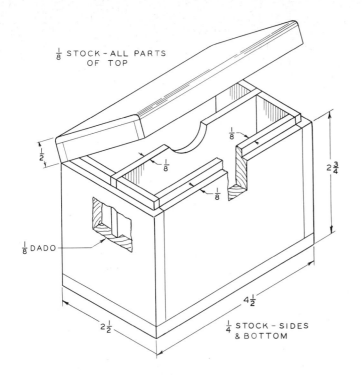

$\frac{1}{8}$ STOCK—ALL PARTS OF TOP

$\frac{1}{2}$

$\frac{1}{8}$

$\frac{1}{8}$

$\frac{1}{8}$

$\frac{1}{8}$

$2\frac{3}{4}$

$\frac{1}{8}$ DADO

$2\frac{1}{2}$

$4\frac{1}{2}$

$\frac{1}{4}$ STOCK—SIDES & BOTTOM

Problem 13·45. Make a working drawing of the playing-card box. Box may be made of wood or plastic.

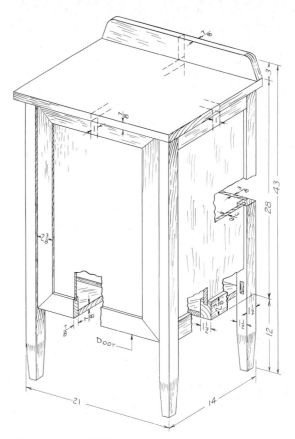

$\frac{1}{16}$

$\frac{1}{3}$

$\frac{3}{8}$

$\frac{7}{8}$

43

28

$2\frac{3}{8}$

$\frac{3}{8}$

$\frac{5}{8}$

$\frac{7}{8}$ $\frac{7}{8}$

$\frac{1}{2}$ $\frac{5}{8}$

$\frac{1}{2}$

12

Door

21

14

Problem 13·47. Make a working drawing of the music cabinet. Supply missing details and hardware.

Problem 13·46. Make a working drawing of the twin bed. Side rails connected to the headboard and footboard with bed fasteners (Broadhead Garrett No. 10 or similar).

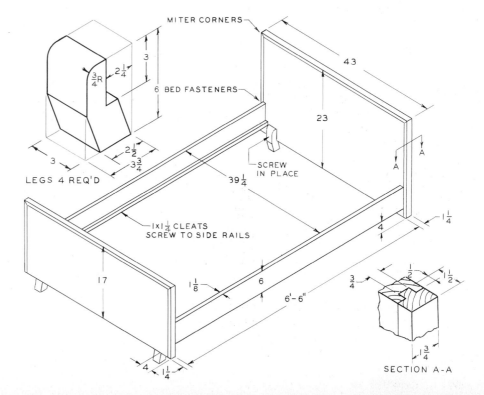

MITER CORNERS

$\frac{3}{4}$R

$2\frac{1}{4}$

3

6 BED FASTENERS

43

23

3

$2\frac{1}{2}$

$3\frac{3}{4}$

LEGS 4 REQ'D

SCREW IN PLACE

$39\frac{1}{4}$

A

A

$1\frac{1}{4}$

4

1x1$\frac{1}{4}$ CLEATS SCREW TO SIDE RAILS

17

$1\frac{1}{8}$

6

6'-6"

4 $1\frac{1}{4}$

$\frac{3}{4}$ $2\frac{1}{2}$ $1\frac{1}{2}$

$1\frac{3}{4}$

SECTION A-A

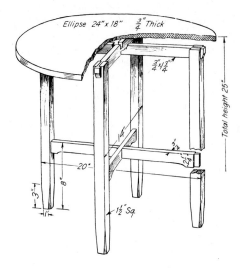

Problem 13•48. Make a working drawing of the typewriter table. Legs, 1¼″ square; top, 18″ × 32″ × ¼″; height, 20″; apron, 4″. Supply details and dimensions not shown.

Problem 13•49. Make a working drawing of the telephone stand. Supply details and dimensions not shown.

Problem 13•50. Make an assembly working drawing, with extra part views if necessary, for the tea table. Supply missing dimensions.

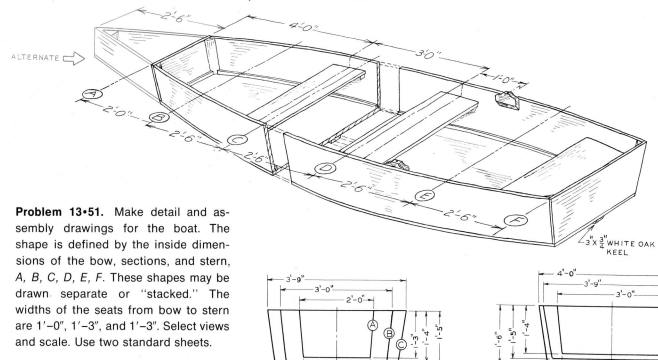

Problem 13•51. Make detail and assembly drawings for the boat. The shape is defined by the inside dimensions of the bow, sections, and stern, A, B, C, D, E, F. These shapes may be drawn separate or "stacked." The widths of the seats from bow to stern are 1′–0″, 1′–3″, and 1′–3″. Select views and scale. Use two standard sheets.

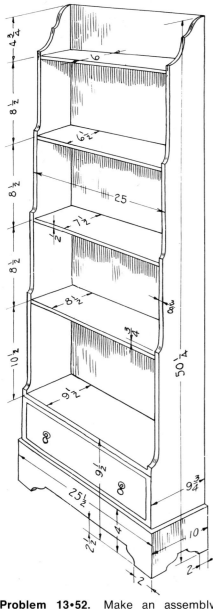

Problem 13•52. Make an assembly working drawing of the book pier. Design the construction of the drawer.

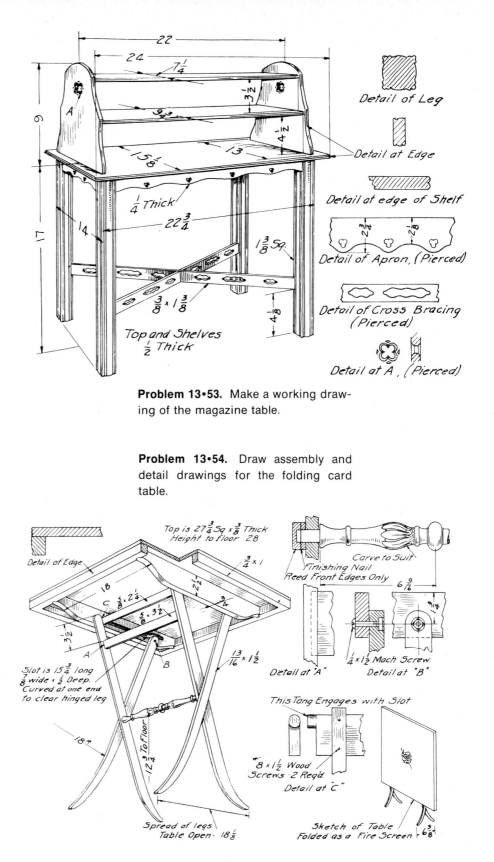

Problem 13•53. Make a working drawing of the magazine table.

Problem 13•54. Draw assembly and detail drawings for the folding card table.

26•27 Before starting Probs. 13·55 to 13·72, study the views given and see just what is required in each case. See how many pieces are to be represented and the best method of showing them. It will be necessary to use judgment to arrange for the spacing of the views for detail drawings of several pieces. Each piece should be completely dimensioned and should be named.

Assembly drawings may have different treatments according to the purpose to be served. They may have no dimensions; they may have dimensions necessary for assembling or erection, for operation, and so forth; or they may have all dimensions. If dimensions are not stated in the problem, consult your instructor.

The chapters on size description, technique of the finished drawing, bolts and screws, and mechanical drafting should be used for study and reference in connection with these assembly and detail drawings.

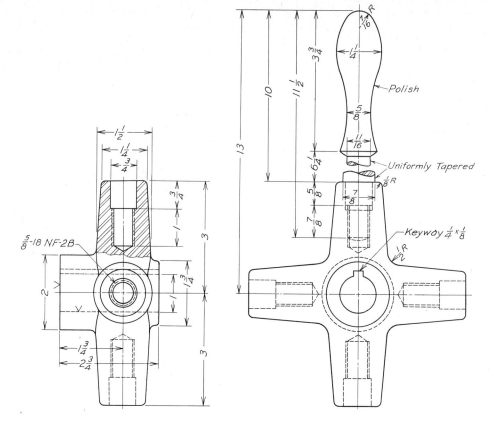

Problem 13•55. Make detail drawings for the pilot hub showing each piece fully dimensioned.

Problem 13•56. Make detail working drawings of the hung bearing showing each piece fully dimensioned. All bolts are ⅝" in diameter.

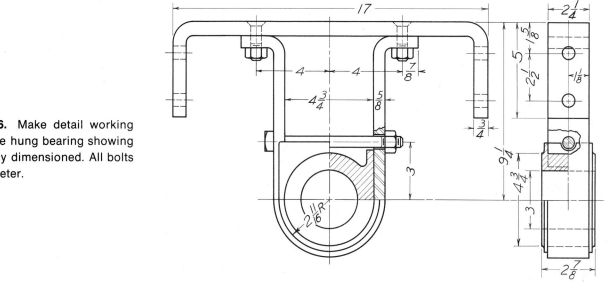

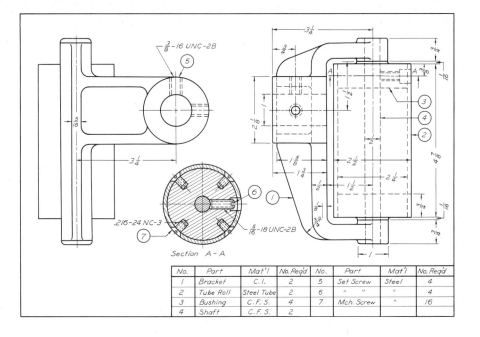

Problem 13•57. Make detail drawings of the pivot-guide roll.

No.	Part	Mat'l	No. Req'd	No.	Part	Mat'l	No. Req'd
1	Bracket	C.I.	2	5	Set Screw	Steel	4
2	Tube Roll	Steel Tube	2	6	" "	"	4
3	Bushing	C.F.S.	4	7	Mch. Screw	"	16
4	Shaft	C.F.S.	2				

Problem 13•58. Make working detail drawings of base, pulley, bushing, and shaft with bill of material for complete pulley-and-stand unit. Full size, three sheets. If necessary, the top view may be a half plan.

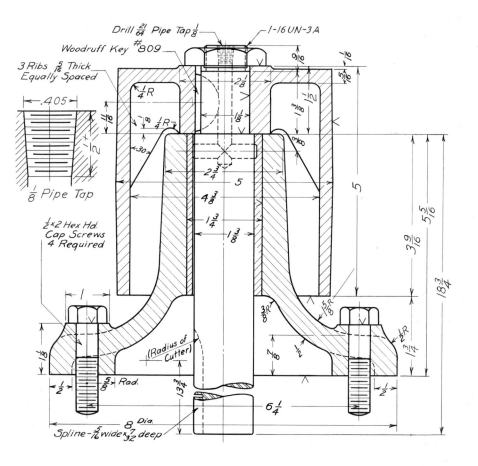

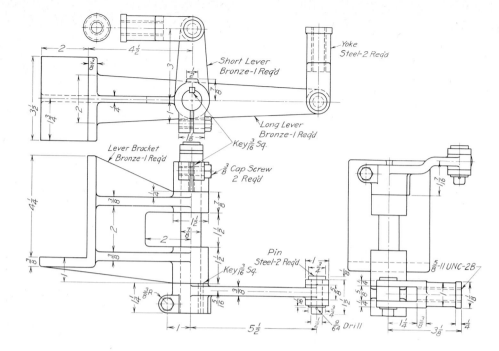

Problem 13·59. Make detail drawings of the bell-crank reverse.

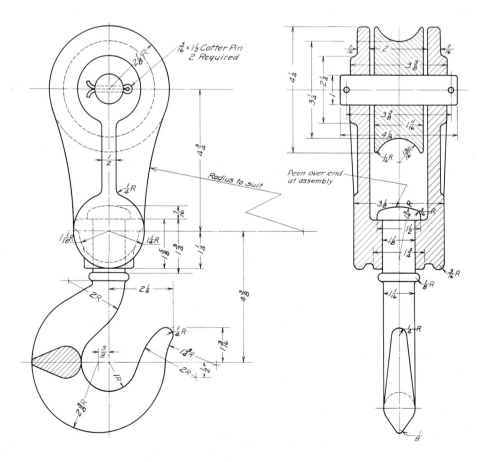

Problem 13·60. Make detail drawings of the crane hook.

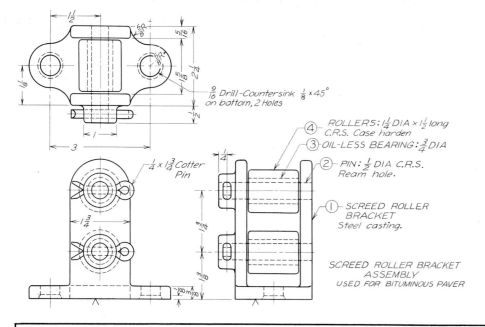

Problem 13•61. Make detail drawings of the roller bracket.

ROLLERS: $1\frac{1}{4}$ DIA × $1\frac{1}{2}$ long
C.R.S. Case harden

④

③ OIL-LESS BEARING: $\frac{3}{4}$ DIA

② PIN: $\frac{1}{2}$ DIA C.R.S.
Ream hole.

① SCREED ROLLER
BRACKET
Steel casting.

$\frac{9}{16}$ Drill-Countersink $\frac{1}{8}$ × 45°
on bottom, 2 Holes

$\frac{1}{4}$ × $1\frac{3}{4}$ Cotter Pin

SCREED ROLLER BRACKET
ASSEMBLY
USED FOR BITUMINOUS PAVER

Problem 13•62. Make a two-view assembly drawing of the tool post.

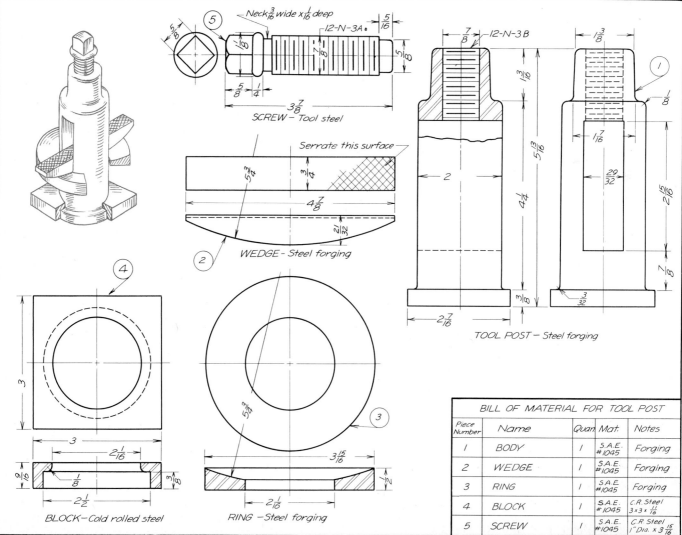

Neck $\frac{3}{16}$ wide × $\frac{1}{16}$ deep

⑤

12-N-3A

SCREW – Tool steel

Serrate this surface

② WEDGE – Steel forging

④

BLOCK – Cold rolled steel

③

RING – Steel forging

12-N-3 B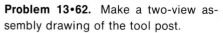

①

TOOL POST – Steel forging

BILL OF MATERIAL FOR TOOL POST				
Piece Number	Name	Quan	Mat.	Notes
1	BODY	1	S.A.E. #1045	Forging
2	WEDGE	1	S.A.E. #1045	Forging
3	RING	1	S.A.E. #1045	Forging
4	BLOCK	1	S.A.E. #1045	C.R. Steel 3×3×$\frac{11}{16}$
5	SCREW	1	S.A.E. #1045	C.R. Steel 1"Dia. × 3$\frac{15}{16}$

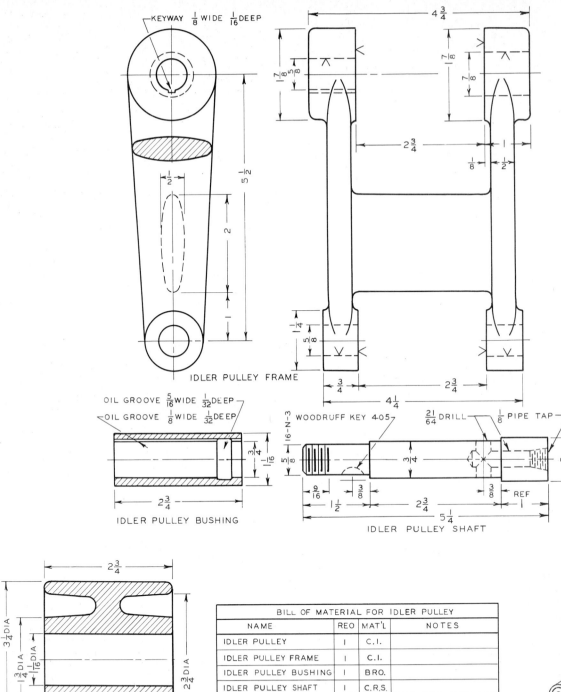

KEYWAY $\frac{1}{8}$ WIDE $\frac{1}{16}$ DEEP

IDLER PULLEY FRAME

OIL GROOVE $\frac{5}{16}$ WIDE $\frac{1}{32}$ DEEP

OIL GROOVE $\frac{1}{8}$ WIDE $\frac{1}{32}$ DEEP

IDLER PULLEY BUSHING

16-N-3   WOODRUFF KEY 405 $\frac{21}{64}$ DRILL $\frac{1}{8}$ PIPE TAP

IDLER PULLEY SHAFT

$\frac{3}{16}$ R

IDLER PULLEY
FINISH ALL OVER

BILL OF MATERIAL FOR IDLER PULLEY			
NAME	REO	MAT'L	NOTES
IDLER PULLEY	I	C.I.	
IDLER PULLEY FRAME	I	C.I.	
IDLER PULLEY BUSHING	I	BRO.	
IDLER PULLEY SHAFT	I	C.R.S.	
$\frac{5}{8}$ SAE HEX NUT	I		$\frac{3}{8}$ HIGH PURCHASED
WOODRUFF KEY 405	I		PURCHASED
$\frac{1}{8}$ OILER	I		PURCHASED

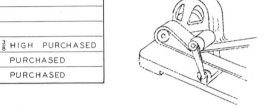

Problem 13•63. Make an assembly drawing of the idler pulley, two views, full size, showing pulley, bushing, and upper end of frame in section.

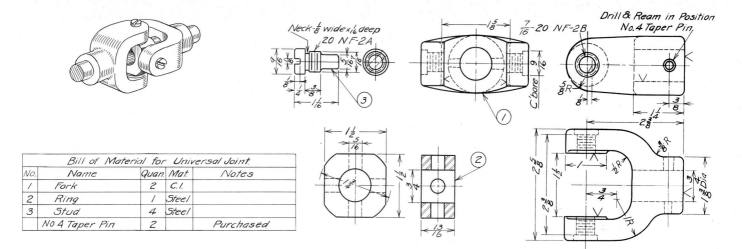

Bill of Material for Universal Joint

No.	Name	Quan.	Mat.	Notes
1	Fork	2	C.I.	
2	Ring	1	Steel	
3	Stud	4	Steel	
	No.4 Taper Pin	2		Purchased

Problem 13·64. Make a two-view assembly drawing of the universal joint in section.

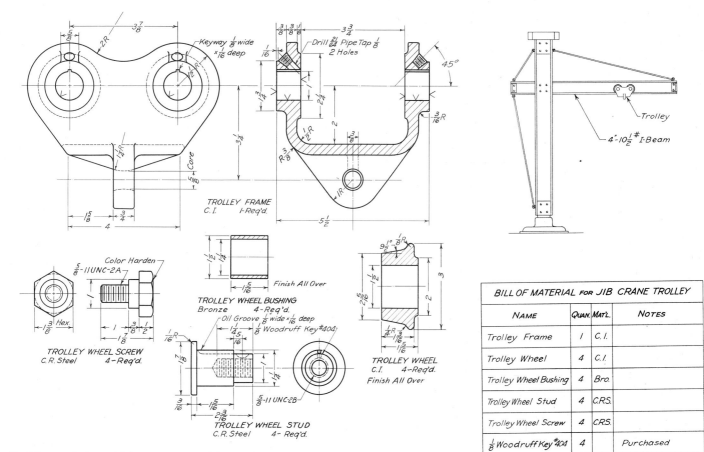

TROLLEY FRAME
C.I.   1-Req'd.

TROLLEY WHEEL BUSHING
Bronze   4-Req'd.

TROLLEY WHEEL
C.I.   4-Req'd.
Finish All Over

TROLLEY WHEEL SCREW
C.R. Steel   4-Req'd.

TROLLEY WHEEL STUD
C.R. Steel   4-Req'd.

Trolley

4"-10½#I-Beam

BILL OF MATERIAL for JIB CRANE TROLLEY

NAME	QUAN.	MAT'L.	NOTES
Trolley Frame	1	C.I.	
Trolley Wheel	4	C.I.	
Trolley Wheel Bushing	4	Bro.	
Trolley Wheel Stud	4	C.R.S.	
Trolley Wheel Screw	4	C.R.S.	
⅛ Woodruff Key #404	4		Purchased
⅛ Std. Alemite Oiler	4		Purchased
1 Lock Washer	4		Purchased

Problem 13·65. Make an assembly drawing of the jib-crane trolley. Draw one view in section. The I-beam may be indicated if desired, obtaining dimensions from a structural-steel handbook.

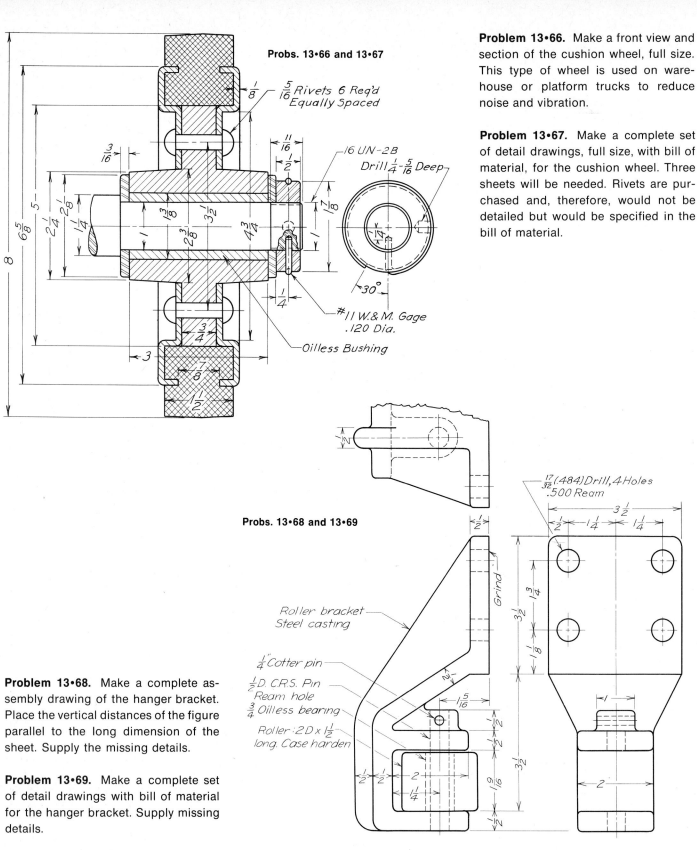

Probs. 13·66 and 13·67

5/16 Rivets 6 Req'd Equally Spaced

16 UN-2B
Drill 1/4 - 5/16 Deep

#11 W.& M. Gage .120 Dia.

Oilless Bushing

Problem 13·66. Make a front view and section of the cushion wheel, full size. This type of wheel is used on warehouse or platform trucks to reduce noise and vibration.

Problem 13·67. Make a complete set of detail drawings, full size, with bill of material, for the cushion wheel. Three sheets will be needed. Rivets are purchased and, therefore, would not be detailed but would be specified in the bill of material.

Probs. 13·68 and 13·69

Roller bracket
Steel casting

1/4" Cotter pin

1/2 D. C.R.S. Pin
Ream hole

3/4 Oilless bearing

Roller: 2 D x 1 1/2
long. Case harden

Grind

17/32 (.484) Drill, 4 Holes
.500 Ream

Problem 13·68. Make a complete assembly drawing of the hanger bracket. Place the vertical distances of the figure parallel to the long dimension of the sheet. Supply the missing details.

Problem 13·69. Make a complete set of detail drawings with bill of material for the hanger bracket. Supply missing details.

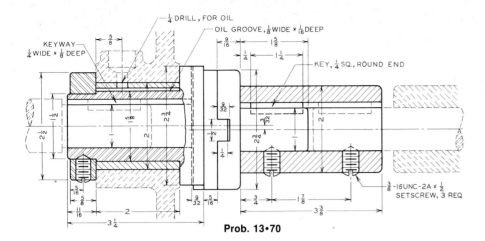

Problem 13·70. Make working detail drawings of clutches, driving and driven; clutch cross; muff coupling; collar; bushing; and key with bill of material for complete unit of the Oldham coupling (for connecting the ends of two rotating shafts, not in accurate alignment). Full size. Two sheets.

Prob. 13·70

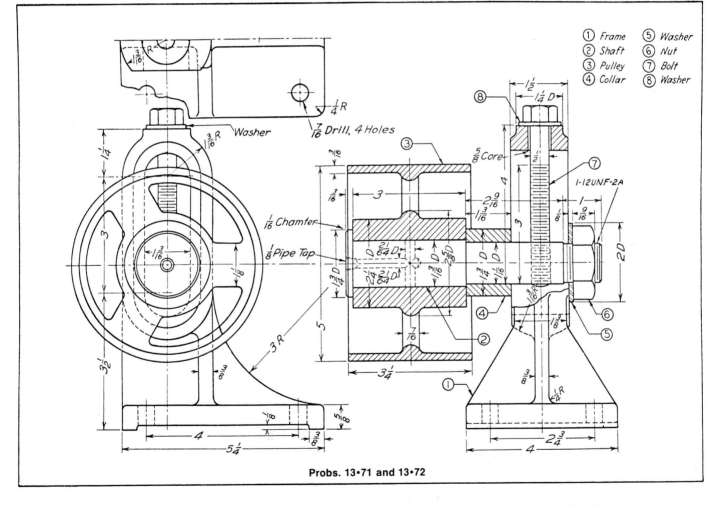

① Frame   ⑤ Washer
② Shaft   ⑥ Nut
③ Pulley   ⑦ Bolt
④ Collar   ⑧ Washer

Probs. 13·71 and 13·72

Problem 13·71. Make an assembly drawing of the belt tightener. Show three exterior views.

Problem 13·72. Make a complete set of detail drawings for the belt tightener.

Problems   503

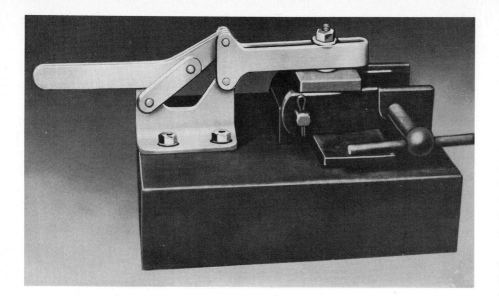

26·28 The Model KP-186 toggle-action clamp, shown, is one of a large variety of clamping fixtures made by Knu-Vise Incorporated, Detroit, Mich. Note the U-shaped toggle bar used to hold work in place. It may be used without the spindle to clamp the work directly. The handle is pivoted on the link and, when raised, it releases the toggle bar. The link and toggle bar are also pivoted on the base. Work out dimensions not given as parts are drawn.

This low-model clamp allows free overhead movement of operating tools in drilling, routing, or end-mill operations. The parts are made of steel, and all parts except the toggle bar are heat-treated. The clamp is cadmium-plated.

Part 1. Base—RH, made of SAE #1020, CRS (Society of Automotive Engineers, No. 1020, cold-rolled steel), thickness #9 (0.1494) USS, GA. (U.S. Standard Gage). Pierce 2 holes 0.238 $^{+0.003}_{-0.000}$ diameter, ream 0.250 $^{+0.001}_{-0.000}$. Distance between centers *B* and *C* is 2.470. Spotweld RH and LH bases together at places marked *X*.

Part 2. Base—RH, same as Part 1 but left hand.

Part 3. Toggle bar, made of SAE #1020, CRS, thickness #11 (0.1196) USS, GA. Pierce 4 holes 0.187 $^{+0.001}_{-0.000}$ diameter.

Part 4. Handle—RH made of SAE #1020, CRS, thickness #9 (0.1494) USS, GA. Pierce 2 holes 0.238 $^{+0.003}_{-0.000}$ diameter, ream 0.250 $^{+0.001}_{-0.000}$. Spotweld RH and LH handles together at places marked *X*.

Part 5. Handle—LH, same as Part 4 but left hand.

Part 6. Link, made of SAE #1020, CRS, thickness #11 (0.1196) USS, GA. Pierce 2 holes 0.187 $^{+0.001}_{-0.000}$.

Distance between centers *C* and *D* is 1.625 $^{+0.001}_{-0.001}$.

Part 7. Shoulder rivet, made of SAE #X-1112, screw stock, cyanide harden.

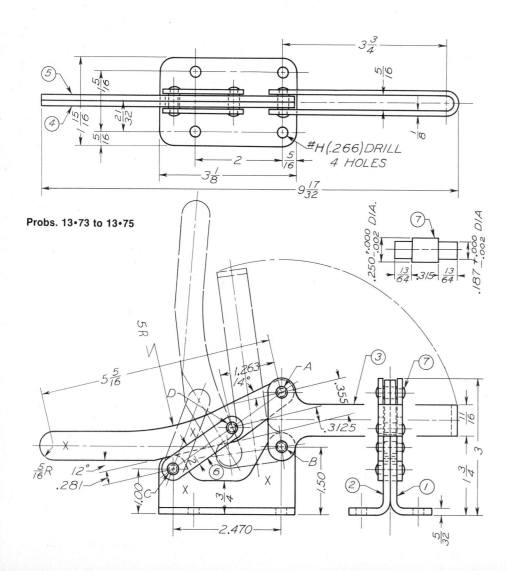

Probs. 13·73 to 13·75

Four required. See enlarged view on the drawing. See photograph and description before and while working Probs. 13·73, 13·74, and 13·75.

Problem 13·73. Make a set of detail working drawings for the parts of the Model KP-186 toggle-action clamp.

Problem 13·74. Prepare a complete parts list for the Model KP-186 toggle-action clamp.

Problem 13·75. Make an assembly drawing of the Model KP-186 toggle-action clamp. Work out the open posi-tion carefully and draw it in with the proper lines for showing an alternate position. A convenient method is to make tracings of parts with accurate center distances, place them in the desired position, and punch the centers with a needle point. The parts can then be drawn.

Probs. 13·76 to 13·78

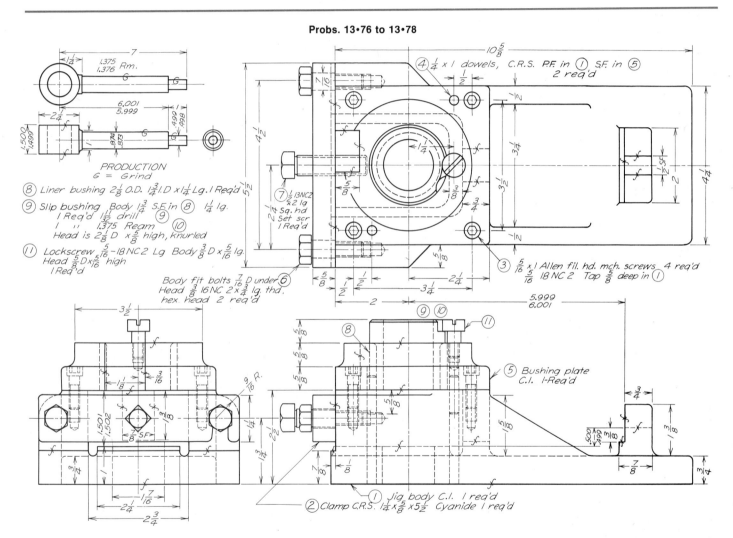

Problems 13·76, 13·77, and 13·78. A jig is a device used to hold a machine part (called the *work* or *production*) while it is being machined, or produced, so that all the parts will be alike within specified limits of accuracy. Note the production shown; upper left corner.

Problem 13·76. Make a detail working drawing of the jig body.

Problem 13·77. Make a complete set of detail drawings for the jig with bill of material. Use as many sheets as necessary or use larger sheets.

Problem 13·78. Make a complete assembly drawing of the jig, three views. Give only such dimensions as are necessary for putting the parts together and using the jig.

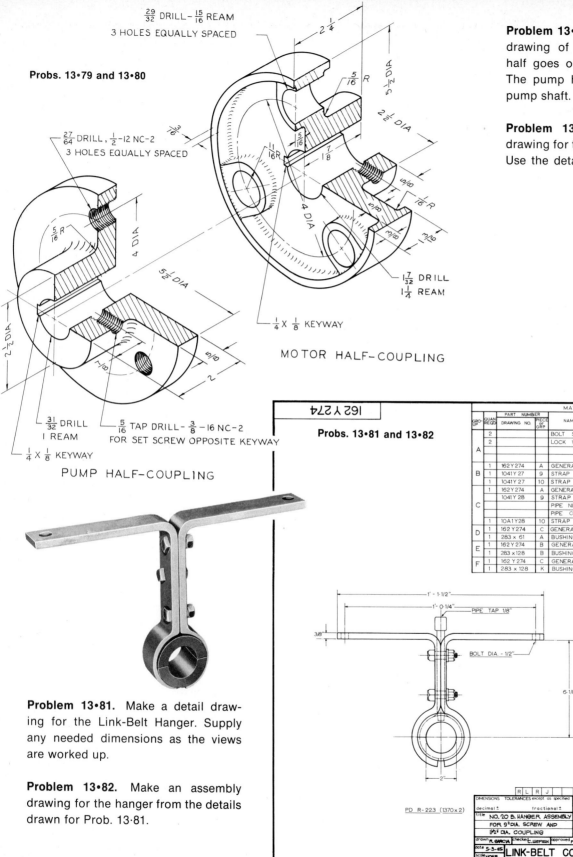

Probs. 13·79 and 13·80

$\frac{29}{32}$ DRILL – $\frac{15}{16}$ REAM
3 HOLES EQUALLY SPACED

$2\frac{1}{4}$

$\frac{5}{16}$ R

$5\frac{1}{2}$ DIA

$2\frac{1}{2}$ DIA

$\frac{3}{16}$

$\frac{5}{16}$

$\frac{11}{16}$ R

$1\frac{7}{8}$

4 DIA

$\frac{1}{16}$ R

$1\frac{7}{32}$ DRILL
$1\frac{1}{4}$ REAM

$\frac{1}{4}$ X $\frac{1}{8}$ KEYWAY

MOTOR HALF-COUPLING

$\frac{27}{64}$ DRILL , $\frac{1}{2}$-12 NC-2
3 HOLES EQUALLY SPACED

$\frac{5}{16}$ R

4 DIA

$5\frac{1}{2}$ DIA

$2\frac{1}{2}$ DIA

$\frac{31}{32}$ DRILL
1 REAM

$\frac{5}{16}$ TAP DRILL - $\frac{3}{8}$ -16 NC-2
FOR SET SCREW OPPOSITE KEYWAY

$\frac{1}{4}$ X $\frac{1}{8}$ KEYWAY

PUMP HALF-COUPLING

Problem 13·79. Make a detail working drawing of the coupling. The motor half goes on an electric motor shaft. The pump half goes on a centrifugal pump shaft.

Problem 13·80. Make an assembly drawing for the coupling of Prob. 13·79. Use the details drawn for Prob. 13·79.

Problem 13·81. Make a detail drawing for the Link-Belt Hanger. Supply any needed dimensions as the views are worked up.

Problem 13·82. Make an assembly drawing for the hanger from the details drawn for Prob. 13·81.

162 Y 274

Probs. 13·81 and 13·82

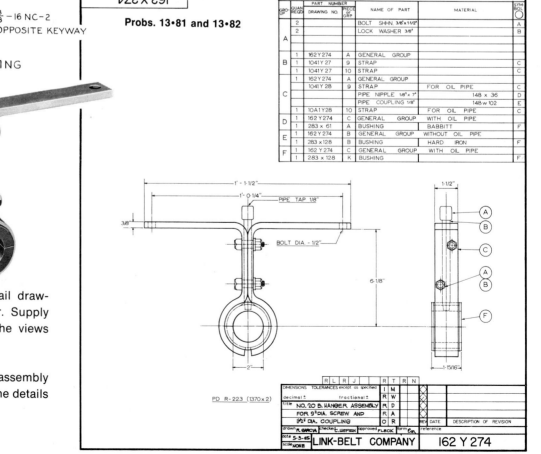

MATERIAL LIST						
GROUP	QUAN REQD.	PART NUMBER DRAWING NO.	PIECE or GRP	NAME OF PART	MATERIAL	SYM BOL
A	2			BOLT SHHN. 3/8"x1 1/2"		A
	2			LOCK WASHER 3/8"		B
B	1	162 Y 274	A	GENERAL GROUP		
	1	1041 Y 27	9	STRAP		C
	1	1041 Y 27	10	STRAP		C
C	1	162 Y 274	A	GENERAL GROUP		
	1	1041 Y 28	9	STRAP	FOR OIL PIPE	C
				PIPE NIPPLE 1/8" x 7"	148 x 36	D
				PIPE COUPLING 1/8"	148 w 102	E
	1	10A 1 Y 28	10	STRAP	FOR OIL PIPE	C
D	1	162 Y 274	C	GENERAL GROUP WITH OIL PIPE		
	1	283 x 61	A	BUSHING	BABBITT	F
E	1	162 Y 274	B	GENERAL GROUP WITHOUT OIL PIPE		
	1	283 x128	B	BUSHING	HARD IRON	F
F	1	162 Y 274	C	GENERAL GROUP WITH OIL PIPE		
	1	283 x 128	K	BUSHING		F

1' - 1 1/2"

1' - 0 1/4"

PIPE TAP 1/8"

3/8"

BOLT DIA. - 1/2"

6 1/8"

1 1/2"

A
B
C
A
B
F

2"

1-15/16"

PD R-223 (1370 x 2)

R	L	R	J		R	T	R	N
DIMENSIONS TOLERANCES except as specified
decimal ±   fractional ±
title NO. 20 B. HANGER ASSEMBLY
FOR 9" DIA. SCREW AND
1½" DIA. COUPLING

REV DATE   DESCRIPTION OF REVISION

drawn R. GARCIA   checked C. WEFIEN   approved FLECK   form $\overline{c_{in}}$ reference
date 5-3-65
scale NONE

LINK-BELT COMPANY   162 Y 274

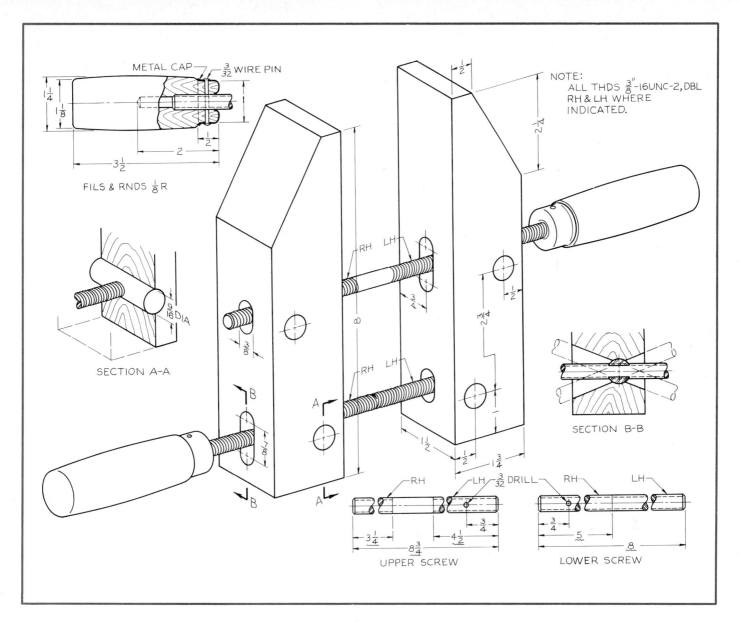

METAL CAP — $\frac{3}{32}$ WIRE PIN

$1\frac{1}{4}$ $1\frac{1}{8}$ $\frac{1}{2}$ 2 $3\frac{1}{2}$

FILS & RNDS $\frac{1}{8}$ R

SECTION A-A

$\frac{9}{16}$ DIA

NOTE:
ALL THDS $\frac{3}{8}$"-16UNC-2, DBL RH & LH WHERE INDICATED.

$\frac{1}{2}$ $2\frac{1}{4}$

RH LH

RH LH

$\frac{3}{4}$ $2\frac{3}{4}$ $\frac{1}{2}$

8 $\frac{3}{8}$

$\frac{7}{8}$

A B

SECTION B-B

$1\frac{1}{2}$ $\frac{1}{2}$ $1\frac{3}{4}$

RH LH $\frac{3}{32}$ DRILL RH LH

$3\frac{1}{4}$ $4\frac{1}{2}$ $\frac{3}{4}$ $\frac{3}{4}$ 5 8

$8\frac{3}{4}$

UPPER SCREW LOWER SCREW

Probs. 13•83 and 13•84

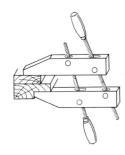

Problem 13•83. Make a detail drawing for the Jorgensen adjustable wood clamp, made by the Adjustable Clamp Company.

Problem 13•84. Make an assembly drawing of the Jorgensen clamp from the details made for Prob. 13·83.

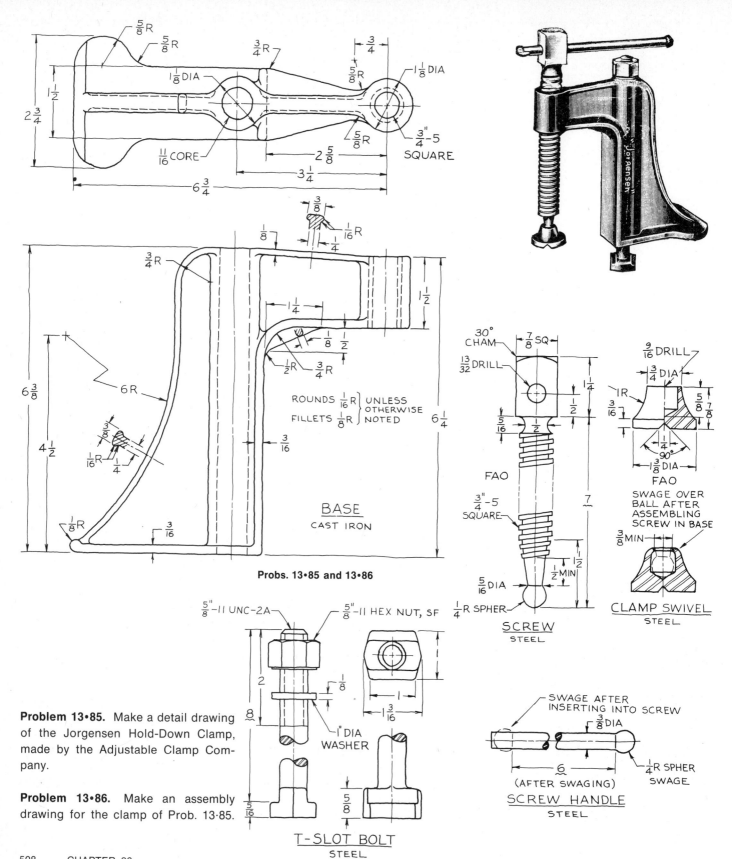

$\frac{5}{8}$R

$\frac{5}{8}$R

$\frac{3}{4}$R

$\frac{3}{4}$

$\frac{5}{8}$R

$\frac{1}{8}$ DIA

$1\frac{1}{8}$ DIA

$1\frac{1}{2}$

$2\frac{3}{4}$

$\frac{11}{16}$ CORE

$\frac{5}{8}$R

$\frac{3}{4}$"–5
SQUARE

$2\frac{5}{8}$

$3\frac{1}{4}$

$6\frac{3}{4}$

$\frac{3}{8}$

$\frac{1}{16}$ R

$\frac{1}{8}$

$\frac{1}{4}$

$\frac{3}{4}$R

$1\frac{1}{4}$

$1\frac{1}{2}$

$\frac{1}{8}$ $\frac{1}{2}$

$\frac{1}{2}$R $\frac{3}{4}$R

ROUNDS $\frac{1}{16}$R } UNLESS
FILLETS $\frac{1}{8}$R } OTHERWISE
                         NOTED

$6\frac{3}{8}$

$6R$

$4\frac{1}{2}$

$\frac{3}{8}$
$\frac{1}{16}$R $\frac{1}{4}$

$\frac{1}{8}$R

$\frac{3}{16}$

$\frac{3}{16}$

$6\frac{1}{4}$

BASE
CAST IRON

Probs. 13·85 and 13·86

30°
CHAM

$\frac{7}{8}$ SQ

$\frac{13}{32}$ DRILL

$\frac{9}{16}$ DRILL

$\frac{3}{4}$ DIA

$1\frac{1}{4}$

1R

$\frac{3}{16}$

$\frac{5}{8}$

$\frac{7}{8}$

$\frac{5}{16}$

$\frac{1}{2}$

$\frac{1}{2}$

$\frac{1}{4}$
90°

$1\frac{3}{8}$ DIA

FAO

FAO

$\frac{3}{4}$"–5
SQUARE

SWAGE OVER
BALL AFTER
ASSEMBLING
SCREW IN BASE

$1\frac{1}{2}$

$\frac{1}{2}$ MIN

$\frac{3}{8}$ MIN

$\frac{5}{16}$ DIA

$\frac{1}{4}$R SPHER

7

SCREW
STEEL

CLAMP SWIVEL
STEEL

$\frac{5}{8}$"–11 UNC–2A

$\frac{5}{8}$"–11 HEX NUT, SF

2

$\frac{1}{8}$

1

$1\frac{3}{16}$

8

1" DIA
WASHER

$\frac{5}{16}$

$\frac{5}{8}$

T–SLOT BOLT
STEEL

Problem 13·85. Make a detail drawing of the Jorgensen Hold-Down Clamp, made by the Adjustable Clamp Company.

Problem 13·86. Make an assembly drawing for the clamp of Prob. 13·85.

SWAGE AFTER
INSERTING INTO SCREW

$\frac{3}{8}$ DIA

6
(AFTER SWAGING)

$\frac{1}{4}$R SPHER
SWAGE

SCREW HANDLE
STEEL

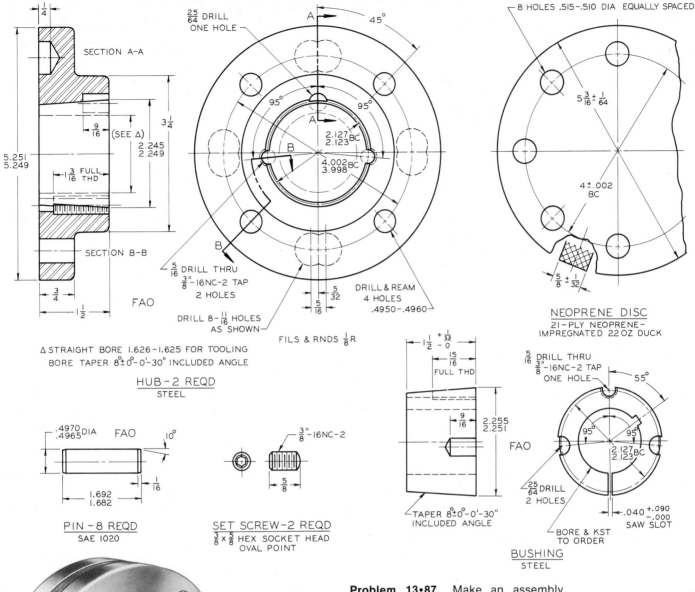

SECTION A-A

$\frac{9}{16}$ (SEE Δ)

2.245
2.249

$1\frac{3}{16}$ FULL THD

SECTION B-B

$\frac{3}{4}$

$1\frac{1}{2}$

FAO

$\frac{1}{4}$

5.251
5.249

$3\frac{1}{4}$

$\frac{25}{64}$ DRILL ONE HOLE

45°

A

95°   95°

B

A

2.127 BC
2.123

4.002 BC
3.998

B

$\frac{5}{16}$ DRILL THRU
$\frac{3}{8}$-16NC-2 TAP
2 HOLES

DRILL 8-$\frac{11}{16}$ HOLES
AS SHOWN

FILS & RNDS $\frac{1}{8}$R

$\frac{5}{32}$

$\frac{5}{16}$

DRILL & REAM
4 HOLES
.4950-.4960

8 HOLES .515-.510 DIA EQUALLY SPACED

$5\frac{3}{16}\pm\frac{1}{64}$

$4\pm.002$ BC

$\frac{5}{8}\pm\frac{1}{32}$

NEOPRENE DISC
21-PLY NEOPRENE-
IMPREGNATED 22 OZ DUCK

△ STRAIGHT BORE 1.626-1.625 FOR TOOLING
BORE TAPER 8°±0'-0'-30" INCLUDED ANGLE

HUB - 2 REQD
STEEL

.4970 DIA   FAO   10°

1.692
1.682

$\frac{1}{16}$

PIN - 8 REQD
SAE 1020

$\frac{3}{8}$"-16NC-2

$\frac{5}{8}$

SET SCREW - 2 REQD
$\frac{3}{8}$ x $\frac{5}{8}$ HEX SOCKET HEAD
OVAL POINT

$1\frac{1}{2}$ $+\frac{1}{32}$ -0

$\frac{15}{16}$

FULL THD

$\frac{9}{16}$

2.255
2.251

FAO

TAPER 8°±0'-0'-30"
INCLUDED ANGLE

$\frac{5}{16}$ DRILL THRU
$\frac{3}{8}$-16NC-2 TAP
ONE HOLE

55°

95°   95°

2.127 BC
2.123

$\frac{25}{64}$ DRILL
2 HOLES

.040 $+.090$ $-.000$
SAW SLOT

BORE & KST
TO ORDER

BUSHING
STEEL

Problem 13•87. Make an assembly drawing of the Dodge Manufacturing Co., No. 5 Taper-Lock Type HH Flexible Coupling. Show a sectional view and an exterior assembly.

Prob. 13•87

GROUP 14. PICTORIAL DRAWING

26•29 Study Chap. 14 carefully before beginning the problems. Use regular sheet with $10\frac{1}{2}'' \times 15''$ working space.

The two starting positions for the isometric axes are shown in Figs. 14-4 and 14-5b. Remember that all measurements must be taken parallel to the axes.

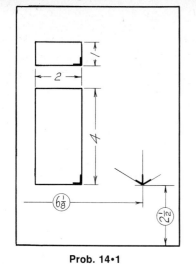

Prob. 14·1

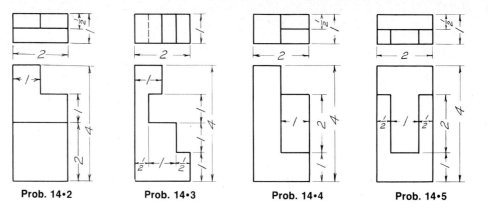

Prob. 14·2   **Prob. 14·3**   **Prob. 14·4**   **Prob. 14·5**

Problems 14·1 to 14·5. Draw the two orthographic views and an isometric drawing using the axes in the second position as indicated.

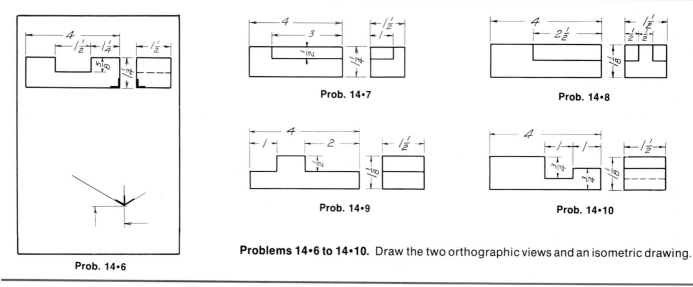

Prob. 14·6

Prob. 14·7   **Prob. 14·8**

Prob. 14·9   **Prob. 14·10**

Problems 14·6 to 14·10. Draw the two orthographic views and an isometric drawing.

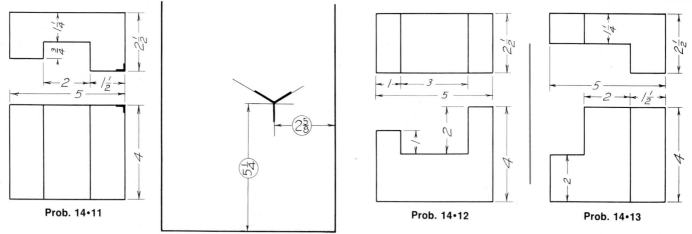

Prob. 14·11   **Prob. 14·12**   **Prob. 14·13**

Problems 14·11, 14·12, and 14·13. Draw the views given and an isometric drawing using the axes in the position indicated.

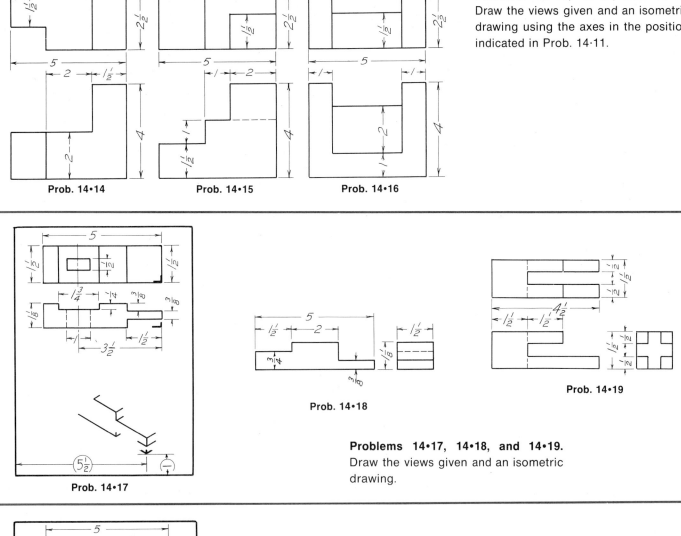

Problems 14·14, 14·15, and 14·16. Draw the views given and an isometric drawing using the axes in the position indicated in Prob. 14·11.

Prob. 14·14

Prob. 14·15

Prob. 14·16

Prob. 14·17

Prob. 14·18

Prob. 14·19

Problems 14·17, 14·18, and 14·19. Draw the views given and an isometric drawing.

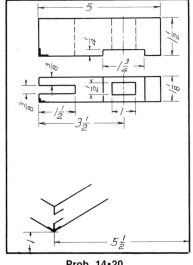

Prob. 14·20

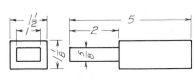

Prob. 14·21

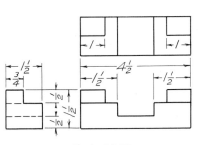

Prob. 14·22

Problems 14·20, 14·21, and 14·22. Draw the views given and an isometric drawing.

Problems 14·23 to 14·26. Draw the views given and an isometric drawing. These problems require the locating of nonisometric lines. Read Art. 14·6 and observe the construction in Fig. 14-6a before starting one of these problems. The layout of Prob. 14·17 may be used. The construction lines should be drawn very lightly and either to the left or the right on the drawing and are not to be erased until they have been inspected by the instructor. The final lines of the isometric drawing should be brightened with a sharp pencil.

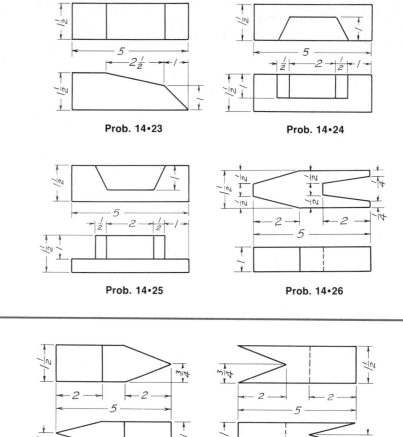

Prob. 14·23

Prob. 14·24

Prob. 14·25

Prob. 14·26

Problems 14·27 and 14·28. Draw the views given and an isometric drawing.

 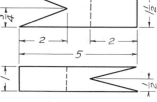

Prob. 14·27

Prob. 14·28

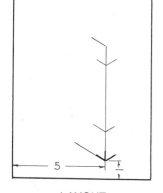

LAYOUT

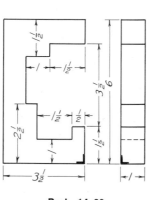

Prob. 14·29

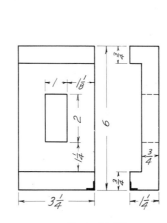

Prob. 14·30

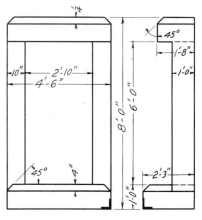

Prob. 14·31

Problem 14·29. Make an isometric drawing of the notched block. Start at the corner indicated by thick lines.

Problem 14·30. Make an isometric drawing of the plate.

Problem 14·31. Make an isometric drawing of the frame using the layout of Prob. 14·29. Use scale of ¾″ = 1′–0″.

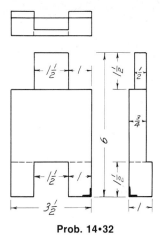

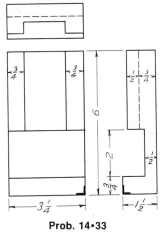

Prob. 14·32

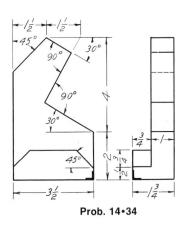

Prob. 14·33

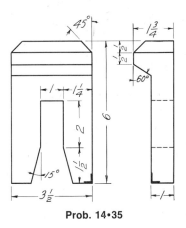

Prob. 14·34

Prob. 14·35

Problem 14·32. Make an isometric drawing of a lock joint.

Problem 14·33. Make an isometric drawing of a rabbited stop.

Problem 14·34. Make an isometric drawing of a notched slide.

Problem 14·35. Make an isometric drawing of a slotted stop.

Problem 14·36. Make an isometric drawing of the stirrup. The drawing is started on the layout at the upper left. Note the thick starting lines.

Problem 14·37. Make an isometric drawing of the brace. The drawing is started on the layout at the upper right. Note the thick starting lines.

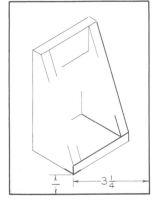

Prob. 14·36

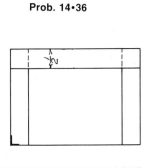

Prob. 14·37

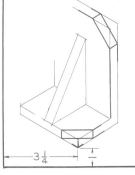

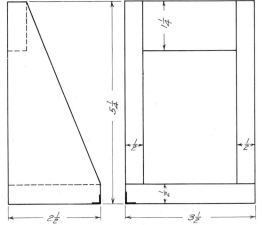

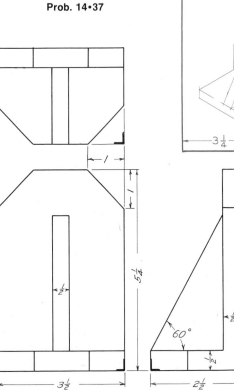

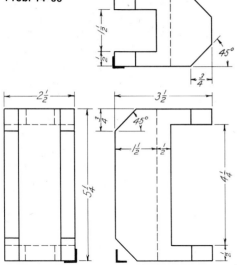

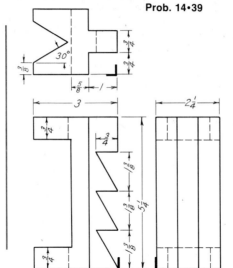

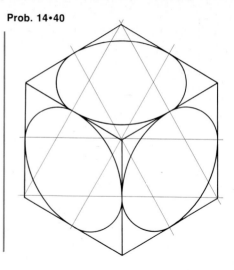

Problem 14·38. Make an isometric drawing of the cross slide. Use the layout of Prob. 14·36.

Problem 14·39. Make an isometric drawing of the ratchet. Use the layout of Prob. 14·36.

Problem 14·40. Make an isometric drawing of a 3″ cube with an isometric circle on each visible face. See Art. 14·7.

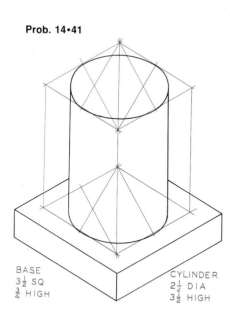

BASE
3½ SQ
¾ HIGH

CYLINDER
2½ DIA
3½ HIGH

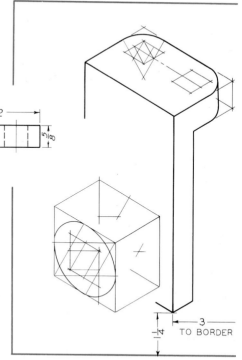

Problem 14·41. Make an isometric drawing of a cylinder resting on a square plinth (square base).

Problem 14·42. Draw the three views given and an isometric drawing of the hung bearing. Most of the construction is indicated on the layout. Make the drawing as though all corners were square and then construct the curves as described in Art. 14·7. Use two small sheets or one large sheet.

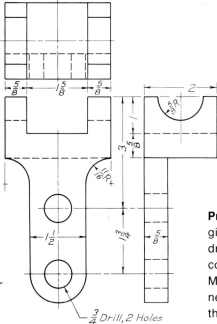

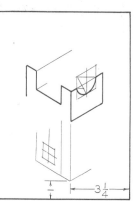

26·30 Sectional views on isometric drawings are often useful in showing interior construction. The cutting planes must be isometric planes, that is, parallel to the faces of the isometric cube. Section lining is done with the 60° triangle. In making a full section, draw the cut surface first, then add the part of the object behind it. For a half section, it is usually best to draw the full isometric view, very lightly first, then cut out the front quarter by two isometric planes.

Problem 14·43. Draw the three views given and then make an isometric drawing of the bracket. Some of the construction is indicated on the layout. Make the drawing as though the corners were square and then construct the curves. Read Art. 14·7. (This is an alternative for Prob. 14·42.)

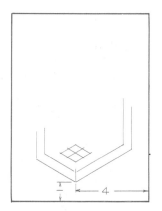

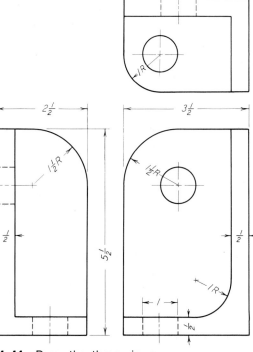

Problem 14·44. Draw the three views given and then make an isometric drawing of the lug. Make the drawing as though the corners were square and then construct the curves. Read Art. 14·7.

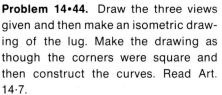

Problem 14·45. Make an isometric drawing in half section of the box step. See layout.

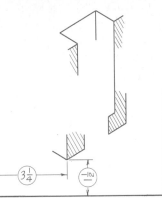

Prob. 14·46

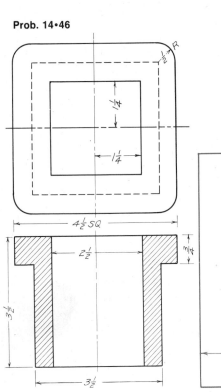

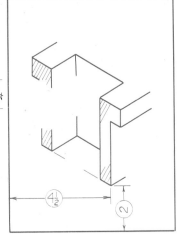

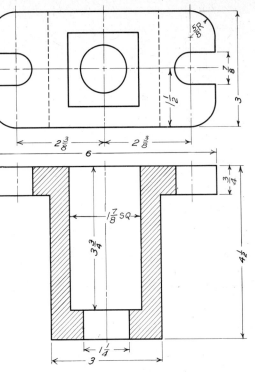

Problem 14·47. Make an isometric drawing in section of the post support. See layout.

Problem 14·46. Make an isometric drawing in section of the post-socket. See layout.

Plate 19

Prob. 14·50

Prob. 14·49

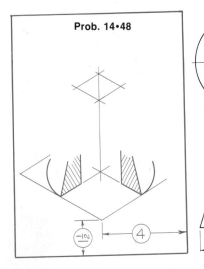

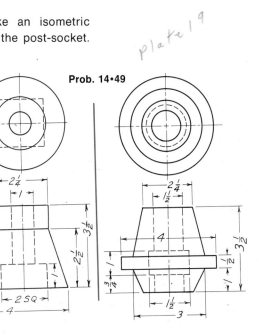

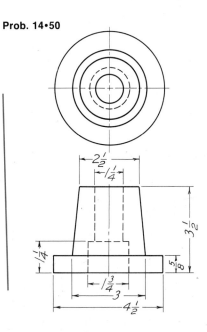

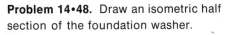

Problem 14·48. Draw an isometric half section of the foundation washer.

Problem 14·49. Draw an isometric half section of the centering cone.

Problem 14·50. Draw an isometric half section of the cone bearing.

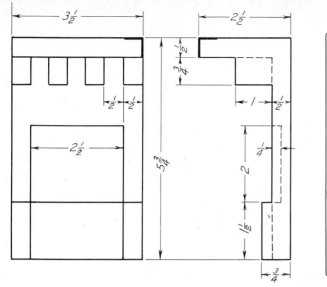

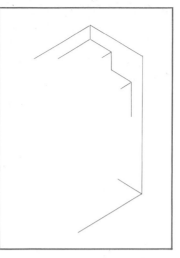

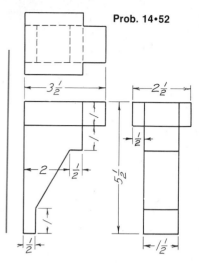

Prob. 14·52

Problem 14·51. Make an isometric drawing of the tablet. Use reversed axes.

Problem 14·52. Make an isometric drawing of the bracket. Use reversed axes.

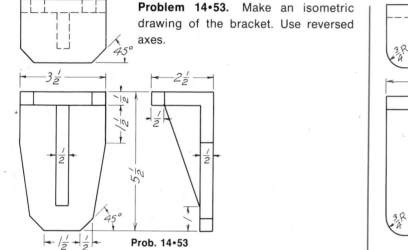

Problem 14·53. Make an isometric drawing of the bracket. Use reversed axes.

Prob. 14·53

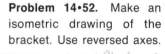

Problem 14·54. Make an isometric drawing of the bracket. Use reversed axes. Note the construction shown for the ogee curve.

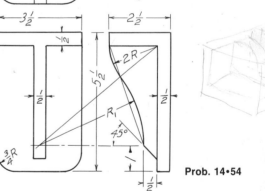

Plate 18

Prob. 14·54

Problem 14·55. Make an isometric drawing of the extension bar. Use long axis horizontal. See Art. 14·13.

Prob. 14·55

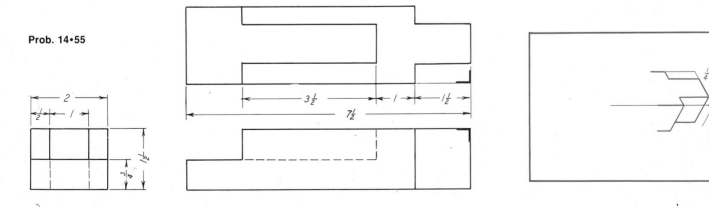

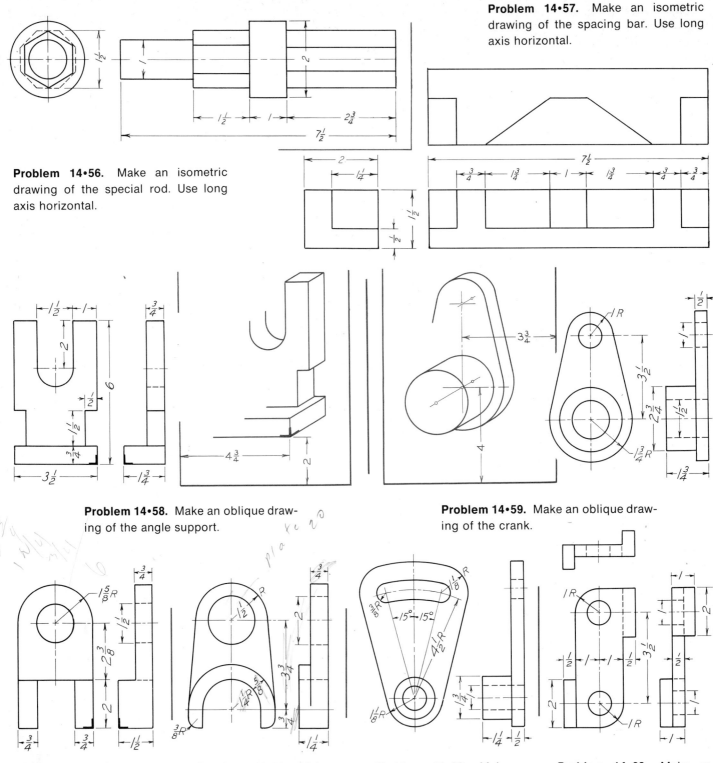

Problem 14•57. Make an isometric drawing of the spacing bar. Use long axis horizontal.

Problem 14•56. Make an isometric drawing of the special rod. Use long axis horizontal.

Problem 14•58. Make an oblique drawing of the angle support.

Problem 14•59. Make an oblique drawing of the crank.

Problem 14•60. Make an oblique drawing of the forked guide.

Problem 14•61. Make an oblique drawing of the guide link.

Problem 14•62. Make an oblique drawing of the slotted sector.

Problem 14•63. Make an oblique drawing of the double stop.

Problem 14·64. Make an oblique drawing of the locating plate. Axis 30° or 45° to the right or left as directed.

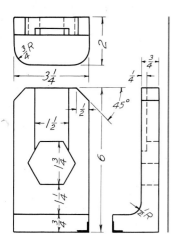

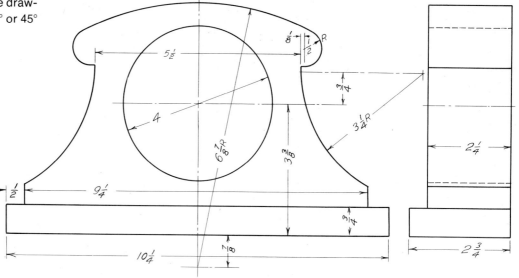

Problem 14·65. Make an oblique drawing of the clock case. Use an axis of 30° to the right.

Problems 14·66 to 14·74. Make pictorial sketches.

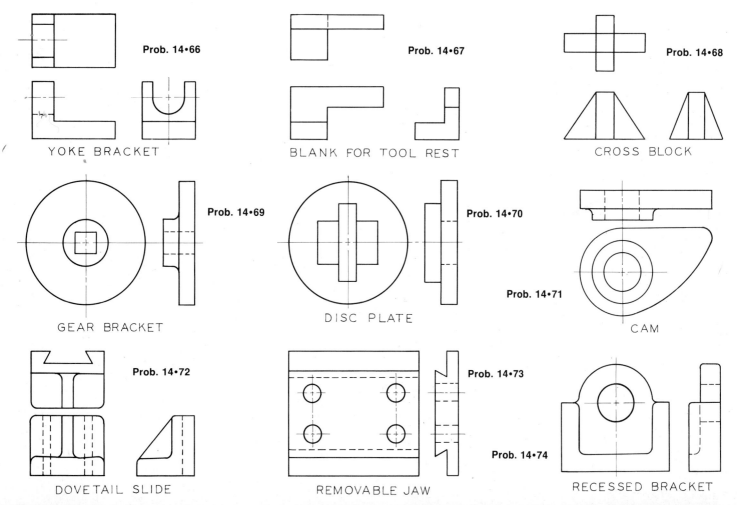

Prob. 14·66

Prob. 14·67

Prob. 14·68

YOKE BRACKET

BLANK FOR TOOL REST

CROSS BLOCK

Prob. 14·69

Prob. 14·70

Prob. 14·71

GEAR BRACKET

DISC PLATE

CAM

Prob. 14·72

Prob. 14·73

Prob. 14·74

DOVETAIL SLIDE

REMOVABLE JAW

RECESSED BRACKET

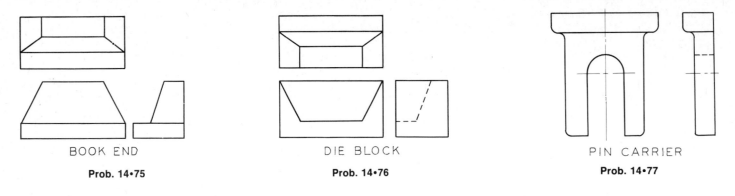

BOOK END

Prob. 14•75

DIE BLOCK

Prob. 14•76

PIN CARRIER

Prob. 14•77

Problems 14•75 to 14•77. Make pictorial sketches.

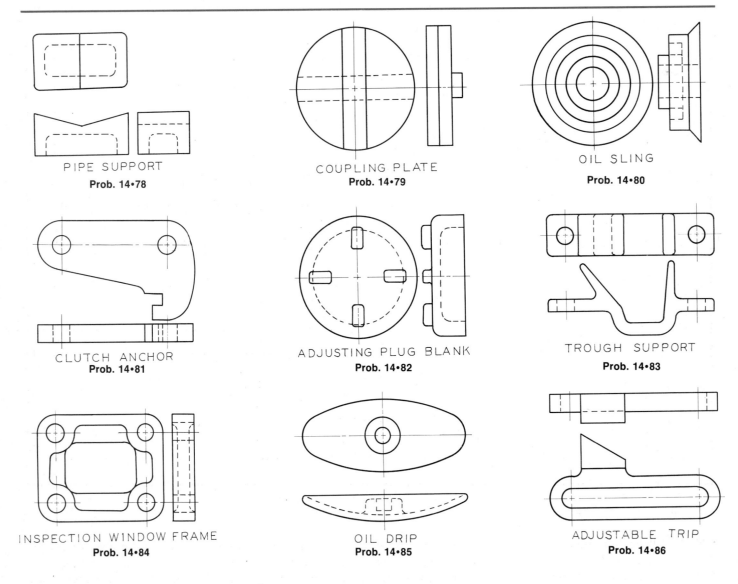

PIPE SUPPORT

Prob. 14•78

COUPLING PLATE

Prob. 14•79

OIL SLING

Prob. 14•80

CLUTCH ANCHOR

Prob. 14•81

ADJUSTING PLUG BLANK

Prob. 14•82

TROUGH SUPPORT

Prob. 14•83

INSPECTION WINDOW FRAME

Prob. 14•84

OIL DRIP

Prob. 14•85

ADJUSTABLE TRIP

Prob. 14•86

Problems 14•78 to 14•86. Make pictorial sketches.

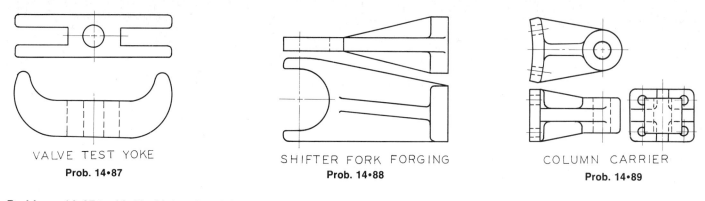

VALVE TEST YOKE
Prob. 14•87

SHIFTER FORK FORGING
Prob. 14•88

COLUMN CARRIER
Prob. 14•89

Problems 14•87 to 14•89. Make pictorial sketches.

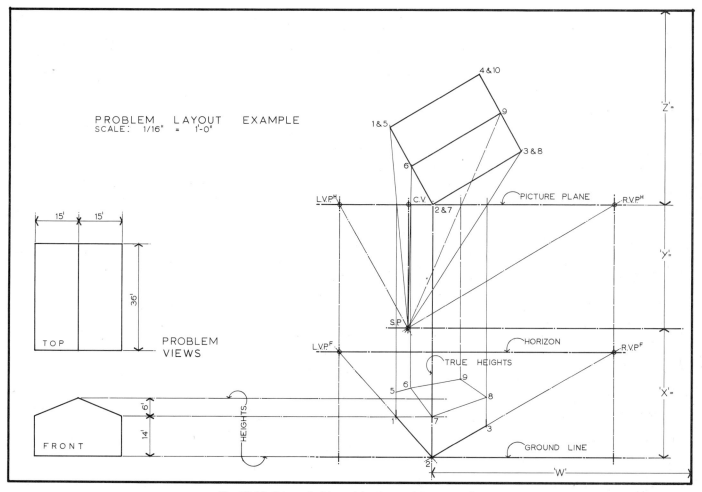

Fig. 26-31. Suggested layout for two-point perspective.

26•31 Perspective problems. Read Arts. 14·26 to 14·29 before starting these problems. Use light, thin lines for construction lines and do not erase them; brighten the result. Use a suitable scale. Locate and indicate the station point, horizon, and ground line. Select scale and position to give a good picture. A suggested layout for a two-point perspective is shown in Fig. 26-31 for a 10″ × 15″ working space. Show construction lines on all problems.

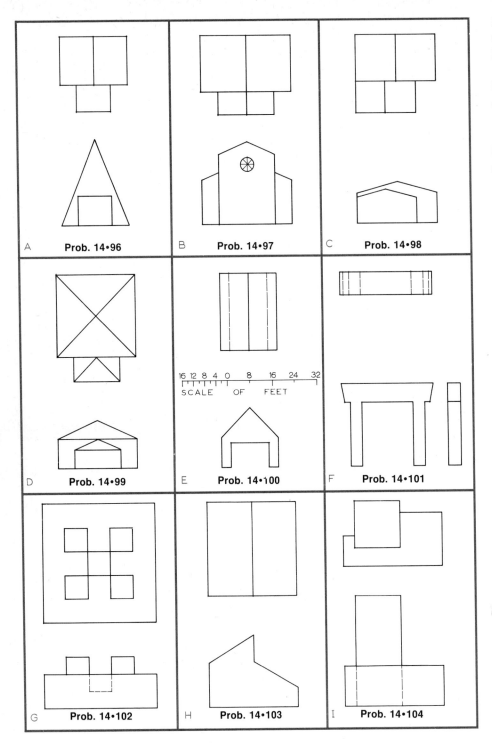

A   **Prob. 14•96**

B   **Prob. 14•97**

C   **Prob. 14•98**

D   **Prob. 14•99**

E   **Prob. 14•100**

16 12 8 4 0   8   16   24   32
SCALE   OF   FEET

F   **Prob. 14•101**

G   **Prob. 14•102**

H   **Prob. 14•103**

I   **Prob. 14•104**

Problem 14•90. Draw a one-point perspective of one of the objects shown in Prob. 14·4 or 14·5.

Problem 14•91. Draw a one-point perspective of one of the objects shown in Prob. 14·13, 14·14, or 14·16.

Problem 14•92. Draw a one-point perspective of the object shown in Prob. 14·36.

Problem 14•93. Draw a one-point perspective of the object shown in Prob. 14·38.

Prob. 14•94. Draw a one-point perspective of the object shown in Prob. 14·58.

Problem 14•95. Draw a one-point perspective of the object shown in Prob. 14·65.

Problems 14•96, 14•97, and 14•98. Make a two-point perspective drawing. Note the graphic scale; make larger if desired.

Problem 14•99. Make a two-point perspective drawing.

Problems 14•100 and 14•101. Make a one-point perspective drawing.

Problem 14•102, 14•103, and 14•104. Make a two-point perspective drawing.

GROUP 15.
TECHNICAL ILLUSTRATION

26•32 Study Chaps. 14 and 15 before beginning these problems. Any suitable problems may be selected by the instructor to be worked as technical illustration drawings. Carefully proportioned pictorial drawings in isometric, oblique, or perspective may be used depending upon the most effective result. A few problems may be drawn with instruments. The amount of rendering should be kept down to the least that will bring out the shapes.

Problem 15•1. Make an exploded-view drawing of the stirrup shown in Prob. 14·36. See Figs. 15-6a to 15-6c.

Problem 15•2. Make an exploded-view drawing of the brace shown in Prob. 14·37. See Figs. 15-6a to 15-6c.

Problem 15•3. Make an exploded-view drawing of the cross slide shown in Prob. 5·23. See Figs. 15-6a to 15-6c.

Problem 15•4. Make an exploded-view drawing of the hung bearing shown in Prob. 14·42. See Figs. 15-6a to 15-6c.

Problem 15•5. Make an exploded-view drawing of the bearing shown in Prob. 5·91. See Figs. 15-6a to 15-6c.

Problem 15•6. Make an exploded-view drawing of the bench hook shown in Prob. 13·36.

Problem 15•7. Make a production drawing of the nail box shown in Prob. 13·38.

Problem 15•8. Make a production drawing of the bookrack shown in Prob. 13·39.

Problem 15•9. Make a production drawing of the babbitted bearing shown in Prob. 13·21.

Problem 15•10. Make an exploded-view drawing of the hung bearing shown in Prob. 13·56.

Problem 15•11. Make an exploded-view drawing of the hanger bracket shown in Prob. 13·68.

Problem 15•12. Make an exploded-view drawing of the pivot-guide roll shown in Prob. 13·57.

Problem 15•13. Make an exploded-view drawing of the tool post shown in Prob. 13·62.

Problem 15•14. Make an exploded-view drawing of the idler pulley shown in Prob. 13·63.

Problem 15•15. Make an exploded-view drawing of the pulley-and-stand unit shown in Prob. 13·58.

Problem 15•16. Make an exploded-view drawing of the belt tightener shown in Prob. 13·71.

GROUP 16. AEROSPACE DRAWINGS

26•33 Study Chap. 16 before starting these problems. It will be helpful to read magazines and books on aeronautics and aerospace vehicles in your school library and the public library as air science is a rapidly changing development.

Consider the size of sheet and a suitable scale for each problem. It is not necessary to include all the tabulated information on every drawing.

Problem 16•1. Refer to Fig. 16-10b. Make a drawing of the fitting assembly.

Problem 16•2. Refer to Fig. 16-7a. Make a drawing of the sheet-metal part shown. Suggest 8½″ × 11″ sheet.

Problem 16•3. Refer to Fig. 16-6a. Make a forging blank drawing of the roller arm. Suggest 8½″ × 11″ sheet.

Problem 16•4. Refer to Fig. 16-6b. Make a forging machine drawing of the roller arm. Suggest 8½″ × 11″ sheet.

Problem 16•5. Refer to Fig. 16-6c. Make a forging drawing of the fitting.

Problem 16•6. Refer to Fig. 16-9. Make a tabulated drawing of the plunger assembly.

Problem 16•7. Refer to page 524 for drawing and directions.

Problem 16•8. Refer to Fig. 16-10a. Make a drawing of the brace assembly.

Problem 16•9. Refer to Fig. 16-5. Make a casting drawing of the bracket.

Problem 16•10. Refer to Fig. 16-7b. Make a drawing of the sheet-metal part.

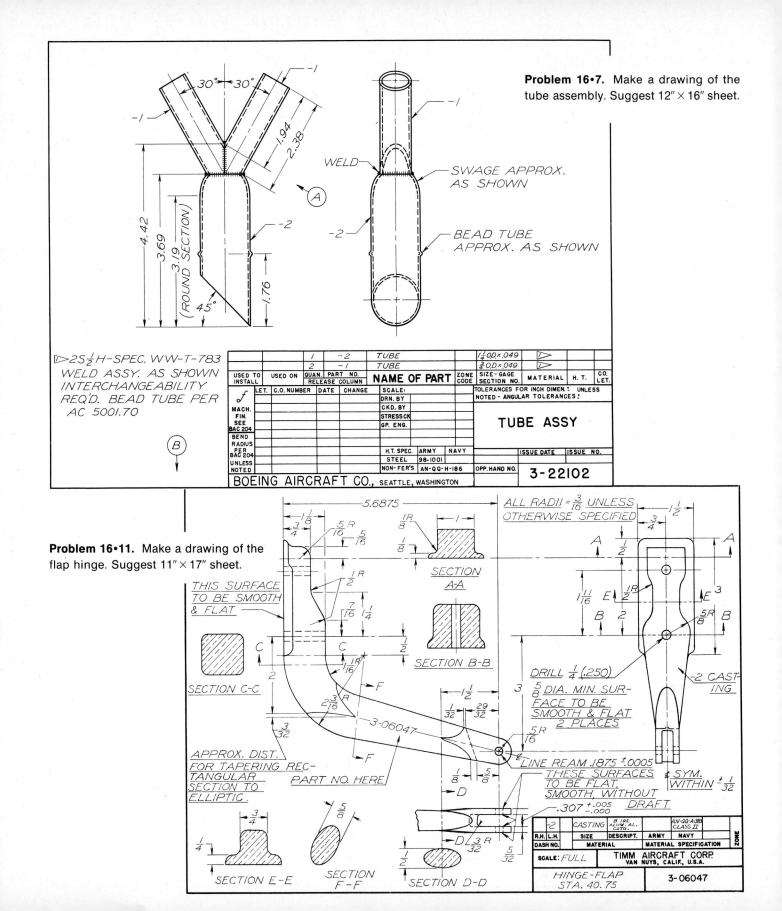

Problem 16·7. Make a drawing of the tube assembly. Suggest 12″ × 16″ sheet.

30° 30°
1.94
2.38
—1
—1
WELD
SWAGE APPROX. AS SHOWN
4.42
3.69
3.19
(ROUND SECTION)
—2
45°
1.76
BEAD TUBE APPROX. AS SHOWN
—2
A
▷2S½H-SPEC. WW-T-783 WELD ASSY. AS SHOWN INTERCHANGEABILITY REQ'D. BEAD TUBE PER AC 5001.70
B

	1	-2	TUBE		1¼ O.D.×.049	▷	
	2	-1	TUBE		¾ O.D.×.049	▷	
USED TO INSTALL	USED ON	QUAN.	PART NO. RELEASE COLUMN	NAME OF PART	ZONE CODE	SIZE- GAGE SECTION NO.	MATERIAL	H. T.	CO. LET.

LET.	C.O. NUMBER	DATE	CHANGE	SCALE:

SCALE:
DRN. BY
CKD. BY
STRESS CK
GP. ENG.
MACH. FIN. SEE BAC 204
BEND RADIUS PER BAC 204
UNLESS NOTED

TOLERANCES FOR INCH DIMEN.± UNLESS NOTED - ANGULAR TOLERANCES ±

TUBE ASSY

H.T. SPEC. | ARMY | NAVY
STEEL | 98-1001
NON-FER'S | AN-QQ-H-186
OPP. HAND NO.

ISSUE DATE | ISSUE NO.

3-22102

BOEING AIRCRAFT CO., SEATTLE, WASHINGTON

Problem 16·11. Make a drawing of the flap hinge. Suggest 11″ × 17″ sheet.

5.6875
ALL RADII = 3/16 UNLESS OTHERWISE SPECIFIED
1½
¾
A
½
A
⅛
¾
5/16 R
5/16
1R ⅛
1
⅛
SECTION A-A
THIS SURFACE TO BE SMOOTH & FLAT
1R ½
7/16 1¼
1 11/16
1R ½
E
E
3
½
B
2
B
5/8 R
SECTION B-B
C
C
1R 1/16
SECTION C-C
2
2 3/16 R
F
DRILL ¼ (.250) 5/8 DIA. MIN. SUR-FACE TO BE SMOOTH & FLAT 2 PLACES
—2 CASTING
3/32
3-06047
APPROX. DIST. FOR TAPERING REC-TANGULAR SECTION TO ELLIPTIC.
F
PART NO. HERE
1½
1/32 29/32
3
5R 16
LINE REAM .1875 ±.0005
THESE SURFACES TO BE FLAT, SMOOTH, WITHOUT DRAFT
℄ SYM. WITHIN ± 1/32
⅛ 5/8
D
.307 +.005 -.000
¾ ¼
5/8
SECTION E-E
SECTION F-F
D 3R 3/32
½
5/32
SECTION D-D

-2	CASTING	B 195. ALUM.-AL. CSTG.	AN-QQ-A-383 CLASS Ⅱ	
R.H. L.H.	SIZE	DESCRIPT.	ARMY	NAVY
DASH NO.	MATERIAL	MATERIAL SPECIFICATION		ZONE

SCALE: FULL
TIMM AIRCRAFT CORP. VAN NUYS, CALIF., U.S.A.
HINGE-FLAP STA. 40.75 | 3-06047

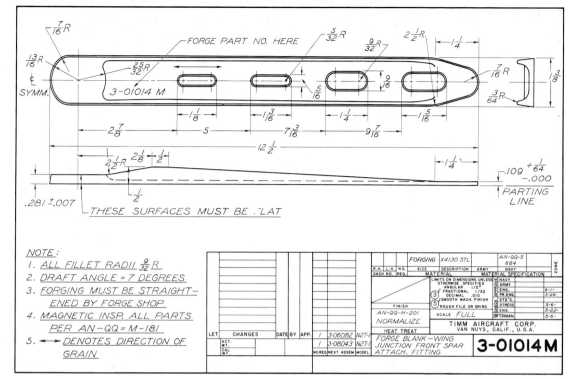

Problem 16•12. Make a drawing of the forge blank. Suggest 11″ × 17″ sheet.

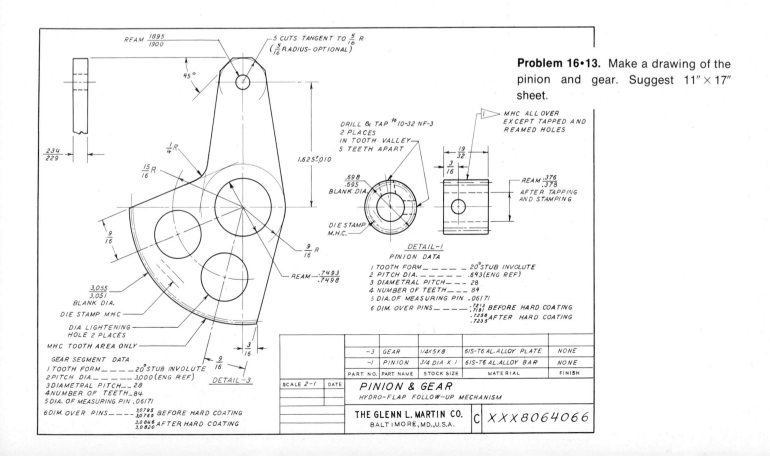

Problem 16•13. Make a drawing of the pinion and gear. Suggest 11″ × 17″ sheet.

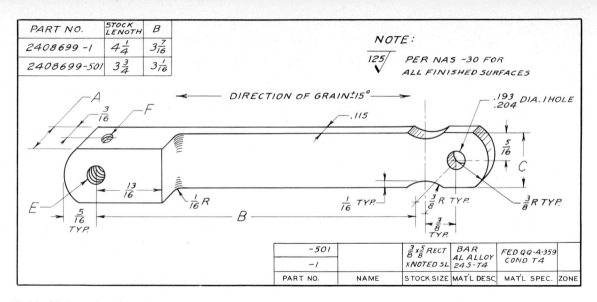

PART NO.	STOCK LENGTH	B
2408699 -1	$4\frac{1}{4}$	$3\frac{7}{16}$
2408699-501	$3\frac{3}{4}$	$3\frac{1}{16}$

NOTE:
$\overset{125}{\diagdown}$ PER NAS -30 FOR ALL FINISHED SURFACES

DIRECTION OF GRAIN±15°

.193 / .204 DIA. I HOLE

-501		$\frac{3}{8}x\frac{5}{8}$ RECT	BAR AL ALLOY 245-T4	FED QQ-A-359 COND T4	
-1		X NOTED 5L			
PART NO.	NAME	STOCK SIZE	MAT'L DESC.	MAT'L SPEC.	ZONE

Problem 16•14. Make a drawing showing the necessary orthographic views and notes for the LEVER-COCKPIT AIR-VALVE CONTROL. Note that the letter B is to be used for the center-to-center dimension since the drawing is for two separate parts as set out in the tabulation in the upper left-hand corner. Replace the letter A with the words STOCK SIZE. Replace the letter C with the words STOCK SIZE. Replace the letter E with the note: $^{0.2113}_{0.2173}$ DIA THRU, CSK 90° × ¼, THD ¼-28NF-3 per AN-S-126. Replace the letter F with the note: $^{0.1042}_{0.1145}$ DIA depth ⁵⁄₁₆, CSK 90° × ⅛, THD 6-32NC-3 per AN-S-126.

Problem 16•15. Make a drawing showing the necessary orthographic views and notes for the ARM-BRAKE-VALVE ACT. LOWER. Indicate the parting line (PL). Indicate an allowance at A to be removed for surface roughness.

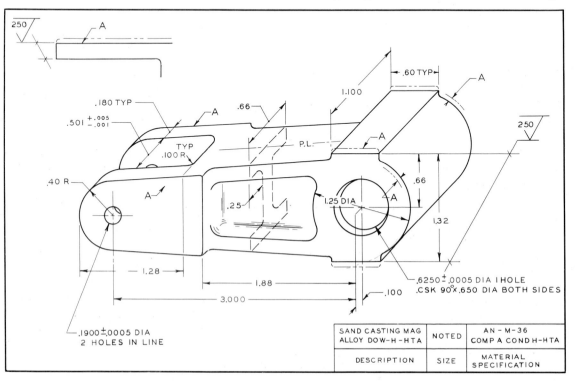

SAND CASTING MAG ALLOY DOW-H-HTA	NOTED	AN-M-36 COMP A COND H-HTA
DESCRIPTION	SIZE	MATERIAL SPECIFICATION

GROUP 17. WELDING DRAWINGS

26·34 Study Chap. 17 before starting these problems. Some knowledge of welding methods is necessary for understanding and making welding drawings. It is desirable to have books on welding, the standards of The American Welding Society, and the ASA Z32.2.1 Graphical Symbols for Welding at hand.

Problem 17·1. Make a drawing showing the basic types of joints shown in Fig. 17-4a.

Problem 17·2. Make a drawing of the grooved joints shown in Fig. 17-4b.

Problem 17·3. Make a drawing of the casting for the sheave housing shown in Fig. 17-3a.

Problem 17·4. Make a welding drawing for the sheave housing of Fig. 17-3b and compare your drawing with Fig. 17-3b.

Problem 17·5. Make a complete welding drawing for the stirrup shown in Prob. 14·36. Show three views with welding symbols.

Problem 17·6. Make a complete welding drawing of the brace shown in Prob. 14·37. Show three views with symbols.

Problem 17·7. Make a complete welding drawing of the hung bearing shown in Prob. 14·42. Show three views with welding symbols.

Problem 17·8. Make a complete welding drawing with welding symbols for the bearing to replace the casting shown in Prob. 5·91. Use $3/8''$ steel for all except the hubs.

Problem 17·9. Same as Prob. 17·8 for the angle plate shown in Prob. 9·39.

Problem 17·10. Make a welding drawing for the bearing holder shown in Prob. 13·30. Use welded steel and show the welding symbols.

Problem 17·11. Make a complete welding drawing for the bracket bearing to replace the casting shown in Prob. 13·29. Use $1/2''$ steel except for the hub. Show the welding symbols.

Problem 17·12. Make a welding drawing of the structural detail shown in Fig. 17-7d.

GROUP 18. ELECTRICAL DRAWINGS

26·35 Problems 18·1 to 18·36. Study Chap. 18 before starting these problems. Note that electrical drawings require some knowledge of electricity and of the great use of symbols.

Problem 18·1 (Fig. 18-9a). Draw symbols as selected by the instructor. Make about two or more times as large as shown in the book.

Problems 18·2 to 18·13. Make a drawing of a circuit similar to the figure. Draw about three times the size shown in the book.

Problem 18·2. Fig. 18-10a.

Problem 18·3. Fig. 18-10b.

Problem 18·4. Fig. 18-10c.

Problem 18·5. Fig. 18-10d.

Problem 18·6. Fig. 18-10e.

Problem 18·7. Fig. 18-10f.

Problem 18·8. Fig. 18-11a.

Problem 18·9. Fig. 18-11b.

Problem 18·10. Fig. 18-11c.

Problem 18·11. Fig. 18-20a.

Problem 18·12. Fig. 18-20b.

Problem 18·13. Fig. 18-20c.

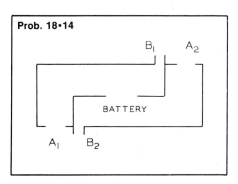

Prob. 18·14

Problem 18·14. Draw the diagram. Show the proper symbols. Push button at A_1 to operate bell B_1 and push button at A_2 to operate bell at B_2. This is a return, or answer, call system.

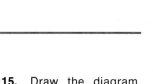

Prob. 18·15

Problem 18·15. Draw the diagram. Show the proper symbols. Three bells are to be operated separately from the battery: bell B_1 by pushbutton A_1; bell B_2 by pushbutton A_2, and bell B_3 by pushbutton A_3.

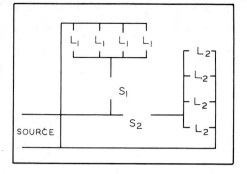

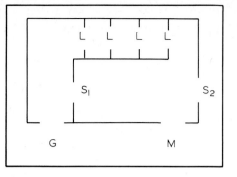

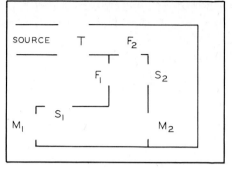

Problem 18•16. Draw the diagram. Show the proper symbols. Current is supplied from an outside source. Lamps at L_1 are operated by a fused switch at S_1. Lamps at L_2 are operated by a fused switch at S_2.

Problem 18•17. Draw the diagram. Show the proper symbols. Generator at G, motor at M, lamps at L, fused switches at S_1 and S_2.

Problem 18•18. Draw the diagram. Show the proper symbols. Transformer at T, motors at M_1 and M_2, switches at S_1 and S_2, circuit breakers at F_1 and F_2.

Problem 18•22 (Fig. 18-20e). Draw symbols as selected by the instructor. Make the symbols about twice the size shown in the book.

Problem 18•23 (Fig. 18-1b). Make a drawing of the simple radio circuit. Make about two or three times the size shown in the book. Do not copy.

Prob. 18•19

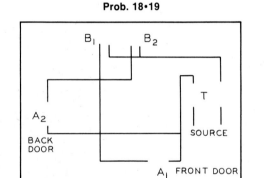

Problem 18•19. Draw the diagram. Show the proper symbols. Transformer at T, pushbutton at A_1 at front door operates bell at B_1, pushbutton at A_2 at back door operates buzzer at B_2.

Problem 18•20 (Fig. 18-20g). Make a drawing of the single-phase starter diagram. Make about three or four times the size shown in the book. Use 11″ × 17″ sheet with long dimension vertical.

Problem 18•21 (Fig. 18-20h). Make a drawing of the diagram. Draw about three times the size shown in the book.

Prob. 18•24

Problem 18•24. Make a drawing of the circuit for the simple regenerative radio.

Make two or three times the size shown in the book.

Problem 18•25. Draw a schematic diagram for the plate circuit. See Fig. 18-1b before starting this problem; also, Figs. 18-9b and 18-20e for symbols. $A = $ A battery; $B = $ B battery; $C = $ input posts; $D = $ output posts for meter, earphones, or other load; $E = $ theostat; $F = $ 1H4G tube.

Prob. 18•25

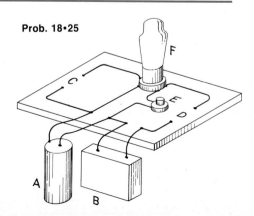

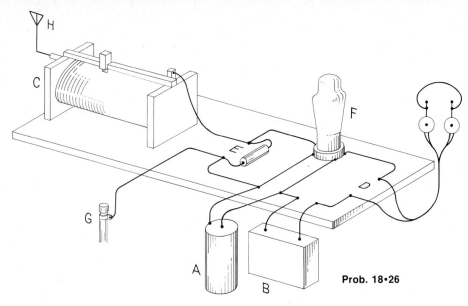

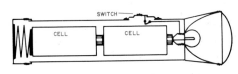

Problem 18·29 (Fig. 18-28e). Make a drawing of the schematic diagram shown. Make two or more times the size shown in the book.

Prob. 18·30

Problem 18·30. Draw a schematic diagram of the circuit for the two-cell flashlight shown in the pictorial diagram. Use correct symbols.

Prob. 18·26

Problem 18·26. Draw a schematic diagram for the radio set using the loading-coil tuner. See Figs. 18-1b, 18-9b, and 18-20e. In the figure, A = A battery, 1½ volts; B = B battery, 22½ volts; D = output; E = grid leak resistor, ½ to 3 megohms; F = 1H4G tube; G = ground; H = antenna; C = loading-coil tuner.

Problem 18·27 (Fig. 18-28c). Make a drawing of the schematic diagram shown. Make two or more times the size shown.

Problem 18·28 (Fig. 18-28d). Make a drawing of the schematic diagram shown. Make two or more times the size shown.

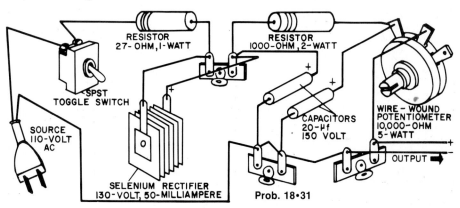

Prob. 18·31

Problem 18·31. Draw a schematic diagram of the circuit for the selenium rectifier power supply shown in the pictorial diagram. Use correct symbols.

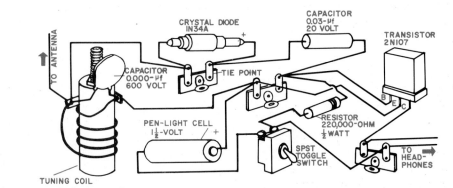

Problem 18·32. Draw a schematic diagram of the circuit for the one-transistor radio receiver shown in the pictorial diagram. Use correct symbols.

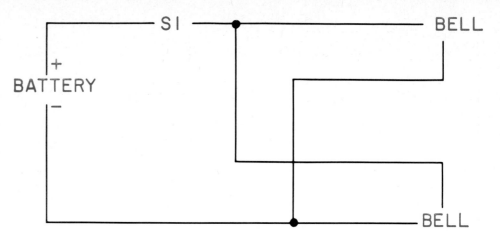

SI: SWITCH, PUSHBUTTON, CIRCUIT CLOSING

Problem 18•33. Draw the diagram using the correct symbols. In this circuit switch *S1* operates both bells at the same time.

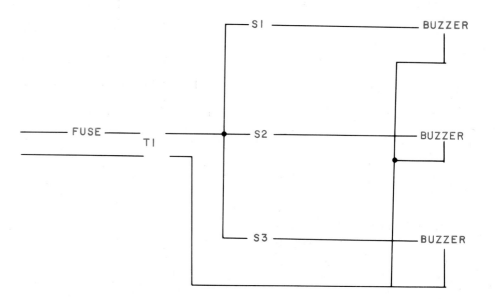

Problem 18•34. Draw the diagram for the signal system in which each switch controls a different buzzer. Use correct symbols.

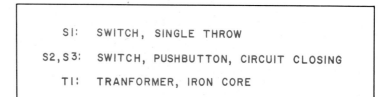

SI:	SWITCH, SINGLE THROW
S2,S3:	SWITCH, PUSHBUTTON, CIRCUIT CLOSING
TI:	TRANFORMER, IRON CORE

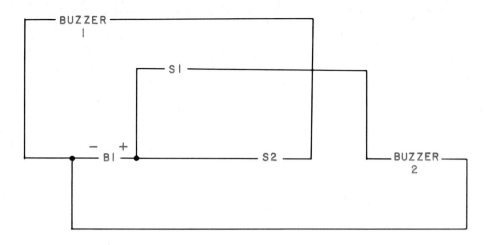

Problem 18•35. Draw the diagram for the return-call signal system. Switch S1 controls Buzzer 2. Switch S2 controls Buzzer 1. Use correct symbols.

BI: BATTERY

SI, S2: SWITCH, PUSHBUTTON, CIRCUIT CLOSING

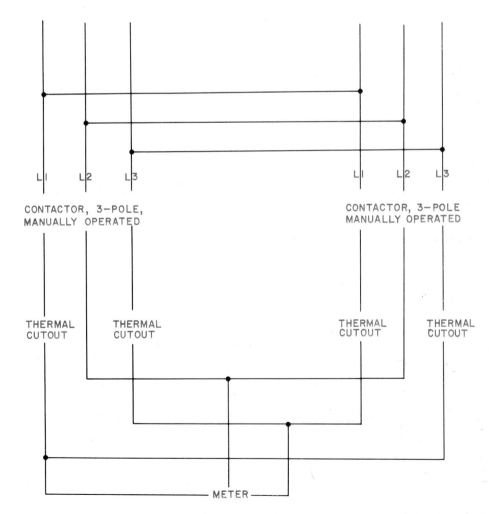

Problem 18•36. Draw the diagram for the three-phase motor reversing starter circuit. Use correct symbols.

GROUP 19.
CAM AND GEAR DRAWINGS

26·36 Cams and gears are machine elements used in many ways for the transmission of motion and power. Study Chap. 19 carefully before starting the problems in this group. It will be necessary to make some calculations to obtain dimensions for the gear drawings. Formulas are given in Art. 19·10. The formulas used, the given values, the calculations, and the figured values should be neatly lettered on the drawing or on a separate sheet as directed by the instructor.

Accuracy and neatness are necessary to obtain satisfactory drawings in this group. The pencil must be kept sharp and the lines fine and light. When the desired result has been obtained, the drawing should be brightened, using a sharp pencil of the proper grade to make the views stand out.

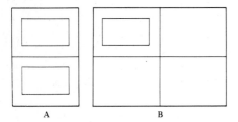

Fig. 26-19a. Sheet layouts for Probs. 19·1 and 19·2.

Problem 19·1 (8½″ × 11″ sheet or one-half 11″ × 17″ sheet). See layout, Fig. 26-19a. In a rectangle 5 in. wide and 2¾ in. high, draw a diagram for uniform rising motion. In a rectangle 5 in. wide and 2¾ in. high, draw a diagram for modified falling motion. See Fig. 19-5.

Problem 19·2 (8½″ × 11″ sheet or one-half 11″ × 17″ sheet). See layout, Fig. 26-19a. In a rectangle 5 in. wide and 2¾ in. high, draw a diagram for harmonic rising motion. In a rectangle 5 in. wide and 2¾ in. high, draw a diagram for gravity falling motion.

Problem 19·3 (11″ × 17″ sheet). Draw a displacement diagram. Refer to Figs. 19-4 and 19-5. Draw a line 9 in. long representing the base circle of a cam. Motion as follows: rise 1¾ in. during 100° with harmonic motion, at rest (dwell) during 40°, drop ⅞ in. during 90° with harmonic motion. Complete and letter the diagram. See Fig. 19-4 at B.

Problem 19·4 (11″ × 17″ sheet). Design a plate cam with point contact (see Fig. 19-3b). Motion as follows: rise 1½ in. with uniform motion during one-half revolution, drop 1½ in. with uniform motion during one-fourth revolution, at rest during the remaining one-fourth revolution. Distance AC equals 2¼ in., Fig. 26-19b.

Problem 19·5 (11″ × 17″ sheet). Design a plate cam with point contact (see Fig. 19-3b). Motion as follows: rise 2 in. with uniform motion during one-third revolution, at rest during one-sixth revolution, drop 2 in. uniformly during one-fourth revolution, at rest during remaining one-fourth revolution. Distance AC equals 1¾ in., Fig. 26-19b.

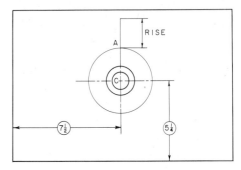

Fig. 26-19b. Sheet layouts for Probs. 19·4 and 19·5.

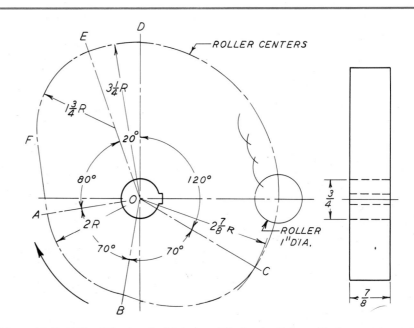

Problem 19·6 (11″ × 17″ sheet). Make a drawing for a plate cam for the conditions given in the illustration. Lay off the angles and draw radial lines from O. Draw the path of the roll centers. From E to D, dwell, radius 3¼ in. From D to C, drop from 4¼ in. to 2⅞ in. uniform motion. From C to B, drop from 2⅞ in. to 2 in. with harmonic motion. From B to A, dwell, radius 2 in. From A to F, straight line. From F to E, radius of 1¾ in. as shown. Draw cam face using 1-in.-diameter roller in sufficient number of positions to determine the outline. Keyway ¼″ × ⅛″. Do not erase the construction lines.

Problem 19·7 (11″ × 17″ sheet). Design a plate cam with roller. Motion as follows: rise 2 in. with uniform motion during 180°, drop 1 in., remain at rest during 75°, drop 1 in. with uniform motion during remaining 105°. Diameter of roller is 7/8 in. Distance AC equals 2¼ in. Refer to Fig. 26-19b.

Problem 19·8 (11″ × 17″ sheet). Design a plate cam with roller. Motion as follows: rise 1¾ in. with harmonic motion during 120°, at rest during 60°, drop 1¾ in. with modified uniform motion during 120°, at rest during remaining 60°. Diameter of roller is 7/8 in. Distance AC equals 2½ in. Draw a displacement diagram first. Refer to Fig. 26-19b.

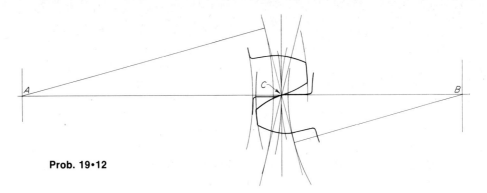

Prob. 19·12

Problem 19·10 (17″ × 22″ sheet). Make a drawing of the face cam shown in Fig. 19-6a in Chap. 19.

Problem 19·11 (11″ × 17″ sheet). Make a drawing of the barrel (cylindrical) cam shown in Fig. 19-6b in Chap. 19.

Problem 19·12 (11″ × 17″ sheet). Refer to Figs. 19-9a and 19-9b. Draw two gear teeth in contact on the line of centers AB (at point C). Gear with center at A has 20 teeth. Pinion with center at B has 14 teeth. Diametrical pitch is 1¼. Draw the line of centers. Calculate the radii of the gear and pinion. Lay off the angle of pressure using 15° for convenience. Draw the pitch circles and addendum and dedendum circles. Draw the base circles. Compute and lay off the circular thickness of a tooth (one-half the circular pitch) from C for the gear and pinion. Starting at point C, construct an involute from the base circles to the addendum circle. Refer to Fig. 4-37 for involute. Draw the fillets. Brighten the two resulting gear teeth.

Problem 19·13. Make a working drawing for a cut spur gear similar to Fig. 19-11a in Chap. 19 but with 72 teeth and diametral pitch = 12.

Problem 19·14. Make a working drawing for a cut spur gear. Diametral pitch = 6. Width of face = 1⅝″. Diameter of shaft or bore = 1⅞″. Length of hub = 2″.

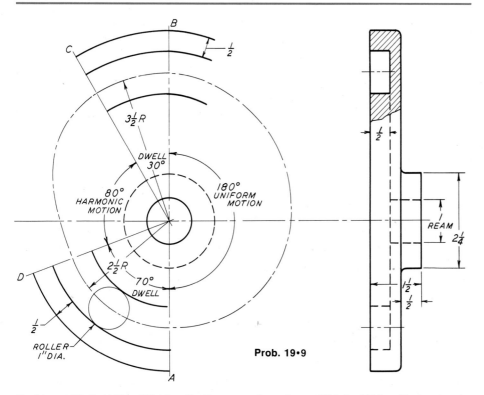

Prob. 19·9

Problem 19·9 (11″ × 17″ sheet). Draw a box (grooved) cam for the conditions given in the illustration. Lay off the angles. Draw the path of the roll centers. From A to B, rise from 2½″ to 3½″, with modified uniform motion. From B to C, dwell, radius 3½″. From C to D,

drop from 3½″ to 2½″, with harmonic motion. From D to A, dwell, radius 2½″. Draw groove, using roller with 1″ diameter in sufficient number of positions to fix outlines for the groove. Complete the cam drawing. Keyway ¼″ × ⅛″. Leave construction lines.

Problem 19·15. Make a working drawing for a cut spur gear and pinion. Outside diameter of gear = 6½″. Width of face = 1¼″. Length of hub = 1½″. Pitch diameter of pinion = 1½″, and number of teeth = 12. Other dimensions to be worked up as views are drawn.

GROUP 20. DEVELOPMENTS AND INTERSECTIONS

26·37 Developments. Study Arts. 20·1 to 20·23 on developments before starting Probs. 20·1 to 20·37. They are planned for convenient working on 11" × 17" sheets (full size) or may be worked on 8½" × 11" sheets (half size).

Problems 20·1 and 20·2. Develop the lateral surface of the truncated prism using the layout given. Read Art. 20·7.

Problems 20·3 to 20·8. Develop the lateral surface of the prism. Use layout of Prob. 20·1.

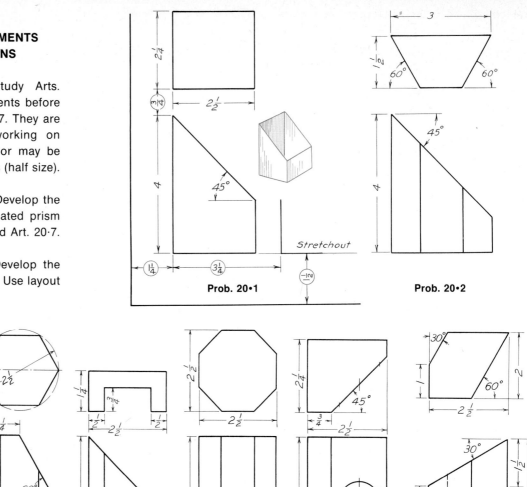

Prob. 20·1

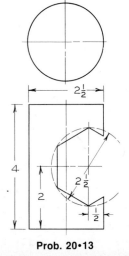

Prob. 20·2

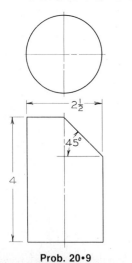
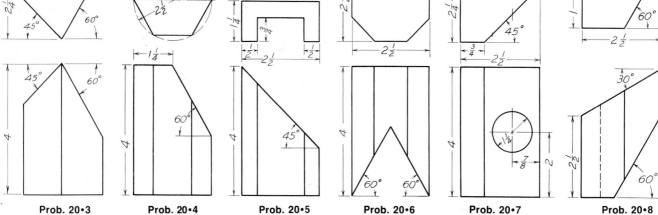

Prob. 20·3   Prob. 20·4   Prob. 20·5   Prob. 20·6   Prob. 20·7   Prob. 20·8

Problems 20·9 to 20·13. Develop the lateral surface of the cylinder. Read Art. 20·9.

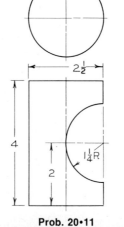

Prob. 20·9   Prob. 20·10   Prob. 20·11   Prob. 20·12   Prob. 20·13

Problems 20·14 to 20·27. Develop the surface.

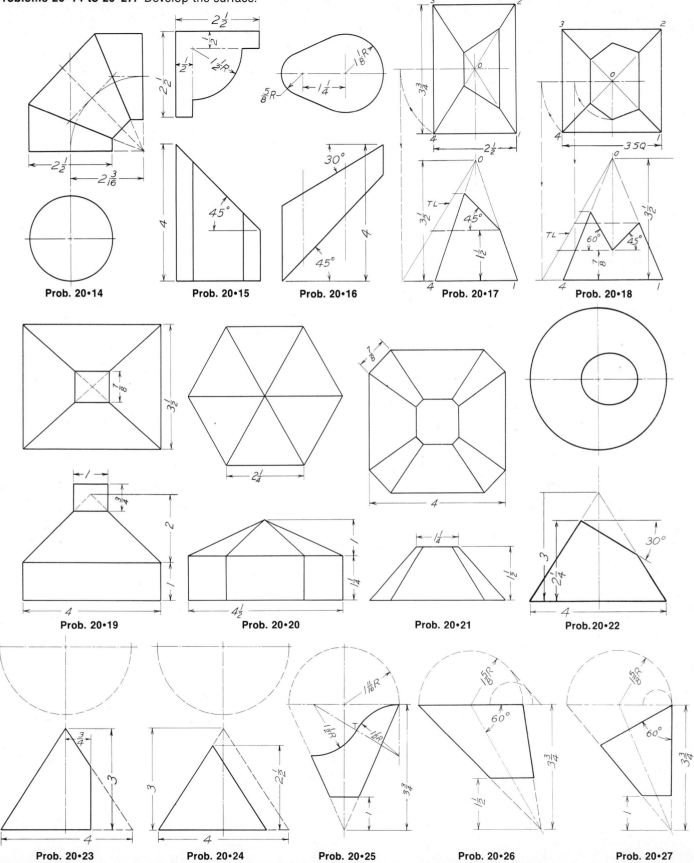

Prob. 20·14

Prob. 20·15

Prob. 20·16

Prob. 20·17

Prob. 20·18

Prob. 20·19

Prob. 20·20

Prob. 20·21

Prob. 20·22

Prob. 20·23

Prob. 20·24

Prob. 20·25

Prob. 20·26

Prob. 20·27

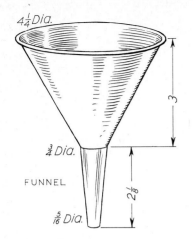

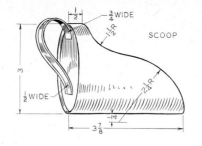

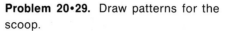

Problem 20·28. Draw patterns for the funnel.

SCOOP

Problem 20·29. Draw patterns for the scoop.

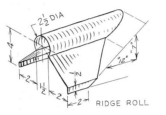

RIDGE ROLL

Problem 20·30. Draw the views and the pattern for the ridge roll.

CANDLESTICK

Problem 20·31. Draw patterns for the candlestick.

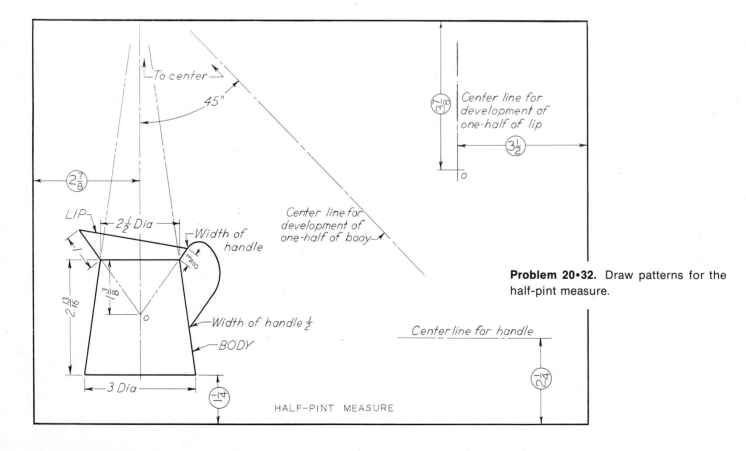

Problem 20·32. Draw patterns for the half-pint measure.

HALF-PINT MEASURE

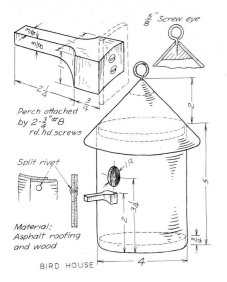

Perch attached
by 2-¾"#8
rd. hd screws

Split rivet

Material:
Asphalt roofing
and wood

BIRD HOUSE

Problem 20·33. Make a working drawing with patterns for the bird house.

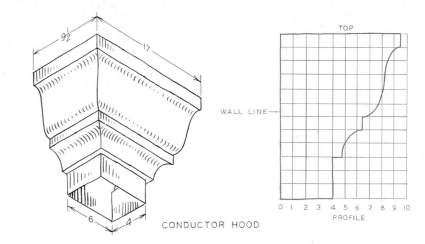

CONDUCTOR HOOD

TOP

WALL LINE

0 1 2 3 4 5 6 7 8 9 10
PROFILE

Problem 20·34. Draw the orthographic
views and the pattern for the conductor
head. Use a scale that will be suitable
for a standard-size sheet. Note that the
profile is defined by the outline on the
squared paper. Each square equals 1″.

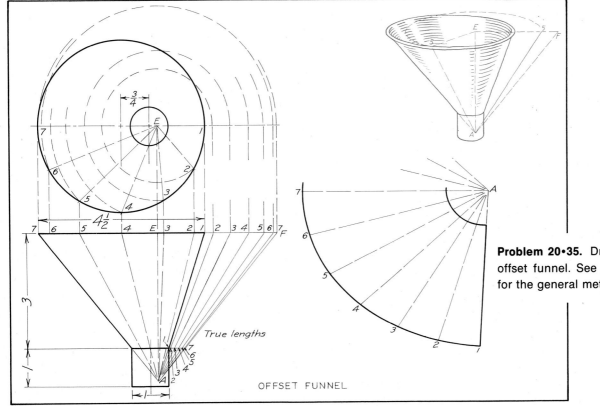

True lengths

OFFSET FUNNEL

Problem 20·35. Draw a pattern for the
offset funnel. See Arts. 20·15 to 20·21
for the general method of solution.

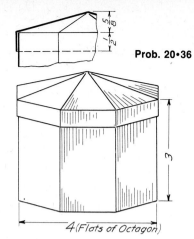

Prob. 20·36

Problem 20·36. Draw the views and the pattern for the jewel box.

4 (Flats of Octagon)

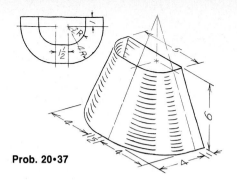

Prob. 20·37

Problem 20·37. Draw a pattern for the bed-lamp shade. Use a scale that will be suitable for a standard-size sheet.

26·38 Intersections. Study Arts. 20·24 to 20·31 on intersections before starting Probs. 20·38 to 20·60. First, observe the kinds of surfaces and the relative positions. Then, see where the limiting planes are needed. Find where the lines cut and locate the points on the lines of intersection, that is, where the lines cut from both surfaces by the same plane cross each other.

These problems are planned for convenient working on 11″ × 17″ sheets. Some may be worked on 8½″ × 11″ sheets.

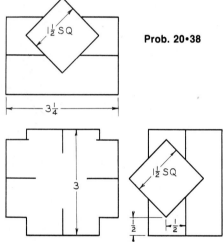

Prob. 20·38

1½ SQ

3¼

3

1½ SQ

Problem 20·38. Find the line of intersection between the two prisms.

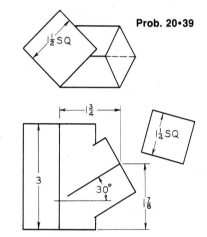

Prob. 20·39

1½ SQ

1¾

3

30°

7/8

1¼ SQ

Problem 20·39. Find the line of intersection between the two prisms.

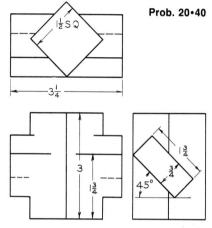

Prob. 20·40

1½ SQ

3¼

3

1¾

1¾

1¾

45°

Problem 20·40. Find the line of intersection between the two prisms.

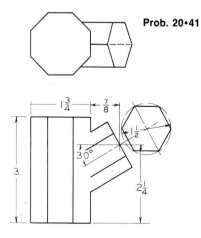

Prob. 20·41

1¾

7/8

30°

1½

3

2¼

Problem 20·41. Find the line of intersection between the two prisms.

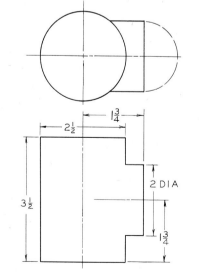

1¾

2½

2 DIA

3½

1¾

Problem 20·42. Find the line of intersection between the two cylinders.

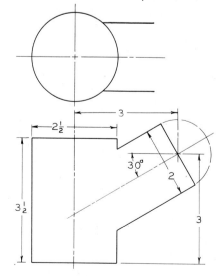

3

2½

30°

2

3½

3

Problem 20·43. Find the line of intersection between the two cylinders.

Problems 20·44 to 20·52. Find the line of intersection.

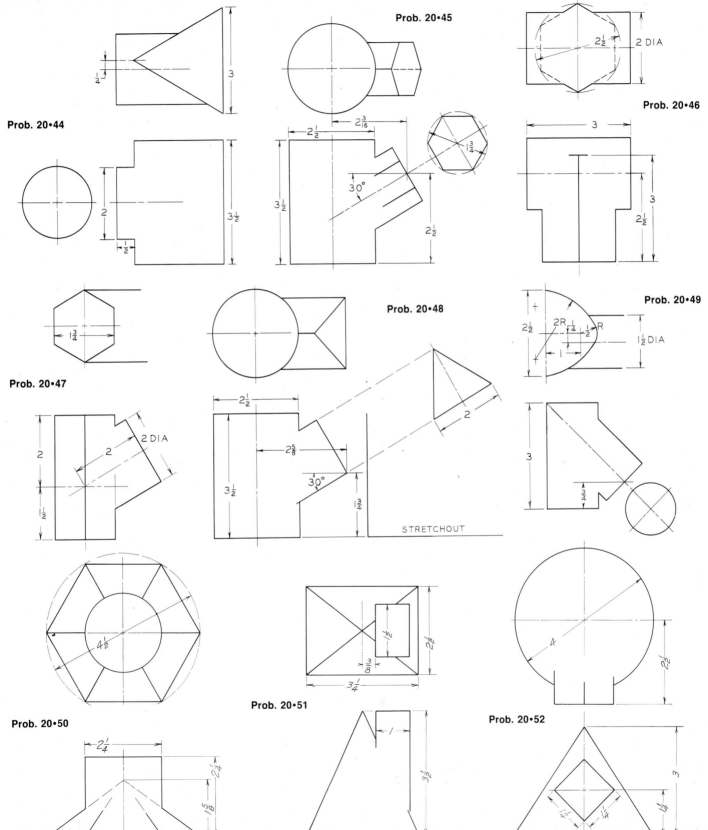

Prob. 20·45

Prob. 20·46

Prob. 20·44

Prob. 20·48

Prob. 20·49

Prob. 20·47

STRETCHOUT

Prob. 20·50

Prob. 20·51

Prob. 20·52

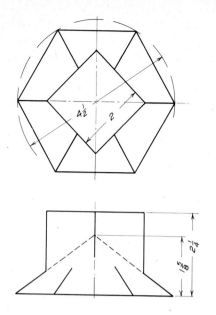
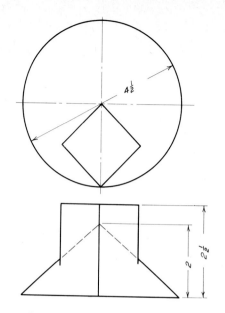
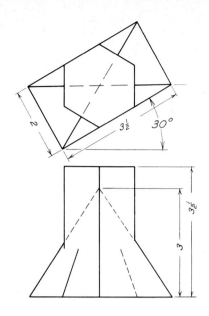

Problem 20·53. Find the line of intersection and develop the pyramid.

Problem 20·54. Find the line of intersection and develop the cone.

Problem 20·55. Find the line of intersection and develop the pyramid.

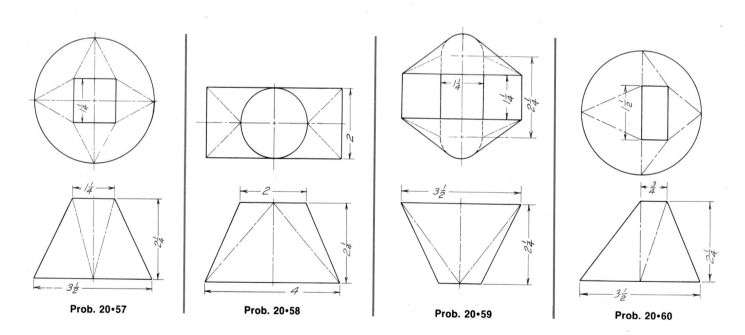

Prob. 20·57

Prob. 20·58

Prob. 20·59

Prob. 20·60

Problems 20·57 to 20·60. Develop the surface of the transition piece. Study Art. 20·23 carefully. Any of the intersection problems may be used for development by solving one problem on a sheet.

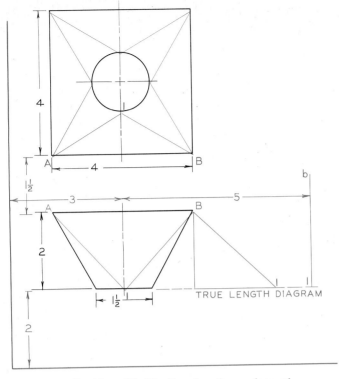

Problem 20•56. Develop the surface of the transition piece. Refer to Arts. 20·22 and 20·23.

GROUP 21.
ARCHITECTURAL DRAWINGS

26•39 The reading and making of house plans are important parts of mechanical drawing. Several houses under construction should be visited at different stages of completion and compared with the working drawings. Study Chap. 21 carefully; see also the set of plans for Prob. 21·30, before starting the problems in this group. Most of the architectural drawing problems are for working on an 11″ × 17″ sheet, but check size required before starting a problem.

Exercises for lettering practice are given in Group 3 where Probs. 3·21 to 3·29 are specifically designed for architectural lettering.

Problem 21•1 (Fig. 21-16b). Turn the sheet with the long dimension vertical. Make an isometric drawing showing balloon framing. Select a suitable scale. Studs and floor joists to be spaced 16″ center to center. Use 2″ × 4″ studs and 2″ × 8″ floor joists.

Problem 21•2 (Fig. 21-16a). Turn the sheet with the long dimension vertical. Make an isometric drawing showing western framing. Select a suitable scale. Studs and floor joists to be spaced 16″ center to center. Use 2″ × 4″ studs and 2″ × 8″ floor joists.

Problem 21•3 (Figs. 21-18a and 21-18b). In the left-hand half of the sheet make a drawing showing a box sill for wood siding. In the right-hand half of the sheet make a drawing showing a box sill for brick veneer.

Problem 21•4. Same as Prob. 21·3 but for the sills shown in Figs. 21-18c and 21-18d.

Problem 21•5. Same as Prob. 21·3 but for sills shown in Figs. 21-18e and 21-18f.

Problem 21•6. Same as Prob. 21·3 but for the sills shown in Figs. 21-18g and 21-18h (or Fig. 21-18i).

Problem 21•7 (Fig. 21-19a). Make a drawing showing diagonal sheathing. Select a suitable scale to show the construction clearly.

Problem 21•8 (Fig. 21-19b). Make a drawing showing horizontal sheathing. Select a suitable scale to show the construction clearly.

Problem 21•9 (Figs. 21-20b to 21-20g). Make a drawing to show two of the cornices illustrated, one in the left-hand half of the sheet and the other in the right-hand half. Select a scale to show the construction clearly.

Problem 21•10. Draw a stair layout similar to the plan and elevations of Fig. 21-21 for a floor-to-floor height of 9′–4″.

Problem 21•11 (Fig. 21-22). Draw details for a fireplace.

Problem 21•12 (Fig. 21-23b). Turn the sheet with the long dimension vertical. Make a drawing of a window with the sash in place showing the framing. Draw an elevation, a vertical section at one side and a horizontal section below.

Problem 21·13 (Fig. 21-23c). Draw detail sections for a double hung window in a brick veneer wall. Use scale of $3'' = 1'-0''$, or larger, and select a suitable-size sheet.

Problem 21·14. Same as Prob. 21·13 but for a masonry wall. Refer to Fig. 21-23d. Use scale of $3'' = 1'-0''$, or larger, and select a suitable-size sheet.

Problem 21·15 (Fig. 21-24a). Make drawings of two of the doors shown. Place them side by side.

Problem 21·16 (Fig. 21-24b). Turn the sheet with the long dimension vertical and make a drawing for door framing details. Show an elevation, a vertical section at one side and a horizontal section below.

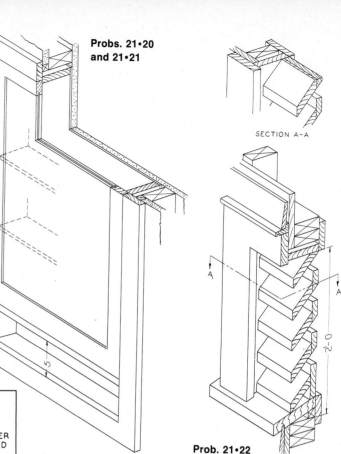

Probs. 21·20 and 21·21

SECTION A-A

Prob. 21·22

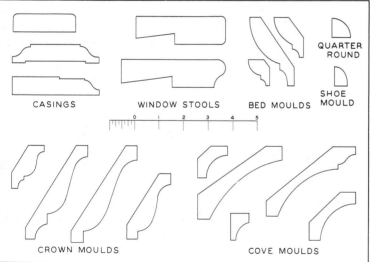

CASINGS

WINDOW STOOLS

BED MOULDS

QUARTER ROUND

SHOE MOULD

CROWN MOULDS

COVE MOULDS

Problem 21·17. Draw full size profiles (sections) of the trim and molding shown. Obtain dimensions from the scale ($11'' \times 17''$ sheet).

Problem 21·20. Make a working drawing of a medicine cabinet including the framing. Inside of closed part to be $1'-9''$ wide and $2'-4''$ high. Show a front elevation and a vertical section. Back of cabinet may be $\frac{1}{8}''$ presswood.

Problem 21·21. Same as Prob. 21·20 but without the open space. Assume a suitable size.

Problem 21·18. Make a drawing of a typical wall section similar to that shown on sheet 4 of illustrations for Prob. 21·30 but for a brick veneer wall and box cornice. Turn sheet with long dimension vertical.

Problem 21·19. Make a drawing of a typical wall section similar to that shown on sheet 4 of illustrations for Prob. 21·30 but for a stucco wall and cornice with exposed rafters. Turn sheet with long dimension vertical.

Problem 21·22. Make a working drawing of a louver to go between studs that are 16'' on centers. Show framing and give necessary dimensions. Select suitable scale and views. Show framing separate from louver.

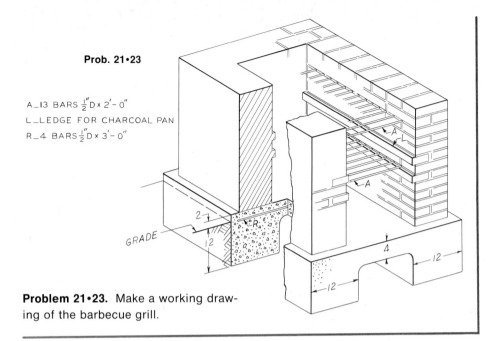

Prob. 21·23

A__I3 BARS ½"D x 2'-0"
L__LEDGE FOR CHARCOAL PAN
R__4 BARS ½"D x 3'-0"

Problem 21·23. Make a working drawing of the barbecue grill.

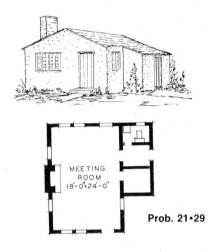

Problem 21·28. Make a bathroom plan showing the size and location of plumbing fixtures. Refer to manufacturer's catalog for sizes and styles of fixtures.

MEETING ROOM 18'-0"x24'-0"

Prob. 21·29

Problem 21·29. Draw a floor plan, foundation plan, and elevations for the club house. No basement. Piers to be placed inside of the foundation where needed to support a central lengthwise girder.

Prob. 21·24

Prob. 21·25

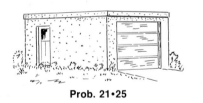

Prob. 21·26

Problems 21·24 to 21·26. Draw plan and elevations for one of the garages. Size to be specified by the instructor. Refer to current descriptive circulars for overall dimensions of automobiles.

Problem 21·27. Make a kitchen plan showing the size and location of both movable and built-in features. Refer to catalogs and trade literature for necessary information.

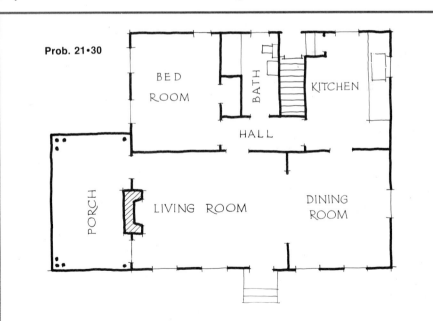

Prob. 21·30

BED ROOM

BATH

KITCHEN

HALL

PORCH

LIVING ROOM

DINING ROOM

Problem 21·30. Make a set of plans for the house illustrated in the sketch and the set of plans on sheets 1 to 5 of the illustrations marked Prob. 21·30. (Sheets 1 to 5 are on pages 544 to 546.)

Prob. 21·30. Pen-and-ink perspective of a house.

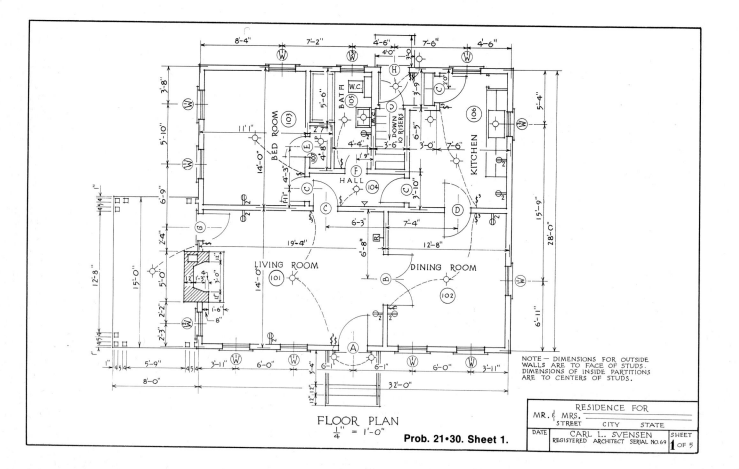

FLOOR PLAN

$\frac{1}{4}'' = 1'-0''$

Prob. 21·30. Sheet 1.

NOTE — DIMENSIONS FOR OUTSIDE WALLS ARE TO FACE OF STUDS. DIMENSIONS OF INSIDE PARTITIONS ARE TO CENTERS OF STUDS.

RESIDENCE FOR
MR. & MRS. _____
STREET   CITY   STATE
DATE   CARL L. SVENSEN
REGISTERED ARCHITECT SERIAL NO.69
SHEET 1 OF 5

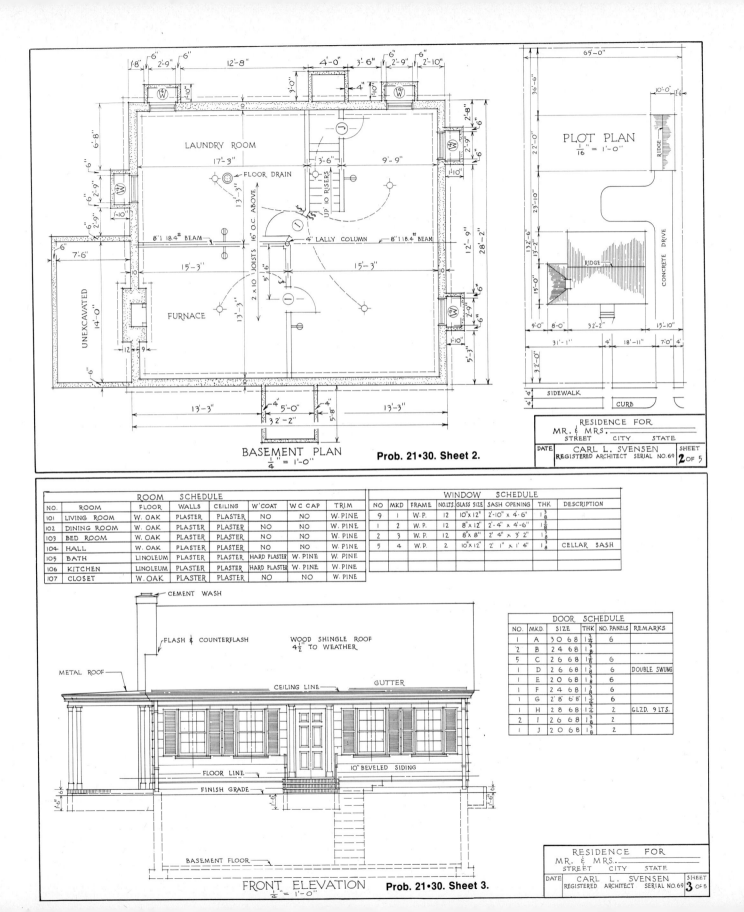

BASEMENT PLAN
¼" = 1'-0"   Prob. 21·30. Sheet 2.

PLOT PLAN
1/16" = 1'-0"

FRONT ELEVATION   ¼" = 1'-0"   Prob. 21·30. Sheet 3.

RESIDENCE FOR
MR. & MRS._____
STREET   CITY   STATE
DATE   CARL L. SVENSEN
REGISTERED ARCHITECT   SERIAL NO. 69
SHEET 2 OF 5

RESIDENCE FOR
MR. & MRS._____
STREET   CITY   STATE
DATE   CARL L. SVENSEN
REGISTERED ARCHITECT   SERIAL NO. 69
SHEET 3 OF 5

ROOM SCHEDULE

NO.	ROOM	FLOOR	WALLS	CEILING	W'COAT	WC CAP	TRIM
101	LIVING ROOM	W. OAK	PLASTER	PLASTER	NO	NO	W. PINE
102	DINING ROOM	W. OAK	PLASTER	PLASTER	NO	NO	W. PINE
103	BED ROOM	W. OAK	PLASTER	PLASTER	NO	NO	W. PINE
104	HALL	W. OAK	PLASTER	PLASTER	NO	NO	W. PINE
105	BATH	LINOLEUM	PLASTER	PLASTER	HARD PLASTER	W. PINE	W. PINE
106	KITCHEN	LINOLEUM	PLASTER	PLASTER	HARD PLASTER	W. PINE	W. PINE
107	CLOSET	W. OAK	PLASTER	PLASTER	NO	NO	W. PINE

WINDOW SCHEDULE

NO	MKD	FRAME	NO.LTS.	GLASS SIZE	SASH OPENING	THK	DESCRIPTION
9	1	W. P.	12	10"x12"	2'-10" x 4'-6"	1 3/8	
1	2	W. P.	12	8"x12"	2'-4" x 4'-6"	1 3/8	
2	3	W. P.	12	8"x 8"	2'-4" x 3'-2"	1 3/8	
5	4	W. P.	2	10"x12"	2'-1" x 1'-4"	1 3/8	CELLAR SASH

DOOR SCHEDULE

NO.	MKD.	SIZE	THK	NO. PANELS	REMARKS
1	A	3068	1 3/4	6	
2	B	2468	1 3/8	6	
5	C	2668	1 3/8	6	
1	D	2668	1 3/8	6	DOUBLE SWUNG
1	E	2068	1 3/8	6	
1	F	2468	1 3/8	6	
1	G	2'8 6'8	1 3/8	6	
1	H	2868	1 3/4	2	GLZD. 9 LTS.
2	I	2668	1 3/8	2	
1	J	2068	1 3/8	2	

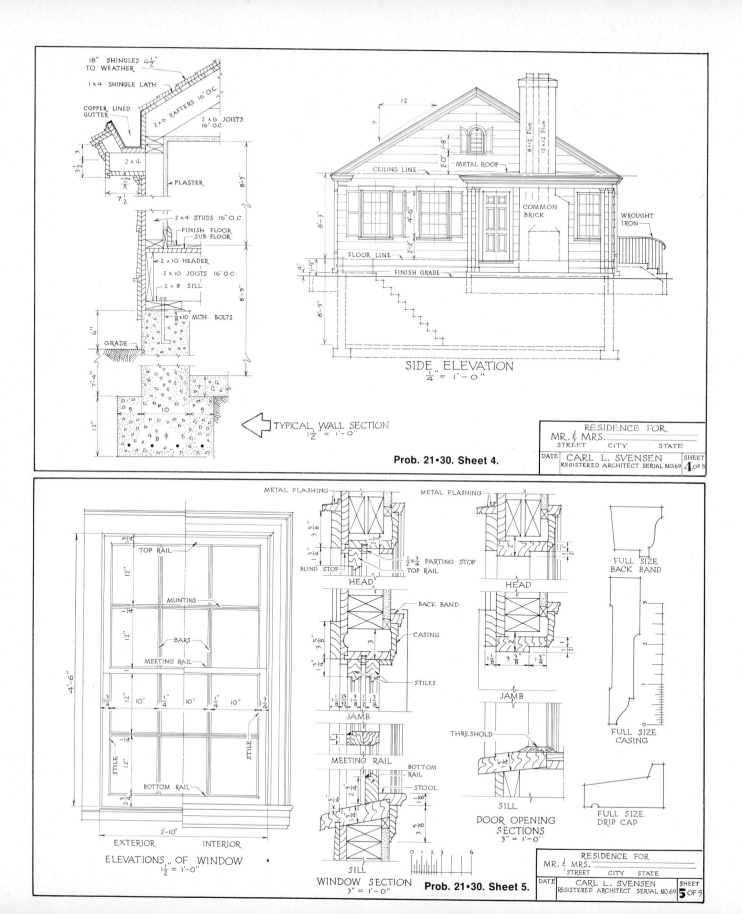

TYPICAL WALL SECTION
$\frac{1}{2}" = 1'-0"$

18" SHINGLES $4\frac{1}{2}"$ TO WEATHER

1×4 SHINGLE LATH

COPPER LINED GUTTER

2×6 RAFTERS 16" O.C.

2×6 JOISTS 16" O.C.

2×4

PLASTER

2×4 STUDS 16" O.C.

FINISH FLOOR
SUB FLOOR

2×10 HEADER

2×10 JOISTS 16" O.C.

2×8 SILL

$\frac{5}{8}×10$ MCH. BOLTS

GRADE

SIDE ELEVATION
$\frac{1}{4}" = 1'-0"$

CEILING LINE

METAL ROOF

COMMON BRICK

WROUGHT IRON

FLOOR LINE

FINISH GRADE

8×12 Flue

12×12 Flue

Prob. 21·30. Sheet 4.

RESIDENCE FOR
MR. & MRS. _____
STREET   CITY   STATE
DATE   CARL L. SVENSEN
REGISTERED ARCHITECT SERIAL NO.69
SHEET 4 OF 5

ELEVATIONS OF WINDOW
$1\frac{1}{2}" = 1'-0"$

TOP RAIL

MUNTINS

BARS

MEETING RAIL

STILE

STILE

BOTTOM RAIL

EXTERIOR   INTERIOR

METAL FLASHING

METAL FLASHING

BLIND STOP

$\frac{1}{2}×\frac{3}{4}$ PARTING STOP

TOP RAIL

HEAD

HEAD

BACK BAND

CASING

STILES

JAMB

JAMB

MEETING RAIL

BOTTOM RAIL

STOOL

THRESHOLD

SILL

DOOR OPENING SECTIONS
$3" = 1'-0"$

FULL SIZE BACK BAND

FULL SIZE CASING

FULL SIZE DRIP CAP

SILL

WINDOW SECTION
$3" = 1'-0"$

Prob. 21·30. Sheet 5.

RESIDENCE FOR
MR. & MRS. _____
STREET   CITY   STATE
DATE   CARL L. SVENSEN
REGISTERED ARCHITECT   SERIAL NO.69
SHEET 5 OF 5

Problem 21·31. Refer to Figs. 21-29, 21-30a, 21-30b, 21-31, 21-32, 21-33, 21-34, and 21-35a. Make a set of plans as illustrated or of such drawings as may be designated by your instructor, with or without changes.

Problem 21·32. Same as Prob. 21·30 but without a basement. Refer also to Fig. 21-35b.

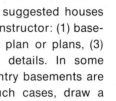

Prob. 21·33

Prob. 21·34

Problems 21·33 to 21·37. Make drawings for one of the suggested houses as directed by your instructor: (1) basement plan, (2) floor plan or plans, (3) elevations, and (4) details. In some sections of the country basements are seldom used. In such cases, draw a foundation plan instead of a basement plan. Piers or a slab foundation may be used.

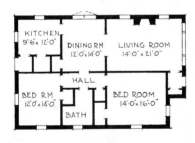

Prob. 21·35

Prob. 21·36

Prob. 21·37

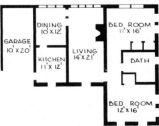

Problems 21•38 and 21•39. Make drawings for one of the suggested houses as directed by your instructor: (1) basement plan, (2) floor plan or plans, (3) elevations, and (4) details. In some sections of the country basements are seldom used. In such cases, draw a foundation plan instead of a basement plan. Piers or a slab foundation may be used.

Prob. 21•38

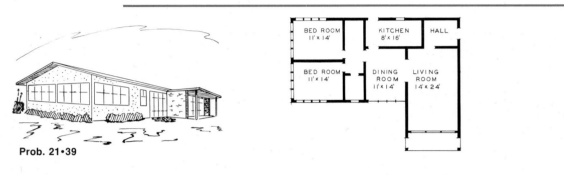

Prob. 21•39

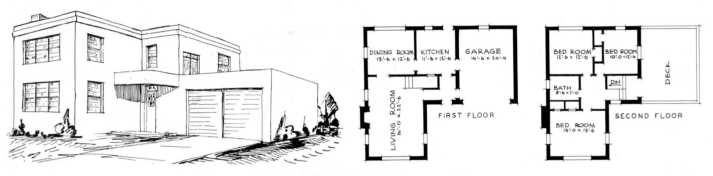

Problem 21•40. Make plans to remodel the house shown.

Problem 21•41. Make plans to remodel the house shown.

Problem 21•42 (Fig. 21-23h). Make a drawing for the casement window details. Select a suitable scale and size of sheet.

Problem 21•43 (Fig. 21-24c). Make a drawing of the entrance details. Select a suitable scale and size of sheet.

Problem 21•44 (Figs. 21-2a and 21-2b). Make a set of plans for the house illustrated, as specified by the instructor.

Prob. 21•45

Prob. 21•46

Prob. 21•47

Prob. 21•48

Prob. 21•49

Prob. 21•50

Prob. 21•51

Prob. 21•52

Problems 21•45 to 21•52. Make floor plans to suit the exterior of one of the houses illustrated, as specified by the instructor.

GROUP 22.
STRUCTURAL DRAWINGS

26•40 Read Chap. 22 before starting these problems. Select a proper scale and size of sheet. Structural drafting is a specialized field and requires some knowledge of structural design. A few problems are presented here to give a general idea of this branch of drafting.

Problem 22•1 (Fig. 22-2a). Make a drawing of the structural-steel shapes shown.

Problem 22•2 (Fig. 22-3a). Make a drawing showing the rivet symbols. Rearrange to make a good appearing sheet.

Problem 22•3 (Fig. 22-8). Make a drawing of the structural-steel detail shown. Consult a structural-steel handbook. Scale: $3/4'' = 1'-0''$.

Problem 22•4 (Fig. 22-7a). Make a structural drawing of the truss shown. Consult a structural-steel handbook. Scales: $3/4'' = 1'-0''$ and $1\frac{1}{2}'' = 1'-0''$.

Problem 22•5 (Fig. 22-10a). Make a drawing of the reinforced-concrete detail shown. Scale: $1\frac{1}{2}'' = 1'-0''$.

GROUP 23.   MAP DRAFTING

26•41 Study Chap. 23 before starting these problems. The size of the required working space is specified for most of the problems. The use of a good quality of tracing paper or tracing cloth is advised.

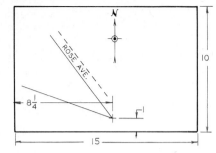

Problem 23•1. Make a drawing of a plat of a survey as shown in Fig. 23-3. Use a working space of 11″ × 15″. Scale: 1″ = 100′. Start the lowest point 8¼″ from the left border and 1½″ up from the bottom border. Use a protractor (Fig. 2-14b) to lay out the angles and a civil engineer's scale (Fig. 2-26) to lay off the distances.

Problem 23•2. Make a city map as shown in Fig. 23-4. Working space: 6⅛″ × 14″. Use dividers to transfer and enlarge sufficient distances from Fig. 23-4 to draw two times the size in the book, or use the graphical scale to obtain measurements and draw to scale of 1″ = 200′.

Problem 23•3. Lay out the tract of land in Prob. 23-1, or trace Prob. 23-1 and divide it into residential lots. Plan most lots with 75-foot frontage and 150 feet or more depth. Rose Avenue is a main thoroughfare along the northeast side of the tract. Use a working space of at least 11″ × 15″. Scale: 1″ = 100′. Provide necessary 40-foot streets.

Problem 23•4. Plot the boundary line by means of bearings for the following survey. Working space: 10″ × 15″. Scale: 1″ = 200′. Locate point 1 at 2″ from left border and up ⅜″ from bottom border.

Course	1–2	2–3	3–4	4–1
Distance	1801.5	1235.0	1775.6	To close
Bearing	East	N12°-30E	N74°-15W	To close

Find the bearing and length of the closing line, 4–1, from your plat.

Problem 23•5. Lay out the tract of land in Prob. 23-1, or trace Prob. 23-1, and divide it into residential lots. Plan most lots with 80-foot, or more, frontage and depth of 200 feet, or more. There are streets along side. Use a working space of 10″ × 15″. Scale: 1″ = 200′. Provide necessary 60-foot streets.

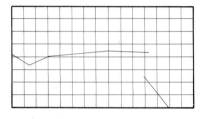

Problem 23•6. Make an operations map as shown in Fig. 23-5. Draw a grid sheet on tracing paper over Fig. 23-5 in the book and trace the figure. Short marks along the border lines are to assist in drawing the small tracing grid. Using an enlarged grid drawn with light, thin lines, redraw the figure in an 8″ × 15″ working space. Note that a metric scale of kilometers is used. Scale is 1:250000. The graphic scale on the original drawing shows 8 centimeters equals 20 kilometers, or 1 centimeter equals 2.5 kilometers (1 kilometer = 0.621 mile and 1 inch equals 2.54 centimeters).

Problem 23•7. Make a contour drawing with profile as shown in Fig. 23-6a. Use a working space of 8½″ × 12½″. Draw two times size shown in the figure. Use dividers or a grid to enlarge the figure (vertical profile scale: 1″ = 20′; horizontal scale: 1″ = 500′).

Problem 23•8. Make a contour drawing as shown in Fig. 23-6a, or trace Prob. 23-7, but take the profile on line B-B or C-C as directed by your instructor. Space 8½″ × 12½″. Draw two times the size shown in the figure. Profile scale: 1″ = 20′.

Problem 23•9. Make a contour drawing as shown in Fig. 23-7a. Draw a grid on the illustration. The short marks on the border are to assist in drawing the grids. Draw an enlarged grid of 1-in. squares for an 8″ × 11″ working space and locate points for drawing the contours.

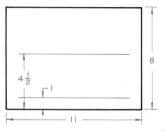

Problem 23•10. Using the drawing made for Prob. 23-9, draw two profiles as directed on horizontal grid lines (A-A and B-B), or (A-A and C-C), or (B-B and C-C). Space: 8″ × 11″. Vertical profile scale: 1″ = 60′. See layout.

Problems 23•11 and 23•12 are on page 551.

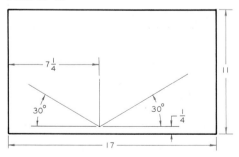

Problem 23•13. Make a block diagram. Develop the figure from the contour map drawn in Prob. 23-9. Space: 11″ × 17″. See layout. Vertical scale: 1″ = 200′.

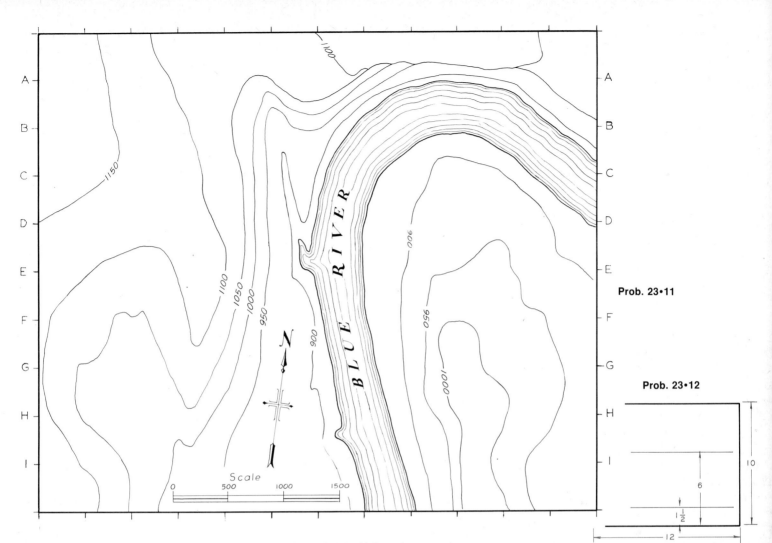

Prob. 23•11

Prob. 23•12

BLUE RIVER

Scale
0   500   1000   1500

Problem 23•11. Make a contour map as shown. Working space: 10″ × 12″. Use grids and dividers to enlarge the map.

Prob. 23•14

Problem 23•14. Draw the conventional symbols and letter them as in Fig. 23-8a. Space: 10″ × 15″. Make the small rectangles 1¾″ × 2″.

Problem 23•12. Using the map drawn for Prob. 23·11, draw two profiles taken on horizontal grid lines as designated by your instructor. Working space: 10″ × 12″. Vertical profile scale: 1″ = 100′.

Problem 23•15. Draw the symbols for Aerodromes and letter them as in Fig. 23-8b. Space: 7″ × 10″.

Problem 23•16. Draw the symbols and notes for Aerodrome Data and Landing Facilities Information (Fig. 23-8b). Space: 9″ × 10″.

Problem 23•17. Draw the symbols and notes for Air Navigation Lights (Fig. 23-8b). Space: 7″ × 10″.

Problem 23•18. Draw the symbols and notes shown under the heading "Miscellaneous" (Fig. 23-8b). Space: 7″ × 10″.

Problem 23•19. Make a geologic surface map as shown in Fig. 23-10. Use the coordinate system indicated and dividers to transfer and enlarge the map. Space: 9″ × 15″.

Problem 23•20. Make a geological section as shown in Fig. 23-11. Space: 10½″ × 15″. Use grids and dividers to enlarge to size specified. Vertical scale: 1:250. Horizontal scale: 1:10000.

Appendix

Military standards (MIL-STD)

Department of Defense Standardization Requirements for Engineering Drawing and Associated Documents. These are mandatory for use by the Departments of the Army, the Navy, and the Air Force. These standards are published in pamphlets which cover all phases of making and using engineering drawings by the Armed Services. Many are in complete or substantial agreement with American Standards. They are, of course, subject to revision as necessary.

American standards

A few standards are listed below that are useful for reference. Standards are subject to revisions and latest issues should be consulted. American Standards, with prices, is published by the American Standards Association, 10 East 40th Street, New York, N.Y., 10016.

Acme Screw Threads	B1.5
Buttress Screw Threads	B1.9
Graphical Electrical Symbols for Architectural Plans	Y32.9
Graphical Symbols for Electrical Diagrams	Y32.2
Graphical Symbols for Heating, Ventilating, and Air Conditioning	Z32.2.4
Graphical Symbols for Pipe Fittings, Valves, and Piping	Z32.2.3
Graphical Symbols for Plumbing	Y32.4
Graphical Symbols for Welding	Y32.3
Hexagon Head Cap Screws, Slotted Head Cap Screws, Square Head Set Screws, Slotted Headless Set Screws	B18.6.2
Pipe Threads	B2.1
Slotted and Recessed Head Screws	B18.6.1
Socket Head Cap Screws and Socket Set Screws	B18.3
Square and Hexagon Bolts and Nuts	B18.2
Stub Acme Screw Threads	B1.8
Unified and American Screw Threads for Screws, Bolts, Nuts, and Other Threaded Parts	B1.1
Woodruff Keys, Keyslots, and Cutters	B17f
American Drafting Standards Manual	
Section 1. Size and Format	Y14.1
Section 2. Line Conventions, Sectioning, and Lettering	Y14.2
Section 3. Projections	Y14.3
Section 4. Pictorial Drawing	Y14.4
Section 5. Dimensioning and Notes	Y14.5
Section 6. Screw Threads	Y14.6
Section 7. Gears, Splines, and Serrations	Y14.7
Section 8. Castings	Y14.8
Section 9. Forging	Y14.9
Section 10. Metal Stamping	Y14.10
Section 11. Plastics	Y14.11
Section 12. Die Castings	Y14.12
Section 13. Springs, Helical and Flat	Y14.13
Section 14. Mechanical Assemblies	Y14.14
Section 15. Electrical and Electronic Diagrams	Y14.15
Section 16. Tools, Dies, and Gages	Y14.16
Section 17. Fluid Power	Y14.17

Aerospace-automotive drawing standards

First edition issued in 1963. Published by The Society of Automotive Engineers, Inc., 485 Lexington Avenue, New York, N.Y., 10017. This is a comprehensive loose leaf volume of standards.

Metric System Equivalents

Length

Centimeter	=	0.3937 inch
Meter	=	3.28 feet
Meter	=	1.094 yards
Kilometer	=	0.621 statute mile
Kilometer	=	0.5400 Nautical mile
Inch	=	2.54 centimeters
Foot	=	0.3048 meter
Yard	=	0.9144 meter
Statute mile	=	1.61 kilometers
Nautical mile	=	1.852 kilometers

Area

Square centimeter	=	0.155 square inch
Square meter	=	10.76 square feet
Square meter	=	1.196 square yards
Hectare	=	2.47 acres
Square kilometer	=	0.386 square miles
Square inch	=	6.45 square centimeters
Square foot	=	0.0929 square meter
Square yard	=	0.836 square meter
Acre	=	0.405 hectare
Square mile	=	2.59 square kilometers

Volume

Cubic centimeter	=	0.0610 cubic inch
Cubic meter	=	35.3 cubic feet
Cubic meter	=	1.308 cubic yards
Cubic inch	=	16.39 cubic centimeters
Cubic foot	=	0.0283 cubic meter
Cubic yard	=	0.765 cubic meter

Capacity

Milliliter	=	0.0338 U.S. fluid ounce
Liter	=	1.057 U.S. liquid quarts
Liter	=	0.908 U.S. dry quart
U.S. fluid ounce	=	29.57 milliliters
U.S. liquid quart	=	0.946 liter
U.S. dry quart	=	1.101 liters

Mass or Weight

Gram	=	15.43 grains
Gram	=	0.0353 avoirdupois ounce
Kilogram	=	2.205 avoirdupois pounds
Metric ton	=	1.102 short, or net, tons
Grain	=	0.0648 gram
Avoirdupois ounce	=	28.35 grams
Avoirdupois pound	=	0.4536 kilogram
Short, or net, ton	=	0.907 metric ton

Metric Equivalents

Mm	In.*	Mm	In.	In.	Mm †	In.	Mm
1 = 0.0394		17 = 0.6693		$\frac{1}{32}$ = 0.794		$\frac{17}{32}$ = 13.493	
2 = 0.0787		18 = 0.7087		$\frac{1}{16}$ = 1.587		$\frac{9}{16}$ = 14.287	
3 = 0.1181		19 = 0.7480		$\frac{3}{32}$ = 2.381		$\frac{19}{32}$ = 15.081	
4 = 0.1575		20 = 0.7874		$\frac{1}{8}$ = 3.175		$\frac{5}{8}$ = 15.875	
5 = 0.1969		21 = 0.8268		$\frac{5}{32}$ = 3.968		$\frac{21}{32}$ = 16.668	
6 = 0.2362		22 = 0.8662		$\frac{3}{16}$ = 4.762		$\frac{11}{16}$ = 17.462	
7 = 0.2756		23 = 0.9055		$\frac{7}{32}$ = 5.556		$\frac{23}{32}$ = 18.256	
8 = 0.3150		24 = 0.9449		$\frac{1}{4}$ = 6.349		$\frac{3}{4}$ = 19.050	
9 = 0.3543		25 = 0.9843		$\frac{9}{32}$ = 7.144		$\frac{25}{32}$ = 19.843	
10 = 0.3937		26 = 1.0236		$\frac{5}{16}$ = 7.937		$\frac{13}{16}$ = 20.637	
11 = 0.4331		27 = 1.0630		$\frac{11}{32}$ = 8.731		$\frac{27}{32}$ = 21.431	
12 = 0.4724		28 = 1.1024		$\frac{3}{8}$ = 9.525		$\frac{7}{8}$ = 22.225	
13 = 0.5118		29 = 1.1418		$\frac{13}{32}$ = 10.319		$\frac{29}{32}$ = 23.018	
14 = 0.5512		30 = 1.1811		$\frac{7}{16}$ = 11.112		$\frac{15}{16}$ = 23.812	
15 = 0.5906		31 = 1.2205		$\frac{15}{32}$ = 11.906		$\frac{31}{32}$ = 24.606	
16 = 0.6299		32 = 1.2599		$\frac{1}{2}$ = 12.699		1 = 25.400	

* Calculated to *nearest* fourth decimal place.   † Calculated to *nearest* third decimal place

Source: Extracted from p. 713 of Thomas E. French and Charles J. Vierck, *Graphic Science*, McGraw-Hill Book Company, New York 1958.

Table 2. Decimal Equivalents of Common Fractions

$\frac{1}{64}$	0.015625	$\frac{17}{64}$	0.265625	$\frac{33}{64}$	0.515625	$\frac{49}{64}$	0.765625
$\frac{1}{32}$	0.03125	$\frac{9}{32}$	0.28125	$\frac{17}{32}$	0.53125	$\frac{25}{32}$	0.78125
$\frac{3}{64}$	0.046875	$\frac{19}{64}$	0.296875	$\frac{35}{64}$	0.546875	$\frac{51}{64}$	0.796875
$\frac{1}{16}$	0.0625	$\frac{5}{16}$	0.3125	$\frac{9}{16}$	0.5625	$\frac{13}{16}$	0.8125
$\frac{5}{64}$	0.078125	$\frac{21}{64}$	0.328125	$\frac{37}{64}$	0.578125	$\frac{53}{64}$	0.828125
$\frac{3}{32}$	0.09375	$\frac{11}{32}$	0.34375	$\frac{19}{32}$	0.59375	$\frac{27}{32}$	0.84375
$\frac{7}{64}$	0.109375	$\frac{23}{64}$	0.359375	$\frac{39}{64}$	0.609375	$\frac{55}{64}$	0.859375
$\frac{1}{8}$	0.1250	$\frac{3}{8}$	0.3750	$\frac{5}{8}$	0.6250	$\frac{7}{8}$	0.8750
$\frac{9}{64}$	0.140625	$\frac{25}{64}$	0.390625	$\frac{41}{64}$	0.640625	$\frac{57}{64}$	0.890625
$\frac{5}{32}$	0.15625	$\frac{13}{32}$	0.40625	$\frac{21}{32}$	0.65625	$\frac{29}{32}$	0.90625
$\frac{11}{64}$	0.171875	$\frac{27}{64}$	0.421875	$\frac{43}{64}$	0.671875	$\frac{59}{64}$	0.921875
$\frac{3}{16}$	0.1875	$\frac{7}{16}$	0.4375	$\frac{11}{16}$	0.6875	$\frac{15}{16}$	0.9375
$\frac{13}{64}$	0.203125	$\frac{29}{64}$	0.453125	$\frac{45}{64}$	0.703125	$\frac{61}{64}$	0.953125
$\frac{7}{32}$	0.21875	$\frac{15}{32}$	0.46875	$\frac{23}{32}$	0.71875	$\frac{31}{32}$	0.96875
$\frac{15}{64}$	0.234375	$\frac{31}{64}$	0.484375	$\frac{47}{64}$	0.734375	$\frac{63}{64}$	0.984375
$\frac{1}{4}$	0.2500	$\frac{1}{2}$	0.5000	$\frac{3}{4}$	0.7500	1	1.0000

Table 3.
Unified and American Thread Series

With Minor Diameters for Tap-drill Sizes

Diameter	Threads per inch		Tap-drill sizes	
	Coarse NC	Fine NF	Coarse NC	Fine NF
$\frac{1}{4}$	20	28	0.1959	0.2113
$\frac{5}{16}$	18	24	0.2524	0.2674
$\frac{3}{8}$	16	24	0.3073	0.3299
$\frac{7}{16}$	14	20	0.3602	0.3834
$\frac{1}{2}$*	13	..	0.4167	
$\frac{1}{2}$	12	20	0.4098	0.4459
$\frac{9}{16}$	12	18	0.4723	0.5024
$\frac{5}{8}$	11	18	0.5266	0.5649
$\frac{3}{4}$	10	16	0.6417	0.6823
$\frac{7}{8}$	9	14	0.7547	0.7977
1	8	12	0.8647	0.9098
$1\frac{1}{8}$	7	12	0.9704	1.0348
$1\frac{1}{4}$	7	12	1.0954	1.1598
$1\frac{3}{8}$	6	12	1.1946	1.2848
$1\frac{1}{2}$	6	12	1.3196	1.4098
$1\frac{3}{4}$	5	..	1.5335	
2	$4\frac{1}{2}$	..	1.7594	
$2\frac{1}{4}$	$4\frac{1}{2}$	..	2.0094	
$2\frac{1}{2}$	4	..	2.2294	
$2\frac{3}{4}$	4	..	2.4794	
3	4	..	2.7294	
$3\frac{1}{4}$	4	..	2.9794	
$3\frac{1}{2}$	4	..	3.2294	
$3\frac{3}{4}$	4	..	3.4794	
4	4	..	3.7294	

* Not Unified.

Source: Extracted from American Standard *Unified and American Screw Threads for Screws, Bolts, Nuts, and Other Threaded Parts* (ASA B1.1–1960), with the permission of the publisher, The American Society of Mechanical Engineers.

Table 4. Sizes of Numbered and Lettered Drills

No.	Size	No.	Size	No.	Size	Letter	Size
80	0.0135	53	0.0595	26	0.1470	A	0.2340
79	0.0145	52	0.0635	25	0.1495	B	0.2380
78	0.0160	51	0.0670	24	0.1520	C	0.2420
77	0.0180	50	0.0700	23	0.1540	D	0.2460
76	0.0200	49	0.0730	22	0.1570	E	0.2500
75	0.0210	48	0.0760	21	0.1590	F	0.2570
74	0.0225	47	0.0785	20	0.1610	G	0.2610
73	0.0240	46	0.0810	19	0.1660	H	0.2660
72	0.0250	45	0.0820	18	0.1695	I	0.2720
71	0.0260	44	0.0860	17	0.1730	J	0.2770
70	0.0280	43	0.0890	16	0.1770	K	0.2810
69	0.0292	42	0.0935	15	0.1800	L	0.2900
68	0.0310	41	0.0960	14	0.1820	M	0.2950
67	0.0320	40	0.0980	13	0.1850	N	0.3020
66	0.0330	39	0.0995	12	0.1890	O	0.3160
65	0.0350	38	0.1015	11	0.1910	P	0.3230
64	0.0360	37	0.1040	10	0.1935	Q	0.3320
63	0.0370	36	0.1065	9	0.1960	R	0.3390
62	0.0380	35	0.1100	8	0.1990	S	0.3480
61	0.0390	34	0.1110	7	0.2010	T	0.3580
60	0.0400	33	0.1130	6	0.2040	U	0.3680
59	0.0410	32	0.1160	5	0.2055	V	0.3770
58	0.0420	31	0.1200	4	0.2090	W	0.3860
57	0.0430	30	0.1285	3	0.2130	X	0.3970
56	0.0465	29	0.1360	2	0.2210	Y	0.4040
55	0.0520	28	0.1405	1	0.2280	Z	0.4130
54	0.0550	27	0.1440				

Source: Extracted from p. 718 of Thomas E. French and Charles J. Vierck, *Graphic Science*, McGraw-Hill Book Company, New York, 1958.

Table 5. Acme and Stub Acme Threads*

ASA-preferred diameter-pitch combinations

Nominal (major) diam.	Threads/in.	Nominal (major) diam.	Threads/in.	Nominal (major) diam.	Threads/in.	Nominal (major) diam.	Threads/in.
$\frac{1}{4}$	16	$\frac{3}{4}$	6	$1\frac{1}{2}$	4	3	2
$\frac{5}{16}$	14	$\frac{7}{8}$	6	$1\frac{3}{4}$	4	$3\frac{1}{2}$	2
$\frac{3}{8}$	12	1	5	2	4	4	2
$\frac{7}{16}$	12	$1\frac{1}{8}$	5	$2\frac{1}{4}$	3	$4\frac{1}{2}$	2
$\frac{1}{2}$	10	$1\frac{1}{4}$	5	$2\frac{1}{2}$	3	5	2
$\frac{5}{8}$	8	$1\frac{3}{8}$	4	$2\frac{3}{4}$	3		

* ASA B1.5 and B1.8–1952. Diameters in inches.

Source: Extracted from p. 718 of Thomas E. French and Charles J. Vierck, *Graphic Science*, McGraw-Hill Book Company, New York, 1958.

Table 6. American Standard Regular Hexagon Bolts

Diameter	Flats	Height		
		Unfinished	Semi-finished	Finished
$\frac{1}{4}$	$\frac{7}{16}$	$\frac{11}{64}$	$\frac{5}{32}$	$\frac{5}{32}$
$\frac{5}{16}$	$\frac{1}{2}$	$\frac{7}{32}$	$\frac{13}{64}$	$\frac{13}{64}$
$\frac{3}{8}$	$\frac{9}{16}$	$\frac{1}{4}$	$\frac{15}{64}$	$\frac{15}{64}$
$\frac{7}{16}$	$\frac{5}{8}$	$\frac{19}{64}$	$\frac{9}{32}$	$\frac{9}{32}$
$\frac{1}{2}$	$\frac{3}{4}$	$\frac{11}{32}$	$\frac{5}{16}$	$\frac{5}{16}$
$\frac{9}{16}$	$\frac{13}{16}$	....	....	$\frac{23}{64}$
$\frac{5}{8}$	$\frac{15}{16}$	$\frac{27}{64}$	$\frac{25}{64}$	$\frac{25}{64}$
$\frac{3}{4}$	$1\frac{1}{8}$	$\frac{1}{2}$	$\frac{15}{32}$	$\frac{15}{32}$
$\frac{7}{8}$	$1\frac{5}{16}$	$\frac{37}{64}$	$\frac{35}{64}$	$\frac{35}{64}$
1	$1\frac{1}{2}$	$\frac{43}{64}$	$\frac{39}{64}$	$\frac{39}{64}$
$1\frac{1}{8}$	$1\frac{11}{16}$	$\frac{3}{4}$	$\frac{11}{16}$	$\frac{11}{16}$
$1\frac{1}{4}$	$1\frac{7}{8}$	$\frac{27}{32}$	$\frac{25}{32}$	$\frac{25}{32}$
$1\frac{3}{8}$	$2\frac{1}{16}$	$\frac{29}{32}$	$\frac{27}{32}$	$\frac{27}{32}$
$1\frac{1}{2}$	$2\frac{1}{4}$	1	$\frac{15}{16}$	$\frac{15}{16}$
$1\frac{3}{4}$	$2\frac{5}{8}$	$1\frac{5}{32}$	$1\frac{3}{32}$	$1\frac{3}{32}$
2	3	$1\frac{11}{32}$	$1\frac{7}{32}$	$1\frac{7}{32}$
$2\frac{1}{4}$	$3\frac{3}{8}$	$1\frac{1}{2}$	$1\frac{3}{8}$	$1\frac{3}{8}$
$2\frac{1}{2}$	$3\frac{3}{4}$	$1\frac{21}{32}$	$1\frac{17}{32}$	$1\frac{17}{32}$
$2\frac{3}{4}$	$4\frac{1}{8}$	$1\frac{13}{16}$	$1\frac{11}{16}$	$1\frac{11}{16}$
3	$4\frac{1}{2}$	2	$1\frac{7}{8}$	$1\frac{7}{8}$
$3\frac{1}{4}$	$4\frac{7}{8}$	$2\frac{3}{16}$	2	
$3\frac{1}{2}$	$5\frac{1}{4}$	$2\frac{5}{16}$	$2\frac{1}{8}$	
$3\frac{3}{4}$	$5\frac{5}{8}$	$2\frac{1}{2}$	$2\frac{5}{16}$	
4	6	$2\frac{11}{16}$	$2\frac{1}{2}$	

Source: Extracted from American Standard Square and Hexagon Bolts and Nuts (ASA B18.2–1960), with the permission of the publisher, The American Society of Mechanical Engineers.

[handwritten note: Slightly bigger than across corners]

Table 7. American Standard Regular Hexagonal Nuts

Diameter	Unfinished		Semifinished		Finished	
	Flats	Thickness	Flats	Thickness	Flats	Thickness
$\frac{1}{4}$	$\frac{7}{16}$	$\frac{7}{32}$	$\frac{7}{16}$	$\frac{13}{64}$	$\frac{7}{16}$	$\frac{7}{32}$
$\frac{5}{16}$	$\frac{9}{16}$	$\frac{17}{64}$	$\frac{9}{16}$	$\frac{1}{4}$	$\frac{1}{2}$	$\frac{17}{64}$
$\frac{3}{8}$	$\frac{5}{8}$	$\frac{21}{64}$	$\frac{5}{8}$	$\frac{5}{16}$	$\frac{9}{16}$	$\frac{21}{64}$
$\frac{7}{16}$	$\frac{3}{4}$	$\frac{3}{8}$	$\frac{3}{4}$	$\frac{23}{64}$	$\frac{11}{16}$	$\frac{3}{8}$
$\frac{1}{2}$	$\frac{13}{16}$	$\frac{7}{16}$	$\frac{13}{16}$	$\frac{27}{64}$	$\frac{3}{4}$	$\frac{7}{16}$
$\frac{9}{16}$	$\frac{7}{8}$	$\frac{1}{2}$	$\frac{7}{8}$	$\frac{31}{64}$	$\frac{7}{8}$	$\frac{31}{64}$
$\frac{5}{8}$	1	$\frac{35}{64}$	1	$\frac{17}{32}$	$\frac{15}{16}$	$\frac{35}{64}$
$\frac{3}{4}$	$1\frac{1}{8}$	$\frac{21}{32}$	$1\frac{1}{8}$	$\frac{41}{64}$	$1\frac{1}{8}$	$\frac{41}{64}$
$\frac{7}{8}$	$1\frac{5}{16}$	$\frac{49}{64}$	$1\frac{5}{16}$	$\frac{3}{4}$	$1\frac{5}{16}$	$\frac{3}{4}$
1	$1\frac{1}{2}$	$\frac{7}{8}$	$1\frac{1}{2}$	$\frac{55}{64}$	$1\frac{1}{2}$	$\frac{55}{64}$
$1\frac{1}{8}$	$1\frac{11}{16}$	1	$1\frac{11}{16}$	$\frac{31}{32}$	$1\frac{11}{16}$	$\frac{31}{32}$
$1\frac{1}{4}$	$1\frac{7}{8}$	$1\frac{3}{32}$	$1\frac{7}{8}$	$1\frac{1}{16}$	$1\frac{7}{8}$	$1\frac{1}{16}$
$1\frac{3}{8}$	$2\frac{1}{16}$	$1\frac{13}{64}$	$2\frac{1}{16}$	$11\frac{11}{64}$	$2\frac{1}{16}$	$1\frac{11}{64}$
$1\frac{1}{2}$	$2\frac{1}{4}$	$1\frac{5}{16}$	$2\frac{1}{4}$	$1\frac{9}{32}$	$2\frac{1}{4}$	$1\frac{9}{32}$
$1\frac{5}{8}$	...	...	$2\frac{7}{16}$	$1\frac{25}{64}$		
$1\frac{3}{4}$	...	...	$2\frac{5}{8}$	$1\frac{1}{2}$	$2\frac{5}{8}$	$1\frac{1}{2}$
$1\frac{7}{8}$	...	...	$2\frac{13}{16}$	$1\frac{39}{64}$		
2	...	...	3	$1\frac{23}{32}$	3	$1\frac{23}{32}$
$2\frac{1}{4}$	...	...	$3\frac{3}{8}$	$1\frac{59}{64}$	$3\frac{3}{8}$	$1\frac{59}{64}$
$2\frac{1}{2}$	...	...	$3\frac{3}{4}$	$2\frac{9}{64}$	$3\frac{3}{4}$	$2\frac{9}{64}$
$2\frac{3}{4}$	...	...	$4\frac{1}{8}$	$2\frac{23}{64}$	$4\frac{1}{8}$	$2\frac{23}{64}$
3	...	...	$4\frac{1}{2}$	$2\frac{37}{64}$	$4\frac{1}{2}$	$2\frac{37}{64}$

Table 8. American Standard Heavy Hexagon Bolts

Diameter	Flats Unfinished semi-finished finished	Height of head Unfinished	Height of head Semi-finished finished	Diameter	Flats Unfinished semi-finished finished	Height of head Unfinished	Height of head Semi-finished finished
$\frac{1}{2}$	$\frac{7}{8}$	$\frac{7}{16}$	$\frac{13}{32}$	$1\frac{5}{8}$	$2\frac{9}{16}$	$1\frac{9}{32}$	$1\frac{7}{32}$
$\frac{5}{8}$	$1\frac{1}{16}$	$\frac{17}{32}$	$\frac{1}{2}$	$1\frac{3}{4}$	$2\frac{3}{4}$	$1\frac{3}{8}$	$1\frac{5}{16}$
$\frac{3}{4}$	$1\frac{1}{4}$	$\frac{5}{8}$	$\frac{19}{32}$	$1\frac{7}{8}$	$2\frac{15}{16}$	$1\frac{15}{32}$	$1\frac{13}{32}$
$\frac{7}{8}$	$1\frac{7}{16}$	$\frac{23}{32}$	$\frac{11}{16}$	2	$3\frac{1}{8}$	$1\frac{9}{16}$	$1\frac{7}{16}$
1	$1\frac{5}{8}$	$\frac{13}{16}$	$\frac{3}{4}$	$2\frac{1}{4}$	$3\frac{1}{2}$	$1\frac{3}{4}$	$1\frac{5}{8}$
$1\frac{1}{8}$	$1\frac{13}{16}$	$\frac{29}{32}$	$\frac{27}{32}$	$2\frac{1}{2}$	$3\frac{7}{8}$	$1\frac{15}{16}$	$1\frac{13}{16}$
$1\frac{1}{4}$	2	1	$\frac{15}{16}$	$2\frac{3}{4}$	$4\frac{1}{4}$	$2\frac{1}{8}$	2
$1\frac{3}{8}$	$2\frac{3}{16}$	$1\frac{3}{32}$	$1\frac{3}{32}$	3	$4\frac{5}{8}$	$2\frac{5}{16}$	$2\frac{3}{16}$
$1\frac{1}{2}$	$2\frac{3}{8}$	$1\frac{3}{16}$	$1\frac{1}{8}$				

Table 9. American Standard Regular Square Bolts and Nuts

Diameter	Bolthead		Nut	
	Flats	Height of head	Flats	Thickness of nut
$\frac{1}{4}$	$\frac{3}{8}$	$\frac{11}{64}$	$\frac{7}{16}$	$\frac{7}{32}$
$\frac{5}{16}$	$\frac{1}{2}$	$\frac{13}{64}$	$\frac{9}{16}$	$\frac{17}{64}$
$\frac{3}{8}$	$\frac{9}{16}$	$\frac{1}{4}$	$\frac{5}{8}$	$\frac{21}{64}$
$\frac{7}{16}$	$\frac{5}{8}$	$\frac{19}{64}$	$\frac{3}{4}$	$\frac{3}{8}$
$\frac{1}{2}$	$\frac{3}{4}$	$\frac{21}{64}$	$\frac{13}{16}$	$\frac{7}{16}$
$\frac{5}{8}$	$\frac{15}{16}$	$\frac{27}{64}$	1	$\frac{35}{64}$
$\frac{3}{4}$	$1\frac{1}{8}$	$\frac{1}{2}$	$1\frac{1}{8}$	$\frac{21}{32}$
$\frac{7}{8}$	$1\frac{5}{16}$	$\frac{19}{32}$	$1\frac{5}{16}$	$\frac{49}{64}$
1	$1\frac{1}{2}$	$\frac{21}{32}$	$1\frac{1}{2}$	$\frac{7}{8}$
$1\frac{1}{8}$	$1\frac{11}{16}$	$\frac{3}{4}$	$1\frac{11}{16}$	1
$1\frac{1}{4}$	$1\frac{7}{8}$	$\frac{27}{32}$	$1\frac{7}{8}$	$1\frac{3}{32}$
$1\frac{3}{8}$	$2\frac{1}{16}$	$\frac{29}{32}$	$2\frac{1}{16}$	$1\frac{13}{64}$
$1\frac{1}{2}$	$2\frac{1}{4}$	1	$2\frac{1}{4}$	$1\frac{5}{16}$
$1\frac{5}{8}$	$2\frac{7}{16}$	$1\frac{3}{32}$		

Source: Extracted from American Standard Square and Hexagon Bolts and Nuts (ASA B18.2–1960), with the permission of the publisher, The American Society of Mechanical Engineers.

Source: Extracted from American Standard Square and Hexagon Bolts and Nuts (ASA B18.2–1960), with the permission of the publisher, The American Society of Mechanical Engineers.

Note: $1\frac{5}{8}$, $1\frac{7}{8}$ not in unfinished or semifinished bolts.

Source: Extracted from American Standard Square and Hexagon Bolts and Nuts (ASA B18.2–1960), with the permission of the publisher, The American Society of Mechanical Engineers.

Table 10. American Standard Heavy Nuts Square and Hexagon

Diameter	Flats — Unfinished semi-finished square and hexagon	Thickness of nut — Unfinished square and hexagon	Semi-finished hexagon
$\frac{1}{4}$	$\frac{1}{2}$	$\frac{1}{4}$	$\frac{15}{64}$
$\frac{5}{16}$	$\frac{9}{16}$	$\frac{5}{16}$	$\frac{19}{64}$
$\frac{3}{8}$	$\frac{11}{16}$	$\frac{3}{8}$	$\frac{23}{64}$
$\frac{7}{16}$	$\frac{3}{4}$	$\frac{7}{16}$	$\frac{27}{64}$
$\frac{1}{2}$	$\frac{7}{8}$	$\frac{1}{2}$	$\frac{31}{64}$
$\frac{9}{16}$	$1\frac{15}{16}$	....	$\frac{35}{64}$
$\frac{5}{8}$	$1\frac{1}{16}$	$\frac{5}{8}$	$\frac{39}{64}$
$\frac{3}{4}$	$1\frac{1}{4}$	$\frac{3}{4}$	$\frac{47}{64}$
$\frac{7}{8}$	$1\frac{7}{16}$	$\frac{7}{8}$	$\frac{55}{64}$
1	$1\frac{5}{8}$	1	$\frac{63}{64}$
$1\frac{1}{8}$	$1\frac{13}{16}$	$1\frac{1}{8}$	$1\frac{7}{64}$
$1\frac{1}{4}$	2	$1\frac{1}{4}$	$1\frac{7}{32}$
$1\frac{3}{8}$	$2\frac{3}{16}$	$1\frac{3}{8}$	$1\frac{11}{32}$
$1\frac{1}{2}$	$2\frac{3}{8}$	$1\frac{1}{2}$	$1\frac{15}{32}$
$1\frac{5}{8}$	$2\frac{9}{16}$	....	$1\frac{19}{32}$
$1\frac{3}{4}$	$2\frac{3}{4}$	$1\frac{3}{4}$	$1\frac{23}{32}$
$1\frac{7}{8}$	$2\frac{15}{16}$	....	$1\frac{27}{32}$
2	$3\frac{1}{8}$	2	$1\frac{31}{32}$
$2\frac{1}{4}$	$3\frac{1}{2}$	$2\frac{1}{4}$	$2\frac{13}{64}$
$2\frac{1}{2}$	$3\frac{7}{8}$	$2\frac{1}{2}$	$2\frac{29}{64}$
$2\frac{3}{4}$	$4\frac{1}{4}$	$2\frac{3}{4}$	$2\frac{45}{64}$
3	$4\frac{5}{8}$	3	$2\frac{61}{64}$
$3\frac{1}{4}$	5	$3\frac{1}{4}$	$3\frac{3}{16}$
$3\frac{1}{2}$	$5\frac{3}{8}$	$3\frac{1}{2}$	$3\frac{7}{16}$
$3\frac{3}{4}$	$5\frac{3}{4}$	$3\frac{3}{4}$	$3\frac{11}{16}$
4	$6\frac{1}{8}$	4	$3\frac{15}{16}$

Note: $\frac{9}{16}$, $1\frac{5}{8}$, $1\frac{7}{8}$ not in unfinished nuts.

Source: Extracted from American Standard *Square and Hexagon Bolts and Nuts* (ASA B18.2–1960), with the permission of the publisher, The American Society of Mechanical Engineers.

Table 11. American Standard Square-head Setscrews and Points

D	H nom.	R nom.	K max.	U min.	V max.	C nom.	J nom.	P max.	Q
10 (0.190)	$\frac{9}{64}$	$\frac{15}{32}$	0.145	0.083	0.027	$\frac{3}{32}$	0.141	0.127	0.090
12 (0.216)	$\frac{5}{32}$	$\frac{35}{64}$	0.162	0.091	0.029	$\frac{7}{64}$	0.156	0.144	0.110
$\frac{1}{4}$	$\frac{3}{16}$	$\frac{5}{8}$	0.185	0.100	0.032	$\frac{1}{8}$	0.188	0.156	0.125
$\frac{5}{16}$	$\frac{15}{64}$	$\frac{25}{32}$	0.240	0.111	0.036	$\frac{11}{64}$	0.234	0.203	0.156
$\frac{3}{8}$	$\frac{9}{32}$	$\frac{15}{16}$	0.294	0.125	0.041	$\frac{13}{64}$	0.281	0.250	0.188
$\frac{7}{16}$	$\frac{21}{64}$	$1\frac{3}{32}$	0.345	0.143	0.046	$\frac{15}{64}$	0.328	0.297	0.219
$\frac{1}{2}$	$\frac{3}{8}$	$1\frac{1}{4}$	0.400	0.154	0.050	$\frac{9}{32}$	0.375	0.344	0.250
$\frac{9}{16}$	$\frac{27}{64}$	$1\frac{13}{32}$	0.454	0.167	0.054	$\frac{5}{16}$	0.422	0.391	0.281
$\frac{5}{8}$	$\frac{15}{32}$	$1\frac{9}{16}$	0.507	0.182	0.059	$\frac{23}{64}$	0.469	0.469	0.313
$\frac{3}{4}$	$\frac{9}{16}$	$1\frac{7}{8}$	0.620	0.200	0.065	$\frac{7}{16}$	0.563	0.563	0.375
$\frac{7}{8}$	$\frac{21}{32}$	$2\frac{3}{16}$	0.731	0.222	0.072	$\frac{33}{64}$	0.656	0.656	0.438
1	$\frac{3}{4}$	$2\frac{1}{2}$	0.838	0.250	0.081	$\frac{19}{32}$	0.750	0.750	0.500
$1\frac{1}{8}$	$\frac{27}{32}$	$2\frac{13}{16}$	0.939	0.283	0.092	$\frac{43}{64}$	0.844	0.844	0.562
$1\frac{1}{4}$	$\frac{15}{16}$	$3\frac{1}{8}$	1.064	0.283	0.092	$\frac{3}{4}$	0.938	0.938	0.625
$1\frac{3}{8}$	$1\frac{1}{32}$	$3\frac{7}{16}$	1.159	0.333	0.109	$\frac{53}{64}$	1.031	1.031	0.688
$1\frac{1}{2}$	$1\frac{1}{8}$	$3\frac{3}{4}$	1.284	0.333	0.109	$\frac{29}{32}$	1.125	1.125	0.750

Note: Threads may be coarse-, fine-, or 8-thread series, class 2A. Coarse thread normally used on $\frac{1}{4}$ in. and larger. When length equals nominal diameter or less $Y = 118°$. When length exceeds nominal diameter $Y = 90°$.

Source: Extracted from American Standard *Hexagon Head Cap Screws, Slotted Head Cap Screws, Square Head Setscrews, Slotted Headless Setscrews* (ASA B18.6.2–1956), with the permission of the publisher, The American Society of Mechanical Engineers.

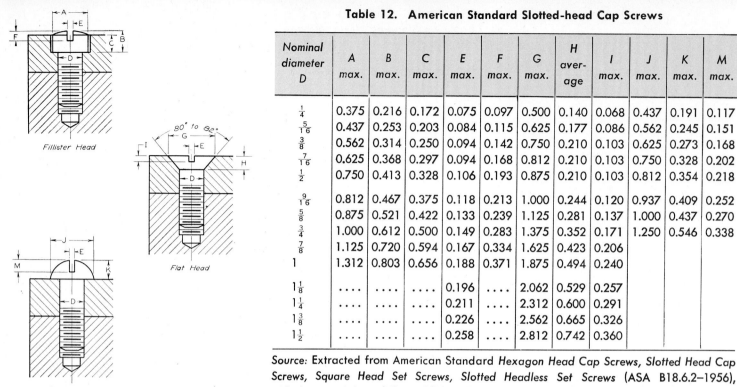

Table 12. American Standard Slotted-head Cap Screws

Nominal diameter D	A max.	B max.	C max.	E max.	F max.	G max.	H average	I max.	J max.	K max.	M max.
1/4	0.375	0.216	0.172	0.075	0.097	0.500	0.140	0.068	0.437	0.191	0.117
5/16	0.437	0.253	0.203	0.084	0.115	0.625	0.177	0.086	0.562	0.245	0.151
3/8	0.562	0.314	0.250	0.094	0.142	0.750	0.210	0.103	0.625	0.273	0.168
7/16	0.625	0.368	0.297	0.094	0.168	0.812	0.210	0.103	0.750	0.328	0.202
1/2	0.750	0.413	0.328	0.106	0.193	0.875	0.210	0.103	0.812	0.354	0.218
9/16	0.812	0.467	0.375	0.118	0.213	1.000	0.244	0.120	0.937	0.409	0.252
5/8	0.875	0.521	0.422	0.133	0.239	1.125	0.281	0.137	1.000	0.437	0.270
3/4	1.000	0.612	0.500	0.149	0.283	1.375	0.352	0.171	1.250	0.546	0.338
7/8	1.125	0.720	0.594	0.167	0.334	1.625	0.423	0.206			
1	1.312	0.803	0.656	0.188	0.371	1.875	0.494	0.240			
1 1/8	....	....	....	0.196	....	2.062	0.529	0.257			
1 1/4	....	....	....	0.211	....	2.312	0.600	0.291			
1 3/8	....	....	....	0.226	....	2.562	0.665	0.326			
1 1/2	....	....	....	0.258	....	2.812	0.742	0.360			

Source: Extracted from American Standard *Hexagon Head Cap Screws, Slotted Head Cap Screws, Square Head Set Screws, Slotted Headless Set Screws* (ASA B18.6.2–1956), with the permission of the publisher, The American Society of Mechanical Engineers.

Table 13. American Standard Machine Screws
Maximum Dimensions

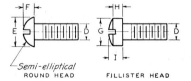

Nominal	Max.	A	B	C	E	F	G	H	I	J	K	M
0	0.060	0.119	0.035	0.056	0.113	0.053	0.096	0.045	0.059	....	....	0.023
1	0.073	0.146	0.043	0.068	0.138	0.061	0.118	0.053	0.071	....	....	0.026
2	0.086	0.172	0.051	0.080	0.162	0.069	0.140	0.062	0.083	0.167	0.053	0.031
3	0.099	0.199	0.059	0.092	0.187	0.078	0.161	0.070	0.095	0.193	0.060	0.035
4	0.112	0.225	0.067	0.104	0.211	0.086	0.183	0.079	0.107	0.219	0.068	0.039
5	0.125	0.252	0.075	0.116	0.236	0.095	0.205	0.088	0.120	0.245	0.075	0.043
6	0.138	0.279	0.083	0.128	0.260	0.103	0.226	0.096	0.132	0.270	0.082	0.048
8	0.164	0.332	0.100	0.152	0.309	0.120	0.270	0.113	0.156	0.322	0.096	0.054
10	0.190	0.385	0.116	0.176	0.359	0.137	0.313	0.130	0.180	0.373	0.110	0.060
12	0.216	0.438	0.132	0.200	0.408	0.153	0.357	0.148	0.205	0.425	0.125	0.067
1/4	0.250	0.507	0.153	0.232	0.472	0.175	0.414	0.170	0.237	0.492	0.144	0.075
5/16	0.3125	0.635	0.191	0.290	0.590	0.216	0.518	0.211	0.295	0.615	0.178	0.084
3/8	0.375	0.762	0.230	0.347	0.708	0.256	0.622	0.253	0.355	0.740	0.212	0.094
7/16	0.4375	0.812	0.223	0.345	0.750	0.328	0.625	0.265	0.368	....	....	0.094
1/2	0.500	0.875	0.223	0.354	0.813	0.355	0.750	0.297	0.412	....	....	0.106
9/16	0.5625	1.000	0.260	0.410	0.938	0.410	0.812	0.336	0.466	....	....	0.118
5/8	0.625	1.125	0.298	0.467	1.000	0.438	0.875	0.375	0.521	....	....	0.133
3/4	0.750	1.375	0.372	0.578	1.250	0.547	1.000	0.441	0.612	....	....	0.149

Source: Extracted from American Standard *Slotted and Recessed Head Screws* (ASA B18.6.3–1962), with the permission of the publisher, The American Society of Mechanical Engineers.

Table 14. American Standard Hexagon-head Cap Screws

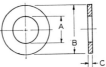

D	W	H	D	W	H
$\frac{1}{4}$	$\frac{7}{16}$	$\frac{5}{32}$	$\frac{3}{4}$	$1\frac{1}{8}$	$\frac{15}{32}$
$\frac{5}{16}$	$\frac{1}{2}$	$\frac{13}{64}$	$\frac{7}{8}$	$1\frac{5}{16}$	$\frac{35}{64}$
$\frac{3}{8}$	$\frac{9}{16}$	$\frac{15}{64}$	1	$1\frac{1}{2}$	$\frac{39}{64}$
$\frac{7}{16}$	$\frac{5}{8}$	$\frac{9}{32}$	$1\frac{1}{8}$	$1\frac{11}{16}$	$\frac{11}{16}$
$\frac{1}{2}$	$\frac{3}{4}$	$\frac{5}{16}$	$1\frac{1}{4}$	$1\frac{7}{8}$	$\frac{25}{32}$
$\frac{9}{16}$	$\frac{13}{16}$	$\frac{23}{64}$	$1\frac{3}{8}$	$2\frac{1}{16}$	$\frac{27}{32}$
$\frac{5}{8}$	$\frac{15}{16}$	$\frac{25}{64}$	$1\frac{1}{2}$	$2\frac{1}{4}$	$\frac{15}{16}$

Note: Bearing surfaces shall be flat and either washer faced or with chamfered corners. Minimum thread length shall be twice the diameter plus $\frac{1}{4}$ in. for lengths up to and including 6 in.; twice the diameter plus $\frac{1}{2}$ in. for lengths over 6 in. Extracted from American Standard *Hexagon Head Cap Screws, Slotted Head Cap Screws, Square Head Set Screws, Slotted Headless Set Screws* (ASA B18.6.2–1960), with the permission of the publisher, The American Society of Mechanical Engineers.

Table 15. American Standard Plain Washers

Inside diameter A	Outside diameter B	Gage	Nom.	Inside diameter A	Outside diameter B	Gage	Nom.	Inside diameter A	Outside diameter B	Gage	Nom.	Inside diameter A	Outside diameter B	Gage	Nom.
$\frac{5}{64}$	$\frac{3}{16}$	25	0.020	$\frac{5}{16}$	$\frac{7}{8}$	16	0.065	$\frac{5}{8}$	$2\frac{1}{8}$	10	0.134	$1\frac{3}{8}$	3	8	0.165
$\frac{3}{32}$	$\frac{7}{32}$	25	0.020	$\frac{11}{32}$	$\frac{11}{16}$	16	0.065	$\frac{21}{32}$	$1\frac{5}{16}$	13	0.095	$1\frac{7}{16}$	3	7	0.180
$\frac{3}{32}$	$\frac{1}{4}$	25	0.020	$\frac{3}{8}$	$\frac{3}{4}$	16	0.065	$\frac{11}{16}$	$1\frac{1}{2}$	10	0.134	$1\frac{1}{2}$	$3\frac{1}{4}$	7	0.180
$\frac{1}{8}$	$\frac{1}{4}$	24	0.022	$\frac{3}{8}$	$\frac{7}{8}$	14	0.083	$\frac{11}{16}$	$1\frac{3}{4}$	10	0.134	$1\frac{9}{16}$	$3\frac{1}{4}$	7	0.180
$\frac{1}{8}$	$\frac{5}{16}$	21	0.032	$\frac{3}{8}$	$1\frac{1}{8}$	16	0.065	$\frac{11}{16}$	$2\frac{3}{8}$	8	0.165	$1\frac{5}{8}$	$3\frac{1}{2}$	7	0.180
$\frac{5}{32}$	$\frac{5}{16}$	20	0.035	$\frac{13}{32}$	$\frac{13}{16}$	16	0.065	$\frac{13}{16}$	$1\frac{1}{2}$	10	0.134	$1\frac{11}{16}$	$3\frac{1}{2}$	7	0.180
$\frac{5}{32}$	$\frac{3}{8}$	18	0.049	$\frac{7}{16}$	$\frac{7}{8}$	14	0.083	$\frac{13}{16}$	$1\frac{3}{4}$	9	0.148	$1\frac{3}{4}$	$3\frac{3}{4}$	7	0.180
$\frac{11}{64}$	$\frac{13}{32}$	18	0.049	$\frac{7}{16}$	1	14	0.083	$\frac{13}{16}$	2	9	0.148	$1\frac{13}{16}$	$3\frac{3}{4}$	7	0.180
$\frac{3}{16}$	$\frac{3}{8}$	18	0.049	$\frac{7}{16}$	$1\frac{3}{8}$	14	0.083	$\frac{13}{16}$	$2\frac{7}{8}$	8	0.165	$1\frac{7}{8}$	4	7	0.180
$\frac{3}{16}$	$\frac{7}{16}$	18	0.049	$\frac{15}{32}$	$\frac{59}{64}$	16	0.065	$\frac{15}{16}$	$1\frac{3}{4}$	10	0.134	$1\frac{15}{16}$	4	7	0.180
$\frac{13}{64}$	$\frac{15}{32}$	18	0.049	$\frac{1}{2}$	$1\frac{1}{8}$	14	0.083	$\frac{15}{16}$	2	8	0.165	2	$4\frac{1}{4}$	7	0.180
$\frac{7}{32}$	$\frac{7}{16}$	18	0.049	$\frac{1}{2}$	$1\frac{1}{4}$	14	0.083	$\frac{15}{16}$	$2\frac{1}{4}$	8	0.165	$2\frac{1}{16}$	$4\frac{1}{4}$	7	0.180
$\frac{7}{32}$	$\frac{1}{2}$	18	0.049	$\frac{1}{2}$	$1\frac{5}{8}$	14	0.083	$\frac{15}{16}$	$3\frac{3}{8}$	7	0.180	$2\frac{1}{8}$	$4\frac{1}{2}$	7	0.180
$\frac{15}{64}$	$\frac{17}{32}$	18	0.049	$\frac{17}{32}$	$1\frac{1}{16}$	13	0.095	$1\frac{1}{16}$	2	10	0.134	$2\frac{3}{8}$	$4\frac{3}{4}$	5	0.220
$\frac{1}{4}$	$\frac{1}{2}$	18	0.049	$\frac{9}{16}$	$1\frac{1}{4}$	12	0.109	$1\frac{1}{16}$	$2\frac{1}{4}$	8	0.165	$2\frac{5}{8}$	5	4	0.238
$\frac{1}{4}$	$\frac{9}{16}$	18	0.049	$\frac{9}{16}$	$1\frac{3}{8}$	12	0.109	$1\frac{1}{16}$	$2\frac{1}{2}$	8	0.165	$2\frac{7}{8}$	$5\frac{1}{4}$	3	0.259
$\frac{1}{4}$	$\frac{9}{16}$	16	0.065	$\frac{9}{16}$	$1\frac{7}{8}$	12	0.109	$1\frac{1}{16}$	$3\frac{3}{8}$	4	0.238	$3\frac{1}{8}$	$5\frac{1}{2}$	2	0.284
$\frac{1}{4}$	$\frac{5}{8}$	18	0.049	$\frac{19}{32}$	$1\frac{3}{16}$	13	0.095	$1\frac{3}{16}$	$2\frac{1}{2}$	8	0.165				
$\frac{17}{64}$	$\frac{5}{8}$	16	0.065	$\frac{5}{8}$	$1\frac{3}{8}$	12	0.109	$1\frac{1}{4}$	$2\frac{3}{4}$	8	0.165				
$\frac{9}{32}$	$\frac{5}{8}$	16	0.065	$\frac{5}{8}$	$1\frac{1}{2}$	12	0.109	$1\frac{5}{16}$	$2\frac{3}{4}$	8	0.165				
$\frac{5}{16}$	$\frac{3}{4}$	16	0.065												

Source: Nominal thicknesses of washers are Birmingham gage sizes. Extracted from American Standard *Plain Washers* (ASA B27.2–1958), with the permission of the publisher, The American Society of Mechanical Engineers.

Table 16. American Standard Cotter Pins

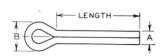

Design of head may vary but outside diameters should be adhered to.

A nominal	B min.	Hole sizes recommended
0.031	$\frac{1}{16}$	$\frac{3}{64}$
0.047	$\frac{3}{32}$	$\frac{1}{16}$
0.062	$\frac{1}{8}$	$\frac{5}{64}$
0.078	$\frac{5}{32}$	$\frac{3}{32}$
0.094	$\frac{3}{16}$	$\frac{7}{64}$
0.109	$\frac{7}{32}$	$\frac{1}{8}$
0.125	$\frac{1}{4}$	$\frac{9}{64}$
0.141	$\frac{9}{32}$	$\frac{5}{32}$
0.156	$\frac{5}{16}$	$\frac{11}{64}$
0.188	$\frac{3}{8}$	$\frac{13}{64}$
0.219	$\frac{7}{16}$	$\frac{15}{64}$
0.250	$\frac{1}{2}$	$\frac{17}{64}$
0.312	$\frac{5}{8}$	$\frac{5}{16}$
0.375	$\frac{3}{4}$	$\frac{3}{8}$
0.438	$\frac{7}{8}$	$\frac{7}{16}$
0.500	1	$\frac{1}{2}$
0.625	$1\frac{1}{4}$	$\frac{5}{8}$
0.750	$1\frac{1}{2}$	$\frac{3}{4}$

Source: Extracted from American Standard *Machine Pins* (ASA B5.20–1958), with the permission of the publisher, The American Society of Mechanical Engineers.

Table 17. American Standard Slotted-head Wood Screws

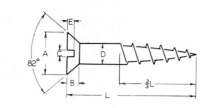
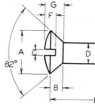

Maximum Dimensions

Nominal size	D	A	B	C	E	F	G	H	I	J	Number threads per inch
0	0.060	0.119	0.035	0.023	0.015	0.030	0.056	0.053	0.113	0.039	32
1	0.073	0.146	0.043	0.026	0.019	0.038	0.068	0.061	0.138	0.044	28
2	0.086	0.172	0.051	0.031	0.023	0.045	0.080	0.069	0.162	0.048	26
3	0.099	0.199	0.059	0.035	0.027	0.052	0.092	0.078	0.187	0.053	24
4	0.112	0.225	0.067	0.039	0.030	0.059	0.104	0.086	0.211	0.058	22
5	0.125	0.252	0.075	0.043	0.034	0.067	0.116	0.095	0.236	0.063	20
6	0.138	0.279	0.083	0.048	0.038	0.074	0.128	0.103	0.260	0.068	18
7	0.151	0.305	0.091	0.048	0.041	0.081	0.140	0.111	0.285	0.072	16
8	0.164	0.332	0.100	0.054	0.045	0.088	0.152	0.120	0.309	0.077	15
9	0.177	0.358	0.108	0.054	0.049	0.095	0.164	0.128	0.334	0.082	14
10	0.190	0.385	0.116	0.060	0.053	0.103	0.176	0.137	0.359	0.087	13
12	0.216	0.438	0.132	0.067	0.060	0.117	0.200	0.153	0.408	0.096	11
14	0.242	0.491	0.148	0.075	0.068	0.132	0.224	0.170	0.457	0.106	10
16	0.268	0.544	0.164	0.075	0.075	0.146	0.248	0.187	0.506	0.115	9
18	0.294	0.597	0.180	0.084	0.083	0.160	0.272	0.204	0.555	0.125	8
20	0.320	0.650	0.196	0.084	0.090	0.175	0.296	0.220	0.604	0.134	8
24	0.372	0.756	0.228	0.094	0.105	0.204	0.344	0.254	0.702	0.154	7

Source: Extracted from American Standard *Slotted and Recessed Head Screws, Machine, Cap, Wood, Tapping, and Slotted Headless Types* (ASA B18.6.1–1956), with the permission of the publisher, The American Society of Mechanical Engineers.

Table 18. American Standard Taper Pins

TAPER PINS   *Maximum length for which standard reamers are available. Taper ¼ in. per ft.

Size No.	0000000	000000	00000	0000	000	00	0
Size (large end)	0.0625	0.0780	0.0940	0.1090	0.1250	0.1410	0.1560
Maximum length*	0.625	0.750	1.000	1.000	1.000	1.250	1.250

Size No.	1	2	3	4	5	6	7
Size (large end)	0.1720	0.1930	0.2190	0.2500	0.2890	0.3410	0.4090
Maximum length*	1.250	1.500	1.750	2.000	2.250	3.000	3.750

Size No.	8	9	10	11	12	13	14
Size (large end)	0.4920	0.5910	0.7060	0.8600	1.032	1.241	1.523
Maximum length*	4.500	5.250	6.000	(Special sizes. Special lengths.)			

Table 19. American Standard Square- and Flat-stock Keys and Shaft Diameters

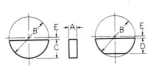

Diameter of shaft D inclusive	Square keys W	Flat keys W × H
$\frac{1}{2} - \frac{9}{16}$	$\frac{1}{8}$	$\frac{1}{8} \times \frac{3}{32}$
$\frac{5}{8} - \frac{7}{8}$	$\frac{3}{16}$	$\frac{3}{16} \times \frac{1}{8}$
$\frac{15}{16} - 1\frac{1}{4}$	$\frac{1}{4}$	$\frac{1}{4} \times \frac{3}{16}$
$1\frac{5}{16} - 1\frac{3}{8}$	$\frac{5}{16}$	$\frac{5}{16} \times \frac{1}{4}$
$1\frac{7}{16} - 1\frac{3}{4}$	$\frac{3}{8}$	$\frac{3}{8} \times \frac{1}{4}$
$1\frac{13}{16} - 2\frac{1}{4}$	$\frac{1}{2}$	$\frac{1}{2} \times \frac{3}{8}$
$2\frac{5}{16} - 2\frac{3}{4}$	$\frac{5}{8}$	$\frac{5}{8} \times \frac{7}{16}$
$2\frac{7}{8} - 3\frac{1}{4}$	$\frac{3}{4}$	$\frac{3}{4} \times \frac{1}{2}$
$3\frac{3}{8} - 3\frac{3}{4}$	$\frac{7}{8}$	$\frac{7}{8} \times \frac{5}{8}$
$3\frac{7}{8} - 4\frac{1}{2}$	1	$1 \times \frac{3}{4}$
$4\frac{3}{4} - 5\frac{1}{2}$	$1\frac{1}{4}$	$1\frac{1}{4} \times \frac{7}{8}$
$5\frac{3}{4} - 6$	$1\frac{1}{2}$	$1\frac{1}{2} \times 1$

Source: Extracted from American Standard *Shafting and Stock Keys* (ASA (B17.1–1943), with the permission of the publisher, The American Society of Mechanical Engineers.

Table 20. Woodruff Keys — Dimensions in Inches

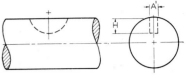

Key No.	Nominal A	Nominal B	Nominal E	Maximum C	Maximum D	Maximum H
204	$\frac{1}{16}$	$\frac{1}{2}$	$\frac{3}{64}$	0.203	0.194	0.1718
304	$\frac{3}{32}$	$\frac{1}{2}$	$\frac{3}{64}$	0.203	0.194	0.1561
305	$\frac{3}{32}$	$\frac{5}{8}$	$\frac{1}{16}$	0.250	0.240	0.2031
404	$\frac{1}{8}$	$\frac{1}{2}$	$\frac{3}{64}$	0.203	0.194	0.1405
405	$\frac{1}{8}$	$\frac{5}{8}$	$\frac{1}{16}$	0.250	0.240	0.1875
406	$\frac{1}{8}$	$\frac{3}{4}$	$\frac{1}{16}$	0.313	0.303	0.2505
505	$\frac{5}{32}$	$\frac{5}{8}$	$\frac{1}{16}$	0.250	0.240	0.1719
506	$\frac{5}{32}$	$\frac{3}{4}$	$\frac{1}{16}$	0.313	0.303	0.2349
507	$\frac{5}{32}$	$\frac{7}{8}$	$\frac{1}{16}$	0.375	0.365	0.2969
606	$\frac{3}{16}$	$\frac{3}{4}$	$\frac{1}{16}$	0.313	0.303	0.2193
607	$\frac{3}{16}$	$\frac{7}{8}$	$\frac{1}{16}$	0.375	0.365	0.2813
608	$\frac{3}{16}$	1	$\frac{1}{16}$	0.438	0.428	0.3443
609	$\frac{3}{16}$	$1\frac{1}{8}$	$\frac{5}{64}$	0.484	0.475	0.3903
807	$\frac{1}{4}$	$\frac{7}{8}$	$\frac{1}{16}$	0.375	0.365	0.2500
808	$\frac{1}{4}$	1	$\frac{1}{16}$	0.438	0.428	0.3130
809	$\frac{1}{4}$	$1\frac{1}{8}$	$\frac{5}{64}$	0.484	0.475	0.3590
810	$\frac{1}{4}$	$1\frac{1}{4}$	$\frac{5}{64}$	0.547	0.537	0.4220
811	$\frac{1}{4}$	$1\frac{3}{8}$	$\frac{3}{32}$	0.594	0.584	0.4690
812	$\frac{1}{4}$	$1\frac{1}{2}$	$\frac{7}{64}$	0.641	0.631	0.5160
1008	$\frac{5}{16}$	1	$\frac{1}{16}$	0.438	0.428	0.2818
1009	$\frac{5}{16}$	$1\frac{1}{8}$	$\frac{5}{64}$	0.484	0.475	0.3278
1010	$\frac{5}{16}$	$1\frac{1}{4}$	$\frac{5}{16}$	0.547	0.537	0.3908
1011	$\frac{5}{16}$	$1\frac{3}{8}$	$\frac{3}{32}$	0.594	0.584	0.4378
1012	$\frac{5}{16}$	$1\frac{1}{2}$	$\frac{7}{64}$	0.641	0.631	0.4848
1210	$\frac{3}{8}$	$1\frac{1}{4}$	$\frac{5}{64}$	0.547	0.537	0.3595
1211	$\frac{3}{8}$	$1\frac{3}{8}$	$\frac{3}{32}$	0.594	0.584	0.4060
1212	$\frac{3}{8}$	$1\frac{1}{2}$	$\frac{7}{64}$	0.641	0.631	0.4535

Note: Nominal dimensions are indicated by the key number in which the last two digits give the diameter (B) in eighths and the ones in front of them give the width (A) in thirty-seconds. For example, No. 809 means $B = \frac{9}{8}$ or $1\frac{1}{8}$ and $A = \frac{8}{32}$ or $\frac{1}{4}$.

Source: Extracted from American Standard *Woodruff Keys, Keyslots and Cutters* (ASA B17f–1930, reviewed 1955), with the permission of the publisher, The American Society of Mechanical Engineers.

Table 21. Wire and Sheet-metal Gages

Dimensions in Decimal Parts of an Inch

No. of wire gage	American, or Brown & Sharpe	Birmingham, or Stubs wire	Washburn & Moen or American Steel & Wire Co.	W. & M. steel music wire	New American S. & W. Co. music wire gage	Imperial wire gage	U.S. Standard gage for sheet amd plate iron and steel
00000000	. . . . . .	. . . . . .	. . . . . .	0.0083			
0000000	. . . . . .	. . . . . .	. . . . . .	0.0087			
000000	. . . . . .	. . . . . .	. . . . . .	0.0095	0.004	0.464	0.46875
00000	. . . . . .	. . . . . .	. . . . . .	0.010	0.005	0.432	0.4375
0000	0.460	0.454	0.3938	0.011	0.006	0.400	0.40625
000	0.40964	0.425	0.3625	0.012	0.007	0.372	0.375
00	0.3648	0.380	0.3310	0.0133	0.008	0.348	0.34375
0	0.32486	0.340	0.3065	0.0144	0.009	0.324	0.3125
1	0.2893	0.300	0.2830	0.0156	0.010	0.300	0.28125
2	0.25763	0.284	0.2625	0.0166	0.011	0.276	0.265625
3	0.22942	0.259	0.2437	0.0178	0.012	0.252	0.250
4	0.20431	0.238	0.2253	0.0188	0.013	0.232	0.234375
5	0.18194	0.220	0.2070	0.0202	0.014	0.212	0.21875
6	0.16202	0.203	0.1920	0.0215	0.016	0.192	0.203125
7	0.14428	0.180	0.1770	0.023	0.018	0.176	0.1875
8	0.12849	0.165	0.1620	0.0243	0.020	0.160	0.171875
9	0.11443	0.148	0.1483	0.0256	0.022	0.144	0.15625
10	0.10189	0.134	0.1350	0.027	0.024	0.128	0.140625
11	0.090742	0.120	0.1205	0.0284	0.026	0.116	0.125
12	0.080808	0.109	0.1055	0.0296	0.029	0.104	0.109375
13	0.071961	0.095	0.0915	0.0314	0.031	0.092	0.09375
14	0.064084	0.083	0.0800	0.0326	0.033	0.080	0.078125
15	0.057068	0.072	0.0720	0.0345	0.035	0.072	0.0703125
16	0.05082	0.065	0.0625	0.036	0.037	0.064	0.0625
17	0.045257	0.058	0.0540	0.0377	0.039	0.056	0.05625
18	0.040303	0.049	0.0475	0.0395	0.041	0.048	0.050
19	0.03589	0.042	0.0410	0.0414	0.043	0.040	0.04375
20	0.031961	0.035	0.0348	0.0434	0.045	0.036	0.0375
21	0.028462	0.032	0.03175	0.046	0.047	0.032	0.034375
22	0.025347	0.028	0.0286	0.0483	0.049	0.028	0.03125
23	0.022571	0.025	0.0258	0.051	0.051	0.024	0.028125
24	0.0201	0.022	0.0230	0.055	0.055	0.022	0.025
25	0.0179	0.020	0.0204	0.0586	0.059	0.020	0.021875
26	0.01594	0.018	0.0181	0.0626	0.063	0.018	0.01875
27	0.014195	0.016	0.0173	0.0658	0.067	0.0164	0.0171875
28	0.012641	0.014	0.0162	0.072	0.071	0.0149	0.015625
29	0.011257	0.013	0.0150	0.076	0.075	0.0136	0.0140625
30	0.010025	0.012	0.0140	0.080	0.080	0.0124	0.0125
31	0.008928	0.010	0.0132	. . . . . .	0.085	0.0116	0.0109375
32	0.00795	0.009	0.0128	. . . . . .	0.090	0.0108	0.01015625
33	0.00708	0.008	0.0118	. . . . . .	0.095	0.0100	0.009375
34	0.006304	0.007	0.0104	. . . . . .	. . . . . .	0.0092	0.00859375
35	0.005614	0.005	0.0095	. . . . . .	. . . . . .	0.0084	0.0078125
36	0.005	0.004	0.0090	. . . . . .	. . . . . .	0.0076	0.00703125
37	0.004453	. . . . . .	. . . . . .	. . . . . .	. . . . . .	0.0068	0.006640625
38	0.003965	. . . . . .	. . . . . .	. . . . . .	. . . . . .	0.0060	0.00625
39	0.003531	. . . . . .	. . . . . .	. . . . . .	. . . . . .	0.0052	
40	0.003144	. . . . . .	. . . . . .	. . . . . .	. . . . . .	0.0048	

Table 22. American Standard Welded and Seamless Steel Pipe

Nominal pipe size	Out-side diam.	Nominal wall thickness			Threads per inch
		Stand-ard wall	Extra strong wall	Double extra strong wall	
$\frac{1}{8}$	0.405	0.068	0.095	. . . .	27
$\frac{1}{4}$	0.540	0.088	0.119	. . . .	18
$\frac{3}{8}$	0.675	0.091	0.126	. . . .	18
$\frac{1}{2}$	0.840	0.109	0.147	0.294	14
$\frac{3}{4}$	1.050	0.113	0.154	0.308	14
1	1.315	0.133	0.179	0.358	$11\frac{1}{2}$
$1\frac{1}{4}$	1.660	0.140	0.191	0.382	$11\frac{1}{2}$
$1\frac{1}{2}$	1.900	0.145	0.200	0.400	$11\frac{1}{2}$
2	2.375	0.154	0.218	0.436	$11\frac{1}{2}$
$2\frac{1}{2}$	2.875	0.203	0.276	0.552	8
3	3.500	0.216	0.300	0.600	8
$3\frac{1}{2}$	4.000	0.226	0.318	. . . .	8
4	4.500	0.237	0.337	0.674	8
5	5.563	0.258	0.375	0.750	8
6	6.625	0.280	0.432	0.864	8
8	8.625	0.322	0.500	0.875	8
10	10.750	0.365	0.500	. . . .	8
12	12.750	0.375	0.500	. . . .	8
14	14.000	0.375	0.500	. . . .	8
16	16.000	0.375	0.500	. . . .	8
18	18.000	0.375	0.500	. . . .	8
20	20.000	0.375	0.500	. . . .	8
24	24.000	0.375	0.500	. . . .	8

Note: To find the inside diameter subtract twice the wall thickness from the outside diameter. Schedule numbers have been set up for wall thicknesses, for pipe and the American Standard should be consulted for complete information. Standard wall thicknesses are for Schedule 40 up to and including nominal size 10. Extra strong walls are Schedule 80 up to and including size 8, and Schedule 60 for size 10.

Source: Extracted from American Standard *Wrought-steel and Wrought-iron Pipe* (ASA B36.10–1959) and American Standard *Pipe Threads* (taper threads) (ASA B2.1–1960), with the permission of the publisher, The American Society of Mechanical Engineers.

Table 23. Steel-wire Nails

American Steel & Wire Company Gage

Size	Length	Common wire nails and brads		Casing nails		Finishing nails	
		Gage, diam.	No. to pound	Gage, diam.	No. to pound	Gage, diam.	No. to pound
2d	1	15	876	$15\frac{1}{2}$	1010	$16\frac{1}{2}$	1351
3d	$1\frac{1}{4}$	14	568	$14\frac{1}{2}$	635	$15\frac{1}{2}$	807
4d	$1\frac{1}{2}$	$12\frac{1}{2}$	316	14	473	15	584
5d	$1\frac{3}{4}$	$12\frac{1}{2}$	271	14	406	15	500
6d	2	$11\frac{1}{2}$	181	$12\frac{1}{2}$	236	13	309
7d	$2\frac{1}{4}$	$11\frac{1}{2}$	161	$12\frac{1}{2}$	210	13	238
8d	$2\frac{1}{2}$	$10\frac{1}{4}$	106	$11\frac{1}{2}$	145	$12\frac{1}{2}$	189
9d	$2\frac{3}{4}$	$10\frac{1}{4}$	96	$11\frac{1}{2}$	132	$12\frac{1}{2}$	172
10d	3	9	69	$10\frac{1}{2}$	94	$11\frac{1}{2}$	121
12d	$3\frac{1}{4}$	9	64	$10\frac{1}{2}$	87	$11\frac{1}{2}$	113
16d	$3\frac{1}{2}$	8	49	10	71	11	90
20d	4	6	31	9	52	10	62
30d	$4\frac{1}{2}$	5	24	9	46		
40d	5	4	18	8	35		
50d	$5\frac{1}{2}$	3	14				
60d	6	2	11				

Table 24. American Standard Large Rivets

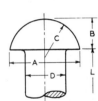
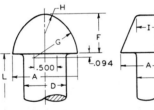
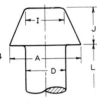
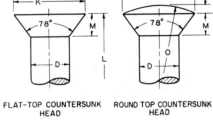
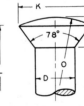
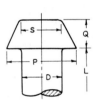

BUTTON HEAD   HIGH BUTTON HEAD   CONE HEAD   FLAT-TOP COUNTERSUNK HEAD   ROUND TOP COUNTERSUNK HEAD   PAN HEAD

Manufactured Shapes

D nominal	A basic	B basic (min.)	C	E basic	F basic	G	H	I basic	J basic (min.)	K basic	M basic (min.)	N	O	P basic	Q basic (min.)	S basic
$\frac{1}{2}$	0.875	0.375	0.443	0.781	0.500	0.656	0.094	0.469	0.438	0.905	0.250	0.095	1.125	0.800	0.381	0.500
$\frac{5}{8}$	1.094	0.469	0.553	0.969	0.594	0.750	0.188	0.586	0.547	1.131	0.312	0.119	1.406	1.000	0.469	0.625
$\frac{3}{4}$	1.312	0.562	0.664	1.156	0.688	0.844	0.282	0.703	0.656	1.358	0.375	0.142	1.688	1.200	0.556	0.750
$\frac{7}{8}$	1.531	0.656	0.775	1.344	0.781	0.937	0.375	0.820	0.766	1.584	0.438	0.166	1.969	1.400	0.643	0.875
1	1.750	0.750	0.885	1.531	0.875	1.031	0.469	0.938	0.875	1.810	0.500	0.190	2.250	1.600	0.731	1.000
$1\frac{1}{8}$	1.969	0.844	0.996	1.719	0.969	1.125	0.563	1.055	0.984	2.036	0.562	0.214	2.531	1.800	0.835	1.125
$1\frac{1}{4}$	2.188	0.938	1.107	1.906	1.062	1.218	0.656	1.172	1.094	2.262	0.625	0.238	2.812	2.000	0.922	1.250
$1\frac{3}{8}$	2.406	1.031	1.217	2.094	1.156	1.312	0.750	1.290	1.203	2.489	0.688	0.261	3.094	2.200	1.009	1.375
$1\frac{1}{2}$	2.625	1.125	1.328	2.281	1.250	1.406	0.844	1.406	1.312	2.715	0.750	0.285	3.375	2.400	1.113	1.500
$1\frac{5}{8}$	2.844	1.219	1.439	2.469	1.344	1.500	0.938	1.524	1.422	2.941	0.812	0.309	3.656	2.600	1.201	1.625
$1\frac{3}{4}$	3.062	1.312	1.549	2.656	1.438	1.594	1.032	1.641	1.531	3.168	0.875	0.332	3.938	2.800	1.288	1.750

Source: Extracted from American Standard *Large Rivets* (ASA B18.4–1960), with the permission of the publisher, The American Society of Mechanical Engineers.

Table 25. Geometrical Shapes

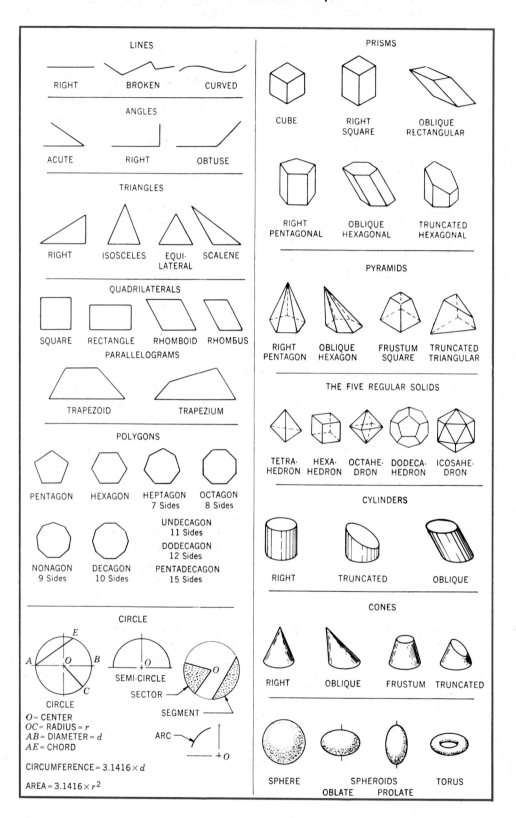

LINES

RIGHT   BROKEN   CURVED

ANGLES

ACUTE   RIGHT   OBTUSE

TRIANGLES

RIGHT   ISOSCELES   EQUI-LATERAL   SCALENE

QUADRILATERALS

SQUARE   RECTANGLE   RHOMBOID   RHOMBUS

PARALLELOGRAMS

TRAPEZOID   TRAPEZIUM

POLYGONS

PENTAGON   HEXAGON   HEPTAGON 7 Sides   OCTAGON 8 Sides

NONAGON 9 Sides   DECAGON 10 Sides

UNDECAGON 11 Sides
DODECAGON 12 Sides
PENTADECAGON 15 Sides

CIRCLE

CIRCLE   SEMI-CIRCLE   SECTOR   SEGMENT

O = CENTER
OC = RADIUS = r
AB = DIAMETER = d
AE = CHORD

ARC

CIRCUMFERENCE = $3.1416 \times d$

AREA = $3.1416 \times r^2$

PRISMS

CUBE   RIGHT SQUARE   OBLIQUE RECTANGULAR

RIGHT PENTAGONAL   OBLIQUE HEXAGONAL   TRUNCATED HEXAGONAL

PYRAMIDS

RIGHT PENTAGON   OBLIQUE HEXAGON   FRUSTUM SQUARE   TRUNCATED TRIANGULAR

THE FIVE REGULAR SOLIDS

TETRA-HEDRON   HEXA-HEDRON   OCTAHE-DRON   DODECA-HEDRON   ICOSAHE-DRON

CYLINDERS

RIGHT   TRUNCATED   OBLIQUE

CONES

RIGHT   OBLIQUE   FRUSTUM   TRUNCATED

SPHERE   SPHEROIDS OBLATE PROLATE   TORUS

Glossary of Shop Terms[1]

(v) = Verb   (n) = Noun

anneal (v) To heat slowly to a critical temperature and gradually cool. Used to soften and to remove internal stresses.

babbitt or **babbitt metal** (n) An anti-friction bearing metal, invented by Isaac Babbitt. Composed of antimony, tin, and copper.

bearing (n) Any part that bears up, or supports, another part. In particular the support for a revolving shaft.

bevel (n) A surface slanted to another surface. Called a *miter* when the angle is 45°.

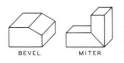

bore (v) To enlarge or to finish a hole by means of a cutting tool called a *boring bar,* used in a boring mill or lathe.

boss (n) A raised surface of circular outline as used on a casting or forging.

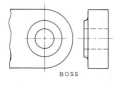

brass (n) An alloy of copper and zinc or copper with zinc and lead.

broach (v) To machine and change the forms of holes or outside surfaces to a desired shape, generally other than round. (n) A tool with a series of chisel edges used to broach.

bronzes (n) Alloys of copper and tin in varying proportions, mostly copper. Sometimes other metals, such as zinc, are added.

bushing (n) A hollow cylindrical sleeve used as a bearing or as a guide for drills or other tools. See oilless bushing in Problem 13·67.

caliper (n) A measuring device with two adjustable legs used for measuring thicknesses or diameters. See Fig. 11-28.

cam (n) A machine part mounted on a revolving shaft used for changing rotary motion into an alternating back-and-forth motion. See Chap. 19.

caseharden (carbonize or carburize) (v) To heat-treat steel to harden the surface by causing it to absorb carbon by quenching in an oil or lead bath.

casting (n) A part formed by pouring molten metal into a hollow form (mold) of the desired shape and allowing it to harden.

chamfer (v) To bevel an edge. (n) An edge which has been beveled.

core (v) To form the hollow part of a casting by means of a part made of sand and shaped like the hollow part (called a *core*) and placed in the mold (see **casting**). The core is broken up and removed after the casting is cool.

counterbore (v) To enlarge an end of a hole to a desired depth and to cylindrical form. Such an enlargement is called a *counterbore.*

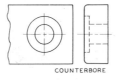

countersink (v) To form a conical space at the end of a hole.

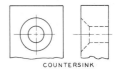

crown (n) The contour of the face of a belt pulley, rounded or angular, used to keep the belt in place. The belt tends to climb to the highest place.

die (n) A hardened metal block of a shape to form a desired shape by cutting or pressing. Also, a tool used to cut external screw threads.

die casting (n) A casting made of molten alloy (or plastic composition) by pouring it into a metal mold or die, generally forced under pressure. Die castings are smooth and accurate.

die stamping (n) A piece which has been formed or cut from sheet material, generally sheet metal.

drill (v) To make a cylindrical hole using a revolving tool with cutting edges, called a *drill,* generally a twist drill.

drop forging (n) A piece formed between dies while hot, using pressure or a drop hammer.

exploded view (n) Separate parts of a single assembly projected away from each other, or separated to show relationships among the parts of one drawing. See Fig. 15-6.

face (v) To machine (finish) a flat surface on a lathe with the surface perpendicular to the axis of rotation.

file (v) To smooth, finish, or shape with a file.

---

[1] Terms defined and illustrated within the text are not included in this list. Such terms may be found by referring to the Index.

fillet (n) The rounded-in corner between two surfaces.

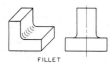

FILLET

flange (n) A rim extension, as at the end of a pipe or similar construction.

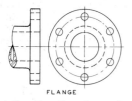

FLANGE

forge (v) To give the desired shape or form to hot metal by hammering or pressure.

functional drawing (n) A drawing using the fewest number of views and the fewest number of lines to provide the exact information required.

galvanize (v) To give a coating of zinc or zinc and lead.

gauge (n) A device for determining whether a specified dimension on an object is within specified limits.

gear (n) A toothed wheel used to transmit power or motion from one shaft to another. A machine element used to transmit motion or force.

grind (v) To use an abrasive wheel to polish or to finish a surface.

key (n) A piece used to fasten a hub to a shaft or for a similar purpose.

keyway or **keyseat** (n) A groove or slot in a shaft or hub into which a key is placed.

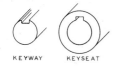

KEYWAY   KEYSEAT

knurl (v) To form a series of regular dents to roughen a cylindrical surface so that it can be held or turned by hand.

limit (n) A boundary. Indication of only the largest and smallest permissible dimensions. See Chap. 11.

lug (n) An "ear" forming a part of, and extending from, a part.

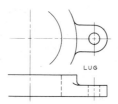

LUG

malleable casting (n) A casting which has been toughened by annealing.

micrometer caliper (n) A measuring device used to determine the exact measurements of diameter thicknesses.

mill (v) To machine a part on a milling machine, using a rotating toothed cutter.

neck (v) To cut a groove around a cylindrical part, generally at a change in diameter.

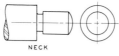

NECK

peen (v) To stretch or head over material with the peen, or ball, end of a machinist's hammer.

photo drawing (n) A drawing prepared from a photograph, or a photograph on which dimensions, changes, or additional parts have been drawn.

punch (v) To pierce thin metal by pressing a tool of the desired shape through it.

ream (v) To make a hole the exact size by finishing with a rotating fluted cutting tool.

round (n) The rounded-over corner of two surfaces.

ROUND

shaft (n) Round stock upon which gears, pulleys, or rotating pieces are attached for support or to transmit power. See Fig. 13-18.

shim (n) A thin plate of metal used between two surfaces to adjust the distance between them.

spot-face (v) To finish a circular spot slightly below a rough surface on a casting to provide a smooth, flat seat for a bolthead or other fastening.

steel casting (n) A part made of cast iron to which scrap steel has been added when melted.

tap (v) To cut threads in a hole with a threading tool called a tap. (n) A hardened screw, fluted to provide cutting edges.

taper pin (n) A piece of round stock made with a gradual and uniform decrease in diameter.

technical illustration (n) A pictorial drawing rendered to simplify and interpret technical information.

temper (v) To reduce the brittleness in hardened steel by heating in various ways, as in a bath of oil, salt, sand, or lead, to a specified temperature and then cooling.

template or **templet** (n) A flat form or pattern of full size used to lay out a shape and to locate holes or other features.

tolerance (n) A specific allowance for variation from a given dimension. The total amount by which a given dimension may vary. The difference between limits. See Chap. 11.

turn (v) To machine a piece on a lathe by rotating the piece against a cutting tool (as when forming a cylindrical surface, and so forth).

upset (v) To make an enlarged section or shoulder on a rod, bar, or similar piece while forging.

vernier (n) A small auxiliary scale used to obtain fractional parts of a major scale.

washer (n) A ring of metal used to form a seat for a bolt or nut.

weld (v) To join pieces of metal, which have been heated to a fusing temperature, by pressing or hammering them together. See Chap. 17.

Index

Metric Equivalents

Mm	In.*	Mm	In.	In.	Mm †	In.	Mm
1 = 0.0394		17 = 0.6693		$\frac{1}{32}$ = 0.794		$\frac{17}{32}$ = 13.493	
2 = 0.0787		18 = 0.7087		$\frac{1}{16}$ = 1.587		$\frac{9}{16}$ = 14.287	
3 = 0.1181		19 = 0.7480		$\frac{3}{32}$ = 2.381		$\frac{19}{32}$ = 15.081	
4 = 0.1575		20 = 0.7874		$\frac{1}{8}$ = 3.175		$\frac{5}{8}$ = 15.875	
5 = 0.1969		21 = 0.8268		$\frac{5}{32}$ = 3.968		$\frac{21}{32}$ = 16.668	
6 = 0.2362		22 = 0.8662		$\frac{3}{16}$ = 4.762		$\frac{11}{16}$ = 17.462	
7 = 0.2756		23 = 0.9055		$\frac{7}{32}$ = 5.556		$\frac{23}{32}$ = 18.256	
8 = 0.3150		24 = 0.9449		$\frac{1}{4}$ = 6.349		$\frac{3}{4}$ = 19.050	
9 = 0.3543		25 = 0.9843		$\frac{9}{32}$ = 7.144		$\frac{25}{32}$ = 19.843	
10 = 0.3937		26 = 1.0236		$\frac{5}{16}$ = 7.937		$\frac{13}{16}$ = 20.637	
11 = 0.4331		27 = 1.0630		$\frac{11}{32}$ = 8.731		$\frac{27}{32}$ = 21.431	
12 = 0.4724		28 = 1.1024		$\frac{3}{8}$ = 9.525		$\frac{7}{8}$ = 22.225	
13 = 0.5118		29 = 1.1418		$\frac{13}{32}$ = 10.319		$\frac{29}{32}$ = 23.018	
14 = 0.5512		30 = 1.1811		$\frac{7}{16}$ = 11.112		$\frac{15}{16}$ = 23.812	
15 = 0.5906		31 = 1.2205		$\frac{15}{32}$ = 11.906		$\frac{31}{32}$ = 24.606	
16 = 0.6299		32 = 1.2599		$\frac{1}{2}$ = 12.699		1 = 25.400	

* Calculated to *nearest* fourth decimal place.   † Calculated to *nearest* third decimal place

Source: Extracted from p. 713 of Thomas E. French and Charles J. Vierck, *Graphic Science,* McGraw-Hill Book Company, New York, 1958.

Decimal Equivalents of Common Fractions

$\frac{1}{64}$	0.015625	$\frac{17}{64}$	0.265625	$\frac{33}{64}$	0.515625	$\frac{49}{64}$	0.765625
$\frac{1}{32}$	0.03125	$\frac{9}{32}$	0.28125	$\frac{17}{32}$	0.53125	$\frac{25}{32}$	0.78125
$\frac{3}{64}$	0.046875	$\frac{19}{64}$	0.296875	$\frac{35}{64}$	0.546875	$\frac{51}{64}$	0.796875
$\frac{1}{16}$	0.0625	$\frac{5}{16}$	0.3125	$\frac{9}{16}$	0.5625	$\frac{13}{16}$	0.8125
$\frac{5}{64}$	0.078125	$\frac{21}{64}$	0.328125	$\frac{37}{64}$	0.578125	$\frac{53}{64}$	0.828125
$\frac{3}{32}$	0.09375	$\frac{11}{32}$	0.34375	$\frac{19}{32}$	0.59375	$\frac{27}{32}$	0.84375
$\frac{7}{64}$	0.109375	$\frac{23}{64}$	0.359375	$\frac{39}{64}$	0.609375	$\frac{55}{64}$	0.859375
$\frac{1}{8}$	0.1250	$\frac{3}{8}$	0.3750	$\frac{5}{8}$	0.6250	$\frac{7}{8}$	0.8750
$\frac{9}{64}$	0.140625	$\frac{25}{64}$	0.390625	$\frac{41}{64}$	0.640625	$\frac{57}{64}$	0.890625
$\frac{5}{32}$	0.15625	$\frac{13}{32}$	0.40625	$\frac{21}{32}$	0.65625	$\frac{29}{32}$	0.90625
$\frac{11}{64}$	0.171875	$\frac{27}{64}$	0.421875	$\frac{43}{64}$	0.671875	$\frac{59}{64}$	0.921875
$\frac{3}{16}$	0.1875	$\frac{7}{16}$	0.4375	$\frac{11}{16}$	0.6875	$\frac{15}{16}$	0.9375
$\frac{13}{64}$	0.203125	$\frac{29}{64}$	0.453125	$\frac{45}{64}$	0.703125	$\frac{61}{64}$	0.953125
$\frac{7}{32}$	0.21875	$\frac{15}{32}$	0.46875	$\frac{23}{32}$	0.71875	$\frac{31}{32}$	0.96875
$\frac{15}{64}$	0.234375	$\frac{31}{64}$	0.484375	$\frac{47}{64}$	0.734375	$\frac{63}{64}$	0.984375
$\frac{1}{4}$	0.2500	$\frac{1}{2}$	0.5000	$\frac{3}{4}$	0.7500	1	1.0000